W9-AHR-900

MENTAL DEFICIENCY

The Changing Outlook

Mental Deficiency

THE CHANGING OUTLOOK

Revised Edition

Edited by

ANN M. CLARKE and *A. D. B. CLARKE*

Fp

THE FREE PRESS
New York

Printed in the United States of America

Library of Congress Catalog Card Number: 65-22286

CONTENTS

Part I: The Background

Part II: Theoretical Problems

Part III: Practical Problems

PLATES

TEXT FIGURES

CONTRIBUTORS

J. M. Berg, M.B., B.Ch., M.Sc., Clinical Research Consultant, Kennedy-Galton Centre, Harperbury Hospital, near St Albans, Herts. Formerly Clinical Research Fellow, Fountain Hospital, London.

Ann M. Clarke, B.A., Ph.D., Research Fellow, Nuffield Unit, Department of Psychology, The University, Hull, Yorkshire. Formerly Principal Psychologist, The Manor Hospital, Epsom, Surrey.

A. D. B. Clarke, B.A., Ph.D., Professor of Psychology, The University, Hull, Yorkshire. Formerly Consultant Clinical Psychologist, The Manor Hospital, Epsom, Surrey.

Margaret Fawcus, L.C.S.T., Director of Studies, Kingdon-Ward School of Speech Therapy, London, S.W.1, Speech Therapist to the Chelsea and Kensington Hospital Group and to the City Literary Institute, London, W.C.2. Formerly Speech Therapist, The Manor Hospital, Epsom, Surrey.

H. C. Gunzburg, M.A., Ph.D.(Vienna), F.B.Ps.S., Consultant Clinical Psychologist, Monyhull Hospital, Birmingham.

N. O'Connor, M.A., Ph.D., Senior Research Psychologist, Medical Research Council's Social Psychiatry Research Unit, Maudsley Hospital, Denmark Hill, London, S.E.5.

Elspeth Stephen, M.A., Dip.Ed., Principal Psychologist, Fountain and Carshalton Hospital Group, Queen Mary's Hospital for Children, Carshalton, Surrey. Formerly Senior Psychologist, Chailey Heritage Craft School and Hospital, Chailey, Sussex.

J. Tizard, M.A., B.Litt., Ph.D., Professor of Child Development. Institute of Education, University of London, Malet Street, London, W.C.1. Formerly Senior Research Psychologist, Medical Research Council's Social Psychiatry Research Unit.

FOREWORD

Traditionally mental deficiency has been a neglected field of study, with the exception of some aspects of neuropathology and genetics. Here some outstanding work has been done, although extremely rare conditions have often assumed relatively greater importance than their numbers might warrant, in comparison with much more common but less clear-cut manifestations of mental subnormality. The fact that there is no 'cure' for the vast majority of clinical conditions subsumed under the wide legal-administrative category of mental deficiency seems to have rendered this aspect of mental handicap the least attractive to therapists and research workers alike. The possibility of capitalizing on the defective's limited assets by the application of learning theories has not yet been sufficiently explored; too often text-books have concentrated upon his deficits. Moreover, the relative complexity of subnormal personalities has all too often been overlooked. Fortunately, however, such pioneers as Binet, Burt and Wallin have laid firm foundations for subsequent work.

Early this century an extreme and over-simplified genetical theory raised profound fears that national degeneracy was imminent; it is nowadays realized, of course, that inheritance does not take place in the simple manner then postulated, and, as Burt has recently stated, it must be supposed that heredity produces differences as often as resemblances. Moreover, the pattern of differential fertility which originally gave rise to alarm is itself changing. Nevertheless, from this original and largely inaccurate premise, a logical belief arose that *custodial care* was the correct solution, on both humanist and scientific grounds, to the social and genetic problems of mental deficiency. This was further reinforced by unemployment between the two World Wars, and the overall effect, among others, prevented any real evaluation of the certified defective's prospects in the community. Similarly, the equally extreme behaviourist view originating from the work of J. B. Watson also had its adherents in the field of mental deficiency research. Nowadays, however, better experimental controls and more sophisticated techniques are beginning to give us more accurate, if less sensational, information about environmental influences. Moreover, much of the earlier work concerned children only, and as this book will endeavour to indicate, the mentally deficient child may in some cases show a different picture in adult life, and certainly his problems will be different.

Mental deficiency is a social-administrative rather than a scientific concept, varying in different countries and within a given country at different times. With the major social and economic changes which have occurred during the last fifteen years, a re-evaluation of the problem has become possible. It is clear that advances have occurred in our understanding of the nature, causes, and treatment of the many conditions which we term mental deficiency, resulting in a steadily changing outlook. Much new research in this country, the United States and Scandinavia has been completed and there has also been increased public interest and understanding, culminating in Britain in the recent Royal Commission. It is being increasingly appreciated that this is a rewarding and often exciting field of study.

In the present volume we have three main aims; first, to summarize as comprehensively as possible the literature on psychological and social aspects of mental deficiency (particularly that of the last decade) against a background of genetics and neuropathology. Second, we have tried to show the intimate, reciprocal and enriching relationship between theory and practice, and the use of experimental method in both areas; and third, an attempt has been made to indicate in a practical manner how the learning difficulties and social problems posed by the subnormal may be ameliorated. We would like to express our gratitude to the contributors who have willingly fitted in with this general plan, and who have patiently tolerated editorial interference over a long period.

Dr Vernon Hamilton read the original manuscript and made many useful suggestions, and Mr Roy Brown provided valuable help at the proofs stage; we are very much indebted to them. We are also glad to record our thanks to Dr J. F. MacMahon who has taught us so much and over many years provided facilities for, and encouraged us in, our endeavours to apply scientific method to the problems of mental deficiency; our debt to him is great. We are also grateful to Professor C. A. Mace, General Editor of the Methuen Manuals of Modern Psychology Series, for his interest and assistance.

ANN M. CLARKE
ALAN D. B. CLARKE

May 1958

ACKNOWLEDGEMENTS

The contributors and Editors have drawn heavily upon the publications of many workers in this field, to all of whom they wish to express their gratitude. They would like in particular to thank the following:

DR J. M. BERG. Professor L. S. Penrose, F.R.S. (for many helpful suggestions and for providing Plate 1*e*). The late Dr D. H. H. Thomas (for permission to photograph the children who were in his care, shown in Plate 1*c*, *f* and *g*). Mr M. A. C. Ridler (for his photography of all the patients shown in Plate 1).

DR H. C. GUNZBURG. Drs C. J. C. Earl and R. J. Stanley (for their stimulating discussions which helped in the formulation of much of the material presented). Dr J. Jastak (for permission to use Fig. 4).

DR N. O'CONNOR. Professor Sir Cyril Burt and the University of London Press (for permission to quote correlations in Table 1 and material on page 190, both from *The Backward Child*). Dr G. Claridge (for permission to quote his work on pp. 202–3). Dr E. M. Gruenberg and the Mental Health Research Unit, Onondaga County, New York (for permission to quote figures in Table 2, and material on p. 38 and Table 5). The Corporation of Glasgow (for permission to use Fig. 1, taken from a pre-war survey). Professors A. R. Luria and A. N. Leontiev (for permission to quote data on pp. 208–11). Dr V. Meyer (for permission to quote his work on p. 232). Professor L. S. Penrose, F.R.S. (for figures in Tables 2 and 4). Dr W. Sloan (for allowing the quotation of a lengthy personal communication, pp. 200–1).

MRS M. FAWCUS. Shulamith Kastein (for permission to quote material on p. 452). Mr James Paterson (for data quoted on p. 461). Messrs B. Schneider and J. Vallon (for permission to quote their writings on p. 455).

MISS ELSPETH STEPHEN. Dr P. Asher (for figures in Table 15). Dr H. V. Bice (for permission to quote figures in Table 15 and Miss J. M. Cockburn (for material quoted on p. 257). Drs W. Cruickshank and G. Raus and the Syracuse University Press (for permission to quote figures in Tables 17 and 18 from their book on *Cerebral Palsy*). Dr M. I. Dunsdon and the National Foundation for Educational Research (for permission to quote Tables 14, 16, part of 18, 20 and 21, and material on pp. 244, 259, 271 and 272, all taken from her book on *The Educability of Cerebral Palsied Children*). Mrs E. B. Floyer (for permission to quote figures in Table 18). Dr V. Meyer (for permission to quote material on p. 258). Dr E. P. Quibell (for help and advice). Mrs F. E. Schonell (for permission to quote figures in Tables 15, 18, 19, 20 and 25, all from her book on *Educating Spastic Children*). Dr Brian Kirman (for reading the revised draft).

PROF. J. TIZARD. Dr C. P. Blacker (for permission to quote his work on pp. 494–5). Professor D. C. Charles (for permission to quote an extended summary of his work, pp. 503–7). Dr J. M. Crawford (for permission to quote material on pp. 497–8). Drs L. T. Hilliard and B. Kirman, and Messrs J. & A. Churchill, Ltd (for permission to include substantial portions of the writer's chapter, and four paragraphs from one of Dr Kirman's chapters in *Mental Deficiency*). Dr T. L. McCulloch (for material on pp. 19–20).

PROF. A. D. B. CLARKE. Dr John Bowlby and the World Health Organization (for allowing a quotation from *Maternal Care and Mental Health* on p. 519. Mrs. M. W. G. Brandon (for supplying data quoted on pp. 522–4). Miss E. L. Evans (for Plate 4). Mrs M. Gresham (for typing much of the manuscript). Mr R. Hermelin (for Plates 3 and 5). Dr H. M. Skeels (for permission to quote Tables 9 and 10 and much data from his studies). Dr R. Worters (for suggesting additions to Chapter V). See also Editorial acknowledgements in Foreword.

DR A. M. CLARKE. Dr E. A. Doll (for permission to quote his criteria of mental deficiency, pp. 60–2). Professor L. S. Penrose, F.R.S., and Messrs Sidgwick & Jackson (for permission to quote

Table 8 from his *Biology of Mental Defect*). See also Editorial acknowledgements in Foreword.

PREFACE TO THE SECOND EDITION

When the First Edition of this book was published in 1958 it was necessary to include a short section on the neglect of mental deficiency. Even so, the trends initiated during that decade enabled us to justify our sub-title: 'The Changing Outlook.' Between 1958 and 1964, however, many developments have occurred, and the pace of change has been greatly accelerated. It may, therefore, be worth reviewing the immediate background in England and in the United States.

In England, the development of the Welfare State in the post-war years sensitized public awareness of deprived members of the population, and this led to particular concern for the conditions of those in mental and mental deficiency hospitals. In the early 1950's it became obvious that custodial care for mildly subnormal persons was no longer appropriate either on humane or economic grounds, and survey and other findings helped to identify the necessary bases for reform.

Public unease about the mental health services undoubtedly played a large part in bringing into being the Royal Commission on Mental Illness and Mental Deficiency, 1954–1957, and ultimately the passing of the Mental Health Act, 1959. The main principles now were firstly, an emphasis on voluntary rather than compulsory admission, and secondly, a shift from hospital care, often in remote isolated areas, to community provisions for the mentally subnormal. Local health authorities were empowered to build training centres for the severely subnormal, as well as hostels for these and for others of higher grade. A great expansion of community services is thus now in progress (Ministry of Health, 1963).

In the United States, a similarly accelerated development has taken place during the last decade. This has been well reviewed by Gibson (1964). Between 1946 and 1960, according to this writer, changing social conditions brought sharply increased community expectations for improved educational and other services. This renaissance in public and professional concern reached its peak in 1962 with the

Report of the President's Panel on Mental Retardation. Indeed, it is clear that the Kennedy family's personal interest in these problems did much to focus attention on the whole field. And before his untimely death in November 1963, President Kennedy was able to sign two major pieces of legislation relating to mental retardation.

The trends outlined have, of course, not merely been confined to Britain and the United States; similar changes have occurred, or are in process of occurring, in many other countries. Indeed, this heightened interest was reflected in the 1960 London Conference on the Scientific Study of Mental Deficiency, attended by nearly 700 delegates coming from twenty-seven countries. During this, the first multidisciplinary international conference, a provisional committee was set up with the aim of fostering an international organization. This latter was inaugurated as a permanent body at The International Copenhagen Conference on the Scientific Study of Mental Retardation in August 1964, with national committees in many countries. Its aim is to encourage research and disseminate scientific information.

Mental deficiency poses two main problems; first, the task of primary prevention of these conditions, whether they be of biological or socio-cultural origin. The second problem is the amelioration of existing mental deficiency wherever possible, again whether by biological, social, or educational means. There have been recent important theoretical advances in the first sphere, even though, as yet, little immediate practical outcome can be expected, and it is very unlikely that, in the immediate foreseeable future, mental deficiency will be substantially reduced in incidence. In the second, however, the increased awareness of mental deficiency as a special problem in learning has already borne practical fruit. Although not wishing to minimize our continuing ignorance, it is now obvious that much can be done to use, develop, and indeed sometimes to create, limited assets in a way thought impossible a mere ten or fifteen years ago. The ground has thereby been cleared and the way is now open for behavioural scientists to explore in depth the details of learning and other processes. Perhaps the most important recent development in the field of mental retardation is the increasing concern by experimental scientists with perception, attention, memory, speech, and concept attainment. Work of this nature takes time to yield applicable knowledge; it seems to us, however, that the foundations of adequate educational programmes for the future will be laid on the basis of research carried out under conditions sufficiently controlled to indicate causes of behavioural deficits and precise methods of overcoming them.

Mental deficiency is a meeting point of a very large number of disciplines; neurology, sociology, biochemistry, psychology, genetics, education, and psychiatry all have some part to play. Work in this field is not only rewarding for its immediate theoretical interest, or practical implications for the handicapped person, but also for its bearing upon the wider study of mankind. As Penrose has put it, 'these unfortunate mentally handicapped individuals can reveal, unwittingly, information of the utmost value to the rest of the human community, and we may well be grateful to them for this service'.

In this, the Second Edition, we have been fortunate to retain the help of our original contributors. In addition, we welcome Dr J. M. Berg to our numbers, and are very grateful for his masterly overview of aetiological principles in pathological deficiency. We have found no reason to alter the general outline of the book, but all Chapters have been revised, in some cases considerably. Advances in various fields also made it necessary completely to re-write and restructure Chapters I, VI, and XIII. And with the greatly increased output of research, all contributors have been forced into a greater selectivity than was necessary in the First Edition. Nevertheless, we hope that the student or research worker will find this book reasonably comprehensive, and that our twelve hundred or so references will enable him to follow up his particular interests without major difficulty.

Mrs M. Phillips prepared the author and subject indexes and references with the assistance of Mr A. S. Henney; we are very grateful to them for undertaking this time-consuming task.

ANN M. CLARKE
ALAN D. B. CLARKE

December 1964

Part I

THE BACKGROUND

Chapter I

INTRODUCTION

by J. Tizard

During the last fifteen years a greater interest has been shown in problems of mental defect than ever before in history. What is happening today in regard to the mentally subnormal is in many respects similar to what is happening, and has happened, to those who suffer from other forms of handicap.

Consider blindness for example. English experience is typical of what has occurred in every civilized country. The first public provision for the blind in England was in workhouses, administered through the Poor Law. According to Sir Ian Fraser (1947) the first institution established expressly for the blind was founded in Liverpool in 1791 on the initiative of two blind men, Edward Rushton, a bookseller, and James Christie, a musician. Rushton had lost his sight at the age of 19 when travelling to the West Indies with a cargo of slaves from whom he contracted malignant ophthalmia. Sixteen years later he brought about the establishment of a School for the Indigent Blind, and this was quickly followed by others.

Sixty years later, however, Miss Elizabeth Gilbert, a blind daughter of the Bishop of Chichester, carried out a survey which showed that of 27,000 blind adults in the United Kingdom at that time, only 1,000 were receiving pensions. The remainder were supported by relatives, or gained a precarious living as best they could. Of 3,900 blind children and young people under 21 years of age, only about half were receiving training in schools or institutions. No provision was made for their after-care or supervision, and usually they found themselves unable to work at the trades for which they had been trained.

Since that time there has been an enormous increase in the

amount of provision made for the blind, and nowadays large numbers of blind people, and in particular of young blind adults, can be trained to be fully independent. In December 1955, for example, there were in England and Wales 253 blind young people between the ages of 16 and 20: of these 68 were at school; 20 in workshops for the blind; 7 were home workers; and 158 were in open employment. While comparable pre-war figures are not available, it is known that the proportion of blind adolescents who find jobs in open employment has greatly increased during the last few years. During the last century suitable methods of educating blind children have been devised, and refined methods for correcting defects in sight have been developed. Advances in our knowledge of the causes of blindness have resulted in a very marked reduction in incidence, especially among children and young people.

What has happened in regard to the blind has also occurred in the case of those who suffer from other forms of handicap. In general two main trends can be observed, one social and educational, and the other medical. Social relief for the handicapped was at first confined to residential institutions. These were, typically, Poor Law Institutions or workhouses which coped with the poor or indigent, the physically disabled, and the mentally afflicted, young and old. Later, specialized asylums of one sort or another were established, for those with one major disability, such as blindness, epilepsy, or mental disorder. In the course of time, if not at the outset, these became custodial institutions, remote from the affairs of ordinary life, separated not only socially but physically from the community. They tended to be built in rural surroundings – to compensate the unfortunate for their afflictions, and because land was cheap.

Inevitably also they became, in Erving Goffman's (1961) phrase, 'total' institutions. The inmates ate, worked, lived, and slept in the same place; large numbers of individuals were herded together, sharing the same wards, messrooms and dayrooms; regimentation was imposed from above; discipline was kept by a small staff who were separated by an extremely wide social distance from the inmates; and the inmates themselves were denied the opportunity, if not the right, to make all but the most trivial decisions affecting their own lives. The institution became self-perpetuating, increasingly remote from everyday life in society, ill-equipped, under-staffed, mean and harsh.

The residential institution for the handicapped has a long and chequered history. It is only very recently indeed that the conception of an institution as 'therapeutic' or 'rehabilitating' has begun to gain general acceptance. Along with this view has come a growth in community services and a concern for the social and family problems of the handicapped person.

What is termed here as the 'medical' approach to problems of handicaps in contrast to the 'social' one, traditionally treated the condition from which the patient suffered, and ignored the person. Thus the child with cerebral palsy or poliomyelitis for example may have had a limb attended to in hospital with the most careful and skilful concern, over a period of months or even years, while the child himself remained bored, unhappy, and lonely, his general social and physical needs being met in only the most perfunctory fashion. Education may have been neglected, or entrusted to staff with no teaching qualifications, such as nurses. Companionship may have been denied him. His need to play may have gone unrecognized. The needs of the child's family, or of the child for his family, may scarcely have been considered at all. Little thought may have been given to after-care.

The traditional narrow medical approach to the handicapped could be as stultifying and as harmful as the custodial. It tended, however, to lend itself to acute rather than chronic illnesses, where spectacular therapeutic successes concealed its other, evil features. In chronic or untreatable conditions it became virtually indistinguishable from the custodial approach, except in the fact that the principal officers were medically qualified and were in consequence paid considerably more than their counterparts in prisons, workhouses, and residential 'colonies' ruled by 'lay' superintendents.

What is new in the contemporary situation is the growing awareness of the complexity of the problems which various mental and physical handicaps entail and the vigour with which measures to deal with them are being taken. From considering merely the handicap we have come to think about the needs of the 'whole child', his family, and the place of the handicapped person in society. Very much more attention is being paid to the provision of medical, educational, and social services which will enable the handicapped person to remain in his own home without undue hardship being imposed upon his family. The patient's, or handicapped person's, education receives much more thought – not only is it customary to provide vocational training of a realistic sort that will enable him to earn his living or take his place in an adult social world, but the importance of a good general education is also coming to be realized. And much more attention is being paid to the development of techniques for studying the assets and deficits of the handicapped person, and their functional significance. In this respect, indeed, we may be on the threshold of a new age, made possible not only by advances in therapeutics which will lead to the prevention of some forms of mental defect and the successful treatment of others, but also by increases in knowledge of psychoneurology and clinical psychology, which will make meaningful functional diagnoses possible, and by advances in educational technique, through teaching machines and similar devices, which will enable instruction to be geared to meet the needs of particular individuals.

It is coming to be seen also that in addition to the particular problems imposed by blindness, deafness, motor disability, mental subnormality, mental illness, or other chronic physical or mental abnormality or handicap, there are problems which are common to all or most of them (Meyerson, 1957), and it seems possible today that we are approaching a time when as a society we shall be more generous, very much better informed, and more honest in our dealings with the handicapped. One can see this happening in relation to the mentally subnormal today. This is one reason why study of mental subnormality is so rewarding.

THE FIELD OF MENTAL DEFICIENCY STUDY

Mental deficiency is not a disease or a single 'entity'. It is, rather, a term applied to a 'condition of subnormal mental development present at birth or in early childhood, and characterized mainly by limited intelligence' (Mayer-Gross, Slater, and Roth, 1954). Mental deficiency is to be distinguished from mental illness in that subnormality of intelligence present from birth or early childhood is an outstanding characteristic. The mentally ill suffer from other forms of mental handicap which arise for the most part during later adolescence or adult life.

It has long been recognized that for most purposes any classification of the mentally subnormal must take into account both the nature of the primary disability from which they suffer, in so far as this is known (e.g. mongolism or phenylketonuria), and the gravity of the mental handicap. Thus the American Association on Mental Deficiency (Heber, 1959) has prepared a *Manual on Terminology and*

Classification in Mental Retardation which is divided into a *medical* classification, for the purpose of which mental retardation is regarded as 'a manifestation of some underlying disease process or medical condition', and a *behavioural* classification in which mental retardation is viewed as being 'characterized by subaverage intellectual functioning associated with deficiences in adaptive functioning'. In the present book we are concerned primarily with behavioural problems. (A brief account of salient medical features is given in Chapters III and VI.) A description of the traditional classification of mental defect by *grade*, or severity of the intellectual or behavioural handicap, and of the confusing terminology used in English-speaking countries to classify defectives behaviourally is therefore given. In the course of this discussion the field of mental deficiency study, as the authors of the book see it, is outlined.

Terminology

The term 'mentally defective' or 'mentally deficient' is used in Great Britain to describe the mentally subnormal as a whole, irrespective of the degree of their subnormality. In general it is applied only to those whose subnormality is marked – for example an I.Q. of 70, or two standard deviations below the mean, is frequently regarded as the upper limit of intelligence which is retarded enough to be considered 'defective' (Tizard, 1950). Until the passing of the Mental Health Act in 1959 the term 'mentally deficient' had a legal as well as a medical and descriptive connotation; but it is now no longer used in Law, having been replaced by the terms 'mental subnormality' and 'severe subnormality'. Synonyms for the term mental deficiency are: oligophrenia, which is widely used on the Continent of Europe; feeblemindedness, which was until recently used in the United States as a synonym for mental deficiency; mental defect; amentia; mental subnormality; mental retardation.

In the United States the term 'mental retardation' is coming to be used in a generic sense to describe the mentally subnormal – thus the American Association on Mental Deficiency *Manual* defines mental deficiency as a synonym for mental retardation, and gives as a reason for using retardation that it is the 'most preferred term among professional personnel in all the disciplines' concerned with their problems.

The A.A.M.D. *Manual* places stress upon backwardness in intelligence as a necessary feature. Mental retardation refers to 'subaverage intellectual functioning which originates during the developmental period and is associated with impairment in adaptive behaviour' (Heber, 1962). By 'subaverage general intellectual functioning' is meant, in this context, an I.Q. of more than one standard deviation below the mean – in other words with an I.Q. of less than about 85 points. The definition appears rather widely drawn, as compared with traditional practice, in that whereas only about 2 per cent. of the population have I.Q.s of less than 70 (i.e. more than two standard deviations below the average), approximately 16 per cent. have I.Q.s of less than 85 (more than one standard deviation below the average). In practice the Americans appear to deal with much the same type of patient as is considered mentally subnormal in Europe, because they insist that both backwardness in intelligence and impaired social adaptation must be demonstrated before a diagnosis can be made. Unfortunately, satisfactory tests of social adaptation are lacking, so that inevitably one is driven back to clinical judgment in attempting to assess this quality. The new classification is thus not very different from the old, except that according to Heber *complete* emphasis is placed on the functioning of the individual at the time the examination is made. In other words 'a person may meet the criteria of mental retardation at one age level and not at another; he may change status as a result of "real" changes in intellectual functioning; or he may move from retarded to non-retarded as a result of a training programme which has increased his level of adaptive behaviour' (Heber, 1962).

Interesting as the United States classification is, however, the traditional, and for many purposes still the most useful, way of classifying the mentally subnormal behaviourally is according to the severity of *grade* of the defect. Three main grades have been distinguished, namely (1) idiots, (2) imbeciles, and (3) feeble-minded persons (British terminology) or morons (United States usage).

Idiots and imbeciles are often collectively described as 'low-grade' defectives in contrast to morons who are described as 'high-grade' defectives. This distinction is a useful one, as the two groups differ qualitatively in many respects, as will be mentioned later.[1]

[1] The terms high-grade, medium grade, and low grade have sometimes also been used to describe patients within each grade – thus a high-grade imbecile is one who is nearing the borderline which separates the imbecile from the moron, whereas a low-grade imbecile is much more severely handicapped, and is nearer the idiot level.

Idiocy and imbecility – low-grade mental deficiency

A classical description of idiocy and of imbecility has been given by E. O. Lewis (1929) who carried out the most thorough large-scale investigation into the prevalence of mental deficiency which has as yet been made in any country. Idiots, he says, are those who are so severely handicapped as to be scarcely capable of receiving permanent benefit from any kind of training. They can seldom be trained in clean habits, to dress themselves, or to use a knife and fork when eating. They may learn to understand a few simple commands, but their own speech is limited to a few isolated words. Their powers of attention and application are so poor that they cannot be trained to do the simplest recreational handwork; but many of them acquire some such habit as a monotonous tapping on a table. Most idiots require during their whole life the attention, nursing, and care that has to be given to infants. Those who are able to walk unaided require supervision because they are unable to guard themselves against common physical dangers.

It is usual to classify as idiots mental defectives who have intelligence quotients of less than 20 points, or in the case of adults, test ages of less than three years. (On the Continent of Europe the definitions have often been drawn more widely – in some cases those with I.Q.s of 30 or even 40 have been called idiots.)

Mental defectives who are capable of guarding themselves against common physical dangers (i.e. who learn to avoid touching hot stoves or swallowing dangerous objects such as pieces of glass), but who are not able to learn the formal skills of reading and writing, are usually classified as imbeciles. Lewis took the view that a child should not be regarded as an imbecile if there was

> some hope that, so far as scholastic attainments are concerned, he would ultimately be able to recognize and form all the letters of the alphabet, to recognize and make simple figures, and perhaps even to read and write a few simple words containing up to three letters, such as 'a', 'it', 'the', 'cat', 'and'; that he would before leaving school be able to make such childish calculations as 'if you had five pennies and lost one, how many would be left?' 'How many do three and two make?' 'What are twice two?' Hence [he said] a child was to be considered an imbecile only in cases where, after a year or two's probation in a special school, or where after two years' training he was still unable to recognize most of his letters,

or where, again, in matters of classroom behaviour and discipline, and in the practical affairs of everyday life – such as dressing, keeping himself clean, playing simple games, finding his way about the building or the neighbourhood – he had not reached the level of a normal child of about half his own age.

In terms of I.Q., Lewis placed the upper limit of imbecility, dividing it from feeble-mindedness or high-grade defect, at 45 to 50 points in the case of children. Educational usage today would probably favour a slightly less stringent criterion. Few children with I.Q.s below 50 or 55 can learn to read or write more than a few words, though it is probable that a good many more of the older ones who attend training centres today could be taught the rudiments of reading. In so far as the concept of imbecility in childhood is linked with formal educability, there is something to be said for making an I.Q. of 50 (on a test with standard deviation of 15 points) a rough dividing line between imbecility and mere educational backwardness, and such a standard has, in fact, been widely adopted.

E. O. Lewis judged adults to be of imbecile grade if they were 'incapable, not only of earning an independent livelihood, but even of contributing materially to their own support'. The best that can be expected of them is 'the simplest of routine tasks under supervision . . . the brightest can usually wash and dress themselves, but only learn to do so very late in childhood, and such matters as buttoning boots or tying shoelaces often remain entirely beyond their powers'.

We know that in his assessment of the potentialities of adult imbeciles Dr Lewis was unduly pessimistic (Chapter XIII). One of the advances in knowledge about the mentally subnormal which has occurred during the last decade and a half has been the discovery that with proper methods of training, and in a society which is prepared and able to make full use of all its members, very much more can be done by even the most handicapped persons than has generally been realized in the past. It is clear that the great majority of imbeciles are too handicapped to lead fully independent lives, even though perhaps one tenth or a fifth of them can do independent work – i.e. can work in open employment.[1] It is not true, however, that they require an excessive amount of supervision, or that they

[1] Lewis placed the 'upper limit' of imbecility in adulthood at about I.Q. 40 rather than I.Q. 50 which is more usual today. Even so his conclusions have been shown by post-war studies to be unnecessarily pessimistic.

cannot be taught to do very complex routine tasks if properly instructed. The majority of imbeciles cannot be employed in open employment, not because their general social behaviour is unsatisfactory, but because they are too simple, and, very frequently, too physically handicapped. They are not usually antisocial, or lacking in persistence, or necessarily unstable temperamentally.

Feeble-mindedness or moronity – high-grade mental deficiency

Great confusion exists in regard to high-grade defectives since the term is applied to an administratively defined group characterized by low intelligence coupled with physical disability, or troublesome or neurotic behaviour, or lack of a proper home. The great majority of those who are merely grossly backward intellectually never come to notice, except in school where they are considered educationally subnormal (E.S.N.) or educationally mentally retarded (E.M.R.) in United States usage. Nor is there any reason why they should be regarded as anything other than ordinary, if somewhat limited, citizens. Whereas imbeciles and idiots suffer from handicaps which are primarily biological in nature, those technically called feeble-minded or morons suffer from handicaps which are in large measure socially determined (Penrose, 1962).

In England high-grade defectives are classified as follows:

Children

Provision is nominally made for about 1 per cent. of children of school age (including those broadly speaking with I.Q.s below 70 but above about 50 or 55) in special schools for the educationally subnormal. The children who attend such schools are called educationally subnormal (often abbreviated to E.S.N.).

If in addition to being intellectually in this grade they present behaviour problems which make them unsuitable for education in school they are legally excluded from school and termed 'subnormal' (formerly 'feeble-minded'). Thus the number of feeble-minded children – or 'subnormal' children under the terms of the 1959 Mental Health Act – is very small, being not more than about one per thousand and usually less in most parts of the country. The number of *educationally* subnormal children is however administratively reckoned to be about 1 per cent. The educationally subnormal remain in the education system; they are educated, or are supposed to be educated, in special schools if on account of their intellectual backwardness they appear to be unable to keep up with the lessons in ordinary classes. In the United States such children tend to be relegated to special classes rather than special schools. The *feeble-minded* or subnormal children, like the imbeciles and idiots, are however excluded from the education system – on the arguable grounds that not being able to be taught to read and write (in the case of idiots and imbeciles) or being so difficult to control in the case of the feeble-minded, they are 'ineducable'. Their 'training', as opposed to education, is in this country arranged by the mental health authorities.[1] In most parts of the United States where training is given at all it is provided by the education authorities (Kirk, 1957; A.A.M.D. Project in Technical Planning in Mental Retardation, 1962).

Adults

The term feeble-minded or subnormal is applied to adults who are both grossly backward in intelligence and who present social problems. Of these the most common is an inability to support themselves, and the second most common is delinquency in the case of men, and sexual promiscuity which demands – or at least receives – attention on the part of public authorities, in the case of women. Dullards with I.Q.s above those of imbeciles but below about I.Q. 70 or 75 who have these additional difficulties are called morons or feeble-minded persons (or simpletons or subnormals). Most people who are dealt with in this way are adolescents – as they get older most of them 'settle down'. Thus just as educational subnormality is a condition diagnosed most commonly among school children in the later years of school life, when school lessons become intellectually taxing, so most feeble-mindedness is a condition of adolescent immaturity which even dull and retarded individuals tend to grow out of, or learn to cope with or conceal. To regard it as anything more precisely definable than this, is scarcely justified by the facts of the situation as we know it today.

Mental deficiency is relatively common – imbecility in children is 10–15 times as common as blindness, and educational subnormality severe enough to warrant education in special schools is five times as common as imbecility. The condition can be brought about by

[1] It would simplify matters if the term feeble-minded or subnormal was not applied at all to children – and a slight change in administrative practice would result in this. 'Feeble-minded' children should, properly, be regarded as maladjusted educationally subnormal children. Their education is thus a matter for an education authority.

many causes, only a few of which are at present known. As Haldane (1949) says, there should be nothing surprising in the fact of multiple causation:

> Everyone knows that visual defect is due to many causes, and that some kinds can be improved by spectacles, others by surgery, while yet others are at present incurable, though the incurable fraction is slowly decreasing. The brain is a vastly more complex organ than the eye, and can go wrong in many more ways.

In imbeciles and idiots the damage to the central nervous system is severe. In most feeble-minded persons the damage is either not severe, or is not demonstrable upon examination or upon autopsy, and the main defects, which are behavioural, are in many cases due rather to environmental factors impairing the efficiency of a vulnerable organism, than to physiological causes in themselves.

Mental deficiency has often been regarded as a barren field of study because, by and large, there are no specific cures for the various diseases which give rise to it. As many writers have pointed out the two terms 'treatment' and 'training' are still practically synonymous. Some rare forms of mental defect, such as that arising from German measles in the mother during the early months of pregnancy, can be largely prevented; in other cases parents may be advised to avoid the risk of producing a mentally deficient child by not having children at all. In most instances, however, neither the genetical basis, if any, nor the underlying pathology are known, and little can as yet be done in the way of primary prevention.

Psychologically, high-grade and low-grade defectives have little in common. Paediatricians and biologists are naturally interested in specific *diseases* and have tended in the past to concern themselves with low-grade rather than high-grade cases; psychologists and social scientists, on the other hand, have tended to concern themselves mainly with the high-grade group. It can be argued that the field of mental deficiency study has its boundaries set by social and administrative conventions, rather than by biological or psychological landmarks. A brief historical survey of the administrative problem enables one to give a better picture of the total field.

SOCIAL PROVISION FOR THE MENTALLY DEFICIENT

That some children are born mentally subnormal has been recognized in all societies, and legal measures to safeguard them or their property have usually been taken. Most countries of the world still, however, have no special mental health legislation (World Health Organization, 1955). In some countries a general Mental Health Act covers both the mentally deficient and the mentally ill, while in others no distinction is made between the two conditions. Some of the main developments in English law relating to mental defect are summarized in Chapter III.

An account of the development of *administrative* provision for mental defectives in England is to be found in Hilliard (Hilliard and Kirman, 1965), who points out that until the nineteenth century legislation applied only to the relatively few members of society who possessed large estates. The jurisdiction of the king was more concerned with feudal rights and duties relating to property than with the welfare of the individual. It did not touch the poorer people, and no provision was made except by a few religious houses, for the care of the mentally ill and mentally subnormal. In Elizabethan England the Poor Law, 1601, began the separation from the community of the poor and afflicted. Workhouses were set up, into which were put the destitute, the unemployed or unemployable, and paupers. This step began the process of segregating social misfits, which has continued until the present day.

The first institutions to be established expressly for mental defectives were built in the nineteenth century. In France Seguin founded a centre for the training of idiots in Paris in 1837. In England, the first mental deficiency asylum was established in London during the 1840's. In 1849 an annexe was built at Colchester for the training of patients in 'simple mechanical employments', and in 1855 the Royal Earlswood Institution was built as a 'model asylum' (Penrose, 1949). By 1886 when the Idiots Act was passed, four hospitals had been built, and by 1913 some 5,000 patients were in mental deficiency hospitals. From the time of the 1913 Mental Deficiency Act the numbers increased steadily, and today there are about 60,000 patients in institutional care.

Parallel with the increase in institutional provision has gone an increase in facilities for community care. About 80,000 mental defectives in England and Wales are today 'supervised' by the local health authorities. Of an estimated total of 25,000 ineducable children of compulsory school age, 18,000 are attending occupation centres for trainable children. In recent years, too, more centres have been built for adult defectives, and today some 14,000 attend these.[1]

In the overall development of its mental deficiency services, the United Kingdom is probably in advance of most of the rest of the world, but a similar process has occurred in many other countries. A particularly valuable and well documented account of the development both of services to meet the needs of the mentally subnormal in the United States, and of the social theorizing that gave rise to them, is to be found in S. P. Davies' *Social Control of the Mentally Deficient* (1930).

As Davies points out, the early pioneers believed that by suitable training the mentally subnormal could be made fully normal, and able to take their place in society. The first institutions were therefore educational ones, and the question of custodial care did not arise. Towards the end of the nineteenth century this hope of restoring imbeciles to complete normality was realized to be a vain one, and plans were made for institutions to care for defectives, if necessary, for life. Unfortunately, just as this decision began to be translated into practice, two new factors changed society's thinking about the whole subject. These were:

(1) The development and application of the Binet–Simon method of intelligence testing.

(2) The development of the eugenics movement, together with the rediscovery of the Mendelian laws of heredity, and resulting heredity studies.

The impact of these discoveries was most clearly seen in the United States where it was soon shown by means of the Binet test that the number of extremely dull (moron) persons was much larger than had ever been thought. At the same time, the proportion of

[1] Fuller accounts of the development of provisions for the mentally subnormal in England and Wales can be found in the Report of the Ministry of Education for the year 1955, and in the Report of the Royal Commission on the Law relating to Mental Illness and Mental Deficiency, 1957. The present position is that educationally subnormal children (i.e. broadly speaking, children with I.Q.s between about 50 and 70) attend, or should attend, special schools run by the education authority. Imbeciles and idiots (i.e. broadly speaking those with I.Q.s below about 50 points) are excluded from school as ineducable. The local health authority has the duty to provide occupation centre training for trainable children – i.e. imbeciles. Most authorities make some provision, though few have done enough for these children.

those in gaols and workhouses, and in receipt of poor relief, who achieved low scores on the Binet test was shown to be extremely high. Family histories seemed to indicate that 'social degeneracy' was transmitted as a unitary trait, through parents to children; and the more degenerate the parents, the larger the number of children who were born to them. (How these studies were carried out, and the mistakes made in the method of inquiry, are discussed in Chapter XVII.)

From faulty premises, and by a series of invalid inferences, alarming conclusions were drawn about the 'menace of the feeble-minded'. A quotation from a speech made in 1912 by Dr Walter E. Fernald, one of the respected figures in the history of psychiatry in the United States, illustrates the state of panic of those most concerned with the problem at this time. The talk was on 'The burden of feeble-mindedness – the synonym of human inefficiency and one of the great sources of human wretchedness and degradation'. Dr Fernald spoke as follows:

> The past few years have witnessed a striking awakening of professional and popular consciousness of the widespread prevalence of feeble-mindedness and its influence as a source of wretchedness to the patient himself and to his family, and as a causative factor in the production of crime, prostitution, pauperism, illegitimacy, intemperance, and other complex social diseases.

And again:

> The social and economic burdens of uncomplicated feeble-mindedness are only too well known. The feeble-minded are a parasitic, predatory class, never capable of self-support or of managing their own affairs. The great majority ultimately become public charges in some form. They cause unutterable sorrow at home and are a menace and danger to the community. Feeble-minded women are almost invariably immoral and if at large usually become carriers of venereal disease or give birth to children who are as defective as themselves. . . . Every feeble-minded person, especially the high-grade imbecile, is a potential criminal, needing only the proper environment and opportunity for the development and expression of his criminal tendencies [quoted in Davies, 1930].

Another writer summed up the situation in these words: 'Our data here reveal that illegitimacy, attempted murder, theft, forgery, arson, prostitution, drunkenness, destitution, and disease are salient features of the social careers of these incompetents.'

The panic about the menace of the feeble-minded reached its height in the years before the First World War. It was only later realized, as a result of more careful sociological and psychological analysis, that the whole basis for the new policy of segregating the mentally subnormal rested on false premises. Fernald was one of the first to modify his views, as his experience showed him that many feeble-minded persons discharged from institutional care were able to make good in society. More sophisticated genetical studies indicated that the determination of the qualities of personality and of intelligence is a highly complex matter, and that the original assumptions were a ludicrous over-simplification of the facts (see Chapter VI). At the same time Watsonian behaviourism began to stress the importance of the environment in moulding the character of individuals, and in some quarters a return almost to the position of the early nineteenth-century sensationist psychology was made.

Before great progress could be achieved in providing comprehensive services for defectives, based on real social and personal needs, the economic depression of the 1930's, followed by the Second World War and its aftermath, retarded further activities. It is only in the last few years that conditions have been favourable for the building of an adequate training and supervision programme, and even today the grip of past prejudice remains strong.

THE EDUCATIONAL PROBLEM

What is common to idiots, imbeciles, and the grosser cases of feeble-mindedness is marked subnormality in intelligence, with which are associated learning difficulties, and in some cases complete inability to benefit from instruction in ordinary schools. It was natural, therefore, that the education and social training of such persons should have led to investigations into methods of teaching and the best ways of organizing educational provision. Indeed, the first detailed studies of mental defectives, though carried out by physicians, would today be regarded as primarily educational rather than medical in their aim.

The first important investigation to be reported was that of the French physician J. M. G. Itard, who published in 1801 an account of his attempts to educate the Wild Boy of Aveyron. A youth of about 11 or 12 had been found living in a wild state in the woods near Aveyron. Filled with the spirit of scientific inquiry, Itard attempted to socialize him by kindness and human association, and to train him 'through the senses'. He was only partially successful, but his account of his work remains one of the great contributions to pedagogy. (His book has been translated into English by George and Muriel Humphrey, 1932; a summary is to be found in Sarason, 1949.)

Itard's theoretical ideas were developed by Seguin (another French physician, who emigrated to the United States in 1850). Seguin called his method 'physiological' because in effect he attempted to train the mind by developing the senses. The organization of institutional care in the United States during the nineteenth century owed much to Seguin, and his principles of training had a profound influence on later pedagogical thinking.

Madame Montessori (1912), an Italian physician who worked first in Italy, and later in many other countries, continued the 'physiological' tradition, though it was now called 'sense training'. Her work with retarded children proved so successful that her experiments in teaching were applied also to the teaching of young, normal children. She is remembered today for her work on educational methods, and as the originator of educational play materials. In Belgium, at about the same time, Decroly, whose work is best known to English readers through the writing of his pupil Mlle Descœudres (1928), was another pioneer in the development of educational methods both for little children and for the mentally subnormal.

All these, and other workers, were concerned with the education of high-grade imbeciles, and educationally subnormal children. (A useful summary of their work is to be found in Kirk and Johnson, 1954.) With the advent of compulsory education in most of western Europe and the United States, towards the end of the nineteenth century, the whole educational problem of backwardness received a quite different emphasis. Public authorities had, for the first time, to build schools and provide teachers for huge numbers of children. Teachers had to deal with very large classes of children differing widely in ability, and the task of weeding out the dull and the 'ineducable' became one of first priority. For this reason, the work of Binet assumed great importance, since he devised the first instruments which gave a promise of accurate measurement of the intelligence. The educational problems of normal children have been such that from the time of the First World War the primary concern of teachers and educational psychologists with imbeciles and idiots has been that of excluding them from school. Research into teaching methods and educability in so far as it has been concerned with the mentally subnormal has been largely devoted to the dull and educationally subnormal, and not to imbecile or 'trainable' children. At the present time the beginning of a new interest in the training of the 'ineducable' child are to be seen (World Health Organization, 1954; Report of the Royal Commission on the Law relating to Mental Illness and Mental Deficiency, 1957; President's Panel on Mental Retardation, 1962).

THE MODERN ADMINISTRATIVE PROBLEM

The administrative problem of mental deficiency was discussed by Burt (1921) in relation to the schooling of London children. A very similar analysis of the more general administrative problem has been undertaken by McCulloch (1947) whose views are summarized below.

From an administrative point of view, mental defectives are persons with gross social incompetence and mental backwardness, who require social action by the community to protect them or to safeguard others. Whether or not a person deviates sufficiently from community norms to warrant action being taken on his behalf depends, as McCulloch points out, partly on the individual's shortcomings, and partly on the thresholds of community tolerance.

Many factors have to be considered, including 'genetic and developmental history, present intellectual ability, emotionality, economic status, family composition, status in family group, moral standards, vocational skill, community tolerance, and potential or latent capacity for development of social competence under favourable conditions'. A diagnosis or classification is made on the basis of the relevant information collected, and this is followed by a recommendation that some particular line of action be taken. (As things are today, the individual must be considered either as defective or not defective, and this arbitrary dichotomy raises most difficult problems of disposal.)

McCulloch argues that the social action taken following the diagnosis of mental defect

> need not imply in any sense that the individual will always remain

> defective. The simplest interpretation is that, when all relevant factors are considered, he is deemed to be socially incompetent in some important sense at the time of analysis, and that he is grossly subnormal in general intelligence. The action in itself need not imply that the condition is incurable, or that the individual may not have the potentiality for social competence at a later time. . . . At the lower and middle ranges the intelligence level sets an upper limit to the degree of social competence possible, and this degree is below the minimum required. At the upper extremes, the intelligence level may set an upper limit, but this limit need not be below the level of community tolerance. Hence, for those with most favourable prognosis, the diagnosis must be considered a temporary classification, and the deficiency is subject to correction.

Among higher grade cases, diagnostic work should be concerned with the analysis of assets and liabilities of the individual in order to determine prognosis and to recommend specific methods to correct his deficiencies. Assets and liabilities should be evaluated not with reference to an ideal environment only, but in relation to actual conditions of the person's life. A case history will give some indication of the extent to which situational and environmental factors are responsible for the individual's shortcomings. Profiles of intellectual abilities, acquired skills, vocational aptitudes, and the dynamic characteristics of the personality should be drawn up, and attempts made to differentiate between remediable and invariant features. The task is to define and assess inadequacies and potentialities in relation to social norms.

Dealing with training, McCulloch points out that the minimum objective is to increase the social competence of higher grade cases to above the community tolerance level. He views a return to the community and a discontinuance of supervision as an operational designation that the persons concerned are no longer mentally deficient, whatever the diagnosis at discharge may be. Discharge may not necessarily mean that individuals have attained a degree of social competence reached by the average member of the community, but merely that they exhibit sufficient competence to be tolerated in the community. Many social and economic factors cause the threshold of community tolerance to fluctuate at different places, and at different times, and fluctuations of the tolerance level may be so great as to decrease very greatly the usefulness of even the best objective measurements.

The administrative problem, and, to a large extent, the psychological problem also, is on the one hand to devise training programmes based on the assets and deficits of mentally subnormal persons, and the possibilities of developing and using their talents in a socially useful way; on the other hand the social administrator has the task of lowering the threshold of community tolerance so as to enable as many as possible of the mentally subnormal and their relatives to live in society happily and usefully.

THE ROYAL COMMISSION ON THE LAW RELATING TO MENTAL ILLNESS AND MENTAL DEFICIENCY, 1954–1957

In 1954 a Royal Commission was appointed to inquire into the law and administrative machinery governing the mentally ill and mentally defective in England and Wales, and to make recommendations; their report was published in 1957. Since the last complete revision of the mental health laws was the Lunacy Act, 1890, and since the Mental Deficiency Act which governs the legal and administrative arrangements regarding mental defectives was passed in 1913, the need for a review of existing legal and administrative practice was clear. As the Commission comment in their Report, both these Acts have been extensively amended, but existing legislation still embodies many general assumptions and attitudes which were current in the late nineteenth and early twentieth centuries but which are not in accordance with present thought. 'Our present mental health legislation considered as a whole is extremely complicated and also in many respects badly out of date.' The Commission therefore was faced with the task of commenting generally on legal and administrative aspects of mental ill-health, in the light of modern knowledge and the present state of public opinion, and with making recommendations which should govern fresh legislation. The recommendations of the Commission were embodied in a new Mental Health Act which was passed in 1959 and came into operation in 1960. It is noteworthy that many other countries and many of the States in the United States, as well as Canada and Australia, are also revising their legislation. This is important not only in that it indicates a changed attitude to the problem which makes existing legal conceptions inappropriate and unacceptable and prepares the way for further changes. It is also symbolic of an intense and widespread interest in the scientific problems of mental defect. The subject has traditionally been a neglected one. Physicians have tended to neglect it as a field because of the seeming hopelessness of effecting specific cures; educationists and psychologists have been primarily concerned with problems of normal children; society as a whole has viewed the social problem of mental defect with a mixture of alarm and embarrassment.

Changes in patterns of fertility, and the decline in infant mortality, have led to a new attitude towards children, and have posed new problems in paediatrics. A century of compulsory education has meant that many of the problems of educating normal people are no longer so pressing. Full employment and a rising standard of living have resulted in a great extension of the social services. For these largely social reasons, mental deficiency is now receiving more attention. There is no doubt that during the next decade or two the extension of present trends will lead to great advances in this field.

Chapter II

THE PREVALENCE OF MENTAL DEFECT

by N. O'Connor

INTRODUCTION

Systematic studies of the number of defectives in France and in England were first made by Binet and Simon (1907) and the Royal Commission on the Care and Control of the Feeble-minded (1908). The subsequent years produced many estimates which varied widely according to definition of criteria and in earlier studies according to the completeness of the investigation. Thus, discussing this first Royal Commission, E. O. Lewis (Wood Report, 1929) states:

> The question that will naturally be asked is whether our figures prove that there has been an increase in the incidence of mental defect in this country in recent years. . . . Our estimate of the total number of mentally defective persons in England and Wales, it is true, is nearly double that based upon the data of the medical investigation for the Royal Commission in 1906; but the increase can be attributed largely to the fact that a much more thorough inquiry is possible at present than twenty years ago.

Lewis then lists a number of ways in which diagnostic methods have improved, and in which standards have been elaborated more precisely.

None the less, despite a more critical attitude concerning criteria of diagnosis or ascertainment, and, for example, a less naïve approach to the invariability of psychometric measures, estimates are often found to vary widely. Thus in the different counties and county boroughs of England and Wales, the number of Mental Deficiency

Ascertainments (Ministry of Health Report, 1951) varied from 0·040 per cent. in Carmarthen and Merthyr Tydfil to 0·579 per cent. in Sunderland. The differences are startling, but probably bear little relationship to the prevalence of mental deficiency and would not do so even in the case of a precisely defined syndrome, which mental deficiency certainly is not. What is introduced in these statistics is undoubtedly an element of local health policy. For example, if the prevalence figures are correlated with the expenditure on the Care of Mothers and Young Children as listed for 1952–3, in 84 county boroughs (Society of County Treasurers Report on Local Health Service Statistics, 1952–3), a coefficient of +0·40 is obtained. Thus, the county boroughs which spend most on maternal health tend to ascertain more cases of defect. This result would be most unlikely, if prevalence alone were being measured. Thus, any study based on returns of such figures must be biased by economic and administrative differences from area to area, and this is only one source of error in arriving at estimates of the prevalence of defect. The difficulties are set out in detail in the section on problems of measurement.

METHODS OF ASSESSING PREVALENCE

In an article on the prevalence of subnormality, Tizard (1953) notes three kinds of research projects: psychometric studies; field studies using intelligence tests and clinical techniques; and a third kind, follow-up investigations of people who at one time in their lives were classified as subnormal.[1] These types of surveys, in addition to employing different methods, are often initiated for different reasons. The survey described by Binet was undertaken with the intention of saving wasted effort and expense in Paris schools; the Royal Commission of 1908 was interested in the social problem of care, training, and control, and the Wood Committee's Survey (1929) in administrative questions of a similar kind as well as in social provision. Sir Cyril Burt's Survey (1946) was prompted by the existence of the problem of backwardness in schools and more recently studies such as those of Baller (1936) and Charles (1953) have been interested in the social competence of those graded mentally deficient at some time in the past (see Chapter XVII). Similarly, the Scottish intelligence surveys set out to answer the question of whether or not

[1] This is not strictly a separate method of assessing prevalence so far as estimates of backwardness are concerned, but it has great value as a survey technique.

national intelligence was declining. The change in the stated intentions of future investigating committees may reasonably be expected to determine the approach to the problem, and to some extent the results.

Writing of psychoses, Goldhamer and Marshall (1949) point out that a real increase cannot be confirmed in the U.S.A. since 1840 although incidence figures suggest this, because habits of hospitalization for older people have altered at the same time as social provision. Likewise, it might be expected that the changing social attitude towards defect might bring about better facilities for care and hence modify the whole problem of incidence surveys.

In a country where education is compulsory, the incidence of defect can be shown to depend on the demands of the educational system. The Wood Report (1929), Tables 2 and 17, justifies the conclusion that defectives are ascertained for the most part in the age group 10–14, which, as Penrose (1954) has pointed out, is of course the age range during which scholastic demands are greatest. Assessment therefore becomes excessively complicated because the criteria are ill defined, methods more or less comprehensive, and because even individual attitudes or financial considerations or group *mores* may affect ascertainment, and, as a consequence, the assessment of the prevalence of mental defect.[1]

It is necessary to make observations of this kind because in the past, despite Penrose's (1954) clear statements, the social determination of the incidence of mental defect has rarely been fully grasped by any but a few research workers. It is probably not fully appreciated, even by those in the field, that responsible people differ in their tendency to put forward pupils for ascertainment as educationally subnormal. The effects on incidence of differences in attitude of this kind are incalculable, but this is only one of a number of factors which may be relevant to the incidence of subnormality or mental defect. There is therefore some reason to devote a section to the problems which may need solution. This will be done below. It remains to say something about the main subject-matter of this section – the methods used. In the psychometric type of study a test or tests will be administered to a sample of people, usually children, or to all persons in a particular category. Thus, for example, the

[1] 'Prevalence' is used in this chapter to mean the number of cases of a disorder existing in any defined population. 'Incidence' is used to describe a rate of occurrence, e.g. the number of defectives born in any one year.

ascertainment of 'ineducability' is made in England of all children who attend school and prove ineducable by ordinary means. Some type of standardized procedure is usually employed in assessing educability. Similarly, intelligence tests commonly form part of the examination which determines grading as Educationally Subnormal.

Apart, however, from tests used to detect illiterates in the armed forces, surveys relying mainly on psychometric tests are rare. In fact, in Great Britain, no surveys of the incidence of mental deficiency have been made which rely solely on such measures. Thus, the two major studies have used either clinical judgment, as in the Royal Commission (1908) investigation, or a mixture of tests and judgment as in the Wood Report (1929). In the latter case exactly the same problem is met with as in comparing the intelligence quotients of pre-school and school-age children. Thus, in the Wood Report, one standard of judgment exists where tests can be given, as in the case of children, and another where they cannot, as with adults. In other words, the I.Q.s of children of different ages may represent quite different qualities and to call them by the same name may simply conceal our ignorance (see Chapter IV).

However, the most common method of making a full census is that which relies on combined testing and clinical judgment, and its difficulties will be more fully discussed in the following pages. The third type of census which may be taken is not strictly relevant to assessing prevalence, except in so far as it takes account of changes in status. Studies such as these follow up people who have been graded as mentally defective, often to discover whether or not they are still ascertainable. A most interesting example is the continuation of Baller's (1936) work by Charles (1953) (for details, see p. 503–6). Tests formed part of these studies, but other social and clinical evidence was taken into account. The method is limited in application and is not intended to answer the same questions as more comprehensive surveys.

PROBLEMS IN THE MEASUREMENT OF SUBNORMALITY

The problems arising under this heading can be classified as those due to (i) lack of precise criteria; (ii) unreliability of instruments of measurement; and (iii) historical, social, and personal variations which alter the likelihood of classifying individuals as retarded.

(i) Lack of precise criteria

It should be noted that surveys including persons regarded as defective but living outside hospitals, generally find that about 75 per cent. of all defectives are feeble-minded and only 25 per cent. are of imbecile or idiot grade. Moreover, no techniques of neurological examination can reveal any relevant nervous dysfunction among a high proportion of cases, particularly the high-grade. In the absence of medical criteria, diagnosis must therefore be made on the basis of a frequently vague and imprecise social history. A clear diagnostic medical criterion is generally lacking.

The diagnosis of mental deficiency is influenced by the fact that even today it is rare to find that the amount of provision is adequate to meet the needs of those so diagnosed. Hence social circumstances inevitably play a large part in determining whether any particular individual is 'ascertained' to be mentally subnormal or not. If the parents cannot provide a proper home, either because they are old, or negligent, or for some other reason, a dull child is likely to be brought to the notice of the public authorities and to be diagnosed as mentally subnormal. Among other things, the educational record must be taken into account, and when this is done it is soon recognizable that backwardness in scholastic achievement may be due to a number of apparently diverse causes. Sir Cyril Burt (1946) lists the following contributory factors and the degree of their relationship with backwardness – which is defined as two years' scholastic retardation.

TABLE 1

Relationships between educational backwardness and other variables

Variable	Correlation with backwardness
Low measured intelligence	0·7
Poor long-term memory	0·5*
Irregular attendance	0·45* to 0·58*
Poor hearing	0·4*
Poor physique	0·3*
Extreme poverty	0·25*

* Correlations with the influence of intelligence held constant.

The association between scholastic level and other variables is further emphasized when Burt points out that correlations between backwardness and poverty are 0·727, backwardness and overcrowding 0·890, and backwardness and size of family 0·348, for 29 boroughs in London.

In Glasgow in 1939 a study of the relationships of backwardness to socio-economic conditions was carried out. This investigation used the provision of free milk in Glasgow districts as a measure of poverty and malnutrition. A positive relationship was found between the backwardness in schools in the different areas and the percentages of free milk issued in these areas (see Fig. 1).

An interesting special experiment was carried out at the same time in Glasgow. The Dobbie Loan School was conducting a special regimen in an attempt to improve scholastic achievement in the pupils at this school in a poor area. Special meals, attention to sleep, health, nutrition, and study habits resulted in this school providing

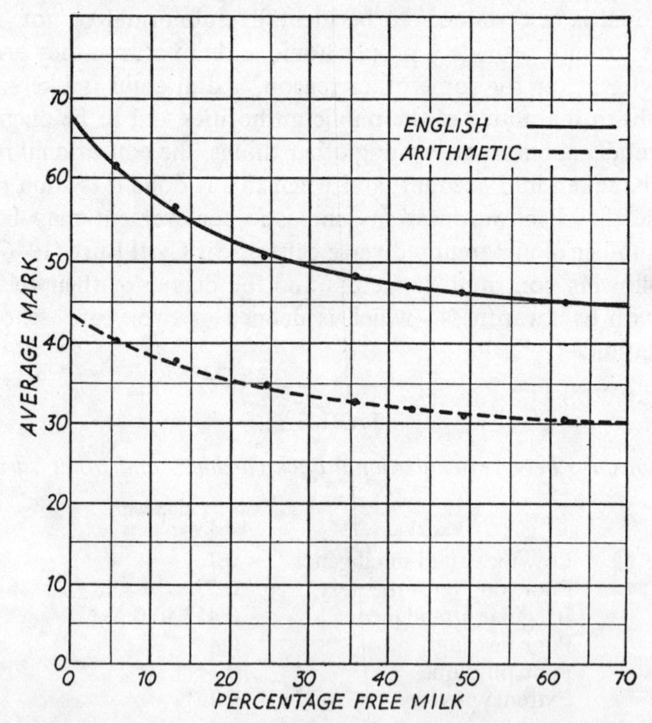

FIG. 1. Backwardness and poverty (*after* Allardyce, 1939)

Showing how the average attainment of a school at the qualifying stage varies with the percentage number of children in the school receiving free milk. English marks are on a scale of maximum 90. Arithmetic marks are on a scale of maximum 70.

an outstanding exception to the curves in Fig. 1. The pupils showed a performance four grades in advance of prediction based on the curves. Results of this kind are confirmed by such studies as those of Seymour and Whittaker (1938). It is possible to make a similar interpretation of the results more recently presented by the Scottish Educational Survey (1947). Thus, criteria of defect can be shown to be educational and social rather than medical, at least for the slightly handicapped.

The criteria of backwardness, if judged on the basis of educational backwardness or intelligence quotient, will inevitably depend on the degree to which such curves fluctuate during school life. On the basis of the Wood Report, Tables 2 and 17, Penrose (1954) has calculated the ascertainment by age in the school populations sampled by Lewis. Table 2 gives these data as well as figures based on a survey conducted for the New York Department of Mental Hygiene in Onondaga County, New York, and findings from the Baltimore Study of Lemkau, Tietze, and Cooper (1942). Figures for the pre-school ages are also included. It can be seen that the incidence varies greatly between age groups, and between the different studies. Penrose comments on the Wood Report figures: 'The incidence represents a complex relationship between social and educational needs and the biological constitution of the population at each age' (op. cit., p. 20).

TABLE 2

Prevalence of defectives by age (per 1,000 of population)
(from Penrose, 1954, and others)

Age	England and Wales (1929)	Baltimore (1942)	Onondaga County (1953) (Whites)
0–4	1·2	0·7	4·5
5–9	15·5	11·8	39·4
10–14	25·6	43·6	77·6
15–19*	10·8	30·2	44·9

* 15–17 for Onondaga County.

The criteria of a survey which, like the Wood Report, aimed to give a comprehensive picture of the number of defectives in England and Wales, could therefore not be expected to be exact. Even if carried out by one person, conditions of case-finding vary a great deal both by age, and even, as Lewis (1929) thinks, according to whether urban or rural occupations prevail in the district.

The degree to which opinion has varied about a syndrome such as feeble-mindedness or mental deficiency in general can be judged from the fact that the proportion supposed to be genetically determined has varied from early estimates of about 77 per cent. (Goddard, 1914) to 29 per cent. (Penrose, 1934) according to Kanner (1948b). In the few well-defined clinical subgroups it is often relatively easy to give a diagnosis, but with those people of I.Q. above 50 but below 75, defect is conceded to be associated primarily with social factors, and therefore definition cannot but be imprecise. Thus early confidence concerning diagnosis has given place to caution. The era surrounding the passing of the 1913 Act, and the anxiety concerning national degeneracy as a result of differential fertility, has now given place to a time when the eugenic attitude has been considerably circumscribed. The change in emphasis has given rise to a reassessment of the meaning of mental deficiency, and especially feeble-mindedness.

The inconsistency of measures of a social kind can be imagined when it is realized that a social worker's or teacher's judgment will often be involved. The diagnosis of severe retardation will thus be in part based on the estimation of a person not necessarily trained to detect dullness, and may in certain instances depend on the size of a special class in a school, or on the presence of vacancies in an E.S.N. school nearby. Variation from school to school, court to court, and social class to social class are likely to occur when diagnosis, ascertainment, or certification depend on an individual's interpretation of the meaning of the term 'social competence'.

(ii) Unreliability of instruments of measurement

This can also be a potent source of error. The fact that social criteria vary between persons, and also from place to place and time to time, has already been emphasized in discussing imprecise criteria, and needs no further consideration.

The reliability of intelligence tests is discussed very fully in Chapter IV, to which the reader is referred. All that need be quoted here is the distinction made between 'unreliability of measurement' (representing, in the main, personal fluctuations) and 'unreliability of persons tested' (that is, their ability to alter in relative standing over long periods of time), which is briefly mentioned below and in Chapters IV and V.

The reliability of measurement is best established by immediate retest, which usually yields a correlation of 0·9 on a properly standardized and validated test. The personal fluctuations which this represents may involve in some cases considerable change in status from one test to the other. Where a precise borderline is used for any purpose, this fact may have repercussions on the way in which, say, a child is dealt with, when one remembers that on one day he might be just below the borderline, and just above it the next.

(iii) Historical, social, and personal changes

These also need little further discussion. It has already been made clear that the problems of measurement of subnormality vary from time to time, depending on current concepts and upon available services. Similarly, the fact that intellectual growth tends not to proceed uniformly and may also vary with gross environmental changes is well known and is considered fully in Chapters IV and V. Suffice it to give as examples the findings of Honzik, Macfarlane, and Allen (1948) and Owens (1953). Honzik *et al.* found that between the ages of 6 and 18, 58 per cent. of a large group of children changed 15 or more I.Q. points at some time during the period, while only 15 per cent. changed by as little as 9 points or less. Owens's interesting study (op. cit.) compares the college entrants of 1919 with the same people in 1950 on subtest of the Army Alpha. Thirty years' increase in age has apparently resulted, contrary to expectations, in increases of score in 7 of 8 subjects. Upward changes were of the order of nearly zero to about 0·5 sigma, 5 of 7 changes were significant at the 1 per cent. (four) or 5 per cent. level (one). It seems probable from the analysis that at least some of this upward change depended on the continuous practice of the function involved. The interest of this conclusion lies in the fact that increased scores were independent of initial scores ($r = 0{\cdot}07$). Although some increase of initial individual differences appeared, these had to be attributed to differences in inter-trial treatment. The study, whilst applying only to graduates, is none the less consistent with the finding that I.Q. increments can occur and that it is sometimes possible to attribute at least part of such changes to differences in training and to cultural influences. In Chapter V, researches showing that positive I.Q. changes can occur in backward children as a result of altering educational or social conditions are discussed in detail.

Each of the problems which have been outlined in this section is likely to affect estimates of the numbers of both grossly defective and feeble-minded children and adults in any civilized community. The brief outline of them given here is inadequate as a treatment of these forces in themselves, but it is intended to give a picture of some of the difficulties which beset census-taking of this nature. In cases where a complete population cannot be examined, which, of course, is the commonest situation, variations in the level of services provided inevitably further complicate the picture. For example, Lewis (1929) points out that sampling of adults in his survey was less adequate than that of children because of the existence of compulsory education for children and the facilities which the schools thus appended for case-finding. Lewis says:

> The ascertainment of adult mental defectives obviously presents much greater difficulty than that of children. Practically all the children between the ages of 5 and 14 are to be found at school, but there is no such aggregation of adults. Even in districts where the men and women are largely employed in the same industry it is not possible to take advantage of this in an investigation such as ours. Except in a few cases, we could not get access to the mentally defective adults who worked in the mines, mills, and factories in the investigated areas; we therefore had to rely for our initial ascertainment of adults upon a large number of sources, some statutory and others voluntary. The following is a list of the chief sources of information:
>
> 1. The Local Authority under the Mental Deficiency Act.
> 2. The Local Education Authority.
> 3. The Poor Law Authority.
> 4. Medical Officers of Health; School Medical Officers; Special Mental Deficiency Medical Officers; Sanitary Inspectors.
> 5. General Practitioners; District Nurses.
> 6. Certified Institutions, Houses and Homes for the Mentally Defective; Mental Hospitals; Epileptic Colonies; Hospitals and Dispensaries.
> 7. Local Branch of the Central Association for Mental Welfare.
> 8. Charitable Institutions and Homes; Shelters; Refuges; Common Lodging Houses.
> 9. Charity Organizations and Societies; Clergy; Social Workers.
> 10. Police and Prison Authorities; Reformatories and Industrial Schools.

Even more confusing perhaps are the 'accidental' reasons which under English law may lead to a person of poor scholastic achievement being declared 'subject to be dealt with', and hence to be certified as defective.

For example, until recently the birth of an illegitimate child to a woman in receipt of relief was sufficient for her to be certified and made the responsibility of the Board of Control.[1] Even the child itself might be certified. It has sometimes been suggested that magistrates have used certification as a means of securing for an unwanted child, conditions which they have judged better than those of children's homes. In other cases, backwardness at school which may or may not have been due to innate lack of ability has been offered as evidence of backwardness which, when combined with a legal offence, may result in permanent hospitalization instead of a jail sentence. In view of the multiple causes of backwardness which may result in educational subnormality, not necessarily of a permanent kind, very great care should be exercised in ascertaining backwardness in such cases.

Such a statement of difficulties is offered to suggest that few estimates of incidence are likely to be repeatable even in the same country a decade or two apart, and certainly not from country to country. In the earlier years of Tredgold's work, and during the earlier years of the Eugenic Society from 1908 to 1914, many students of mental deficiency took the view that it was possible to detect the presence of backwardness with some certainty, and that defect was frequently inherited, and generally incurable. Just as similar views about the ease of diagnosis of schizophrenia, and the possibility of agreeing about its incidence rates, are giving place to increased sophistication, so it is with defect. The scientifically naïve views represented by early studies of the Juke and Kallikak families, and some of the statements of such eminent writers as Galton (1909–10), are now regarded with much greater caution. As a result of the current valuation of incidence, it is now possible to arrive at a certain kind of estimate, but the nature of any such estimate must be accepted as relevant only to the purpose of the survey. The possibility of judging prevalence in a syndrome such as mental deficiency might very well be discarded as a mistaken idea, resulting from a confusion of many distinct and separate entities, each given the blanket title of mental defect. Once having made clear the difficulties, it becomes possible to evaluate results.

[1] The Board of Control until the passing of the National Health Service Act was the Central Authority corresponding to the Commissioners in Lunacy which was responsible for the supervision and administration of the Mental Deficiency Acts.

SURVEY FINDINGS

The first extensive surveys were those mentioned at the beginning of this chapter. In the case of the Report of the Royal Commission on the Care and Control of the Feeble-minded (1908), the purpose of the survey was, as stated, in order to make such provision for the care of this class of person, that hardship or danger 'to such persons and the community' would be avoided. The situation was regarded as serious by the Medical Investigators, who drew information from twelve sources: schools, Poor Law Institutions, those in receipt of relief, sanitary authorities, medical charities, G.P.s, training homes and charitable institutions of various kinds, police, idiot asylums, prisons, houses for inebriates, and 'other sources'. The Commission found 'in the whole population (32,527,843) 149,628 mentally defective persons or 0·46 per cent., apart from certified lunatics'. This was the percentage of those who would now be called mentally defective, although at that time mental defect was a term used to cover all kinds of mental disturbance and abnormality. The Commission found variations in the nine areas examined, showing prevalence figures in some cases as low as 1·35 per 1,000, and in others as high as 4·68 per 1,000. Figures over 4 per 1,000 were most common. The distribution of grades was found to be about 24 per cent. for idiots and imbeciles (6 per cent. and 18 per cent.) and 76 per cent. for the feeble-minded.

Many investigations conducted in subsequent years up to and during the First World War found prevalence rates of about 4 per 1,000. Tredgold (1949) gives a table of American figures from seven surveys, only two of which are considerably different from this rate. These were the 1915 Porter County (Indiana) Survey, 7·35 per 1,000, and the 1917 Nassau County (New York) Survey with a rate of 5·44 per 1,000.

The next important estimate of prevalence was that made and published for the Interdepartmental (Wood) Committee largely by E. O. Lewis. Both this survey and that of the Royal Commission, and in fact most surveys reported here, were field studies aimed at determining the number of cases of defect in a community. The Wood Committee used both tests and clinical diagnosis in its survey. Wood Report findings resulted in an overall figure of 8·57 per 1,000 as an estimate of prevalence, i.e. nearly twice the ratio found by the Royal

TABLE 3

Prevalence figures for England and Wales by age, sex, and grade (per 1,000 population) (Wood Report)

	Feeble-minded			Imbeciles			Idiots			Total		
	M	F	Total	M	F	Total	M	F	Total	M	F	Total
Children	1·81	1·55	3·36	0·38	0·29	0·67	0·09	0·06	0·15	2·28	1·90	4·18
Adults	1·58	1·76	3·34	0·46	0·39	0·84	0·11	0·09	0·19	2·14	2·24	4·38
Children and adults	3·39	3·31	6·70	0·84	0·68	1·52	0·19	0·15	0·35	4·42	4·14	8·57

Commission. Table 3 summarizes some of the findings of this investigation.

The proportion of idiots to imbeciles to feeble-minded cases is similar to that of the Royal Commission, namely, 4, 18, and 78 per cent. This fact is thought to be of considerable administrative importance.

Two other important aspects of prevalence are illuminated by this survey. These are the prevalence of backwardness by social class and the difference in ascertainment noted by age. Just as stillbirths and neonatal mortality can frequently be shown to be related to socio-economic grade in the community as Titmuss (1943) and others have shown, so backwardness is associated with poverty. Sometimes this finding has been presented as if the relationship were genetic. Thus, for example, Tredgold (1909–10) drew attention to the danger of defectives having children.

> . . . I would lay it down as a general principle that as soon as a nation reaches that stage of civilization in which medical knowledge and humanitarian sentiment operate to prolong the existence of the unfit, then it becomes imperative upon that nation to devise such social laws as will ensure that the unfit do not propagate their kind.

This viewpoint was reflected also in the controversy concerning the decline in the national intelligence. The Scottish Council for Research in Education planned a careful research aimed at clarifying the issues involved in the question of national intelligence, and it was predicted with confidence that the general level of intelligence would decline. This prediction was based on differential fertility, i.e. the lower I.Q. of the children of large families and the negative correlation (about $-0{\cdot}224$) between intelligence and family size. Sir Godfrey Thomson (1950) stated:

> 'It is clear that if there is a negative correlation between size of family and intelligence, and if the explanation is that intelligence is largely an inherited quality, and that intelligent people tend to produce smaller families, then the average intelligence will sink generation by generation. There is indeed some direct evidence that this is so.'

Sir Godfrey Thomson thought it unlikely to be as high as a figure estimated by Cattell, namely 3 points per generation, but thought that it might be high as $1\frac{1}{2}$ points. This statement was made about 1944.

On other occasions, similar facts have been presented from an opposite point of view, arguing that environment may in some measure determine intelligence and hence the incidence of defect. There would seem to be a small yet significant relationship between I.Q. and family size, now based on many thousands of cases, but the national intelligence, on the findings of two surveys of the Scottish Council for Research in Education, has not declined between 1932 and 1947. In a later work (1953) the question to which this unexpected result gives rise is discussed (pp. 103 seq.) by referring to a model suggested by Penrose (1950). On the basis of this he shows that it is possible to have a genetically stable level of intelligence even given a negative relationship between family size and I.Q. Environmental explanations are rejected.

However, any study of incidence must also take account of the fact that a number of studies have shown a relationship between intelligence level and socio-economic status. Even though a correlation exists within any one social group between family size and intelligence, Penrose noted a relationship affecting the feeble-minded only, in his Colchester Survey (1938). In the accompanying Table 4 his data are recombined to show the prevalence of dullness plus feeble-mindedness on the one hand and the lower grades of deficiency on the other in professional as opposed to other occupational grades. It should be remembered that the figures refer only to patients in an institution.

TABLE 4

Defect by parental occupation and grade of defect
(in Penrose's Colchester Survey)

	High-grade defect	Imbeciles and idiots
Professional occupations	55	113
Clerical and manual occupations	514	507

A chi square based on these figures is highly significant ($p < 0{\cdot}001$), showing that high-grade defect and low-grade defect are differently distributed in the occupational grades of parents.

The distribution of backwardness in London was mapped by Burt (1937), and most subsequent surveys have confirmed his findings. Recently a thorough analysis of the position in L.C.C. schools has been carried out for the Local Education Authority. This survey was completed some time ago, and although the results have not been published they are believed to show a similar pattern of backwardness to that found by Burt. Burt stated that backward children are to be found in greatest numbers in poor and overcrowded districts. He proceeded to define the areas of backwardness and poverty and provides a table which shows a 0·934 correlation between infant mortality and backwardness. As this correlation is based on 29 boroughs its confidence level is presumably well beyond 0·001.

Thus there seems to be a very great likelihood that some forms of backwardness, probably including feeble-mindedness, are found more frequently in the economically depressed sections of society, and that as Burt notes, 'The various agencies which increase the death rate during infancy presumably tend at the same time to lower the physical and mental vitality of the survivors even when insufficient to cause their early death' (op. cit., p. 104).

Interesting figures have recently been provided by a survey carried out in Onondaga County (1955), directed by the Mental Health Research Unit. They confirm the suggestions made by Burt (1937), Lewis (1929), and Penrose (1938), that the socio-economic status of parents is reflected in the incidence of mild backwardness. Table 5 is taken from one preliminary report of the survey. It confirms also the differential incidence by age. A suggestion of great interest is made in reporting these two findings. This is that habits of reporting vary in different geographical regions. Although tentatively advanced

TABLE 5

Prevalence rates of mental retardation by socio-economic area: Syracuse City, N.Y., 3.1.53

(Rates are per 1,000 enumerated population on 4.1.50)

Socio-economic areas	Rate
I and II	17·0
III	27·8
IV	33·8
V	33·4
VI	65·3

it may be relevant in one form or another to social class and to age differences in prevalence as well as to geographical area. In this study the reported prevalence for males was twice that for females. In the Wood Report the ratio appears to be much more nearly equal for both children and adults. The final summary from the Onondaga County Survey is quoted in full.

A special census of children believed to be possibly retarded was conducted through local child-care agencies in a New York State metropolitan area. One per cent. of all children under 18 years of age were reported as retarded, measured by an intelligence quotient less than 75. Two-tenths (0·2) per cent. were severely retarded, with an intelligence quotient less than 50. Including children known to have an intelligence quotient greater than 75, a total of 3·5 per cent. were referred as 'possibly retarded'.

Reported suspected prevalence rates were observed to vary markedly with age, sex, colour, and place of residence. Rates increased to a peak at age 14 years, then fell off sharply. The reported male rate was nearly twice the female, and non-whites higher than whites. Residence in the economically depressed central area of the city was accompanied by higher rates for all colours.

These data suggest strongly that behaviour leading to the social suspicion of 'mental retardation' is not necessarily a fixed characteristic of individual children but is rather a complex set of manifestations of some children's relationship to their immediate environment.

Other interesting material revealed by the New York State Department of Mental Hygiene Survey is that the relationship between referred mental retardation and other forms of handicap, provides information on the factors which are likely to lead to referral in the first instance. For example it appears that 70 per cent. of 442 children (reported from a group of 3,789 as suffering from brain damage of some kind) also had one form of physical handicap. Speech problems were present in 33 per cent. of cases. The figure for detected brain injury is low and the relative proportions of idiocy, imbecility, and feeble-mindedness as judged by test are in fact closely similar to the Wood Report findings, namely, 6·6 per cent. idiots, 18·6 per cent. imbeciles, and 74·8 per cent. feeble-minded. The calculation is, however, based on only 868 cases abstracted from a table dealing also with children of higher, but nevertheless subnormal, I.Q.s.

The recent studies by Stein and Susser (1962) take the argument a step further. Like many other investigators they distinguish two types of mental subnormality, namely those with presumptive brain damage, and those who appear to be without brain damage. The first group is found among children of all social classes. The second group occurs only among those whose families belong to the lower social groups. Stein and Susser argue that it is not possible to posit a genetical mechanism which would segregate children so sharply by social class (consider the great overlap between classes in the distribution of children in stature for example, where differences in mean stature of children in different social classes are also found). They therefore argue that there is a 'Cultural' syndrome of mental retardation' which accounts for at least 75 per cent. of the educationally subnormal, and which is in principle preventable.

One other investigation is of interest as revealing the change in the use of criteria over a period of years in England. This is the hospital survey of O'Connor and Tizard (1954), who studied twelve hospitals in the London area and sampled 5 per cent. of the total number of 11,850 patients. It was found that idiots and imbeciles formed 42 per cent. of all patients (3 per cent. and 39 per cent.), and the feeble-minded the remaining 58 per cent. Thus it would seem that the distribution of grades in hospitals is different from their distribution in the community.

The other important fact relevant to incidence noted in this study was that the average Matrices Raw Score of a sample of feeble-minded adult patients was 23·9, Standard Deviation 10·4, for men; and 21·4, Standard Deviation 10·0, for women. These figures are equivalent to I.Q.s of approximately 74 and 71 respectively for the age groups involved. The finding thus confirms Penrose's (1938) institutional study, and Tizard's (1950) study, and six other studies made in the post-war period. If the assumption is made that mental deficiency can only be notified when I.Q.s fall below 70 points, an assumption often made by psychiatrists for convenience, although having no legal force, then half the feeble-minded patients in English hospitals at that time would fall outside the category of mental deficiency. This is therefore another example of a survey in which differences in criteria or social attitude may alter prevalence figures or our attitude towards them.

PREVALENCE OF SEVERE MENTAL DEFECT

The discussion so far has been concerned mainly with methodological problems. These arise particularly in the case of high-grade mental subnormality or moronity. When we turn to imbecility and idiocy we are on firmer ground, because the criteria are more clear-cut, and depend to a much greater extent upon the personal qualities of the defective and to a much smaller extent upon the circumstances of his family, than is the case with high-grade defectives. This is particularly true of children, where the fact of compulsory education makes case-finding relatively easy.

Two recent papers investigating the prevalence of severe mental subnormality in children deserve mention: these are an article by Carter (1958) dealing with the prevalence of mongolism, and one by Goodman and Tizard (1962) dealing with the prevalence of idiocy and imbecility in a Metropolitan area.

Carter prepared a life-table for nearly 700 mongols attending the Great Ormond Street Hospital for Sick Children in London between 1944 and 1955. This hospital, which is the largest children's hospital in the country and which is also the leading teaching hospital for paediatrics, probably sees a representative sample of sick and handicapped children including those who suffer from mongolism. Carter calculated that of live-born mongols who make up one in six to seven hundred of all live births 30 per cent. are dead by the age of one month, 53 per cent. by the end of one year and 60 per cent. by the end of 10 years. If one considers survival to the age of 10 there is evidence that the numbers have quadrupled in 30 years. (The prevalence of children with mongolism among 10-year-old children in 1958 was approximately one in every thousand. In 1949 only one in 2,000 was a mongol, and in 1929 probably only one in 4,000. Thus the prevalence at age 10 doubled between 1929 and 1949 and doubled again between 1949 and 1958.) The fall in mortality for mongols is believed to be of the same order as, though a little less than, that for children in general. There is no evidence to suggest that there has been a change in the incidence (or numbers born alive) during that period.

Stoller (1960) and Collman and Stoller (1962b) suggest that the pattern of mongol births at least in Victoria between 1942 and 1957 shows (*a*) an urban predominance, (*b*) a significant periodic variation with three periods of peak incidence, 1944–5, 1950–1, and 1955, and (*c*) a preponderance (40 per cent.) of mongol births confined to a specified area and during limited periods of time. Collmann and Stoller (1962c) also claim a periodic variation for three other disorders, anencephaly, spina bifida, and hydrocephaly.

The presumed rise in the number of mongols and of children with some other forms of congenital malformation who survive to adolescence and perhaps adult life led Goodman and Tizard (1962) to carry out a survey of the prevalence of all forms of idiocy and imbecility in children in the Metropolitan County of Middlesex. This survey provides what are probably the most complete data on the prevalence of severe mental defect in any large urban area since the survey by Dr E. O. Lewis. The County of Middlesex forms part of Greater London; it has an area of 232 square miles and a population of two and a quarter million. The Local Health Authority maintains a register of all mentally subnormal children brought to notice and the records were supplemented for purposes of his study by extensive inquiries made in special schools, and hospitals, to seek out other children who might not be known to the health authority. Table 6 gives the numbers and the age specific rates per thousand reported in this study.

A comparison was made with E. O. Lewis's findings for urban and rural areas of England, obtained 30 years before. For children aged 7–13 (the age group best able to be compared) the numbers and rates are given in Table 7.

Goodman and Tizard found that, as would have been expected, the rates for mongolism had increased fourfold. For all other forms of idiocy and imbecility there was a decline of about one-third in the prevalence rate (2·31 as compared with 3·37 per thousand). They argue that the decline may be due entirely to an artefact, or to different criteria being employed; on the other hand it seems possible that in part at least it is due to a true decline in incidence brought about by better nutrition, better medical care, better antenatal and obstetric services, and more adequate child welfare provision. The problem has been more fully discussed by Tizard (1964).

TABLE 6

'True' prevalence of imbecility and idiocy among children, Middlesex (January 1, 1960)

Age group	Estimated population	Imbeciles and Idiots				
		No.* known to health authority	No. still in education system†	Others‡	Total	Rate per 1,000 population
0–	154,700	146	0	5	151	0·98
5–	138,122	398	14	5	417	0·98
10–14	158,978	547	24	3	574	3·61
0–14	451,800	1,091	38	13	1,142	2·53

* Including those unclassified or called feeble-minded, but properly imbecile or idiot.

† Including residential schools and schools for the physically handicapped, excluding those children already known to the health department.

‡ Including Board of Control approved homes, Sunshine Homes, certified institutions, excluding those children already known to the health department.

TABLE 7

Prevalence of idiocy and imbecility among children aged 7 and under 14 years in 1925–9 and in 1960 (rates per 1000)

	Population	Rates	Number
	1925–9		
All urban areas	39,930	3·71	148
„ rural „	31,930	5·61	179
Total	71,860	4·55	327
	1960		
Middlesex	213,945	3·45	738

1925–9 figures from Lewis's Tables 15 and M.

1960 population figures are estimated from the Middlesex 5–14 population by dividing them in the proportion known to obtain in London.

CONCLUSIONS

A great number of different sources of error exist which might be expected to give rise to considerable variation in prevalence figures. It is therefore remarkable that with difficulties of case-finding, criteria, and changing social attitudes, rates should have been so nearly the same in the many surveys conducted between 1904 and 1917, and between 1918 and 1955. The main differences seem to have been between the earlier and the later periods. With few exceptions the earlier studies find a general prevalence of all grades of defect of about 0·4 per cent., whereas most studies made since the Wood Report have found prevalence to centre about 0·8 to 1·0 per cent., sometimes rising to 1·5 per cent. It may be that more recent studies have had better testing techniques, more experience, and better facilities. Lewis (1929) suggested that his findings were different from those of the 1908 Royal Commission for such reasons. It is possible that the transfer of some responsibility for diagnosis and training to the Ministry of Education under the 1944 Education Act, and subsequent re-examination of provisions for care, may be making as yet undetected changes in the prevalence figures in this country.

However, at present few are concerned about any possibility of a rapid increase in the number of defectives in the community, rather there is concern for more training facilities for the handicapped. Provision either for hospital care of idiots or imbeciles or for the education of the dull and backward has always lagged behind demand. If in the next decade it is possible to reverse this situation, we may find that a complete nation-wide census of those receiving guidance or training because of mental subnormality will be a matter of simply collating returns.

Such an estimate of provision made for different categories of backwardness would in many senses be more meaningful than an effort to arrive at an estimate of the incidence of mental defect considered as a biological entity.

Part II

THEORETICAL PROBLEMS

Chapter III

CRITERIA AND CLASSIFICATION OF MENTAL DEFICIENCY

by Ann M. Clarke

INTRODUCTION

In considering the problem of classification of the mentally deficient it is perhaps worth making several elementary, but none the less important, general points. Firstly, classification always has a purpose; frequently it seeks to rationalize administrative decisions which have already been implemented, and to invest them with a scientific flavour and precision which they do not in fact possess. It seeks to find a quality common to a group of persons heterogeneous in aetiology, in present status and in prognosis, who have been found to need some form of special assistance. Secondly, while no doubt boundaries do exist in nature, they are seldom as clearly defined and rigid as we seek to make them. We tend to impose on nature boundaries which may not in fact exist. These first two considerations particularly apply to the division of mentally deficient persons from the normal population, although, as has been implied, there is general agreement that mental characteristics form a graded continuum from genius to idiocy. Thus, any such division must be to some extent arbitrary.

Many systems of classification are concerned with the problem of sub-division of the whole class known in this country as mentally subnormal persons (and in America as the feeble-minded). Here again, the first consideration applies: classification always has a purpose. The sub-division may have an educational bias, separating the educable from the totally ineducable; it may be concerned with problems of aetiology, for example the universally accepted divisions of inborn and acquired mental deficiency. It may be concerned with levels of psychological functioning, or with levels of social functioning, as in the legal definitions of subnormality, severe subnormality, and psychopathy (Mental Health Act, 1959).

From the foregoing, it will be readily appreciated that, with different purposes and with a lack of natural boundaries, systems of classification of the mentally deficient are frequently arbitrary, overlapping, or even mutually exclusive or contradictory. It is intended in this chapter to examine in detail the views of the most prominent authorities in the field, to show where they agree and where they disagree, where their theories are internally inconsistent, and to offer a critical commentary.

Probably in every society at all times it has been obvious that certain of its members have differed from the rest by virtue of mental or physical abnormalities. Sometimes such persons have been revered, sometimes pitied, and sometimes feared. Different societies at different times have thus reacted to the problem of mental subnormality and disorder, with widely varying degrees of tolerance or intolerance.

LEGAL CLASSIFICATION IN ENGLAND[1]

In England, statutory mention of mental defectives dates as far back as the reign of Edward I (dates: 1272–1307), when the distinction was made for the first time on record between the born fool and the lunatic; in the Statute of Prerogatives in the reign of Edward II, a similar division is recorded, between 'born fool' (*fatuus naturalis*) and the person of unsound mind who may yet have certain lucid intervals (*non compos mentis*, *sicut quidam sunt per lucida intervalla*).

The purpose of this distinction in feudal times was to facilitate the disposal of property: thus, if a man were found by inquisition to be a lunatic, the Crown took possession of his belongings only during the period of his illness; whereas, if a man were found to be an idiot, his property reverted permanently to the Crown, subject only to an obligation to provide for his person and estate.

In later centuries, the distinction between these two categories of mental abnormality disappeared, but as society became more complex, so it became necessary to deal with the unsound in mind in

[1] This account of the historical background is summarized from the Report of the Mental Deficiency Committee (1929), Part I, Chapter III.

various statutes, and discrepancies arose between the criteria of law and of medicine.

Lunatics and mental defectives are clearly distinguished in the Idiots Act of 1886. This Act, furthermore, recognized a class of people less defective than the idiot, referring incidentally to the imbecile. Later, when the Education Act of 1870 had been in operation for some years, it was realized that in the case of children, there were those who, though defective in mind, were capable of being educated to a higher level than those who could be certified as imbeciles; these were termed 'feeble-minded'.

The Royal Commission on the Deaf and Dumb (1889) was asked to include in its deliberations other children who, from special circumstances, might require special methods of education. They concluded that there was a class of children who were 'educable imbeciles', and another type, 'feeble-minded children', who should be separated from ordinary scholars and receive special attention.

In 1897, a Departmental Committee inquiring into the existing educational facilities for defective children, regarded 'idiot' and 'imbecile' as denoting children who could not be educated to become wholly or partially self-supporting, and 'feeble-minded' as describing children who could be so educated.

Thus, over the years, there was a gradual emergence of the nomenclature finally employed in the classification of the Mental Deficiency Act of 1913, which added a fourth category of 'moral imbeciles', to those already in use.

The Mental Deficiency Act

The 1913 Act, which was amended in 1927, defined 'mental defectiveness' as meaning 'a condition of arrested or incomplete development of mind, existing before the age of eighteen years, whether arising from inherent causes or induced by disease or injury'.

The law described four classes of persons who 'shall be deemed to be defectives within the meaning of this Act':

(*a*) Idiots, that is to say, persons in whose case there exists mental defectiveness of such a degree that they are unable to guard themselves against common physical dangers.

(*b*) Imbeciles, that is to say, persons in whose case there exists mental defectiveness which, though not amounting to idiocy, is yet so pronounced that they are incapable of managing themselves or their affairs or, in the case of children, of being taught to do so.

(*c*) Feeble-minded persons, that is to say, persons in whose case there exists mental defectiveness which, though not amounting to imbecility is yet so pronounced that they require care, supervision and control for their own protection or for the protection of others or, in the case of children, that they appear to be permanently incapable by reason of such defectiveness of receiving proper benefit from the instruction in ordinary schools [in effect amended by the 1944 Education Act].

(*d*) Moral defectives, that is to say, persons in whose case there exists mental defectiveness coupled with strongly vicious or criminal propensities and who require care, supervision and control for the protection of others.

It will be noted that the legal definition of mental deficiency gave no exact criteria of the condition, and, as Wallin (1949) has pointed out, is so general and vague as to be worthless as an attempt at scientific description. Wallin says

> there are many degrees and kinds of 'arrested or incomplete development of mind before the age of 18 years', most of which do not constitute 'mental defectiveness' as a legal category, and some of which represent processes of deterioration rather than 'arrested or incomplete development'.

So far as the definitions of the sub-categories of defects were concerned, the criteria were based exclusively on the individual's social competence. Thus, an idiot was said to be unable to guard himself from common physical dangers; imbeciles were unable to manage themselves or their own affairs; the feeble-minded required care, supervision, and control for their own protection or for the protection of others, or, in the case of children, were ineducable; and moral defectives were possessed of strongly vicious or criminal propensities.

Mental Health Act, 1959

In England the Mental Health Act of 1959 repealed all previous legislation dealing with lunacy, mental treatment, and mental deficiency, and provided a single code for all types of *mental disorder*, defined as 'mental illness, arrested or incomplete development of mind, psychopathic disorder or disability of mind'.

'Arrested or incomplete development of mind' comprehends two categories, 'severe subnormality' and 'subnormality', defined as follows:

1. *Severe subnormality:* 'A state of arrested or incomplete development of mind which includes subnormality of intelligence and is of such a nature or degree that the patient is incapable of living an independent life or of guarding himself against serious exploitation, or will be so incapable when of an age to do so.'

2. *Subnormality:* 'A state of arrested or incomplete development of mind (not amounting to severe subnormality) which includes subnormality of intelligence and is of a nature or degree which requires or is susceptible to medical treatment or other special care or training of the patient.'

Psychopathic disorder is defined as 'a persistent disorder or disability of mind (whether or not including subnormality of intelligence) which results in abnormally aggressive or seriously irresponsible conduct on the part of the patient and requires or is susceptible to medical treatment'.

All these definitions are subject to the proviso that persons are not to be regarded as suffering from any form of mental disorder 'by reason only of promiscuity or other immoral conduct'.

Perhaps the most constructive aspect of the Act in respect to mental deficiency was to make it administratively possible for both types of subnormal patient and the psychopathic to be admitted to hospital on an informal basis for 'treatment', without the deprivation of personal liberty implicit in legal certification.

On the other hand, a Working Party of the British Psychological Society, convened in 1962 in order to examine the working of certain aspects of the Act, makes a number of criticisms. Much depends upon how one defines the phrase 'including subnormality of intelligence'. It was clear that a large number of persons with I.Q.s well above 70 were still being dealt with as subnormal. Moreover, the useful distinction between low- and high-grade defective was being lost since different authorities placed the borderline at different points in the scale. It should be added that the distinction between idiots and imbeciles is also being abandoned because of the use of the blanket category 'severely subnormal' to cover both clinical grades. Among other recommendations of the Working Party is the warning that the Binet test should not be used for the assessment of adult subnormal patients.

A further difficulty is that the Mental Health Act makes it much easier to detain compulsorily patients over the age of 25 if they are severely subnormal. This is an obvious temptation, therefore, to use this category in the case of difficult patients – a temptation that is apparently not always being resisted.

TREDGOLD'S SOCIAL CRITERIA

Several authorities have advocated social criteria as the best means of separating the mentally deficient from the normal population. One of the most prominent exponents of this view was A. F. Tredgold (1952), whose arguments on the subject (which have for many years had a profound influence) will be briefly summarized.

Starting with a definition of mental deficiency (amentia) as being a condition in which the mind has failed to reach normal development, Tredgold examines three criteria of such a failure, the educational, intellectual (by means of intelligence tests), and the biological and social criterion.

The first he rejects on the grounds that there are such wide individual differences in responses to educational instruction and in the ability to learn particular subjects, that some people who fail scholastically may be in the normal range of variation; he points out that a large proportion of those who are backward at school later are capable of earning their living and fending for themselves. Tredgold believes, therefore, that it would be unjustifiable and unscientific to use an arbitrary standard such as scholastic educability as the criterion of mental defect.

Intelligence tests are similarly rejected as providing a useful standard of mental deficiency. Tredgold argues that by taking as the criterion an I.Q. below which all would agree that the individual was defective, one would exclude as not defective many persons in institutions, whom no one doubts to be in need of care and control, but whose I.Q. is considerably higher than that of others fending for themselves satisfactorily in the general community. On the other hand, if the dividing line were placed high enough to include all those whom Tredgold regards as defective, it would certainly also include many usually considered normal.

Tredgold, therefore, advocates the use of what he calls a biological and social criterion, based on the assumption that the essential purpose of mind is to enable the individual 'so to adapt himself to his environment as to maintain an independent existence'. From the biological and social aspect, the one who can do this is to be regarded as normal, while the one whose mental development does not admit of this is to be regarded as defective. Tredgold recognizes that the ability to maintain existence is not entirely dependent upon mind, but is influenced by the nature of the individual's surroundings; he says, 'To constitute abnormality and defect, the failure must be due to psychological and not to economic and social causes; and there is usually little difficulty in distinguishing between the two.' He does not, however, give any indication of the criteria to be employed in coming to such a distinction. Tredgold rightly regards as intolerable the possibility that a person capable of holding a job and managing his affairs should be stigmatized as defective because he is either an educational failure, or has an I.Q. below an arbitrary standard, but ignores the fact that social criteria (particularly those which are not operationally defined) are just as arbitrary as the I.Q., if not more so, and have not even the advantage of being based on norms for an entire population. Furthermore, subjective judgments of psychological qualities in other people are notoriously unreliable, and it has repeatedly been found that judges attempting such assessments on the same people differ considerably amongst themselves. It is puzzling that Tredgold should make criticisms of educational and intellectual criteria which he fails to consider in relation to his social criterion, although they would be equally applicable.

Tredgold can also be criticized for the theoretical structure underlying his bio-social considerations, based as it is on McDougall's system of instincts and sentiments, which few scientists today would accept as being either valid or useful.

In discussing the implications of the then legal definition of mental deficiency in Britain, Tredgold states that although the Act made no reference to the permanency of the condition, there is no doubt that mental arrest, sufficient to cause the social incapacity envisaged by the Act, will be permanent and incurable. He further points out that when the Act refers to 'arrested development of mind', there is no legal justification for assuming that the only really important aspect of mind is the intellectual one: 'an arrested development of any process or department of mind, provided it resulted in social incapacity, constitutes mental deficiency'.

This latter interpretation has been advocated by several experts, and is typified by the British Medical Association and Magistrates' Association's memorandum of 1947 (Interpretation of Definitions in the Mental Deficiency Act, 1927), which states that 'the purpose of this memorandum is to point out that the concept of mind is wider than that of intellect, and that mental defect (i.e. deficiency of mind) is not the same thing as intellectual deficiency, though it includes it'. A similar point of view was expressed more recently by the Board of Control (1954) and the Royal Medico-Psychological Association (1954) in their memoranda to the Royal Commission on the Law relating to Mental Illness and Mental Deficiency. Thus, the Board of Control say: 'We regard the present definitions as enabling medical practitioners to certify mentally defective patients on the ground that they have characteristics from early youth which make them anti-social, although their intelligence might be quite normal.' The R.M.P.A. in its discussion of the nature of mental deficiency states

> This 'condition of arrested or incomplete development of mind' may, however, be manifested in very varied ways. A usual manifestation is failure to develop what is commonly known as intelligence – functions which can be measured by psychometric methods and assessed under such terms as 'mental age' or 'intelligence quotient'; but this is by no means invariable, and in other cases the undeveloped mind may be manifested chiefly by failure to attain normal control of the emotions or to achieve the qualities needed for normal social behaviour.

The practical outcome of this point of view has been that in England a large number of individuals of dull-normal and normal intellect have been certified as mentally defective. O'Connor and Tizard (1954) showed that in their 5 per cent. sample of nearly 12,000 patients, over half were classified as 'feeble-minded'; they found, in conformity with their previous researches, and that of other psychologists working in institutions, that the *average* I.Q. of young adult feeble-minded defectives was a little above 70 points. Various tests have been used by different examiners with substantially similar results. Commenting on this state of affairs, the British Psychological Society (1955) says, 'During this century, the British concept of mental deficiency has widened until it is no longer closely related to biological, psychological, or genetic definitions of the condition.' It seems that something like one-quarter of all institutionalized mentally deficient patients had I.Q.s of 70 or above at the time these reports were made, a fact never envisaged by Tredgold or Lewis. As already implied, this position does not appear to have altered substantially (apart from a welcome and dramatic drop in the numbers compulsorily detained) since the passing of the 1959 Mental Health Act.

Conclusion

It will be seen from the foregoing that the adoption of a concept of social incompetence as the sole criterion of mental defect is scientifically invalid and administratively dangerous because: (*a*) such a procedure will necessarily result in the classification of a considerable number of neurotics, psychopaths, and criminals as mentally defective; (*b*) standards of what constitutes a satisfactory social adjustment are quite arbitrary, and differ widely in different societies at different times, and (*c*) there will, therefore, be imperfect agreement among those concerned with the classification of mentally deficient persons as to who should and who should not be included.

THE I.Q. AS A CRITERION OF MENTAL DEFICIENCY

Another approach to the subject of classifying mentally deficient persons, which has been advocated by several authorities, is the use of standardized intelligence tests and the scores derived from them.

It is of interest to note that the original impetus to the development of this technique of mental measurement came from the practical and administrative necessity of finding a means of selecting and segregating in special classes children who did not reach normal standards of educability. In 1904, the Minister of Public Instruction in Paris appointed a commission to investigate methods of discriminating between the normally educable and those who would require special instruction. Alfred Binet was a member of this commission, and in 1905 he published jointly with Simon a formal scale for the measurement of intelligence. The original scale did not employ age standards (as did later revisions), but indicated the levels of performance expected to diagnose the three classes of mental deficiency, idiocy, imbecility, and feeble-mindedness. In 1908 the scale was revised, and again in 1911, the test items being arranged according to the age at which they were usually passed. On the basis of this scale, Binet and Simon regarded a retardation of three years during childhood as being roughly indicative of mental defect, although they stress that such a diagnosis should not be regarded as final.

In 1910, the Binet–Simon scales were translated into English by Goddard in America, and standardized on a population of mentally defective children at Vineland, New Jersey, and normal children in neighbouring schools. Goddard proposed to call a child under 9 feeble-minded if he was more than two years backward on the 1908 Binet scale, while a child over 9 who was three years backward, would be similarly classified.

From the time of Goddard's translation of the Binet–Simon scale, research on intelligence testing has increased at an astonishing rate, particularly in America, but also in England with the work of Sir Cyril Burt; a great many psychologists and psychiatrists have used mental ages and intelligence quotients as crucial evidence in their diagnosis of mental defect. Wallin (1949) states: 'Because of its simplicity and reputed value, the practice of diagnosing mental defectiveness or feeble-mindedness by means of the Binet I.Q. became well-nigh universal after the appearance of the Stanford revision of the Binet scale in 1916.' This statement applies to America, but in England the use of intelligence tests has had widespread repercussions, particularly in fields of educational selection.

The question naturally arose of what standard to employ in separating those to be considered of normal intellect from those to be classified as mentally deficient. The defects of an absolute standard such as that used by Goddard became apparent, and the relative standard, originally proposed by Stern, was adopted to provide a more constant unit of measurement. This index, called the intelligence quotient or mental ratio, is obtained by dividing the subject's mental age on an intelligence scale by his chronological age.

Stern (1914) suggested the adoption of I.Q. 61 to 70 as being diagnostic of imbecility, 71 to 80 for the feeble-minded (morons), while he classed I.Q.s 81–90 as not abnormal. Terman (1916) classified those whose I.Q.s lie in the range 80–90 as dull, those between 70 and 80 as borderline defective, and those below I.Q. 70 as definitely mentally defective.

Pintner (1933) placed the upper limit of mental deficiency at about I.Q. 60, a figure also used by Bernreuter and Carr (1938). Kuhlmann gives the range of 85–94 as dull, 75–84 as borderline, and below 75 as mentally defective. Porteus (1941) suggested I.Q. 60 as the borderline between deficiency and dull-normality, if the score were based on the average I.Q. by the Binet and Porteus mazes (or other standard performance tests); or an I.Q. of 65 if the results were based on both these tests. Wechsler (1944), while objecting to Terman's classification of intelligence as somewhat arbitrary, offers a scheme based on statistical frequencies, which seems little superior in this respect. He classifies as dull-normal those who lie between 1 and 2 probable errors below the mean (I.Q. 80–90); as borderline those lying between 2 and 3 P.E.s below the mean (I.Q. 66–79), and as mentally defective those below I.Q. 65, or over 3 probable errors from the mean.

In England, Burt (1922) stated that the prime factor in mental deficiency is retardation in intelligence, with the reservation that there are rare and peculiar cases distinguished by defect in character and temperament. He provisionally adopted I.Q. 70, on his revision of Binet's scale, as the borderline between normals and defectives, so far as children were concerned. For adults, he provisionally proposed a mental age of 8, or I.Q. 50, as distinguishing between those who are almost invariably social parasites and those who can, albeit at a low level, fend for themselves in the community. He adds, however, 'as accommodation increases, as public opinion advances, the limit will doubtless rise'.

Lewis (1929), in his investigation into the incidence of mental deficiency, adopted criteria of classification suggested by Burt, and found in his sample very few idiots who had a mental ratio as high as 20; on Burt's revision of the Binet scale, adult imbeciles were regarded as having I.Q.s below 40, though a few in the border zone of 40–45 were included, while the upper limit for child imbeciles was taken as I.Q. 45 to 50. The higher grades of mental subnormality were divided into two classes: the feeble-minded and the morally defective. So far as the former class is concerned, an upper limit was fixed at I.Q. 60 in the case of adults, 65 in the case of adolescents, and 70 for children of school age. Concerning the morally defective, Lewis says: 'Although we have given the standards and criteria of "intellectual" and "moral" deficiency separately, many of the cases ascertained in this investigation were of the hybrid type.' 'The cases of moral deficiency ascertained which manifested no intellectual subnormality were so few that these also have been placed in the feeble-minded class; the conditions of a mass investigation such as this did not permit of the ascertainment of many such cases.'

It will be seen from the many systems of classification presented that there are some differences in the standards adopted by various investigators; on the other hand, it is also clear that there is considerable agreement in regarding as mentally deficient those whose I.Q.s. fall in the range 0–75. The conventional sub-divisions of this class of people are given by Kirk and Johnson (1954): idiots – I.Q. 0 to 20 or 25; imbeciles – I.Q. 20 or 25 to 40 or 50; moron (feeble-minded) – roughly I.Q. 50 to 70.

The many dangers inherent in the use of the I.Q. as the *sole* diagnostic criterion of mental deficiency have repeatedly been expressed. The main criticisms of such a procedure may be summarized as follows:

(a) Lack of a perfect relationship between I.Q. and social behaviour

This is probably the most trenchant criticism, particularly of those who would classify everyone having an I.Q. below 70 as being necessarily mentally defective. As Wallin points out (op. cit., p. 23), no particular I.Q. constitutes indubitable proof of mental defectiveness in the socio-legal sense, and there is a danger in the transmutation of I.Q. standards of diagnosis into categories of social defectiveness. Wechsler, in his discussion of the concept of mental deficiency (op. cit., p. 50), mentions the fact that the New York State mental hygiene law provides that individuals attaining I.Q.s below 75 on the 1916 revision of the Stanford–Binet can be classified as mental defectives. In the case of adults, 16 is to be taken as the denominator in calculating this ratio; thus, Wechsler states '. . . actual application of the criterion would automatically classify some 20 per cent. of the white and a considerably larger per cent. of the adult coloured population of the United States as mental defectives'.

Anyone who has worked in the field of mental subnormality can cite examples of individuals who fail to achieve an I.Q. of 70 on intelligence tests, yet are quite capable of managing themselves and their own affairs, and, on the other hand, of individuals who may score above I.Q. 70 on tests, yet are incapable of acquiring the rudiments of formal education, holding a job, or keeping within the limits of community tolerance with regard to social behaviour. In this connexion, however, we must remember that in practice two distinct points are usually considered in classifying a person as mentally subnormal: firstly, does he conform to the definition of the condition, and secondly do his circumstances or behaviour justify official action?

(b) Unreliability of the I.Q.

For any group of people tested and retested shortly thereafter on a well-standardized intelligence test, the commonly expected correlation between the two sets of scores will rarely exceed 0·9. Shapiro (1951b) demonstrates the practical implications of this statistical fact by showing that on a test with a mean of 100 and a standard deviation of 16, for every three children making an average score, on retest one would obtain an I.Q. of above 107 or below 93 because of errors of measurement. Similarly, one out of every ten children would score above 112 or below 88 on the second test. Furthermore, where a test has varying standard deviations at different ages, as, for example, the 1937 revision of the Stanford–Binet scale, a given I.Q. will fluctuate at different ages for reasons of test standardization alone. Tizard (1953b) gives as an example an I.Q. of 74 achieved by a 6-year-old child being equivalent to an I.Q. of 60 at 12 years on the Stanford–Binet, unless the corrections calculated by McNemar (1942) are applied. This subject is discussed in greater detail in Chapter IV.

(c) The same I.Q. on different tests may not mean the same thing

Since a person's status on an intelligence test is gauged not with reference to some baseline, but rather to the average of the distribution of scores for the general population of his age, the I.Q. obtained will therefore depend in part on the distribution of test scores for the population. To take a hypothetical example, let us assume that a test has a mean of 100 and a standard deviation of 25 points, and that another test has a similar mean and a standard deviation of 16 points (a more usual degree of scatter). The properties of a normal distribution curve are such that approximately 68 per cent. of the population lie between plus or minus one standard deviation from the mean. Thus, on the first hypothetical test, with its unusually wide distribution, 68 per cent. will lie between I.Q. 75 and 125, and 32 per cent. will lie above and below this range (that is, 16 per cent. below I.Q. 75). On the second test, with its more usual distribution, 68 per cent. will lie between I.Q. 84 and 116, and 32 per cent. above and below this range (that is, 16 per cent. below I.Q. 84). A person scoring two standard deviations below the average on the first test will have an I.Q. of 50, and on the second test an I.Q. of 68. In reality, differences as wide as those quoted in this example rarely exist, but it will be appreciated that a classification of individuals according to I.Q. ratings obtained on one test cannot be used without correction for ratings on another test. The use of standard scores overcomes this difficulty, and is essential in comparing a person's performance on several intelligence tests (see Chapter IV).

(d) The I.Q. is not always constant

Some critics of the use of the I.Q. for diagnosis may raise the fact that the I.Q. is often inconstant for a variety of reasons, which will be discussed in Chapter IV. Where the reason for inconstancy is delayed mental maturation rather than errors of measurement, such an argument cannot be considered relevant. Mental deficiency describes a level of functioning, and although many would argue that permanency is an essential feature of the condition, it is found in practice that a proportion of those dealt with as such improve over a period of years. A further reference to this topic is made later in this chapter (see also Chapter V).

Conclusion

In the author's opinion, the I.Q. must, like the concept of social incompetence, be rejected as a possible *sole* criterion for the diagnosis of mental defect. Although intelligence tests have the advantage of being precise, objective, and standardized on a cross-section of the whole population, yet even the most perfect are subject to a certain degree of error, and the use of an arbitrary dividing line between the mentally defective and the 'subnormal normal' would classify in the former category some who were socially competent, and in the latter some who were quite incompetent. Nevertheless, a considerable degree of intellectual subnormality as measured on reputable and appropriate intelligence tests should be a *sine qua non* of certification as a mental defective. This view is advanced by a Joint Expert Committee of the World Health Organization (1954) and by other international authorities.

DOLL'S SIX CRITERIA OF MENTAL DEFICIENCY

Edgar Doll, a leading American authority on mental deficiency, has suggested six criteria as being essential to a definition of mental deficiency. They are: (1) Social incompetence, (2) due to mental subnormality, (3) which has been developmentally arrested, (4) which obtains at maturity, (5) is of constitutional origin, (6) is essentially incurable.

These are expanded and classified as follows (1941):

(1) *Social incompetence*, that is, the functional inability to manage one's affairs with ordinary prudence, to sustain oneself economically without undue assistance from others, to discharge the ordinary responsibilities of citizenship.

(2) *Mental subnormality*, that is, a degree of intelligence so low as to make social incompetence as just defined likely and to identify that social incompetence as not being the result of physical disabilities, infirmity, or unfortunate social-economic circumstances.

(3) *Developmental retardation*, that is, arrested mental development in order to discriminate between the mental incompetence of mental deficiency and that of mental deterioration such as insanity or epilepsy.

(4) *A condition obtaining at maturity*, that is, a condition which is essentially incurable or unremediable, which is not outgrown, and which is not essentially altered by treatment, training, or favourable social-economic circumstances except through habit formation and routine activities.

(5) *Of constitutional origin*, that is, a condition which has its roots in hereditary lack of potential for normal developmental attainment, or is a condition produced by untoward events (trauma, disease, deprivation) which so affect the physical organism as to render development to adult normal status unlikely.

He adds that it is important to observe that mental deficiency is not to be determined by any one of these criteria taken alone.

Doll has attempted to make the evaluation of his first criterion of social incompetence more precise, objective, and valid by developing a scale by means of which the clinician can compare the behaviour of a particular patient of any given age with that expected in a normal person in the same age group. The Vineland Social Maturity Scale differs from an intelligence test in that it is based on the everyday activities of children from birth to 25, and can be employed in the absence of the subject by interviewing someone who has observed in detail his behaviour. For example, among the 117 items are the following: age 3–4, 'walks downstairs one step per tread . . . buttons coat or dress'. Age 5–6: 'prints simple words . . . goes to school unattended'. Age 7–8: 'tells time to quarter hour . . . participates in pre-adolescent play'. Age 9–10: 'cares for self at table . . . goes about home town freely', etc. It is Doll's opinion (1940) that the Social Maturity Scale measures with a considerable degree of accuracy the abilities essential for social adequacy and occupational success.

The most difficult of Doll's criteria to satisfy at the time of making a diagnosis is that of incurability (also held by Tredgold and others), since this must inevitably be a retrospective judgment. When Muench (1944), in his follow-up study of children who in early adolescence had been considered defective by Adams and Doll, showed that four of the ten individuals traced appeared no longer to satisfy the criteria, Doll (1947) commented that this did not prove 'that some feeble-minded individuals can and do make a suitable social adjustment, but rather that Adams and Doll could and did make an unsuitable clinical diagnosis!' The fact observed by many investigators that individuals sometimes advance over a period of years to a higher level of social and intellectual functioning than they had previously demonstrated, has led in America to the formulation of the concept of 'pseudo-feeble-mindedness'. The numerous articles on this subject have been reviewed by Cassel (1949a) who observed that implicitly a diagnosis of pseudo-feeble-mindedness is retrospective and involves an earlier error in diagnosis. However, as several writers have pointed out, children who later show accelerated mental growth seem to have been no different from 'ordinary' feeble-minded children of the same general functional level when they were originally assessed. Clarke and Clarke (1955) therefore propose that the term 'pseudo-feeble-mindedness', if it is to be used at all, should be reserved for cases where an erroneous diagnosis of mental deficiency was the result of insufficient examination by the clinician, but should not be applied to those who show (by reliable criteria) real changes, intellectual or social.

Benton (1956) in an exhaustive discussion of the subject, points out that the term 'pseudo-feeble-mindedness' has been employed in two ways: (1) as a mistaken diagnosis; and (2) as mental deficiency of atypical aetiology. In connexion with the former usage, he suggests that errors of diagnosis ought not to be given the status of a clinical entity; and in the latter case, he comments that an impermanent pseudo-feeble-mindedness is more readily diagnosed than a permanent one, but that this cannot be taken to mean that permanent conditions do not exist.

EDUCATIONAL CRITERIA OF MENTAL DEFICIENCY

The M.D. Act of 1927 in its definition of those to be classed as feeble-minded says '. . . in the case of children, that they appear to be permanently incapable by reason of such defectiveness (already defined) of receiving proper benefit from the instruction in ordinary schools'. This definition was in effect amended by the 1944 Education Act, which makes provision for the teaching of educationally subnormal children of all sorts, including the cognitively defective (above I.Q. 50), without certification as mentally deficient. Persistent educational failure has never been regarded as a sole criterion of mental defect and, as Wallin (1949) points out, such a procedure would classify as defective millions of children of backward and borderline levels of intelligence, who cannot be regarded as feeble-minded, socially considered. Nevertheless it is commonly used as one of the facts supporting a diagnosis of mental deficiency, and deserves, therefore, a passing reference.

THE A.A.M.D. COMMITTEE

In an endeavour to bring order into the chaotic status of terminology and classification in the field of mental retardation, the American Association on Mental Deficiency set up a broadly based committee of experts to inquire into the problem and make proposals. The recommended new system of classification was published (Heber, 1959), and represents an important advance in the field. Since the definitions and concepts proposed differ substantially from, for example, those embodied in the new British Mental Health Act, passed in the same year, it remains to be seen how effective the American Association on Mental Deficiency classification will be in producing a more uniform system of statistical reporting on an international basis.

The Manual starts with a section on definition, presenting a general concept of mental retardation which is interdisciplinary in character and which serves to distinguish mental retardation from other disorders of behaviour.

Definition: 'Mental retardation refers to subaverage general intellectual functioning which originates during the development period and is associated with impairment in one or more of the following: (1) maturation, (2) learning, and (3) social adjustment.'

'Subaverage' refers to performance more than one standard deviation below the population mean; 'general intellectual functioning' may be assessed by one or more of the various objective tests developed for the purpose; the upper age limit of the 'developmental period', although it cannot be precisely defined, is regarded as approximately 16 years; rate of 'maturation' refers to the rate of sequential development of self-help skills of infancy and early childhood and is regarded as of prime importance as a criterion during the pre-school years; 'learning' ability refers to the facility with which knowledge is acquired as a function of experience, and is particularly important as a qualifying condition during the school years. Social adjustment is particularly important as a qualifying condition of mental retardation at the adult level where it is assessed in terms of the degree to which the individual is able to maintain himself independently in the community and in gainful employment as well as his ability to meet and conform to other personal and social responsibilities and standards set by the community. Since adequate population norms and highly objective measures of the various aspects of adaptive behaviour are not yet available, it is not possible to establish precise criteria of functioning in these areas.

The report stresses finally that within the framework of the present definition, mental retardation is a term descriptive of the *current* status of the individual.

The Manual outlines excellent classificatory schemes under medical and behavioural headings, and also includes a section on statistical reporting. For details, the reader is referred to the original source (Heber, 1959).

The reader is referred to an interesting polemic on some of the concepts used in the A.A.M.D. Manual between Garfield and Wittson (1960a and 1960b) and Cantor (1960 and 1961). In the latter paper the author discusses at length the concept of 'incurability', and stresses the dangers inherent in the persistent tendency of clinicians to 'entitize' mental retardation.

SUB-CLASSIFICATIONS OF THE MENTALLY DEFICIENT POPULATION

So far in this chapter we have dealt with some of the main criteria which have been used to distinguish the mentally deficient from the normal population. There have also been various attempts to produce sub-classifications of the heterogeneous collection of people designated mental defectives. The first has already been mentioned, namely the legal divisions: idiot, imbecile, feeble-minded, and moral defectives. The first three of these are used internationally in clinical practice, and their designations in terms of I.Q. have already been given (p. 53). Sarason (1949) sounds a salutary note of warning to those who tend to project on to a patient, who has been classified in a particular way, all the characteristics which have been associated with the label. He says that sub-dividing the defective group according to I.Q. score increases the number of labels, however convenient they may be, without increasing our knowledge. Labelling a person an imbecile does not tell us any more about him than the knowledge that he has an I.Q. of 30, and, as has been shown by Clarke and Hermelin (1955), the knowledge of an imbecile's I.Q. tells one extremely little in detail about his ability to deal with his environment or to learn.

Another broad method of classification, which has been adopted in different forms by various authorities, is according to aetiology; here the two principal groups are, (1) those whose condition is due to heredity and (2) those whose condition is due to accident, disease, or injury.

Tredgold divides cases of mental deficiency into four groups: (1) Amentia or mental deficiency due to inheritance – *primary amentia*; (2) amentia or mental deficiency due to environment, in which the defect is exogenous in origin – *secondary amentia*; (3) amentia or mental deficiency due to both inheritance and environment; (4) amentia or mental deficiency without discoverable cause. By secondary amentia, Tredgold means conditions in which a non-genetic factor has produced irreparable damage to the central nervous system; he thus uses the term environment in a restricted sense.

Sarason discusses critically the efficacy of such a system of sub-divisions, and points out the difficulty of attributing patterns of behaviour to genetic mechanisms. MacMahon (1952), in his consideration of the legal definition of deficiency, states that in practice a condition which is not obviously attributable to 'disease or injury' must be ascribed to 'inherent causes', whether or not there is crucial evidence to support such a conclusion. Furthermore, neurological investigation will not always reveal physical defects, which are later discovered at post-mortem examination, while in the meanwhile the condition may have been attributed to heredity.

A somewhat similar classification was made by Lewis (1933). He states that the term mental deficiency is an abstraction used to cover a heterogeneous and complex group of clinical conditions due to a variety of biological factors, and prefers, therefore, to speak of 'mental deficiencies'. On the basis of clinical studies in the field, he suggests there are two forms of variation: (1) the *pathological* type, and (2) the *subcultural* type. Adopting Tredgold's classification of clinical varieties of secondary amentia, Lewis includes in the pathological group all cases of mental deficiency attributable to trauma, inflammatory conditions, hydrocephalus, syphilis, epilepsy, cretinism, and nutritional and sensory defects. He also includes several other conditions, such as mongolism, amaurotic family idiocy, hyperteliorism, naevoid amentiae, progressive degeneration, and many cases of sclerotic amentiae. In the causation of all these varieties of defect, one finds the intervention of some new or alien factors of a pathological character, not found in the normal constitution.

On the other hand, the subcultural group includes those cases of defect in which no alien factor is found, and where the deficiency is only an extreme variety of the normal variation of mental endowments. Thus, the higher grades of subcultural deficiency merge imperceptibly into the lower grades of dullness or temperamental instability in the normal population. Although Lewis inclines to the view that subcultural deficiency is inherited, he believes that unfavourable environmental factors may in some cases account for the condition.

In Lewis's classification, such conditions as phenylketonuria and amaurotic idiocy, which are known to be due to recessive genes, are included in the pathological type, whereas in Tredgold's, they would belong with the primary amentiae. Thus Lewis's subcultural group would be more homogeneous in type than those classified in Tredgold's primary group, referring only to those who are dull, backward, or unstable, or what in America are sometimes referred to as garden-variety mental defectives. Some of the difficulties encountered in the accurate allocation of individuals to such typologies will be discussed in the chapter on aetiology (Chapter VI).

Penrose (1949) discusses the statistical grounds for Lewis's classification, pointing out that there are far too many people whose abilities are more than three or four standard deviations below the population mean than can be fitted under a 'normal' Gaussian curve. Although he believes that Lewis's dichotomy is the best so far devised, he finds it difficult to apply in clinical practice, particularly in so far as actual institutional cases are concerned, since it is not always certain, in those patients where no known disease can be identified, whether a more detailed examination with more knowledge could not have detected significant anomalies. Penrose studied a very large group of institutional defectives with reference to several qualities, and summarized the descriptions of the two classes into which defectives can be roughly divided as follows on Table 8.

A typology frequently used in clinical practice in America is Strauss's exogenous-endogenous dichotomy. Strauss uses the term endogenous to cover those whom Lewis would regard as 'subcultural'; the exogenous defective is assumed to be brain-injured, and the term is used exclusively in connexion with such cases, with whom Strauss and his colleagues have been chiefly concerned. Strauss's definition is:

> A brain-injured child is a child who before, during, or after birth has received an injury to or suffered an infection of the brain. As a result of such organic impairment, defects of the neuromotor system may be present or absent; however, such a child may show disturbances in perception, thinking, and emotional behaviour, either separately or in combination. These disturbances can be demonstrated by specific tests. These disturbances prevent or impede a normal learning process. Special educational methods have been devised to remedy specific handicaps.

The work of Strauss and his colleagues will be described in detail in another chapter, so no evaluation is called for here beyond mention of the fact that some of the psychological tests which Strauss regards as diagnostic of brain injury are not universally considered as of good validity.

A passing reference should be made to the clinical classification of

TABLE 8

The two main groups of institutional cases of mental defect

(from Penrose's *Biology of Mental Defect*, 1949)

Group:	I	II
Degree of defect	Mild	Severe
Incidence of group in general population	Common: 2 per cent.	Uncommon: ¼ per cent.
Proportion of group institutionalized	Few: 3 per cent.	Many: 25 per cent.
Sex incidence	Females predominate	Males predominate
Psychological classification	High-grade, simpleton, moron, feeble-minded (modal I.Q. about 57)	Low-grade, imbecile, or idiot (modal I.Q. about 17)
Predominant medical classification	Physiological, aclinical, residual, associated with behaviour disorders	Pathological, clinical associated with physical malformations
Mental capacity in absence of disease	Subcultural	Normal
Biological classification	Fertility normal or increased	Infertile
Traditional view on causation	Hereditary, primary, endogenous	Environmental, secondary, exogenous
Status of relatives	Parents, brothers, and sisters rather frequently defective, but not sharply distinguished from normals	Parents rarely defective; brothers and sisters occasionally defective and sharply distinguished from normals
Typical hereditary causes	Common genes: multiple additive genes	Rare genes: specific recessive genes
Typical environmental causes	Deprivation; cerebral disease or injury in childhood; anti-social environment	Pre-natal maternal influences; cerebral disease or injury in very early life
Aims of treatment	Special education, socialization	Elementary training, nursing
Physical measurements	Means and variabilities within normal range	Means below normal, increased variabilities

special types in mental deficiency proposed by Gibson (1950). He proceeds on the assumption of two basic groups, namely those proposed by Lewis, and is concerned with a detailed classification of the 'pathological' type of defective. This he divides into six basic groups: skeletal, neuromuscular, cutaneous, special senses, psychiatric, and post-infective, the largest of these being further sub-divided. Some of the conditions included in each of these groups are:

(1) *Skeletal* (sub-divided into anomalies of craniofacial size, craniofacial shape, and dwarfism): microcephaly, hyperteliorism, mongolism, and the chondrodystrophies. (2) *Neuromuscular group:* the cerebral palsies, phenylketonuria, and Friedrich's ataxia. (3) *Cutaneous group:* congenital ichthyosis, anhydrotic ectodermal dysplasia, and the naevoid amentias. (4) *Special sense group:* congenital blindness, deafness, and alexia. (5) *Psychiatric group:* Epileptic, psychotic, neurotic, and moral defective. (6) *Post-infective group:* encephalopathic, meningitic, encephalitic, and congenital syphilitic conditions.

A comprehensive list of references on the topic of classifying special types of deficiency is given, but, as Gibson points out, the subject is controversial, and there is no generally accepted system of classification.

Finally, it should be borne in mind in making a critical evaluation of the various principles of classification and sub-division that many of the disagreements existing among the advocates of the various systems result from their differing purposes in making their selection.

CONCLUSIONS

It will be seen from the material presented in this Chapter that any *rigid* system of criteria or classification in mental deficiency is not only of doubtful validity but may be dangerous because, as Kirman (Hilliard and Kirman, 1957) has pointed out, it may give a misleading sense of precision.

To the extent that mental deficiency is a social concept, with fluctuating threshholds of community tolerance, classification is bound to be somewhat arbitrary, and no system is likely to be either comprehensive or permanent. Clearly, for purposes of research, general orientation and legal definitions, principles of classification are essential; in clinical practice, however, nothing can replace careful observation of an individual case and the objective assessment of his assets, deficits, social history, aetiological and prognostic factors.

Where, for practical and administrative purposes, society demands categorization, then the arbitrary boundaries need as clear and objective definition as possible. This is of paramount importance where the liberty of the subject is involved. In this connexion, wide categories tend to be imprecise, and the tendency for all the characteristics associated with the particular class of persons to be projected on to individual cases all the greater.

Chapter IV

THE MEASUREMENT OF INTELLIGENCE: ITS VALIDITY AND RELIABILITY

by A. D. B. Clarke

INTRODUCTION

In this book considerable space is devoted to the measurement of intelligence and to the factors influencing its development. There are two reasons for this: firstly, serious intellectual subnormality has traditionally been accepted as the main feature of mental deficiency so that investigations concerning the intellect are particularly relevant; and, secondly, there have been many more studies devoted to intelligence than to other aspects of mind. Consequently more is known about this than about other mental functions.

It is worth pointing out that intelligence is an inference from behaviour; it can be inferred in a variety of ways, the size of a person's vocabulary, his ability to solve problems in the abstract or in practical and concrete situations – all these are clearly 'intelligent' in varying degrees. There can be no measure of 'pure intelligence', even though the early workers thought that this was possible, simply because all actions recognized as intelligent are expressed via certain attainments such as speech, motor co-ordination, writing and so forth. No doubt these attainments are based on the efficient working of the central nervous system, but we cannot tell to what extent they are thus dependent. Let us take vocabulary as an example, for it often forms part of intelligence tests and indeed of subjective assessment. Knowledge of word meanings is certainly dependent on the nervous system but clearly does not blossom *in vacuo*; to varying extents it is related to the background, reading, schooling, and cultural level stimulating the child. It is thus partly a function of opportunity.

It should be clear from the foregoing that intelligence is highly complex, so much so that writers such as Hebb (1949) and others have distinguished two main concepts: Intelligence A or 'pure intelligence', and Intelligence B or intelligence as expressed in everyday life or as understood by the man-in-the-street. Vernon (1955a) adds to this scheme Intelligence C, or that which is measured by an intelligence test. Intelligence C should be a good and representative sample of B, but there is no way of knowing how far B is also a measure of A, which can only be inferred. Indeed A in this argument becomes a philosophical abstraction of use only in theoretical discussion.

Further problems, however, remain that are pertinent to the interpretation of intelligence test scores. These problems are concerned with the statistical validity of a given test, the reliability of the measuring device in view of errors of measurement, chance fluctuations, and genuine change of intellectual status; and, arising from a discussion of these factors and the influence of maturational and social factors, the prognostic value of intelligence test data (see Chapters V and XVIII).

Validity

Validity can be defined as the degree to which the test measures what it purports to measure. The main difficulty which confronts validation is the problem of criteria, which is, of course, not confined to the validation of psychological tests, for it exists in many other scientific fields. One can find either arbitrary criteria or empirical ones; one can say that a new test seems to involve abstract thinking, and that therefore 'intelligence is what the test measures', or one can compare results with other intelligence tests which, by a sort of apostolic succession, have been correlated with earlier versions of the Binet test. Yet this, too, is ultimately a subjective technique. If, on the other hand, intelligence tests are validated against success in life situations such as academic work, once again one is confronted with an imperfect criterion. It is obvious that success in academic work involves other personality factors as well as intelligence, and, further, the degree of a person's achievement is itself not an objective uncontaminated criterion, since examination results or teachers' ratings are themselves to some extent subjective.[1] Yet satisfactory validation coefficients can be obtained in spite of these drawbacks.

While validation of tests apparently rests upon insecure foundations, these are perhaps not so inadequate as at first sight they may seem. Adverting to the undisputed fact that all mental activities which can be termed intellectual, even if only remotely so, correlate together positively, the problem at once becomes that of selection of adequate samples of those activities with the lowest possible intercorrelation and the highest possible correlation with the total score gained from them all. In general, the lower the intercorrelations of the test items, the wider the spectrum of intellectual activity they will cover; and hence the better the test of general intellectual ability. These features will be found in reputable tests, and it is no accident that the latter also possess reasonable coefficients of external validity.

Reliability

The reliability of an intelligence test can be defined in terms of the degree to which it measures the same thing in the same way at different times, and this is somewhat easier to establish. There are, of course, three main methods of assessing reliability: the 'split-half' method, which measures internal consistency (itself implying reliability); the use of a parallel version (such as Stanford–Binet Form M compared with Form L) and finally by retest. The latter is probably the most useful method.

Sometimes the words 'test reliability' have been misunderstood because they relate to at least two variables; firstly, does the test measure the same thing in the same way on different occasions, and secondly, does the quality measured itself alter? As we shall see, both variables tend to overlap. Nevertheless we will be concerned with what might reasonably be termed 'reliability of measurement' and 'reliability of persons tested' (that is, their ability to change) both under the general heading of test reliability.

Later discussion will make it clear that in any retest coefficient both variables play a part. 'Reliability of measurement' can best be assessed by immediate retest. If a group of persons are tested and then retested on the following day with the same scale, various factors combine to reduce perfect reliability from $+1{\cdot}0$ to an actual $0{\cdot}9$

[1] For an enlightening discussion of some of the factors involved, see Bull, G. M., 'An examination of the final examination in medicine', *Lancet*, 1956, ii, 368–72.

(Thorndike, 1933). These in all cases represent personal fluctuations; the examiner may make minor errors in scoring, or in giving instructions, or in the establishment of rapport, while in the subject, alterations in mood, in physical condition, fatigue, boredom, anxiety, changes in incentive, practice effects and misunderstanding of instructions may be relevant. Combined, these errors of measurement certainly reduce the value of test results, and should always be taken into account.

It will be seen that over longer time-intervals retest coefficients tend to decrease steadily, and that since errors like those discussed above are unlikely to be cumulative, this must reflect a real change in the qualities tested, that is, 'unreliability of persons'. This is a point which results in considerable confusion; it is by no means uncommon for the following apparently tautological argument to be advanced: 'over several years test scores change, owing to imperfect correlation'. It is further implied that such changes are statistical and have no psychological significance. It is difficult to see why it should be assumed that it is more likely that the expressed statistical relationship should cause alterations in individual test performance, rather than vice versa, that the quality measured itself may undergo a certain degree of progressive change, which is inevitably reflected in a decreasing coefficient of correlation. It should be unnecessary to labour this point, but the distinction is frequently overlooked in otherwise sophisticated literature.

Much of the remainder of this chapter will in fact be concerned implicitly with the validity and reliability of intelligence tests.

SOME GENERAL ASSUMPTIONS UNDERLYING INTELLIGENCE TESTING

1. 'Intelligence can be measured'

It has long been recognized that people vary in their capacity to deal effectively with their surroundings, and everyday life provides countless natural intelligence tests. The most significant fact in the whole field is that all cognitive activities, including those which might only remotely be termed intellectual, correlate together positively. This indicates that from the assessment of the level of cognitive ability in any one sphere, better than chance predictions of the level of the other abilities are possible. Theoretically, several alternative but equally valid explanations of these findings may be made. One may, for example, account for them by postulating a fundamental or master ability that is to varying degrees present in all cognitive activities, that is to say, involving differential amounts of general cognitive ability or of a general 'factor' of intelligence. In addition, specific abilities, different for different activities, may be postulated to account for the findings that a person may be much better or much worse at some tasks than at others. Alternatively, it may be held that cognitive activities may be grouped according to their functional similarity. Group abilities or group 'factors' may then be postulated to account for the high correlations between the activities within a certain group. Or again, the sampling theory accounts for the intercorrelation of cognitive activities by postulating the existence of numerous independent abilities. These, though each limited in scope, each enter into a great many activities, and the correlation between tests will depend on the number of abilities these have in common. A good intelligence test attempts to be an effective small sample of cognitive processes, which like all good samples carries within it a microcosm of the whole. It ensures this, as mentioned earlier, by choosing items with relatively low intercorrelations yet each of which correlates well with the total score derived from them all. Clearly, the lower the intercorrelations, the wider the spread of activities sampled.

In theory, therefore, it is clear that a relatively short test can be produced with implications wider than the individual test items themselves, and in practice this can be demonstrated by the correlation between some real-life intellectual activity and the intelligence test result. There is thus no doubt that the first proposition 'intelligence can be measured' is largely correct.

2. 'Intelligence is normally distributed'

From the early days of intelligence testing the assumption has been made that the majority of persons are of medium or near average intelligence, with relatively few of very superior or very inferior ability, and that mental qualities are akin to some physical factors such as height or weight in forming a Gaussian curve of distribution. This assumption can be neither proved nor disproved in detail since its criterion, the test, is arranged precisely to meet the requirement of normal distribution. Arguments about it are thus circular. While this reservation must be made, it is nevertheless not an unreasonable assumption in terms of everyday experience.

Similarly, arguments about the precise shape of average mental growth curves tend to be unprofitable, for arrangement or rearrangement of test items is bound to influence such curves. In fact, a mental growth curve is the result of complex interaction between the persons tested and the test items, and it is thus only possible to relate a given curve both to the specific test and to the specific standardization sample. It is illegitimate to argue that because mental growth on the Binet test gives a curve of such-and-such a shape that therefore mental growth in general proceeds in this form.

3. 'The I.Q. is constant'

This proposition was made very early in the history of the mental testing movement, indeed so early that it had to be an untested assumption simply because insufficient time had elapsed since the invention of intelligence tests. It is noteworthy that Binet himself (quoted by Skeels and Dye, 1939) commented that

> Some recent philosophers appear to have given their moral support to the deplorable verdict that the intelligence of an individual is a fixed quantity, a quantity which cannot be augmented. We must protest and act against this brutal pessimism. We shall endeavour to show that it has no foundation whatsoever. . . . A child's mind is like a field for which an expert farmer has advised a change in the method of cultivating, with the result that in place of desert land we now have a harvest. It is in this particular sense, the only one that is significant, that we say that the intelligence of children may be increased. One increases that which constitutes the intelligence of a school child; namely the capacity to learn, to improve with instruction.

Binet's use of the words 'Some recent philosophers . . .' is surely significant. The theory of I.Q. constancy was a philosophical one congruent with the somewhat mechanistic attitude to man current fifty years ago, and thus the majority view simply accepted that a child's relative status was fixed and unalterable.

As data began to accumulate over the years, one or two experts had doubts about I.Q. constancy. Thus Burt (1921), discussing retests over periods of several years, notes that I.Q. constancy 'is but imperfectly realized'. Mental growth curves appearing in the textbooks, however, implicitly supported the theory. Such curves, while true of *averages*, neglect individual variability which is the rule rather than the exception. For example, the late developer is one in whom mental growth does not proceed by uniform increments as the curve suggests. Indeed, if individual mental growth were a uniform process, then this would represent the one form of biological growth not characterized by 'fits and starts'.

Two papers by Nemzek (1933) and Thorndike (1940) summarize in all 359 studies carried out before 1940; Clarke and Clarke (1953) point out that these researches show consistently that: (*a*) the predictive value of the I.Q. (as measured by test–retest correlation) decreases as the interval between the tests lengthens; and, as a corollary, (*b*) although the group or population average may not alter greatly, there will be considerable change of status of some individuals within that group (subsequent retests showing that to varying extents some subjects increase in I.Q., some decrease, some fluctuate, and some remain constant); and (*c*) mental tests given to children during the pre-school years have usually little predictive value, and that assessments during infancy have no relationship with later status (except, of course, in cases of severe mental deficiency, the early diagnosis of which is discussed in Chapter XVIII). It should, however, be noted that mental tests designed for early childhood are really tests of sensori-motor development, and their failure to relate to later status may be due either to the fact that different personal qualities are being meaured at different times, or to the fact that the period of infancy and the pre-school years is one of maximum variability in growth, or both.[1]

To illustrate conclusions (*a*) and (*b*), the practical implications of commonly observed test–retest correlations may be considered. Reviews by Nemzek (1933), Thorndike (1933), and Thorndike (1940) have shown that retest correlations are rarely as high as 0·95, and that on *immediate* retest the most probable value is 0·90. Shapiro (1951) demonstrates the implication of this latter as follows:

> Let us assume that we have a test with a test–retest correlation of 0·9 and a standard deviation of 16. These data mean that, out of every three children obtaining an average score of 100, one would obtain a retest score above 107 or below 93. On the basis of the same data, out of every 10 children obtaining an average score on

[1] The work of Maurer (1946) provides a notable exception to conclusion (*c*). It was found that, on a long-term follow-up, certain non-verbal items on the Minnesota Pre-School Scale yielded significant correlations with later status. Much more research is, however, needed on pre-school tests before their commonly poor predictive validity can be fully explained.

the first test, one child would obtain a score above 112 or below 88 on the second test. (These illustrations assume that no learning has taken place.)

Over time-intervals of several years, test–retest correlations are usually much lower than 0·9. Honzik, Macfarlane, and Allen (1948) found a retest correlation of about 0·6 for a time-interval of 12 years, after following up a representative sample of urban children from infancy to the age of 18 years. They tested over 150 children at the ages of 6 and 18, and found that the I.Q.s of 58 per cent. changed 15 or more points; the I.Q.s of 35 per cent. changed 20 or more points; and the I.Q.s of 9 per cent. changed 30 or more points. In only 15 per cent. of cases was the change 9 points or less. Individual I.Q. constancy over this period was thus exceptional. The group averages, on the other hand, showed a maximum shift in I.Q. over this time of only 5 points. The maximum individual I.Q. change was 50 points.

Both some supporters and some opponents of these findings have, however, been misled by their somewhat vague use of the word 'change'. It seems clear from examination of the text (op. cit., p. 312) and of the graphed mental test performance of their case 967 (op. cit., p. 320), that by change they mean maximum variation between any two tests during a given period of time. Consequently, the above figures have sometimes been wrongly interpreted as indicating the change in I.Q. between test results at age 6 and the test results at age 18, whereas they represent *maximal variations for individuals during the whole time period.* Recognition of this ambiguity would seem to go a long way towards reconciling Vernon's (1955a) criticism that I.Q.s are more stable than some writers deduce from this and other researches. In another paper (1955b), implying that the reported changes are greater than would seem possible from the correlation coefficient, he points out that Honzik *et al.* obtained a median variation of about 16 points over the 6–18 year age range. 'This is exaggerated because the group was superior in ability and because it was tested mainly with Terman–Merrill, which has a large standard deviation.' His first point, that I.Q.s are more variable towards the higher end of the scale, is naturally common to all other studies of persons of high ability, but the second point seems to be incorrect, since at age 6 the subjects were tested with the 1916 revision of the Stanford–Binet which Hilden (1949) estimates from Terman's data (in the absence of published material) has a standard deviation of

13 points. At age 18 the subjects were retested with the Wechsler, which has a standard deviation of 14·5 points. If the writer's interpretation is correct, the 'median variation of about 16 points' mentioned above is really the 'median maximal variation' for all subjects. There would then be no discrepancy with Vernon's calculation (personal communication) that the true median variation of scores between the 6 and 18 year tests is about 8 points, corresponding to the obtained correlation of 0·61. Thus, half the group changed within plus and minus 8 points, and half altered more than this, some by very much larger amounts. With these provisos in mind this study appears to be a very important one.

Similarly, Hilden (1949), who is in the process of studying the intellectual growth of 100 children, has reported findings on 30 of these examined from early childhood to late adolescence. In this small sample, too, individual variability in I.Q. was often found: the mean variation was 0·42 S.D. points (6·8 I.Q. points) and the mean maximum variation 27·0 points.

Dearborn and Rothney (1941) have reported findings from the important Harvard Growth Study in which both mental and physical development in children were investigated over many years; their book gives results from many different researches on several hundred children. They conclude that

> 'prediction of growth at various ages is extremely hazardous, but is particularly so during the period of adolescence . . . marked variability in individual growth curves appears throughout the course of the growth period . . . The principle of individual variability goes right to the root of such problems as constancy of the I.Q. . . . We have established the fact that variability rather than consistency of growth is the rule, that prediction except for average of groups is extremely hazardous. . . .'

It has commonly been accepted that in adult life the I.Q. tends to be much more constant than in childhood or adolescence. This may in general well be true, but until recently there has been a dearth of longitudinal research in this field. A number of such studies of rather special groups have, however, come to fruition during the last decade. Owens (1953), for example, carried out a careful thirty-year follow-up of 127 males to whom Army Alpha, Form 6, had been administered as an entrance test at the Iowa State College during 1919. On most sub-tests there was a significant increase in scores, and for the total group on all sub-tests the increment averaged half a sigma. It was not possible to be certain whether these increases had occurred during college life and had been maintained, or whether there had been small and slow improvement during the whole period. Moreover, these tests only measured verbal abilities. Nevertheless, these findings are of great importance.

Bayley and Oden (1955) and Bayley (1955) have also challenged the belief that intellectual growth necessarily ceases in adolescence. This investigation of the adult intelligence of the subjects of the Terman Study of Gifted Children showed that scores on the difficult Concept Mastery test increased over a twelve-year period by about half a sigma. The age range of the thousand subjects varied from 20 to about 50 years. When grouped into five-year age intervals, the increments were found at all ages and with curves of very similar slope.

Similarly, Nisbet (1957) retested after twenty-four years a group of 141 graduates who had first taken a shortened version of the Simplex Group Test at the age of 22. The average increment over this period was estimated to amount to 0·7 or 0·8 sigma. Nisbet quotes a further five American studies with similar implications.

Bradway and Thompson (1962) have reported an interesting twenty-five year study in which pre-school and adolescent I.Q.s were compared with adult Stanford–Binet and W.A.I.S. I.Q.s. The Stanford–Binet I.Q. showed a mean increment of 11 points from adolescence to adulthood, the averages for the subjects in 1931 being 113; in 1941, 112; and in 1956, 123, with similar sigmas of 15–16 points throughout.

Much more work is needed on the natural history of adult intellectual growth and decline, particularly in relation to environmental factors. It is already clear, however, that the view that intellectual growth necessarily ceases in adolescence is no longer tenable so far as verbal abilities are concerned, and, as will be pointed out in the next chapter, studies of some types of subnormal persons show increment in tested intelligence as age increases.

To illustrate conclusion (*c*), namely that mental tests in the pre-school years have little predictive value, Honzik *et al.* can again be cited. Tests at 21 months correlate less than 0·1 with the results at the age of 18 years. Similarly, Bayley (1940) found that mental scores derived from tests at 7, 8, and 9 months, while correlating highly with scores a few months later, had a relationship in the region of zero with all measurements after the age of 30 months. Indeed, in at least three researches quoted by Jones (1946) small negative correlations were found between intelligence scores in infancy and test scores in later life (see also Chapter XVIII). As age increases, however, so does the correlation with later intellectual status. Thus, Bayley (1949) found that for 27 children tested from infancy onwards, the correlations with the test score at the age of 18 years became positive at the age of two, and by the age of four had become 0·52.

From the wealth of available data it is clear that, in the general population, the concept of a rigidly constant I.Q. is contradicted by the facts; I.Q. constancy over long periods of time during the years of mental growth is the exception rather than the rule. It should be remembered, however, that I.Q. constancy is a relative concept, and that radical changes (over 25 points in either direction) are rare.[1] In the literature, however, a few most unusual and apparently authentic cases have been reported where over many years I.Q. variations of 50 or so points have occurred.

If the I.Q. tends to change in many individual cases, what are the causes of this? An understanding of such processes might give us powerful aid in controlling them and might have major implications for education and child care. The causes of I.Q. variability can be subsumed under four headings, the first three of which do not represent real change at all:

I.Q. VARIABILITY

A. *Errors of measurement*

The I.Q. may vary because of alterations in mood of the person tested, to misunderstanding of the instructions, to the cultural bias of the questions, or to errors of scoring. Similarly the I.Q. may vary

[1] Vernon (1955a) suggests the following formula for the calculation of the median variation of I.Q. changes: $0{\cdot}6745\sigma\sqrt{1 - r^2}$ for a single retest, and $1{\cdot}349\sigma\sqrt{1 - \bar{r}}$ for repeated retests. Thus, with the standard deviation of 15, and a retest correlation of 0·7 over a five-year period during childhood, a median variation of 7 points is obtained; that is, 50 per cent. of the sample change within $\pm$ 7 points, and 50 per cent. by more than this (17 per cent. may rise or fall 15 or more points and nearly 1 per cent. may vary as much as 30 points either way). Vernon states that with repeated retesting, fluctuations are about half as wide again. This formula, however, while it appears to be a useful way of deducing the amount of change in normal groups in which increment and decrement are balanced, nevertheless underestimates the amount of variability in admittedly rare groups where there is a strong tendency for most members to increase or to decrease in I.Q. In such cases the test–retest correlation will be higher than in a normal group, because the changes are unidirectional (see p. 115 et seq.).

from one test to another simply because of differences in the standardization of the two tests. Thus, an I.Q. of 80 on a test with a standard deviation of 15 points does not mean the same thing as an identical I.Q. on a test with a standard deviation of 20 points. In fact, it would be equivalent to an I.Q. of 73 on the second. On the 1937 Stanford revision of the Binet, for example, the scatter of scores varies at different ages, and unless corrections are made, the I.Q. of a child will vary over the years for reasons of standardization alone; and the further the I.Q. from the mean the greater the variation (see also Chapter XI, pp. 290–1).

Statistical regression to the mean is another concept used to explain I.Q. changes, especially at the extremes of high or low intelligence. Where errors of measurement on the same or different tests are concerned, or where different tests have a low initial correlation, regression of extreme scores is inevitable and of little psychological significance. The whole concept of statistical regression is far less simple than it might sound, however, and has been responsible for considerable confusion in discussions of I.Q. changes. It is not difficult to appreciate, for example, that on a test such as the Progressive Matrices a person who makes a very low score, say 8/60, is more likely to score higher on retest (test practice of course adds to this possibility) simply because 'chance' tends to be normally distributed and there are more possible changes in the positive than in the negative direction. The opposite argument holds good for scores near the maximum. But it is difficult to see how these factors would influence I.Q.s in the 80's or 90's to any extent.

McNemar (1940) has discussed the whole problem in detail but there remain a number of dubious points in his argument which neglects to attempt explanation of the phenomenon. He gives two main examples. First he suggests that a group of 8-year-old boys of Swedish extraction will have a mean height half a sigma above the American average for that age. If these same boys are measured again at the age of 16, the correlation between the two sets of measures will not be high, that is, there will have been considerable change of relative status in height. The group will still be half a sigma above the American mean (presumably for genetic reasons) and there will have been no general regression. We would expect regression within the group, however; the extremes of 8-year-old tallness or shortness would be relatively less extreme at the age of 16, while others less deviant at age 8 would have become more deviant later.

In contrast, McNemar gives a second example. If, on the basis of measurement, a group of boys had been chosen as above average, a general tendency would occur for the group mean to be nearer the universe mean upon later measurement. It will be seen, therefore, that regression to the general mean in McNemar's view is dependent upon initial selection on the basis of test score. 'In other words, an inferior or superior group will not move toward the general mean on a retest unless they have been selected as inferior or superior on the basis of an initial test' (op. cit., p. 89). Now statistical regression is usually stated to be due to measurement errors; in the examples given, however, it is likely that measurement errors would be negligible, so other factors must be relevant. What these may be McNemar does not say, although he admits that the concept is descriptive rather than explanatory.

Clarke, Clarke, and Brown (1959) have given examples of the confused way in which writers have used regression as an explanatory device, and have suggested two different mechanisms. The first involves errors of measurement of two different kinds, which are far less simple than they sound, and the second, the tendency for growth to be a non-linear process (see section D). There seems to be a tendency for groups selected on the basis of extreme test score to include members whose position at the time of selection is either partly the result of 'chance' or an unusual growth fluctuation. At points later in time, neither is likely to operate to the same extent, either because 'chance' tends not to favour or disfavour the same person twice, or because of the cyclic nature of individual growth, or indeed, a combination of both.

Thus regression is likely to be due both to 'chance' and 'real' factors. In both events, it will tend to be balanced in the general population by others moving outwards from the average.

B. *Test practice*

Increments in I.Q. tend to occur as a result of having taken a particular test on more than one occasion. Practice effects are, however, rather small, averaging 4 or 5 points. Where deliberate 'coaching' takes place, on the other hand, then the increment may be very large and as much as an average of 15 points with intelligent persons (see Vernon, 1954).

C. *Incorrect testing*

One factor which has tended to bring the I.Q. into disrepute is incorrect testing by persons inadequately qualified in psychometrics. The main errors are as follows:

(*a*) A very short test is given. Generally speaking it should take at least an hour to obtain a valid I.Q. on an individual test.
(*b*) No new test is given, but a previous result is quoted as indicating present status. This might not be unreasonable if the individual were adult, and if the I.Q. remained rigidly constant; but this latter is unlikely with the majority of children.
(*c*) The wrong test is given. For example, a person with many years of institutionalization cannot be accurately assessed on tests demanding a good degree of general knowledge. Or again, a purely verbal test for a deaf person will obviously tend to reflect mainly his restricted verbal experiences. Similarly, the administration of the Binet to adults is quite incorrect owing to lack of standardization.
(*d*) The test is given in a traumatic situation which disturbs the person so much that he cannot do himself justice.
(*e*) Abbreviations of a standard test are given, yet the results are based on the norms for the full test. This is analogous with a medical examination which is limited to testing the condition of the C.N.S.

These five forms of incorrect testing almost inevitably result in underestimation of the I.Q.

D. *Variations in the rate of intellectual growth*

Perhaps the most important single fact in this field is that test–retest correlations decrease as the interval between the tests lengthens. On immediate retest the inter-test correlation is usually about 0·9, but as Eysenck (1953) has pointed out, the correlation on the average steadily decreases by about 0·04 per year (for large groups), so that, for example, the most likely value after seven years would be 0·62. This indicates relative and progressive change of status by members of the group under study; some increase, some decrease, some fluctuate about a given point, and some remain constant. Since there is no reason to suppose that errors of measurement are cumulative, this must be a *reflection of real change in intellectual level due to different rates of development*. Intellectual growth is thus comparable with physical growth in proceeding at different rates at different times. Clarke, Clarke, and Brown (1959) give examples of both types of growth curve for individuals and show their essential similarity.

Various authorities cite internal or external factors as being separately or jointly responsible for variations in the rate of mental growth, but research is only now beginning to clarify aspects of the old nature–nurture controversy. It is very likely, however, that the search for a precise formula for their relative importance is founded on the same sort of misconception as the belief in I.Q. constancy. Much will depend on the bio-social background of the particular sample under study. Thus a group of persons suffering from phenylketonuria may owe their condition almost entirely to hereditary factors, while a group from extraordinarily adverse social circumstances may be affected in the main by their nurture.

To sum up, therefore, we can say that in general the I.Q., if properly applied and interpreted, gives a most valuable indication of a person's *present* status on the functions tested, and relates him to others of similar age. For predictive purposes, however, although undoubtedly useful (particularly in a constant enviroment), it is fallible and the longer the time for which prediction is made, the greater the possibility of change. In addition, the I.Q. is an invaluable tool for research. Much of the current criticism of the I.Q. is related to its misuse. For example, it has been used in a somewhat rigid way for educational selection, and Vernon (1955b) has pointed out that a relatively inflexible system cannot do full justice to relatively flexible children. The attack by teachers and others has been directed rather more to the *method* of selection than to selection as such; there is little doubt, however, that if one is forced to select, then use of the I.Q. will improve the process, which will nevertheless continue to result in error to varying extents. The alternative methods, mainly subjective, such as teachers' opinions or clinical judgment are susceptible to rather greater errors due to 'halo' and other effects.

Nowadays psychologists are increasingly critical of the global nature of the I.Q. Moreover, early attempts by such persons as Wechsler to seek test patterns as diagnostic instruments have largely failed. Recent work by Kirk and McCarthy (1961) and Kirk (1962), however, has revived the hope of a measuring instrument which will reveal intellectual strengths and weaknesses, which will have a real meaning in suggesting therapeutic methods for those with learning difficulties, and which will allow the effects of such procedures to be evaluated. Kirk and McCarthy have produced the Illinois Test of Psycholinguistic Abilities based upon Osgood's model of the communication processes. The model involves two channels of communication: (1) auditory and visual inputs and (2) vocal and motor outputs. It involves two levels of organization, a representational or meaning level and an automatic sequential level. It also involves three processes: decoding, association, and encoding. From this nine discrete tests have been constructed, each of which taps a level or process through one of the channels of communication. The resulting cognitive profile for the subject identifies his particular strengths and weaknesses. This approach may well prove to be extremely valuable for research, and the results of further investigations using this instrument are awaited with great interest.

UNITS OF MEASUREMENT

In continuing our discussion of the background and assumptions underlying intelligence testing, the way in which test results are quantified should be considered.

Mental age and the I.Q. The term mental age was coined by Binet and has played an important part in the mental test movement. As many have indicated, the phrase is nothing more than a test score – its reality is entirely dependent on the items in the test and on its standardization.

Greene (1941) has summarized some of the main disadvantages as follows: (1) *inequality of steps.* Since increments in ability during the years of mental growth become progressively less, clearly a mental age year in early childhood has a greater weight than in early adolescence.

(2) *Changes in meaning of mental ages above adult level.* Greene points out that the Stanford investigators have arbitrarily extrapolated mental age scales into the adult range, but that obviously, with increments in average test score ceasing in mid-adolescence,[1] a mental age of, say, 20 years is far from being what the majority of 20-year-olds achieve, and thus possesses an entirely different meaning from, say, a mental age of 10. As will be seen, Wechsler (1937) has also given a detailed and critical case against the term mental age.

(3) *Different processes measured at different ages.* Binet-type scales

[1] As will be seen in Chapter V, this is only true on the average; a number of studies of both subnormals and persons of high ability have shown that intellectual growth may continue well into adult life under special circumstances.

show a definite change from performance to more abstract verbal skills with increase in mental age. Thus different sorts of ability may be sampled at different mental ages.

(4) *Components of equal mental ages.* The question has often been raised whether the same mental age at different chronological ages means the same thing, and it is generally agreed that in fact there may be considerable differences in meaning. One can go further than Greene in pointing out the same mental age at the same chronological age may not have the same meaning for different persons, since after all an M.A. represents the sum of various component successes, and the same sum can obviously be achieved with widely differing components. This applies, perhaps, particularly to the mentally deficient, who in the higher grades characteristically show a wide scatter of subtest scores.

The intelligence quotient or I.Q. has already been discussed, but it remains to detail criticisms of it as a unit of measurement. Since the original equation leading to the estimation of the I.Q. uses M.A. as the numerator, the above criticisms of mental age must in part apply to the I.Q. (except as estimated by Wechsler's method, see below).

It is necessary in comparing I.Q.s on different tests to ensure that means and standard deviations are similar, and also within a given test that the same holds true at different ages. In the 1937 revision of the Stanford–Binet, for example, the adjusted means vary from 104·1 at age 3 to 99·8 at age 6. The standard deviations, however, show serious and considerable variability, ranging from a standard deviation at 6 of 12 points and at age 12 of 20 points. It was not until five years after the publication of this scale that a table of corrections was published by McNemar (1942), and unfortunately to this day many who use the Stanford–Binet test are unaware of the necessity to correct their I.Q.s at certain ages, and that failure to do this will result in individual I.Q. changes for reasons of test standardization alone. The 1960 revision, however, makes allowances for this type of error by inserting corrections in the tables.

The calculation of the I.Q. is, of course, affected by the artificiality of mental ages used for adults. Terman tried to solve the problem by retaining C.A. at 15 in the equation for all those whose real age exceeded that amount. The phenomenon of deterioration in ability with increase of age raises an additional difficulty for his solution.

Wechsler (1937) has critically reviewed the whole field and done much to overcome confusion by calculating the I.Q. in a novel way. He points out that, (*a*) although means tend to remain very similar, this does not imply that scores well above or below the mean will not be variable due to varying standard deviations at different ages, and (*b*) that intellectual growth does not proceed by equal amounts throughout its development. Thus, any method assuming a linear relationship between M.A. and C.A., as in the Binet test, cannot give constant values for any considerable proportion of the growth period. This latter has three consequences: (i) for the average individual the mean value of the I.Q. will change from age to age; (ii) numerators used in the I.Q. equation increase more slowly than do the denominators, and this difference is considered to be most marked in cases of low ability. This is believed to be an effect of the particular logarithmic relationship that connects mental with physical age; and (iii) the ultimate arrest of mental growth in mid-adolescence has absurd results, as already indicated, in the calculation of adult I.Q.s. Wechsler concludes that such I.Q.s are not I.Q.s at all.

Wechsler proposed to overcome these difficulties by expressing raw scores in terms of standard deviation units. For historical reasons the mean was set at 100. He used the Probable Error (0·6745 times the standard deviation) and defined I.Q. 90 as one P.E. below the mean (the P.E. was chosen as the appropriate unit because plus and minus one P.E. from the mean embraces 50 per cent. of the general population, taken to represent the average person). I.Q. 90 is normally regarded as the lower limit of average ability, and from this zero point the calculation of all other I.Q.s becomes a matter of simple arithmetic; having obtained the mean and standard deviation of the distribution, a table of '*z*-scores' is prepared, and for each actual score simple substitution gives a corresponding I.Q.

Wechsler considers that this method has the advantages of (1) dispensing with all assumptions about the precise relations between intellectual and chronological ratings at birth; (2) relieving us of the need for committing ourselves to any fixed adult mental age; (3) enabling us to calculate I.Q.s with the same meaning at all other ages; and (4) retaining the original and only important meaning of the I.Q. as an index of relative brightness.

While Wechsler's method has a decisive advantage over earlier ones, it is only fair to point out that his I.Q.s, to use his own words referring to the work of others, 'are not I.Q.s at all'. As Mursell (1949) indicates, the method is really a variant of standard deviation scoring.

Standard deviation scores and standard scores

Standard deviation scores are obtained by dividing the difference between the test score and the mean of the distribution by the standard deviation. Thus, if a person's I.Q. is 90 on a test, with a mean of 100 and a standard deviation of 15 points, the equation becomes $\frac{90-100}{15} = -\ 0{\cdot}67$. Such a method is very useful in comparing the subject's status on tests with differing standard deviations (see p. 74), since it gives a common unit of measurement independent of differing test distributions.

Standard scores eliminate decimal points and minus signs. The mean is arbitrarily set at 50 and the standard deviation given the value of 10 points. The formula $\frac{(X - M)10}{\sigma} + 50$ is used for calculating standard scores; thus the example quoted above would yield a standard score of 43.

The particular advantage of standard scores, apart from the fact that they give a common unit for test results, is that the units are equal throughout their range of 20–80. Hence they can be added or subtracted without any resulting distortion due to inequality of the scale.

It will be appreciated that although, following Greene (1941), a distinction has been made between standard deviation and standard scores, these are in fact variants of the same procedure and indeed are sometimes both given the same generic name, 'standard' or '*z*-score'.

Percentiles

The use of percentiles as units into which raw scores can be transformed has been quite popular. This method has the advantage of being particularly easily understood; thus someone scoring on the 40th percentile achieves a position higher than the lowest 39 per cent. of the population, and lower than the top 60 per cent. There are, however, considerable disadvantages. Owing to the bunching of scores in the middle of the distributions, the scale is not one of equal steps. Thus at the two extremes of a distribution, a difference of, say, five percentiles is far greater than a similar amount at the centre. Therefore it is not legitimate to add and subtract percentile scores for a person from a number of tests.

The three main units of measurement have been considered, but there are others such as the Personal Constant of Heinis (1926) and the Percent of Average of Kuhlmann (1939), but considerable controversy has existed over some of their assumptions, and nowadays there is little interest in them. There seems no doubt that some type of standard deviation score or standard score is the best unit that we have for the quantification of test results.

CONCLUSIONS

Provided intelligence tests are properly standardized and carefully administered, they provide an objective and valid measure of a person's present intellectual status. This is achieved by comparing the individual score with the relevant norms for the particular age group of the general population. All activities of a cognitive nature correlate together positively, and a good intelligence test will represent an effective and valid sample of such processes, and will correlate well with those activities in life which are commonly recognized as depending on intelligence.

For prediction of future status, intelligence tests are less reliable (although still valuable) not so much because of unreliability of the *test* but because within limits people alter in relative standing. During childhood and adolescence, mental (like physical) growth does not proceed at a uniform rate and the individual's position with respect to others in his age group thus tends to vary from year to year, this being reflected in changes in I.Q. Granted normal and relatively unchanging material and cultural opportunities, however, the I.Q. tends to be constant within broad limits (e.g. while under normal conditions a change in I.Q. in a child from 80 to 140 would be exceedingly unlikely to occur, a change from 80 to 95, or 118 to 110, would be a not uncommon finding after a period of several years from the first test). If, however, during childhood, a change occurs from or to an environment *markedly* inferior to the population average, then there is likely to be considerably greater variation in intellectual status during an individual life-span, and the same may of course occur to victims of diseases of the nervous system. The former applies particularly to a large proportion of subcultural high-grade mental defectives (see next chapter), while instances of the latter will be found at all levels of mental deficiency as well as in the normal population.

Chapter V

GENETIC AND ENVIRONMENTAL STUDIES OF INTELLIGENCE

by A. D. B. Clarke

INTRODUCTION

In the previous chapter the strengths and weaknesses of intelligence testing have been outlined; we now turn to the age-old problem of the effects of nature and nurture upon intelligence. The literature on this subject is immense and to review it fully would require a separate book; the present chapter will therefore present a selection of the most relevant investigations, but the references given should enable the interested reader to obtain most of the basic material. It is proposed to consider (*a*) the rationale and (*b*) the peculiar difficulties of each main method of investigation before discussion of results. In addition, it should be borne in mind that general statements about the relative importance of heredity and environment may be, like all averages, misleading when applied to an individual case or group. Thus, the intellectual condition of a person suffering from phenylketonuria is likely to be due entirely to hereditary factors; on the other hand, a person brought up in an exceptionally bad social environment may be impaired largely because of his adverse experiences. We need, therefore, always to inquire about the specific genetic and cultural factors which might be operative in any particular sample studied, and to be cautious of generalizing the findings to other and different populations. It is probable that lack of caution in this respect has been at least partly responsible for apparently contradictory findings by investigators of this field.

The word environmental needs definition for the purposes of this chapter. It is perfectly correct to regard brain damage due to trauma or resulting from the effects of maternal rubella in early pregnancy as environmental in origin (see Chapter VI), and there is seldom any controversy over these or allied conditions. The present chapter, however, will be concerned only with the rather less obvious and much more controversial effects of social environments; thus in this section, environmental is used as a synonym for cultural. For those who need a very detailed text on this subject, which obviously cannot be achieved in one chapter, Sarason and Gladwin's (1958) excellent book should be consulted.

In the past the problems to be outlined here have been the subject of heated and often bitter controversy, but the dust raised by the protagonists of nature or nurture served largely to obscure the issues. It is apparent that extremists on both sides overstated their case; the geneticists believed that heredity was the only potent factor while the environmentalists postulated a naïve and mechanical behaviourism. It is significant that in the past a chapter such as this might have been headed 'Nature *versus* Nurture', with the implication that only one of these was relevant; nowadays it is better realized that nature and nurture reciprocally interact and cannot be conceived of apart. This remains, however, a central issue in psychology for both theoretical and practical reasons and is obviously of particular relevance to the causation and treatment of high-grade mental deficiency. It is to be hoped that, with passions cooling a little, the way is now clear for the undertaking of crucial experiments which will help to settle the many outstanding problems.

The data to be presented mainly concern the mentally deficient of high grade but in each context one or more researches will be mentioned in which normal persons have been involved. In summary therefore, the main aim of this chapter is to examine evidence on the effects of environment in the aetiology of mild, as opposed to severe, subnormality. It should be read in conjunction with the following chapter on pathology.

STUDIES OF FAMILIES

Rationale. This is the oldest method of investigating the genetics of intelligence, having been employed by Galton and Goddard. The assumption was that if certain qualities such as genius or mental deficiency appeared in a given family generation after generation, then that quality must he inherited.

Difficulties. The study of families is the classic method in animal genetics where breeding is rapid, life-span short, and where the environment can be rigidly controlled. In man, however, the converse is true; thus investigations have to be retrospective, and material relating to persons more than a generation or two in the past tends to be fragmentary, anecdotal, and hence of low reliability. The second problem is the difficulty of separating out the relative effects of heredity and environment. Thus while it is true that some families have been distinguished and powerful for many generations, it is difficult to establish how far this may have been due to native ability, or to the exceptional environment and privileged position provided by each generation for the next. On the other hand, it might be expected that if environmental factors were prepotent then among the monarchies a high rate of outstanding intellect would be found, and this is manifestly incorrect. In summary, the difficulties presented by this method of investigation render the material thus gained of no more than general interest, and interpretation of it far from crucial.

It is common knowledge that in England such families as the Cecils, Wedgwoods, Darwins, and Galtons, have produced an unusually high proportion of persons of outstanding ability for many generations. The best known study of the mentally deficient was carried out by Goddard (1912), who described in detail the two families stemming from the same father, Martin Kallikak. This man joined one of the many military companies that were formed at the time of the American Revolution, and while on service formed an association with a feeble-minded girl whom he had met in a tavern. He had an illegitimate son by this girl who gave the child his father's name in full. At the time of the study, there were 480 descendants, of whom 143 were known to have been feeble-minded, while only 46 were considered normal. The rest were unknown or their status doubtful. These persons married others of similar type and Goddard had on record 1,146 individuals: 'of this large group we have discovered that two hundred and sixty-two were feeble-minded, while one hundred and ninety-seven are considered normal, the remaining five hundred and eighty-one being still undetermined . . .'

The first Martin Kallikak provided for posterity a control group by marrying later a respectable girl of good family by whom he had further children. At the time of the investigation these numbered

496 in direct descent, none of whom were mentally deficient, although three were said to be 'somewhat degenerate'. In general, these descendants had a superior social and economic status, married into the best families in their state, produced a large number of professional people, 'in short, respectable citizens, men and women prominent in every phase of social life'.

The record of the Juke family described by Dugdale (1910) through five generations, has been used to show familial incidence of criminality, destitution, and mental subnormality. The original finding was that of 709 descendants of one morbid couple, a small proportion were socially competent, while the vast majority were in the criminal and social problem group.

As already stated, the main difficulty in studying such families as these is that the basic data are of unknown validity, and that genetic and environmental factors cannot be assessed separately. Thus, little is really known about the girl who gave birth to Kallikak's illegitimate son; if she was feeble-minded it would have been important to know something about the cause of her condition but in retrospective research this was clearly impossible. Further, the state of squalor in which she lived, together with her own mental subnormality, regardless of genetics, would seem likely to have had a profoundly adverse effect upon her son, and as is well known, a vicious circle is often initiated in such circumstances.

For genetic research, the study of family histories is, of course, essential and much more fruitful where conditions are involved which sharply distinguish affected from unaffected persons (e.g. defect due to the action of recessive genes). Penrose (1949) gives an excellent account of such investigations.

STUDIES OF TWINS

Rationale. Identical twins result from the splitting of one fertilized ovum, and therefore possess identical heredity; fraternal twins, on the other hand, arise from two ova, separately fertilized, and, in terms of probability, their hereditary similarity need be no greater than for ordinary siblings. Thus comparison of identical with fraternal twins, and with siblings, may be expected to yield information on both genetic and environmental influences. Particularly valuable information may be expected to emerge from a study of identical twins brought up together, and similar pairs reared apart, especially if in the latter case environmental differences have been great and separation from an early age. This method of study in human genetics can theoretically be regarded as crucial.

Difficulties. Unfortunately several practical difficulties have so far limited the usefulness of the theoretically best method for evaluating the contribution of nature and nurture (and their interaction) to the development of intelligence; they are summarized as follows:

(1) The differentiation of identical from fraternal twins is not perhaps as straightforward as it might seem, and if not checked at birth by examination of the placenta is often a matter of inference some years later. Identical twins must of course be of like sex and are commonly physically very similar; finger-prints, iris pigmentation, presence or absence of mid-digital hair, scapular shape, and a number of other factors are commonly used for establishing identity (cf. Eysenck, 1952).

(2) There is reason to believe that the environment, both pre- and post-natal, of identical twins is more similar for each pair than for fraternals, and for fraternals more similar than for siblings. Thus identical heredity may be accompanied by a more nearly identical environment than is found in children reared together. (On the other hand, however, it is known that multiple births are more hazardous than single births, and not infrequently one twin may be injured or even still-born.)

(3) So far as the crucial study of identical twins reared apart is concerned, very few such pairs have been discovered and studied and of these even fewer were found to have been reared in widely differing socio-cultural conditions. Thus, with heredity 'held constant', the variable 'environment' has not been fully accessible. For full information on the effects of environment on intelligence, a group of about 30 pairs of identical twins would be needed, one half of which were brought up in adverse circumstances and the other half in the best and most stimulating environment.

The correlation between the I.Q.s of randomly selected pairs of unrelated children is zero; of cousins about 0·25; of siblings brought up together about 0·5; of fraternal twins reared together about 0·7; of identicals reared together 0·9. This progressive increase of correlation associated with a progressively closer genetic relationship, has been interpreted as indicating that heredity plays the dominant part in determining intelligence. (It must be remembered that a correlation of 0·9 between two sets of persons is as high as can be gained by retesting the same set of persons on two occasions separated by a short time-interval and using the same test.) That such an interpretation is at least over-simplified is obvious for two main reasons: firstly, if environment had little relevance one would expect that correlations between fraternal twins and between siblings would be similar and about 0·5, because both fraternals and untwinned siblings arise as separate fertilized ova. The discrepancy between 0·7 and 0·5 provides a rough measure of environmental difference in groups which usually have fairly similar conditions of upbringing, and it is by no means negligible. Using the technique of squaring the correlation coefficient as a rough measure of 'the contribution of one variance to the other', we can estimate the environmental effect at about 24 per cent. Adding to this an error variance of at least 19 per cent., the remaining variance, namely 57 per cent., could be ascribed to heredity, a figure rather similar to that proposed by Penrose (1949) on rather different grounds. And it has already been stressed that heredity will be seen as important in the case of subjects whose environmental experiences are fairly similar. Thus it could be argued that such an estimate would reflect a maximal influence of genetical factors, and that where conditions were less uniform then environmental factors would increase in importance. Moreover, compared with normals, the high-grade mentally deficient come in the main from markedly inferior conditions and it might therefore be assumed that such factors would play a considerable part in the aetiology of intellectual defect.

There are no general studies of mentally deficient twins, although a number of interesting investigations of pathological defect occurring in one or both of a given twin pair can be found in the literature. A most important study of normal twins is that reported by Newman, Freeman, and Holzinger (1937), whose sample included 50 pairs of fraternals, 50 pairs of identicals, and 19 pairs of identical twins reared apart. These latter had been separated in most cases at a very early age and for a long period of time and they were studied in adult life.

The Binet I.Q. correlations for the three groups were as follows: identicals, 0·910, fraternals, 0·640, and separated identicals, 0·670. The mean I.Q. difference for the latter was 8·2 with a range from

0 to 24 points. In a highly critical review, McNemar (1938) suggests that the correlations should be corrected for age and range when they become 0·888, 0·631, and 0·767, respectively. He goes on to challenge the statement of Newman *et al.* that 'the correlation for the separated cases are . . . much lower than the corresponding values for unseparated identical twins'. After such correction, McNemar believes that it cannot be claimed that there is a significant difference between the resemblances of unseparated and separated twins. There follows a highly technical argument which in Holzinger's (1938) view was without much point, but he does admit to some minor errors and to some 'clumsiness' in analysis. Such criticism, however, did not in general show the study of Newman *et al.* to be vulnerable. McNemar's cautious conclusion is nevertheless worth quoting:

> it appears that the only evidence which approaches decisiveness is that for separated twins, and this rests ultimately upon the fact that four pairs reared in really different environments were undoubtedly different in intelligence. This fact can neither be ignored by the naturite nor deemed crucial by the nurturite.

An examination of these 19 pairs of identical twins reared apart shows, as Thorpe (1946) points out, that the significant differences between them were always in the same direction as differences in educational opportunity. Marked differences in mental ability, as indeed McNemar conceded, were in every case associated with similarly marked differences in educational and other opportunity. Thus, although it is obvious that this study has controversial features which make interpretation also equivocal, it appears that environment can have a marked effect upon development. To illustrate these points, a brief account of two twin pairs reared apart can be given. Twins A and O, studied by Newman (1929), were separated at the age of 18 months, one being brought up in a crowded middle-class part of London during the First World War, with an interrupted elementary education. The other was brought up in an adoptive home by a socially superior family in Canada; she received an uninterrupted academic education. In the end, both became secretaries, having had nine years of schooling, but O scored 12 points higher on the Stanford–Binet than her twin who had been brought up in London. Another pair, studied by Newman *et al.* (1937), differed in educational and cultural opportunities, one never getting beyond elementary school due to frequent moves on the part of her family, while the other, though reared in a modest home, completed a college education. The former became a saleswoman and later an office worker, while the latter became a teacher of history and English. They were studied at the age of 35, when the social and intellectual superiority (24 I.Q. points) of the twin who had had the better opportunities was apparent. These environmental differences are the most marked occurring in the cases studied by Newman and his colleagues; but it is apparent that even within Western cultures much wider social and cultural differences exist; for example, the difference between the environment of a child in a 'breakdown' family in a London slum in contrast to the opportunities of a child with professional parents is much greater than in the cases studied by Newman. It would be assumed, therefore, that environmental influences would be more potent if twins were separated into vastly different homes such as these.

This same point, as the author indicates, applies to the much more ambitious investigation recently reported by Shields (1962). Forty-four pairs of monozygotic separated twins were studied on physical measures, intelligence, extraversion, neuroticism, and other factors. A control group of non-separated monozygotic twins was also used. The separated twins showed very close resemblance on many measures; on a combined intelligence score, for example, the correlations for non-separated and separated identical twins were + 0·76 and + 0·77 respectively. These correlations were substantially higher than those for dizygotic twins reared together, and certainly point to the strong influence of genetic factors. Nevertheless, it seems probable that the influence of environment was masked by the cultural similarity of the homes in which the children lived. In two-thirds of the separated twin pairs, for example, one twin was brought up by relatives, and Shields notes that 'the degrees of social and cultural differences between the families . . . were as a rule not remarkable. . . .' Although this is an excellent and careful study, it cannot reveal the full role of environment although it certainly demonstrates the strength of hereditary forces.

STUDIES OF CHILDREN IN FOSTER HOMES

Rationale. If children are separated for any reason from their true parents, a comparison of their intellectual and social status (*a*) with their true parents, and (*b*) with their foster parents, should give an estimate of the relative parts played by heredity and environment. In their simplest form, the following propositions may be made: if heredity were prepotent, it would be expected that whatever the new environment of the foster home, the child would approximate to the true parental level. If, on the other hand, environment were prepotent one would expect the converse, namely that whatever the level of the parents, the child would approximate to the level of the foster parents, and further, the longer the time spent in the foster home, the closer this correlation would be.

Difficulties. There are certain drawbacks to this method which may be summarized as follows:

(1) Adoption and fostering of children usually take place when they are very young, and sometimes when they are new-born. Except for obvious and gross mental deficiency, it is impossible to predict future status from tests or clinical observation at this age. Such tests rely very largely on measures of sensori-motor development which have little in common with later intelligence tests, and which intercorrelate rather poorly with themselves. Thus the basis (*a*) for equating groups, and (*b*) for follow-up study tends to be unsatisfactory.

(2) Selective placement of the potentially or actually brighter children in better homes, and duller in homes of lower status, has in fact bedevilled much of the experimental work in this field. Thus when later evaluations reveal the superiority of children in the better foster homes this could result from either their better genetic potential, or the better environment, or a combination of both.

(3) Once again, a full range of environmental possibilities is for obvious reasons not employed in the placement of homeless children, and the levels of foster homes are likely to be more homogeneous than for the general population.

As Jones (1954) points out, we are particularly in need of experimental placement, planned randomly, to overcome such factors, thus avoiding retrospective research which may often fail to reveal biases of this kind (see also Chapter XVIII).

A pioneer study by Freeman, Holzinger, and Mitchell (1928) contrasted mental test variations of children placed in superior foster homes with those shown by children in more average homes. Those in the former gained 10 points in I.Q. on the average over about four years, while the latter gained only 5 points. In general, the earlier the placement, the greater the gain. A study of correlations between foster children reared together and siblings reared apart also indicated environmental effects, and correlations between I.Q.s of foster children and their foster parents increased from 0·34 to 0·52 over four years. This early study has been criticized on the usual grounds that the results may be due to selective placement, which undoubtedly must have occurred (note the initial correlation of 0·34 between children's and foster parents' I.Q.).

Burks (1928) studied the development of over 200 foster children, as well as a control group of over 100 children living with their own parents in similar socio-economic conditions. At the end of the study, foster children's I.Q. correlated to the extent of 0·42 with a combination of father's mental age, vocabulary, mother's vocabulary, and the family income. On the same variables the control children's I.Q.s correlated to the extent of 0·61. Differential increments had occurred, favouring the control children, due in Burks' view to innate differences in ability, and she concluded that home environment contributes only about 17 per cent. of the variance in I.Q. The interpretations by Freeman *et al.* and Burks of somewhat similar findings are very different, and, according to Thorpe (1946), who reviews them excellently, this divergence is due to the strongly hereditarian outlook of Burks; Freeman, on the other hand, seems to appreciate the evidence for hereditary forces, but is willing to explore the influence of superior homes and educational facilities on the social and intellectual development of children. In his view, the results indicated the importance of such facilities, and of early placement. A detailed review of these and other general studies is to be found in Jones (1954).

Skeels and Harms (1948) have studied the mental development of children with inferior social histories who had been placed in adoptive homes. They pointed out that a research of this nature would be likely to have important implications almost whatever the results; thus, if children failed to benefit from placement in superior homes, then it would seem that selective placement would be desirable. If, however, data relating to social background and parentage have little predictive value, then the emphasis shifts to the quality of the foster homes. Their study concerned children selected on the basis of inferior social history and who were placed in adoptive homes in infancy or under 2 years of age.

There were three groups. Group I consisted of 107 children whose mothers had been classified as mentally retarded with I.Q.s of 75 or less. All were committed to an orphanage at less than 6 months of age, and placed in adoptive homes when less than 2 years old. Approximately 80 per cent. were illegitimate, and all but 20 had been tested at the close of the study. These 20 appeared to be not very different from the remainder, as judged on the basis of the histories of the true parents. In contrast to the homes of the true parents, the foster homes were selected in general for their adequate adjustment in the community; foster parents were regarded as intelligent, dependable, and stable. The occupational level was higher than that of the true fathers, and was above that of the population as a whole. Mean age at the time of placement was 5·3 months (range: 8 days to 23 months), and two-thirds of the group were fostered under 6 months of age. The mean I.Q. of the 87 children at an average age of 5½ was 105·5 with a standard deviation of 16·7, and a range of from 55 to 141. These results were in some cases gained on the Kuhlmann–Binet, in others on the 1916 Stanford–Binet, and in others on the 1937 Stanford–Binet. Children's intelligence showed a small but significant correlation with the intelligence of true mothers, the results on the Kuhlmann–Binet being largely responsible for the correlation of the whole group.

Group II was composed of children whose fathers had low occupational status; a reasonable inference was that on the average their intellectual level would also tend to be low. The mothers of these children seemed also likely to be in the lower ranges but this was not so marked or uniform as in Group I. The foster homes for the children were markedly superior to those from which the child issued and somewhat superior to those in Group I. The children, 111 in number, were placed in foster homes at a mean age of 5 months, with a range from 8 days to 21 months. The average age at the time of assessment was a little over 5 years, and the mean I.Q. (Kuhlmann–Binet, 1916 Stanford–Binet, and 1937 Stanford–Binet) was 110, standard deviation of 15, and a range from 55 to 154. Where the I.Q.s of both the child and the true mother were known (75 cases) the correlation between them was on the borderline of significance at the 5 per cent. level. There was some evidence of selective placement when true mother's I.Q. was considered in relation to occupational level of the foster home.

Group III was composed of 31 children whose mothers were

known to have I.Q.s below 75 and whose fathers were unskilled or slightly skilled labourers, hence very probably of low I.Q. Occupationally the foster homes were markedly above that of the population from which such children were drawn, and slightly above the general population as a whole. The mean I.Q. of the true mothers was 62·6, standard deviation of 8·6, and a range from 40 to 75. All but seven of the true fathers were in the lowest occupational classification.

The children were tested at a mean age of 5 years 4 months, ranging from 1 year 1 month (a totally unreliable age for predictive assessment) to 10 years 6 months. On the same tests as previously the children averaged 104 with a standard deviation of nearly 16 points. Correlations with true mothers' I.Q. and with the educational level of the foster mothers were not significant. There was no evidence of selective placement in terms of true mother education in relation to foster mother education, nor between true mother I.Q. and foster mother education. But there was a tendency for children of duller mothers to be placed in homes which were occupationally lower; the difference (5·6 I.Q. points) did not, however, reach statistical significance.

These studies are of considerable interest and appear to be free from many of the weaknesses of some of the earlier work from the University of Iowa. At the very least they indicate that children from poor or adverse backgrounds tend to do better than might be expected if early in life they are given the advantage of average or above average foster homes. The genetic implications are, however, less clear. We do not know, for example, whether any of the true mothers may have been mentally deficient for 'organic' reasons (e.g. because of disease or injury); such persons are as likely as any to be genetically normal, and the same might be said for true fathers. The fact that some mothers were as low as I.Q. 40 is suggestive of organic factors in their cases. The authors, however, are careful not to draw any genetic conclusions, which would clearly be unwarranted so far as Groups I and II are concerned, and very doubtful in the case of Group III. Ideally, a study such as this should have a group of fathers and mothers of known low I.Q., and in whom an organic aetiology had been excluded. Even this would be insufficient for genetic research if these persons had functioned well below their potential because of poor environmental conditions. In fact, genetic and environmental influences in groups such as these are almost inextricably mingled, but it is none the less important to show that children from such poor backgrounds at these ages appear to have a normal chance of superior, average, or subnormal intelligence, because far too often an over-simplified genetical viewpoint has resulted in such persons being given no alternative to institutional upbringing, with all that this implies.

At the same time it should be recognized that a clear indication of the presence of forces other than environmental ones (presumably genetic) also emerges from the data, and the authors fail to draw the reader's attention to this. If environment alone were responsible for the status of the children we would expect only a small scatter of I.Q.s in the moderately homogeneous foster homes in which they were placed. Yet we find a fairly normal distribution of ability with a considerable proportion below average while enjoying the advantages of above average environments. This study is important in demonstrating that people are not born equal nor do they respond or change uniformly when introduced to similar conditions.

Skodak and Skeels (1949) summarize their earlier studies (Skeels, 1938; Skodak, 1939; and Skodak and Skeels, 1945) on a group of foster children followed up from infancy until adolescence. While there exist a large number of cross-sectional studies of children in foster homes, repeated evaluations of the same children into adolescence or early adulthood have been rare. Their earlier reports provoked intense controversy (see McNemar, 1940; and Wellman, Skeels, and Skodak, 1940), but in this final paper the authors feel that the intensity of such discussion had dissipated in the previous decade as evidence accrued showing that modifiability of intelligence was not an unusual phenomenon.

The foster homes in these studies were above the average of their community in economic security and in educational and cultural status. The primary factors in the matching of the infants to prospective homes were, owing to meagreness of information about the child's family background, the stipulations of the foster parents regarding religion, sex, and hair colour, in that order. This method of placement of children from relatively inferior socio-economic backgrounds into substantial homes thus provided the setting for these studies, and, as the authors say, it did not seem possible that children with such meagre potentials, as predicted from the intellectual, academic, and occupational attainments of the true parents, could measure up to the demands of cultured, educated foster parents.

Skodak and Skeels indicate that children committed to public agency care have parents whose general social, vocational, and adjustment levels are substantially below that of children who become wards of private agencies or who are adopted through private channels. The criteria used for inclusion of children in these studies were (*a*) the child was placed in an adoptive home under the age of 6 months; (*b*) the child had been given an intelligence test prior to November 1936, and after one year's residence in the adoptive home; (*c*) some information, though of variable amount and reliability, existed concerning the natural and adoptive parents; (*d*) the child was white, and of north European background. This group was representative of the available children, because there was no systematic withholding of children because of poor histories, nor was there a group excluded because of low intelligence test scores.

In the first follow-up report (Skodak, 1939), out of a total of 180 children it was possible to retest 152 during 1937–8. On the third examination (Skodak and Skeels, 1945) 139 children were reassessed. The fourth and final visit in 1946 resulted in the present sample of 100. It was concluded that this final group was representative of the original total group.

Table 9 shows the main results, and it will be noted that the mean I.Q. for this group had remained above average throughout early childhood, school age, and into adolescence. The Kuhlmann–Binet was used for all children under 3 years, and at later ages the 1916 Stanford–Binet. At the time of final examination, the 1937 Stanford–Binet was also given.

TABLE 9

Longitudinal data on 100 adopted children

(after Skodak and Skeels, 1949)

Test	Age	Mean I.Q.	S.D.	Range
I	2 yrs. 2 mo.	117	13·6	80–154
II	4 yrs. 3 mo.	112	13·8	85–149
III	7 yrs. 0 mo.	115	13·2	80–149
IV (1916)	13 yrs. 6 mo.	107	14·4	65–144
IV (1937)	13 yrs. 6 mo.	117	15·5	70–154

Rather wide fluctuations in I.Q. between tests were found throughout the entire period. The general trend was towards losses when the first infant test was taken as a standard for comparison. But by and large, such fluctuations tend to occur normally and the children did not greatly change their positions relative to the general population as a whole. Where marked changes did occur, there were related factors which could usually be identified in the individual case.

If a comparison was made of the occupational status of 73 of the true and the 100 foster fathers, it became apparent that not only were the foster fathers above the average of the population as a whole, but were conspicuously above the mean for true fathers, who were well below the population mean. Thus the children of parents at one occupational extreme were placed in homes the occupational level of which was at the other. Similarly, the educational status of the true parents was significantly below that of the foster parents, and the mean of the whole population. There was no significant relationship at any period between foster parents' education and the foster children's I.Q.s, but, of course, the range of both variables was somewhat limited. Intelligence test results were available for 63 true mothers, 59 of which were based on the 1916 Stanford–Binet, 1 on the Terman Group Test, 2 on Otis, and 1 on Wechsler–Bellevue. Tests were given by trained examiners under ordinary conditions, usually after the mother had decided to release the baby for adoption. The mean I.Q. of these true mothers was 85·7 points with a standard deviation of 15·8. The mean I.Q. of the children at the age of 13½ on the same test was 106 with a standard deviation of 15·1 points. This 20-point difference between the two means is highly significant and of considerable social consequence. It should be noted that there was no difference between the mean I.Q.s of children whose mothers had been examined and those whose mothers' I.Q.s were unknown.

Some of the most controversial data emerge from the correlations between true mother and child I.Q.s at different stages in the child's development. Thus, at test I, the relationship was zero; at test II, the correlation was 0·28; at test III, 0·35; at test IV (1916), 0·38; at test IV (1937), 0·44. It appeared, therefore, that test scores during the first two years of life bore no relationship to the scores of mothers, nor did they show a very high relationship to the children's own later scores (the correlation was 0·35). By 7 years of age a substantial correlation with true mothers' I.Q. was reached, which remained of the same magnitude in adolescence provided the 1916 Stanford–

Binet was used with both children and mothers; it was further increased if the 1937 revision is used. The authors agree that many reasons can be advanced for the low correlations between infant and later measures, and state that there is considerable evidence for the belief that as a group these children received maximal stimulation in infancy with optimum security and affection following placement at an average of 3 months of age. The quality and amount of such stimulation seemed to have little relation to the foster family's educational and cultural status. Available data such as occupational status and formal education are not in the authors' view sufficiently sensitive to be useful in measuring these less tangible differences in child-rearing practices, an attitude also advanced most cogently in the recent monograph by Wittenborn (1956). The correlational findings can be interpreted in two ways; if the genetic interpretation is favoured, then the mother's mental level at the time of her examination is considered to reflect her fundamental genetic constitution and ignores the effects of whatever environmental deprivations or advantages may have influenced her own mental development. Thus it would be assumed that children of the brighter mothers would turn out to be brighter regardless of the type of foster home into which they were placed. The increasing correlation might support this view, since the occupational differences between foster parents are not large. Both biological regression to the mean, and the role of the unknown fathers, complicate the picture, however, even though the mean I.Q. of the children is so much higher than that of the true mothers. If, on the other hand, the environmental interpretation is favoured, then the question is raised whether the increasing correlation between true mother and child reflects the tendency to selective placement, with the influence of the foster home having a greater effect as the child grows older. In fact, it is clear that there was a small tendency towards selective placement, probably particularly prevalent at the extremes. The authors conclude, however, that the 'increasing correlation . . . cannot be attributed to genetic determinants alone'.

The relationship between the educational status of 92 of the true mothers and the children's I.Q. was also assessed; correlations were zero at test I, but thereafter varied between 0·31 and 0·37 during the four remaining tests. Jones (1954) quotes some interesting unpublished data by Honzik, in which she showed a close similarity between these correlations and those obtained on a sample of about

200 children living with their own parents. This similarity in Jones's view provides added evidence as to the relatively small weight of environmental factors in producing parent-child resemblances in the variables studied. On the other hand, selective placement may again complicate the issue, but the correlations between foster parent education and child I.Q. were approximately zero at all age levels.

It will be apparent that a longitudinal research of this nature, while in many ways superior to cross-sectional studies, leaves many questions unanswered or unclear. This is partly the result of it having been originally begun as a service project rather than as a planned research which might have overcome methodological defects and informational lacunae. The use of relatively crude indices is a further limiting factor, and there is little doubt that future work of this nature must study in far greater detail the dynamics of the foster home situation. Nevertheless, a relatively conservative general conclusion would be that these children on the whole showed a marked difference from their natural parents, particularly from their mothers. Once again, it is clear that the children show a very different picture from what might have been expected in view of their background; but the mechanisms at work in producing such a difference are somewhat unclear.

Wittenborn's (1956) monograph, reviewed in detail in Chapter XVIII, is mentioned here because its results indicate a way in which some environmental effects, in spite of selective placement, can be measured. It also shows the need for a more intensive study of home conditions and child-rearing practices. Wittenborn pointed out that heredity can be suspected as 'a confounding third variable' in correlations between developmental criteria and environmental measurements when the particular aspect was usually considered to have an hereditary component (e.g. intelligence). Such correlations would be a likely effect of selective placement. Where, however, developmental aspects not considered to have an hereditary basis were shown to relate to conditions of child rearing in the foster home, there would be some reason to believe that these were not due to selective placement but emerged as a response to these particular practices. For example, it was shown in the younger sample of foster children that there was a correlation of 0·33 between phobic reactions and unsympathetic child-rearing practices (operationally defined.) Such relationships were not particularly strong, and if, as the author and his collaborators suspect, many are an expression of the formative role of the environmental differences, they should not be taken as indications of the possible maximal importance of such differences; their importance may be much greater than indicated. It seems likely, they conclude, that inharmonious, incompatible, and rejective adoptive parents may tend to produce children who are aggressive and fearful. Such findings as these help us little to answer questions concerning the relative importance of nature and nurture in producing *intellectual differences*, but do indicate a method of approach to the study of home conditions and foster parental attitudes which might be useful with the question of intelligence and overcome the crudity of earlier work.

STUDIES OF THE EFFECTS ON INTELLIGENCE OF SPECIAL ENVIRONMENTS AND OF ENVIRONMENTAL CHANGE

Rationale. This method either measures the intelligence of children before and after some major environmental change, or compares the level of functioning of individuals in special circumstances with those of similar age and type in the population as a whole. The assumption is that if cultural differences affect intellectual development, then poor environments will on the whole produce lower test scores than good environments; and further, that removal from one cultural milieu into a very different one will produce increments or decrements in I.Q. according to the nature of the environmental change.

Difficulties. One of the main difficulties of this method is the establishment of proper experimental controls. Bias may result from equating groups at early ages before mental tests give reliable prognostic estimates; from various selection factors, and from failure to take into account normal variability and maturation. Other shortcomings of this technique will be mentioned in the text in connexion with individual researches.

Probably the most satisfactory study of the effects of special environments on normals is that by Husén (1951) quoted by Vernon (1955a and 1955b). Husén showed that adults who obtain full secondary and university education have a 12-point increment on the average over others of the same initial I.Q. who left school at the age of 15. Similarly, Vernon's demonstration that there is a differential decline in mental test performance such that those in non-intellectual jobs decline more rapidly than those in intellectual work is another indicator of environmental effects. Moreover, Honzik *et al.* (1948) considered that children whose mental test scores showed the most marked fluctuations had life histories which showed unusual variations with respect to disturbing and stabilizing factors. Nevertheless, there were other children whose scores remained constant despite highly disturbing experiences.

An interesting study by Skeels and Dye (1939) investigated the effects of differential stimulation on mentally retarded children. The initial observation was accidental. Two children under 18 months old, in residence at a state orphanage, gave unmistakable evidence of marked mental retardation. Kuhlmann–Binet intelligence tests were given to both, the results on one (at 13 months) being I.Q. 46, and on the second (aged 16 months) I.Q. 35. Qualitative and behavioural assessments supported these results. There was no indication of organic defects.

These two children were recommended for transfer to a state school for the mentally deficient but the prognosis was at the time regarded as poor. After transfer, they were placed in a ward of older girls whose ages ranged from 18 to 50 years and in mental age from 5 to 9 years. Six months later the psychologist visiting the wards of this institution was surprised to notice the apparently remarkable development of these children. They were accordingly re-examined on the same test as before, this time gaining I.Q.s of 77 and 87 respectively. A year later their I.Q.s had risen to 100 and 88. At the age of about 3½ the two children's scores were 95 and 93.

The hypothesis to explain these results was that the ward attendants had taken a particular fancy to these two babies who were the only pre-school children in their care. They were given outings and special play materials. Similarly, the older and brighter inmates of the ward were particularly attached to the children and would play with them during most of their waking hours; for these two it was clearly a stimulating environment. It was considered that a further change would be desirable if the intellectual alteration was to be maintained, and accordingly they were placed in rather average adoptive homes at the age of 3½. After about fifteen months in these homes re-examination, this time with the Stanford–Binet, resulted in

I.Q.s of 94 and 93 respectively. These unexpected findings raised a number of important questions. Observation suggested that similar children left in an orphanage nursery made no such gains in the rate of mental growth. Adult contacts were at a minimum and limited largely to physical care. Adoptive placement was clearly inappropriate, owing to the lack of certainty that progress would occur. The most reasonable solution would seem to lie in a repetition of the 'accidental experiment' but this time in a planned and controlled manner. Thus research was started involving an experimental group of 13 children whose ages ranged from 7 to 30 months, and Kuhlmann–Binet I.Q.s from 35 to 89. Mean age at the time of transfer to the state school was 19 months and mean I.Q. was 64. Once again, clinical observation supported the I.Q. classification; for example, a 7-month-old child in the group could scarcely hold his head up without support, while another at 30 months could not stand alone and required support while sitting in a chair. After the close of the experimental period it was decided to study a control group of children remaining in the orphanage. This group consisted of 12 children, whose ages ranged from 11 to 21 months, and I.Q.s from 50 to 103. Mean age at the time of the first test was 16 months, with a mean I.Q. of 86. No marked differences in the birth histories of the two groups were observed, nor in their medical histories. Family histories indicated that the majority came from homes of low socio-economic levels with parents of low intellect, and there were no important differences between them.

The members of the experimental group in general repeated the experiences of the first two children and also attended the school kindergarten just as soon as they could walk. In the case of almost every child, some adult, either older girl or attendant, would become particularly attached to him or her and would figuratively 'adopt' him. This probably constituted an important aspect of the change. Members of the control group, however, had environments rather typical of the average orphanage. The outstanding feature was the profound lack of mental stimulation or experiences usually associated with the life of the young child in an ordinary home. Up to the age of 2 years, the children were in the nursery of the hospital. They had good physical care but little beyond this; few play materials were available and they were seldom out of the nursery room except for short walks or periods of exercise. At the age of 2, they graduated to cottages where overcrowding was characteristic. Thirty to thirty-six children of the same sex under 6 years of age were under the care of one matron and three or four untrained and reluctant teen-age girls. The matron's duties were so arduous that a necessary regimentation of the children resulted. No child had any personal property. The contrast between these two environments is obvious (cf. Bowlby, 1951).

During the course of the experiment the average increase in I.Q. of the experimental group was 27·5 points, the final I.Q. at the conclusion being a mean of 91·8. The difference was highly significant, the '*t*' value being 6·3. Gains ranged from 7 to 58 points; three made increments of 45 points or more, and all but two increased by more than 15 points. The length of the experimental period depended in an individual case upon the child's progress, varying from 5·7 months to 52·1 months, with a mean of 18·9 months.

The development of the children in the control group was almost precisely the opposite from those in the experimental group. The average I.Q. at the beginning was 86·7 and at the end was 60·5, an average loss of 26·2 points. The '*t*' value of 6·1 showed the clear significance of the findings. Apart from one child who gained 2 points, all showed losses varying from 8 to 45 points. Ten of the twelve children lost 15 or more points. The average length of the experimental period was 30·7 months.

Table 10 summarizes the main findings, and the implications are, on the face of it, clear. Children brought up in psychologically poor environments show relative deterioration, while those brought up in environments more nearly similar to the normal will advance to varying extents, and both types will faithfully tend to follow in the direction of the environmental shift. The writers tell us that subsequent to this and other experiments, orphanage conditions have been considerably improved.

There are several criticisms which must nevertheless be made of this study. First, the testing of the infants in both groups was done at ages when these are anyway unreliable from a long-term point of view; thus their level at the commencement would normally give little clue about subsequent development, although admittedly gross developmental anomalies (particularly motor) seemed to have been present. Second, the groups were by no means matched even for I.Q. The experimental group had a lower mean initial I.Q. than the control; this raises the possibility of unknown selection factors. The

TABLE 10

Mental test results, mainly Kuhlmann–Binet

	Experimental group		Control group	
	Before transfer	After transfer	First test	Last test
Mean	64·3	91·8	86·7	60·5
S.D.	16·4	11·5	14·3	9·7
N	13	13	12	12

experimental periods for both groups was markedly different; the experimental group had a shorter time on the average in better conditions, while the control group had a longer period under extremely poor conditions (30 months versus 18 months). A straightforward comparison of the effects of the two environments cannot therefore legitimately be made. Third, the inclusion of a control group was apparently an afterthought at the conclusion of the main experiment. Clearly, proper planning would have involved a control group from the outset. In a sense there was some sort of control, although it was not as efficient as it could have been; it is of interest that in both groups the initial I.Q.s at these early ages gave little prediction of a relatively short-term outcome. The fourth point is that although members of both groups had apparently the same early experiences in the orphanage, they were not identically impaired at the commencement of the experiment. Thus, the initial differences between them were clearly due to factors other than environmental ones in infancy. Later, however, environmental factors apparently reversed the relationship. This must mean that unknown selection factors were operating, although, in fairness, it must be added that the initial superiority of the control group should have aided rather than penalized it. This, then, is an extremely interesting study, which, however, is not free from criticism. The results are strongly suggestive, and more recent work seems to have supported the findings.

The work reported by Bernardine Schmidt (1946) is probably the most controversial in the literature. She studied 322 children between the ages of 12 and 14 who had been placed because of low intelligence in special schools. Three such schools were experimental, using intensive methods, while the remaining two were regarded as controls, in which the traditional approach to such children was maintained. The mean I.Q.s of the experimental groups ranged between 49 (S.D. 10) and 56 (S.D. 10), while the two control means were 61 (S.D. 2·3) and 63 (S.D. 2·1). The special programme for the first three groups was directed not only to assisting them while at school but at preparing them for community adjustment later. There were six specific goals: (1) development of desirable personal behaviour, (2) improvement of basic educational skills, (3) the development of the manipulative arts, (4) improvement in work and study habits, (5) learning of occupational and relational vocational information, and (6) pre-employment experience. This programme lasted for three years, and every eighteen months the Stanford–Binet, Bernreuter Personality Inventory, and Vineland Social Maturity Scale were given, and there was a follow up for a period of five years after the end of the school programme. The control groups showed a slight decrease in average I.Q. after five years but the Experimental Groups made very large increments, from a mean of 52 to a mean of 89. Similar striking gains were reported in other spheres. Sarason (1953) wonders whether some of the controversy that has been raised by Schmidt's data is not due to differences in the various concepts of mental deficiency, pointing out that if incurability is regarded as a necessary criterion, then on that view these subjects were not mental defectives. However, this suggestion is overshadowed by Kirk's (1948) trenchant challenge which cast considerable doubt on the validity of the data. When investigating these findings, he was unable to gain access to the original data, and found discrepancies in the class records with the data published by Schmidt. He pointed out that the author did not explain how retarded semi-literate children could have been given the Bernreuter Personality Inventory, with its necessary high level of comprehension. Her reply (1948) can scarcely be considered impressive, and does not attempt to deal with each of Kirk's points one by one. There is thus some doubt about the whole study; nevertheless, as will be seen, several researches since then may indicate that some at least of her findings were correct, even if the interpretation she gave may not have been entirely so.

Two papers by Guertin (1949 and 1950) discuss the characteristics of 25 patients whom he regarded as pseudo-feeble-minded (for discussion of this concept, see pages 130–1); that is, persons who had shown large increments of I.Q. and who had advanced towards intellectual normality. A control group of patients was selected on the basis of matched pairs, all relevant variables being held constant; this group increased in I.Q. by only 3·2 points (range of changes: −38 to +13). The experimental group, however, had altered from a mean of 59 points to a mean of 83 (range of changes +6 to +43 points) and these gains had occurred until nearly the age of 30. The subjects were of course selected on the basis of having made large increments, so were not typical of the general mentally deficient population with which Guertin was working; no doubt some of the increase was spurious because different tests were used at different times for the assessments.

Guertin indicated that it had yet to be demonstrated that there were true differences in cross-sectional clinical data between those who are truly feeble-minded (by which he meant permanently so) and those who show deferred maturation. Pre- and post-admission data were extracted from the case histories under twelve different headings (e.g. age of walking, adjustment while on parole, family background, etc.). Four professional and experienced persons were asked to judge which of each pair (experimental and control) was the more likely to have made large I.Q. changes. All judges scored better than chance (50 per cent.), ranging from 64 per cent. to 74 per cent. correct. The most useful criteria for assessing the likelihood of later improvement appeared to be a history of inadequate home care, and the absence of a familial history of mental deficiency. Guertin pointed out that there were stable trends occurring in the longitudinal data, and that therefore these changes could not be due to errors of measurement. The best explanation, he believed, was that delayed maturation stemmed from environmental under-stimulation. Those who showed marked increases did so after the age of 16, and tended to come from less adequate home environments.

Clarke and Clarke (1954b) have described a study of cognitive changes in the feeble-minded which was undertaken as a result of observing that in a small group of high-grade patients there had occurred in some cases quite large changes in I.Q., ranging from a decrease of five points to an increase of 25 points on the Wechsler–Bellevue Test, Form I, over a time-interval of about 18 months. A control group was matched for initial I.Q. and age and retested after a short time-interval to find the maximal effects of test practice, errors of measurement, and underestimation at the time of the first test. It was found that the increases in the first group were significantly greater and could not be accounted for by these factors.

It was further noted that several writers such as Burt (1947), McKay (1942), Roberts (1945b), Spaulding (1946), and Guertin (1949) had noted such changes, and in some cases had suggested hypotheses to explain them. Seldom, however, were such hypotheses submitted to experimental verification.

In order to ascertain how often such changes were likely to occur a representative sample of 59 patients were retested with the same test, and Table 11 shows the main results.

TABLE 11

Results of test and retest on Wechsler, Form I, for 59 patients retested after an average interval of 27 months

	Original full scale I.Q.	Retest full scale I.Q.	Difference scores
Mean	66·2	72·7	6·5
S.D.	14·0	13·4	6·2
N	59	59	59

t (correlated means) = 8·074, significant beyond 0·1 per cent. level
I.Q. range at original test: 35 to 98
I.Q. range at retest: 40 to 97
Age range at retest: 14 to 50 years,* mean 23·5, S.D 8·1
Period between test and retest: mean 27 months, S.D. 6 months
Range of I.Q. changes: − 7 to +25 I.Q. points

* Only nine patients were over 30 years of age.

Almost half these patients showed gains of 8 points or more, and it was obvious that for the majority of such persons the increments occurring over this relatively short interval did not represent the total change which the individual had already made or would make in the future. The picture presented by the data showed a considerable proportion of the certified feeble-minded advancing towards or into intellectual normality.

Several hypotheses were examined to explain the results; control group data disposed of the possibility of test practice or initial underestimation due to nervousness affecting to any extent the data. There was a small but significant tendency for those of lower I.Q. to make the larger changes ($r = -0{\cdot}311$), but no other relevant relationships emerged except for one. This final hypothesis was that those whose history included early adverse environmental circumstances would be those who made the larger increases. Twelve criteria such as 'neglect', 'N.S.P.C.C. intervention', 'cruelty', etc. were formulated, and an independent investigator, who knew neither the patients nor their test scores, applied them to the 59 case histories, separating them into two groups, those from very bad homes and the remainder (many of whom came from fairly bad homes). The former showed a mean increment of 9·7, S.D. 6·3, and the latter a mean of 4·1, S.D. 4·9, very similar to control group data. Table 12 shows the distribution of these changes.

TABLE 12

Distribution of I.Q. changes

Change	Very bad homes	Remainder	Controls*
−7 to 0 I.Q. points	1/25 = 4%	8/34 = 24%	4/29 = 14%
+1 to +7 I.Q. points	6/25 = 24%	17/34 = 50%	19/29 = 65% } 100%
+8 I.Q. points or more	18/25 = 72%	9/34 = 26%	6/29 = 21%
+10 I.Q. points or more	12/25 = 48%	5/34 = 15%	1/29 = 3%
+15 I.Q. points or more	7/25 = 28%	0	0
+25 I.Q. points	1/25 = 4%	0	0

* The control group consisted of patients retested after a time-interval averaging 3 months, in order to establish the maximal effects of test practice, errors of measurement, and underestimation.

The difference between the gains made by the two groups was significant at the 0·1 per cent. level, and confirmed the hypothesis that a record of early adverse experiences was related to I.Q. improvement, often many years later. This suggests that such experiences tend to retard mental development for many years, after which the effects begin to fade, I.Q. increments thus occurring. It was concluded that the increments seemed to be more the effect of being removed from a very adverse environment rather than of entry into a relatively better one, since there was no correlation with length of institutionalization, nor with particular type of treatment and training. These changes were related to I.Q. variability in normals, being different only in three respects: first, they tended to be unidirectional; second, they were relatively large in relation to the fairly short time-interval; and third, they took place at ages when mental growth is normally assumed to have ceased. It was suggested that further research might show how such relatively spontaneous changes could be both accelerated and improved.

Marchand (1956) studied changes in psychometric test results in a group of patients who had had outside employment experience after institutional training; 123 patients were investigated and the interval between initial test and final retest averaged about 11 years. Before placement, their I.Q.s ranged from 40 to 91, with a mean of 58·8, while the final range was from 36 to 99, with a mean of 68, the average rise being 9·2 I.Q. points. It was found that 88 per cent. attained higher I.Q.s after having had outside employment experiences, 50 per cent. rising by from 1 to 9 points, and 38 per cent. increasing by from 10 to 31 points. A control group of 20 patients who were of similar I.Q. range, but lower average (52·9), and whose members had not been in employment outside the institution over a period of about 9 years, showed a slight average decrease of 1·4 I.Q. points. It was considered that there had occurred consistent differences in the drives and attitudes of those who had shown significant I.Q. changes.

Marchand is at pains to point out that this was a retrospective study, using very loose criteria which cannot be considered as scientific research but merely as a survey suggesting possible future work. He does not consider that it has proven that outside employment for mental defectives has been the sole cause of general I.Q. rises, but does believe that when institutions offer enriching and satisfying experiences, one of which may be outside employment, the individual patient has a better chance of responding nearer to maximal functioning. Clearly there may well have been selection factors involved originally when the particular patients were chosen for outside placement, and a similar bias presumably operated in the fact that the members of the control group were not so chosen. A further difficulty is that apparently some of the tests were different, such that an initial assessment may have been on the Stanford–Binet and a final one on the Wechsler. This would in itself perhaps account for some of the variability. Further, we are not told whether the Stanford–Binet I.Q.s for the younger patients were corrected for variability of standard deviation at different ages, where relevant, and this might again result in some spurious changes. Nevertheless, provided these results are looked at with some caution, as the author wishes, the study is suggestive and interesting.

Clarke, Clarke, and Reiman (1958) have followed up the earlier work of the first two authors, and have reported the results of three further studies of cognitive and social changes in the feeble-minded. Their first new study followed up those persons who were still available in 1955–6 from the 1954 research. Nine patients from the original group of 25 patients from very bad homes were still accessible, and 19 of the original 34 from not such bad homes were also accessible. A large proportion of the remaining 31 had been discharged, so that those who remained were likely to be the less satisfactory members of the samples; hence estimates of I.Q. change over nearly six years would probably be minimal for the whole of the original group. The differential availability of the members of the two groups is in itself of social note. The fact that relatively fewer of those from very bad homes were still available, once again

TABLE 13 (a)

Test–retest data, Wechsler, Form I, over six years

Group from very bad homes

	1949 F.S. I.Q.	1952 F.S. I.Q.	1955 F.S. I.Q.	Diff. '49/'52	Diff. '52/'55	Diff. '49/'55
Mean	59·6 (66·4)	70·7 (76·1)	75·8	11·1 (9·7)	5·1	16·2
S.D.	9·7 (14·1)	11·4 (13·4)	10·3	4·2 (6·3)	5·0	6·1
N	9 (25)	9 (25)	9	9 (25)	9	9
t (1-tail test)				7·929 sig. 0·1% level	3·059 sig. 1% level	7·969 sig. 0·1% level

I.Q. range: 1949 47–72
1952 58–86
1955 64–91

Age at final retest: Mean 26·4, S.D. 5·5 yrs.
Period between first and final test: Mean 70·9 mos., S.D. 2·5 mos.
Range of I.Q. changes: +3 to +22 points. (10 points and above: 8/9 = 89 per cent.; 15 points and above: 7/9 = 78 per cent.)

TABLE 13 (b)

Group from less adverse homes

	1949 F.S. I.Q.	1952 F.S. I.Q.	1955 F.S. I.Q.	Diff. '49/'52	Diff. '52/'55	Diff. '49/'55
Mean	62·3 (66·1)	66·8 (70·1)	72·5	4·5 (4·1)	5·7	10·2
S.D.	13·4 (14·1)	13·0 (13·1)	13·3	4·4 (4·9)	5·1	6·6
N	19 (34)	19 (34)	19	19 (34)	19	19
t (1-tail test)				4·460 sig. 0·1% level	4·872 sig. 0·1% level	6·737 sig. 0·1% level

I.Q. range: 1949 35–87
1952 40–89
1955 48–100

Age at final retest: Mean 27·9, S.D. 9·5 yrs.
Period between first and final test: Mean 74·2 mos., S.D. 5·3 mos.
Range of I.Q. changes: −2 to +21 I.Q. points. (10 points and above: 10/19 = 53 per cent.; 15 points and above: 5/19 = 26 per cent.)

t (between Group from very bad homes and Group from less adverse homes) = 2·403 (sig. above 2·5 per cent. level, 1-tail test).

The figures in brackets show the data for the original group of which the present subjects formed a part.

underlined the better prognosis of those from the worst social conditions. Further, of the 9 from very bad homes, 8 were already working in the community whereas only 4 of the 19 from not such bad homes were so placed.

The previous Table (13a and b) shows the main results.

It will be noted that the members of the very bad home group had increased by about 16 points over six years (significant at the 0·1 per cent. level), while those from the less adverse homes had improved by about 10 points (significant at the 0·1 per cent. level) over a similar period. Particularly the former group now showed a substantially different cognitive picture than originally, and the authors considered that the results confirmed the earlier study; those with the greater damage due to deprivation in early life made a greater recovery. It was unlikely that the I.Q. increments *caused* the better social adaptation noted earlier; rather the increase must be regarded as one facet of more or less total personality development, as Marchand (1956) suggested, which may well be associated with the same general causation.

The second study (1958) involved the retesting of those who remained from the high-grade patients admitted to the hospital about four years previously. The main question for investigation was whether I.Q. changes in this type of person were a function of time-interval between tests, as is sometimes implied for normals. The present time-interval was roughly double that of the 1954 research. Thirty-two of an original 60 were still available, and once again it appeared that these were the less satisfactory members of the original sample. An independent investigator, knowing neither the patients nor their test scores, applied the twelve criteria to the case notes, and once again divided the sample into two groups, those from the very bad homes, and those from the not such bad homes. Subsequently retesting was carried out by a psychologist who knew neither the patients nor their histories nor their earlier test scores. The mean increment of the very bad home group was 11·5 points, with a standard deviation of 6·3 points, while the increase of the remainder was an average of 7·2 points, with a standard deviation of 6·6 points. In the former, the increment over the doubled time-interval was not so very much larger than the one found in the 1954 research (11·6 versus 9·7). Clearly, therefore, increment is not a direct function of length of the period between test and retest for this group. This supports a subsidiary result of the first (1958) study, where it was found that such persons made their maximum change in the earlier period and thereafter changed more slowly. The group from the less adverse homes made an increment much more nearly double that of the similar group in the 1954 research (7·2 points versus 4·1), which again links with a finding in the first (1958) study that I.Q.s on the average increased steadily throughout the six-year period for those patients whose early histories had been less adverse.

The third (1958) study was devoted to a special problem; the original (1954) research had suggested that I.Q. increments in this population resulted more as an effect of removal from adverse conditions rather than of entry into relatively better ones. It was important to determine whether a special environment would stimulate and accelerate I.Q. increments in this age range and population.

The subjects selected for the testing of this hypothesis were a group of 21 who had received intensive training followed by placement in industrial work in the community. This was in all cases expected to lead to discharge of these patients from care, and success rates of this and similar groups had already indicated the superiority of this over traditional methods of training and placement. Once again home conditions were independently assessed and followed by independent retesting. It was found that those from the worst homes had increased by 14 points on the average, while those from less adverse conditions had gained an average of 10 points. These were not very different from results of the second study (1958) over a similar time-interval and indicated only very small effects of the difference in environments. Thus, while early *negative* environmental influence had profoundly adverse effects, *positive* stimulation in adolescence or later exerted little influence upon the I.Q. It seemed that entry into any non-adverse environment would allow intellectual damage to fade to varying extents.[1] Socially, however, these special conditions had resulted in profound changes in the subjects. Clarke and Clarke (1959) have further considered the implications of their studies, and summarized the results in graphical form as in Fig. 2 below. They draw attention to the almost linear increase, over six years, in the proportion of persons in the groups drawn from very bad homes, making given increments in I.Q. Using comparable criteria and similar populations, the findings of the Clarkes have been independently confirmed by Roswell Harris (1958).

Mundy (1955) carried out both a pilot and main study of environmental influences upon the I.Q. In the latter she used an experimental and control group, each consisting of 28 adult females certified as feeble-minded, and considered that the two were initially equated on a number of important variables, the only difference being that one had had employment experiences while the other had not. These groups were tested and then retested after two years, during which the controls remained in the institution, while members of the experimental group enjoyed normal life experiences, mostly in residential wage-earning employment. The Wechsler and Progressive Matrices tests were used, and on retest, the controls showed an

[1] These authors draw attention to some remarkably similar findings (Widdowson and McCance, 1954) in an entirely different field of deprivation. Following malnutrition, German war-time orphanage children showed increased physical growth rates, and difference in diets did not result in differential increases; rather the children grew equally well and more rapidly than normal on all diets.

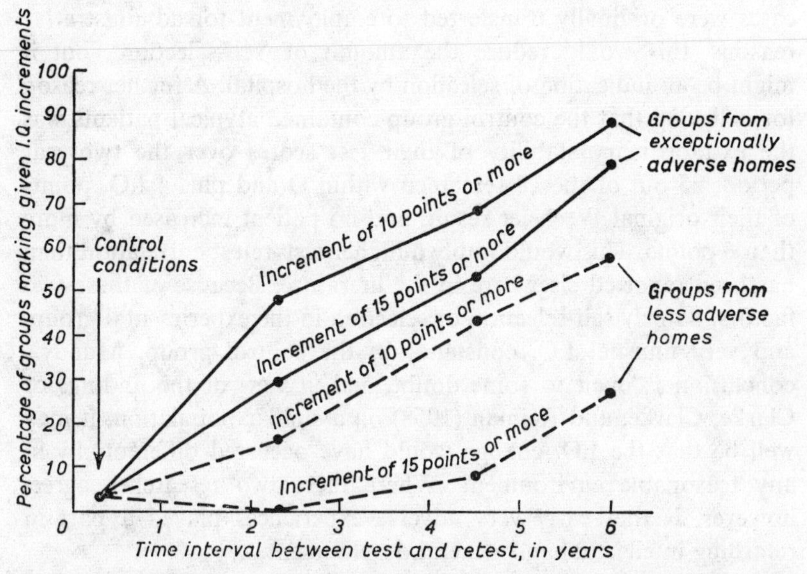

Fig. 2. Cognitive recovery from deprivation. This shows the increasing proportion of different but comparable groups of feeble-minded patients exhibiting increments in I.Q. of 10 and 15 points with increase in time-interval between test and retest. Increments of 20 points or more are not shown, but for the six-year interval 33 per cent. of the group from exceptionally adverse homes and 5 per cent. of those from less adverse homes made gains of this order.

average Wechsler increment of 2·25 points, and on the Matrices, 3·46 points. The experimental group, however, gained an average of 11 and 9·82 points respectively. Mundy believed that these results indicated that present environmental differences induced differential gains, but the validity of this conclusion clearly rests upon whether control and experimental groups were in fact initially equal in all respects. We are told, however, that there was no clinical selection by the hospital for outside employment, and that 'any able-bodied patient who wished for outside work was found suitable employment as soon as this was feasible'. This suggests that members of the experimental group had, through drive, ambition, and initiative, asked for outside employment and hence gained it, while for several years at least the members of the control had been content to remain within a good institution; there was thus a difference between the groups in terms of 'self-selection'. It should be added, however, that in a personal communication the author has stated that some cases were originally transferred to employment for administrative reasons; this would reduce the amount of 'self-selection', but it might be an indication of selection by the hospital. A further reason for believing that the control group contained atypical patients was the extraordinary stability of their test scores over the two-year period; 25 out of the 28 remained within O and plus 4 I.Q. points of their original Wechsler result, and no patient increased by more than 6 points. This would imply a higher test–retest correlation than has been reported elsewhere in the literature. Because of these two factors, namely self-selection or selection in the experimental group, and very unusual I.Q. constancy in the control group, Mundy's conclusion is open to some doubt, and in view of the findings of Clarke, Clarke, and Reiman (1958) on a similar population, it may well be that the I.Q. change would have occurred differentially in any reasonable environment. Where these two researches agree, however, is that early very adverse experiences played a part in retarding intellectual and general development.

Kirk (1958) has reported the results of a very carefully controlled experiment on the effects of pre-school education on the intellectual and social development of mentally retarded children. The investigation was designed to provide factual data for or against the general contention that special educational provision early in life could alter the children's rate of development.

Eighty-one defective children, aged between 3 and 6, were identified and studied for between three and five years. Twenty-eight formed the Community Experimental Group, attending a pre-school in the community and being followed up for between one and four years after leaving. Fifteen children were members of the Institution Experimental Group, attending an institution pre-school, and being followed up in the same way as in the first group. Twenty-six children constituted the Community Contrast Group and a further 12, in a different institution from the second experimental group, constituted the Institution Contrast Group.

The I.Q.s of the subjects ranged from 45 to 80. They were examined at the beginning of the experiment, during the pre-school period and again on follow-up after leaving the pre-school. The results were analysed both by case studies of the children in the experimental groups, and by the more conventional type of statistical comparisons. For the former, each child was placed in one of seven developmental levels, ranging from 'uneducable' to 'average'. It was found that

30 of the 43 children who had received pre-school stimulation showed an acceleration in growth rates during the experimental period and retained that level subsequently. They had raised their developmental classification from between one and three levels.

Analysis of test scores showed differential increase on the Binet, Kuhlmann, and Vineland scales, all significant beyond the 0·05 level. On the Binet, for example, the range of I.Q. changes from the beginning to the end of the study for the Institution Experimental Group varied between a loss of 17 points and a gain of 33. The average increment was 10 points. For the Institution Contrast Group, however, there was an average decrement of 6½ points, with a range of from −19 to +10. The Community Experimental Group showed a total average Binet increment of nearly 12 points, while the Community Contrast Group showed a 7-point increment. The difference between the two Contrast Groups is interesting, and obviously has a bearing upon interpretation of the effects of some kinds of institutional upbringing. In brief, it was clear that pre-school education whether in the community or the institution had positive and, within the time limits of the study, lasting effects on intellectual and social development. Nevertheless, as Kirk indicates, group comparisons may well mask intra-group differences. It became apparent that it was much more difficult to displace the growth rates of those children with definite organic aetiologies. This finding is in accord with the Clarkes' work on I.Q. changes reported earlier. The results also suggested two further conclusions: first, that 'within limits the greater the changes that are made in the environment, the greater are the changes in the rate of growth'; and second, that holding the home factor constant by studying siblings from the same family one of whom did, and the other who did not, attend pre-school, it was clear that the pre-school had provided compensation for inadequate home environment.

An unexpected finding by Kirk was that the Community Contrast Group after a year in school showed an upward trend in I.Q.s and S.Q.s, thus narrowing the gap between its members and those who had had the advantage of pre-school stimulation. Kirk notes that 'this could mean that pre-schools for mentally-handicapped children are not necessary, since the children will accelerate their rate of development after entering school at the usual age of six'. A further study of the Community Contrast Group, however, suggested that children from adequate homes tend to accelerate their growth rates during later school experience, while those from inadequate homes did not. This difference was, however, not significant statistically, no doubt partly because of the small number (8 out of 26) in this group who came from inadequate homes.

The general inference from the study, then, is that both pre-school and early school education have beneficial intellectual and social effects. Pre-school stimulation, however, seems to be particularly important for those from inadequate homes. Kirk's investigation is likely to prove a fruitful stimulus to later ones. It is one of the few in the whole literature which cannot be criticized on methodological grounds. It has thus shown, among other things, that the complex problems studied can be brought under experimental control.

The work reviewed by Bowlby (1951) is too well known to need summary; it is highly relevant to some of the findings already quoted on the effects of early adverse environment in childhood which have played some part in producing mental deficiency. His review is, however, almost entirely concerned with deprived children rather than with adolescents or adults, a point which he notes with care. Bowlby is pessimistic about the recovery of children from early psychological damage, particularly if they do not receive full psychotherapy. Yet some of the subjects in the researches quoted here could scarcely have had worse early environmental influences, and many in adult life had done better than might have been expected from either Bowlby's thesis or the traditional viewpoint. Part of this greater success was naturally due to improved economic conditions, but a substantial part also to individual change. Yet few subjects received psychotherapy. Similarly, some of the social studies of defectives from adverse conditions, particularly the exemplary monograph by Charles (1953), have shown that they tend not to develop according to a rigid stereotype, and that many eventually function at a dull-normal or normal level. Two very important questions arise; first, to what extent is human resilience an important variable, and what in fact is it? Does it depend upon the basic resources of the nervous system, genetically determined, or upon early learning experiences or both; why is it that some children succumb while others do not; why are some utterly overwhelmed by such experiences while others emerge apparently unscathed? Second, is it possible that when other deprived children are studied in adolescence or later from Bowlby's point of view, it will be found that initial psychological damage, as in many high-grade defectives, tends steadily to be repaired? This is the view of Clarke and Clarke (1959) who have briefly reviewed the whole field of deprivation, concluding that to varying extents there exists a tendency towards spontaneous recovery from the effects of early adversity.

THE MECHANISMS OF ENVIRONMENTAL INFLUENCE

All too little is understood about the mechanisms of environmental influence, although the correlates of subcultural deficiency have been well known since Burt's pioneer surveys. The conclusions then advanced were that poverty, bad housing conditions, and lack of stimulation were contributory but not prime causal agents. The main cause, writes Burt, was 'unquestionably heredity'.

There is no doubt that a proportion of those with I.Q.s between 50 and 75 do in fact owe their condition almost entirely to genetic factors. With a correlation of only about 0·5 between parents and their children, it is to be expected that for parents with average I.Q.s of, say, 90, some of their children will fall well below this figure and some well above. Nevertheless, from the recovery of many of the most deprived and neglected high-grade defectives, many of whom ultimately achieve borderline- or dull-normality in I.Q., it seems reasonable to suppose that their condition is quite largely environmental in origin. That is to say, various factors combine to prevent the subcultural defective from reaching his genetic potential. In brief, then, we can identify three sub-populations which make up the group we know as high-grade or educable defectives: first, the genetic cases; second, the subcultural, who under the best child-raising conditions would seldom be average members of the population, but whose present condition is largely environmental in origin; and third, those with minor neurological or biochemical anomalies of development.

A brief summary may now be given of what is known of environmental agencies which operate in the aetiology of subcultural high-grade deficiency.

1. Lack of childhood stimulation

In its most extreme, and fortunately very rare, form, there is little doubt that social isolation can even cause low-grade deficiency. One of the two cases described by Davis (1947) of illegitimate children secreted in attics for the first five or six years of life, made a dramatic recovery from imbecility and speechlessness. This girl, reared by a deaf-mute mother in conditions of semi-darkness and silence, eventually attained intellectual normality after rescue from these conditions and special skilled treatment. One or two other cases of this type seem to owe their deficiency primarily to such isolation.

The damaging effects of bad institutions upon young children have already been mentioned. A number of careful studies have underlined the virtual impossibility of permanent attachments to adults (Rheingold, 1956, 1960) as well as the relative lack of adult contacts. While the popular insistence upon maternal–child interaction is probably partly a cultural value judgment, studies of kibbutzim children also emphasize the importance of *permanence* in adult–child relationships, as well as of generous staff–child ratios.

In the institution, the child's main learning model is other children rather than adults, and this would seem to be a potent reason for retardation of development. Kellmer Pringle and Tanner (1958), for example, showed that at the age of 4 years, a group of residential nursery children living in excellent material conditions were retarded in speech to the extent of 10 months, in comparison with a group of day nursery children of similar background, who lived in poor conditions with their mothers.

Large numbers of careful studies have revealed the correlates of low social and economic class (e.g. Douglas, 1964). These include poor material and often, though not invariably, poor psychological conditions. There can be little doubt that both have a direct effect in preventing children from reaching their full potential. Where the environment is actively adverse (e.g. cruelty or neglect) these effects are more profound in all areas of psychological development.

2. Speech and cognitive development

It is increasingly recognized that language is of immense importance in development. Until recently the view was held that for the young child speech had two functions: first, and obvious, the need to communicate and understand; and, second, the role of egocentric commentary, proposed by Piaget. Luria (1961), however, has revived interest in the relation between speech and thought. In a series of brilliant experiments with young pre-school children, he has shown that speech is also externalized thinking, essential to problem-solving. It is a means whereby behaviour is regulated and integrated.

This being so, speech retardation due to environmental influence is likely to weaken the earlier stages of cognitive development. And since each stage depends upon the integrity of previous stages, this situation tends to be perpetuated.

Approaching this problem from a new sociological angle, Bernstein has suggested the existence of two very different speech modes. The first, termed 'restricted', is to be found in the lower socio-economic groupings of the population. It is characterized by non-analytical, here-and-now statements, tends to be direct and concrete, using, for example, 'heavy-duty' verbs. In contrast, the middle and upper classes also possess an 'elaborated' speech mode. This is analytical and explanatory, with many qualifications and precision of vocabulary. Bernstein gives evidence which underlines the penalty paid by children reared under restricted speech as compared with those with elaborated. He argues that education necessarily employs elaborated speech and concepts, so that it must more and more tend to become a foreign language for many working-class children.

In one experiment, for example, Bernstein (1960) compared a group of 61 working-class messenger boys with a group of 45 subjects matched for age and sex, drawn from one of Britain's well-known public schools.[1] These two groups were given the Progressive Matrices, a non-verbal test, the difference between them averaging 8–10 I.Q. points. For Mill Hill vocabulary, however, the differences reflected 23–24 I.Q. points superiority by the non-working-class group. Later work (1962a and b) has revealed more clearly the nature of linguistic differences between social classes.

Large-scale social and psychological surveys also yield findings of relevance to the nature–nurture problem. The Scottish Survey of 1947, for example, confirmed the significance of the inverse relationship between family size and verbal intelligence, irrespective of social class. Nisbet's (1953) interpretation that, in effect, dilution of parental care in larger families is responsible seems far the most plausible explanation. Maxwell (1961) points out that although high scorers are to be found in all social categories, their respective proportions differ. Moreover, in the upper strata (where in general one assumes nature and nurture to be excellent) the proportion of low scorers is very small indeed.

Research upon concept formation and concept attainment (e.g.

[1] American readers should note that these are, in fact, independent schools catering for the highest socio-economic groups of the population.

Furth, 1964) lends support to the view that the relationship between speech and intelligence is probably even more complex than is perhaps implied above. A useful start has, however, been made, and one can expect this field of investigation to prove rewarding.

PSEUDO-FEEBLE-MINDEDNESS

No account of I.Q. changes in the mentally deficient is complete without some discussion of the concept of pseudo-feeble-mindedness. During the last decade or so, many articles have appeared on this subject, and these have been well reviewed by Cassel (1949a). Implicit in the relevant literature is the fact that the diagnosis of pseudo-feeble-mindedness is retrospective and involves an earlier diagnostic error. Such a viewpoint is exemplified by Porteus' (1941) statement that: 'Very wide differences in intellectual status merely indicate that the first diagnosis was wrong. Any child who finally functions at a normal level proves thereby that he never was feeble-minded.' In effect, Doll's (1941) attitude is similar; essential incurability is suggested as a necessary criterion of mental deficiency, and, therefore, no firm diagnosis can be made for many years in most cases. These attitudes have been challenged by Clarke and Clarke (1955), who argue that pseudo-feeble-mindedness does not involve *mistaken diagnosis*, since most studies show that at the material time the child seemed no different in level of functioning from the ordinary feeble-minded child, and test results gave no indication of unreliability or underestimation. Rather, there has been *mistaken prognosis* by the clinician. Mental deficiency can only be regarded as a broad term under which are subsumed a whole variety of conditions arising from a large number of different causes. Broadly speaking there are two types of level of mental arrest, the one permanent (as in most low-grade imbeciles and idiots), and the other impermanent to varying degrees (as in some high-grade cases). Different causes can obviously produce the same symptoms, and this is true of mental deficiency where these may involve low I.Q., social incompetence, abnormal behaviour, and so forth. Clarke and Clarke believe that the term pseudo-feeble-mindedness is quite inappropriate when applied to cases showing deferred intellectual maturation, because it obscures the fact of real change, arguing circularly that if there has been change, this cannot really have taken place because people do not really change. Kirk (1958) quotes with approval Stoddard's

(1943) view that 'to regard all changes in mental status as an artifact is to shut one's eyes to the most significant and dramatic phenomenon in human growth'.

THE INFLUENCE OF DRUGS UPON THE I.Q.

Although the effect of drugs upon the I.Q. should not properly be discussed in a chapter on genetic and environmental studies of intelligence, as defined at the outset, nevertheless there has been sufficient interest in this sphere to justify inclusion of a short section.

Rationale. Tradition as well as empirical research have suggested that certain chemical substances can improve a person's intelligence. Administration of the drug under controlled conditions thus enables such claims to be validated.

Difficulties. The only difficulties in this method are those of experimental control. It is essential that control groups should be used; that the effects of test practice be precisely known; that the tester be unaware of whether a particular subject is experimental or control; that the administration of placebos and the drug be carried out in such a way that both the nurse and the patient are unaware of its identity; and that matched groups chould be selected and assigned at random either to experimental or control conditions. All these are straightforward steps, and it is significant that few studies have followed them completely; more often they have been in the nature of relatively uncontrolled observations. Without these controls, such factors as the interest taken by the experimenters or nurses in the patients (leading to increased motivation in the test situation) may alter radically the outcome.

Glutamic acid

Since 1943 there have been reports in the literature claiming improvement in cognitive function following the administration of glutamic acid both to animals and man. As Lombard, Gilbert, and Donofrio (1955) indicate, the reasons for choosing glutamic acid in attempting to improve human intelligence are

> that . . . (it) appears to be the only amino-acid which will cause increased oxygen uptake by brain tissue; that the enzyme glutaminase, which synthesizes glutamine from glutamic acid, is utilized in brain metabolism; and that glutamic acid has been shown to be

a catalyst for the formation of acetyl-choline, whose release is intimately connected with the electrical change of nerve activity (op. cit., p. 122).

Researches on the value of glutamic acid therapy have been excellently reviewed by Milliken and Standen (1951) and more recently by Lombard, Gilbert, and Donofrio (1955). In general it may be said that the better controlled studies gave negative results and the less controlled researches have tended to give positive findings. Such workers as Albert, Hoch, and Waelsch (1946) claimed that eight mentally deficient patients showed test score increases following glutamic acid therapy followed by decreases when the same patients were given placebos. In the excellently controlled study of Milliken and Standen (op. cit.) two groups of mentally deficient adults, one group of mentally deficient children and two groups of normal boys were divided each into an experimental and control section. Before and after treatment with glutamic acid or a placebo, each was given verbal, performance, and personality tests. After the second test administration, each subject was transferred to the other group for a further period of treatment or placebo-treatment as the case might be, and subsequently a third testing took place. Results of cognitive testing provided no evidence in favour of the hypothesis. Similarly, the findings of Lombard, Gilbert, and Donofrio (op. cit.), another very carefully controlled study, yielded negative findings. Thus in spite of the logical rationale of this method, it must be concluded that real evidence of its efficacy is lacking.

Celastrus paniculata

Morris, MacGillivray, and Mathieson (1954) point out that the seeds of this oriental plant have for centuries enjoyed repute among Hindu physicians as a stimulant both of intelligence and memory. These authors carried out a carefully controlled study on high-grade patients, testing and retesting after treatment a large number of cognitive functions. They found that the drug was of little value and believed it possible that the euphoria sometimes produced by its administration may be responsible for its traditional reputation.

Hormone treatment and replacement therapy

It is well known that some cases of specific endocrine dysfunction such as hypothyroidism, which leads to cretinism if severe, can be successfully treated if this is started sufficiently early in life (see Chapter VI). Early work (Woolf, Griffiths, and Moncrieff, 1955) suggested that the recessively inherited metabolic disorder known as phenylketonuria may also be treated with a diet low in phenyl-alanine. Three children are described, two aged 2 years 8 months, and the third aged 5 years at the start of treatment. They were carefully observed and tested (Griffiths' mental development scale) for periods of nine, ten, and five months, respectively. Increments in I.Q. were as follows: 20–30, 42–49, and 11–14, respectively; these are of course very small but the time-intervals were similarly short, and in fact the qualitative differences in behaviour seemed to be greater than the changes might imply. Nevertheless, recent controlled studies indicate the success of careful long-term biochemically-controlled treatment. Such children do not quite reach the level of their unaffected siblings but develop far above the level of the untreated child (Waismann, 1964). It is to be expected that other rare metabolic defects may ultimately prove susceptible to treatment.

In general, except where known rare disorders can be diagnosed early before irreversible changes in the nervous system have occurred, and where replacement therapy is possible, the hope that there exist drugs which may increase intelligence has not been realized. Indeed, since it is known that, so far as subcultural defect is concerned, the aetiology is a complex and relatively ill-understood process of reciprocal interaction between social and genetic and constitutional factors, it would appear unlikely *a priori* that the problems of low intelligence could be solved in this way.

CONCLUSIONS

The reader may well feel that, after detailed discussion of nature and nurture in relation to high-grade mental deficiency, he is in need of more precise statements in which the various threads of argument are drawn together. An attempt will therefore be made to outline some general conclusions which emerge from this review.

It may be assumed that heredity plays an essential part in determining the limits of intellectual development, but these limits are considerably wider than was formerly thought. With moderate uniformity of environment, individual differences result largely from genetic variations. The feeble-minded, however, more than any other group in western culture have been reared in most adverse circumstances, followed in many cases by further lengthy periods in residential schools and institutions, with all that this implies. Thus the feeble-minded in such conditions seem likely to be functioning towards the lower end of their spectrum of potentialities, while normals under ordinary conditions of life approximate more closely to their upper limits.

It is possible to assess in a cautious and conservative manner the extent to which the observed cognitive deficiency of institutionalized subnormal patients results from their conditions of nurture. This estimate can be made from the data on I.Q. increments among typical high-grade patients considered in detail earlier (pp.115–22), and is based on the *assumption that the amount of measured recovery is equivalent to the degree of original psychological damage*. Such a procedure is, however, likely to *underestimate* the effect of adverse nurture for three reasons:

(1) A very long follow-up would be needed to measure the total process of recovery, and this has only been carried out systematically on social aspects of high-grade mental deficiency (Charles, 1953), with results, incidentally, consistent with those on I.Q. increments. Thus assessments based on a six-year period between test and retest in the decade and a half (age 15 to about 30) in which increments are most common, are likely to be minimal.

(2) It is possible that the range of potential development already referred to is itself narrowed by adverse experiences and there is indeed some evidence from other research that this may be so. Thus the amount of measured recovery (i.e. of increment) is again likely to underestimate the degree of intellectual damage induced by adverse nurture in this group.

(3) The data obtained in these researches were based on persons still available for retesting, and strong evidence existed that these were the less promising members of the original samples; thus, once more, minimal assessments are probable.

Nevertheless, bearing all these limitations and provisos in mind, and using measured recovery over six of the crucial years as the criterion, it is evident that the most adverse conditions, characterized by cruelty and neglect in childhood (representative of about 40 per cent. of subnormals in institutions), retard intellectual development by *at least* an average of 16 points (S.D. 6). Similarly, unsatisfactory social conditions, or life-long institutional upbringing but not involving such a severe degree of deprivation (characteristic of something like 45–50 per cent. of subnormal patients), retard intellectual development by *at least* an average of 10 points (S.D. 6). It may well be, however, that the total effect is considerably greater and research will eventually establish more accurate figures. It is indeed likely that a much higher proportion of such persons will make large changes than occurs in the normal population.

It seems very probable that findings such as these represent one of the factors accounting for Penrose's (1949) demonstration that the incidence of high-grade mental deficiency declines markedly from the age of 15 onwards. Thus, from these two entirely different approaches, a similar picture emerges.

It is also evident that environmental deprivation does not operate in a rigid and mechanical way; a wide variation in individual susceptibility to psychological damage and resilience thereafter is maintained, and that individual outcome is immensely varied. What these factors of susceptibility and resilience are based upon is an obvious field for research.

The main conclusion is that for children or young adolescents, with I.Q.s in the 50's, 60's, or 70's, a necessarily bad outcome cannot be predicted if they have also been reared in adverse conditions either in their own homes or in institutions. This clearly has implications both for theory and practice. These findings fit well the general thesis that, contrary to psycho-analytical theory, non-reinforced early experiences tend to have effects which in man usually fade or at least show a shift in severity as time increases (Clarke, 1965).

Finally, the methodological imperfections so characteristic of much research in this field are nowadays well understood; it is to be hoped, therefore, that future investigations will be planned in such a way as to avoid these weaknesses. The main problem now seems to be to investigate experimentally the mechanisms involved both in environmentally induced retardation and recovery from the effects of deprivation, as well as research upon genetic influences which are no less important. In particular, the work and theories of Piaget, Hebb, and Harlow seem likely to provide the impetus to new research upon the fundamental problems of human development.

If we consider the nature–nurture problem generally, it is already clear that reliable evidence is being accumulated. The search for precise formulae for the importance of either factor is being abandoned in favour of isolating particular effects of particular conditions.

If it be true, as we have stated, that extreme social isolation can cause imbecility, or that crowded and inadequate institutions can cause gross motor retardation, among other things (Dennis and Najarian, 1957; Dennis, 1960), then it is obvious that nurture is all-important. It is equally obvious that nature falls into precisely the same category. In general, the hereditarians have dominated the field for most of the century, while those who held to the opposite extreme spoiled their arguments by relying upon methodologically inadequate work. It is probable that what has diminished the appreciation of the effects of nurture has been the fact that this will not be *seen* as being very important where children under rather similar environmental conditions are being compared. In the same way, the effect of pressure upon the temperature of gas would not be understood unless pressure is varied.

Put very simply, it is self-evident that concept formation must ultimately depend upon informational input from the environment. Where such input is lacking, concept development must also be lacking. What is not yet clear is to what extent later environmental enrichment will compensate for earlier impoverishment. It seems that while with man we cannot speak of critical periods of learning, there are nevertheless optimal periods for different functions.

Accepting, therefore, an interaction theory of nature and nurture we can reach the rough equation that where environment is adequate the observed differences between children must be largely genetic in origin, and where it is adverse, the environmental effects (masked in the earlier case) are superimposed upon genetic differences. This being so, it is at once apparent that large sections of the population are underfunctioning to varying degrees. This problem has recently been considered by Hunt (1961) in a scholarly book. He writes that:

> The hope of increasing the average level of intelligence by proper manipulation of children's developmental encounters with their environments, a hope which becomes reasonable with the evidences surveyed here and with relinquishing the assumptions of fixed intelligence and predetermined development, provides a challenge of the first order. It has great implications for human welfare as the growth of technology in Western cultures demands a higher and higher percentage of people who can manipulate symbols and solve complex problems. In this challenge the theory of man's nature and the fate of his welfare are obviously intertwined.

Hunt's view is completely in accord with that advanced in this chapter. And while we remain in comparative ignorance of some of the mechanisms which retard development, we already know enough to be able to say that some forms of higher-grade mental deficiency can be alleviated or perhaps even prevented by appropriate environmental manipulation.

Chapter VI

AETIOLOGICAL ASPECTS OF MENTAL SUBNORMALITY: PATHOLOGICAL FACTORS

by J. M. Berg

INTRODUCTION

A wide variety of individuals with different clinical characteristics and different degrees of intellectual retardation are considered to be mentally defective or subnormal. Criteria of social competence and educational capability enter into such considerations, as well as the intellectual level *per se* as measured by tests of intelligence. Persons who can be classified as mentally subnormal on the basis of these criteria range from the helpless idiot to the dullard whose behaviour is regarded as disturbed or otherwise inappropriate. From the aetiological point of view, the term mental subnormality has no more meaning than, for example, a term such as diminished head size. Like smallness of the head, mental subnormality is not a disease entity but a symptom which can be determined by a large number of different causal agencies. These agencies operate, in given circumstances, to produce the symptom, in varying degrees of severity, together with other clinical manifestations.

GENERAL APPROACH TO THE PROBLEM

Some subnormal persons, in particular those with severe mental defect, suffer from demonstrable organic disease or pathology which, however determined, can reasonably be regarded as being responsible for the subnormality. Aided by knowledge of the personal and family history, these pathological conditions may be detected by means of various diagnostic techniques including clinical, neuropathological, biochemical and cytological ones. In other cases of subnormality, no physical abnormality can be found which could account for the mental defect. A considerable clinical problem which arises in these cases is that of trying to decide whether the inability to demonstrate organic pathology is due to inadequacy of available methods of diagnosis or due to the absence of such pathology. Important diagnostic aids have been developed in recent years, notably in the fields of biochemistry and cytogenetics, which have led to the detection of previously undifferentiated pathological types of mental subnormality. There is little doubt that more such types will be recognized in the future, though very many persons are likely to remain who function at a low intellectual level for reasons other than the operation of specific disease processes. Lewis (1933) called such cases 'subcultural', as opposed to 'pathological', and regarded them as representing the lower end of the normal variations in intelligence which occur in the general population. Most of these cases have relatively mild intellectual deficit and many are not obviously distinct from the normal population as a whole.

Lewis's (1933) subdivision of the mentally retarded into those who are organically diseased variants of the general population and those who are normal variants provides a helpful approach to the aetiology of mental subnormality. Two groups of causal agencies emerge for consideration:

1. Specific organic pathological processes directly responsible for, or closely associated with, mental defect. In the main, these lead to severe subnormality. However, a few (for example, the triple-X condition in females) are more usually associated with mild defect and many (for example, phenylketonuria) can result in intellectual states varying from gross idiocy to levels within the range of normality.
2. An interaction of genetical and environmental influences, of the same kind as those operating in the normal population, not responsible for specific physical disease but sufficient to produce some (usually mild) impairment of intellectual function. This will lead to a diagnosis of subnormality if the individual is considered also to be socially incompetent.

The influences mentioned in the second group have been considered in Chapters V and XVIII and will not be discussed further here. In this chapter an account is given of specific pathological causes of, and distinct physical syndromes closely associated with, mental subnormality. The subject cannot be dealt with extensively within the confines of one chapter, so that the data are presented with emphasis on principles rather than details.

HEREDITY AND ENVIRONMENT IN THE CAUSATION OF PATHOLOGICAL TYPES OF MENTAL SUBNORMALITY

The pathological types of mental subnormality can conveniently be divided into those which are genetically and those which are environmentally determined. It should be borne in mind, however, that the two sets of causal factors are not mutually exclusive. The effects on the individual of abnormal events and diseases having their origin in the environment will be influenced by the inherited constitution of that individual; for example, the occurrence of an obviously environmental event, such as injury at birth, will be dependent to some extent on characteristics of the new-born infant, like his birth weight, which are partly genetically determined. Conversely, inherited defects can be determined by earlier environmental events as, for instance, when irradiation produces mutations in germ cells (ova and sperms) which are harmful to offspring derived from these cells. Further, even when mental subnormality is due to inherited disease, environmental influences, such as a stable and stimulating home, appropriate educational facilities, and specific medical treatments, can have a substantial effect on the actual level and quality of mental function achieved. Haemolytic disease of the newborn, due to *Rhesus* incompatibility between mother and foetus, provides a notable example of the interaction between hereditary and environmental factors in the production of mental effects. In this condition, an inherited antigenic difference between the mother and her foetus can result in the formation of maternal antibodies which constitute an environmental hazard to the foetus; its red cells may be haemolysed and the products of the haemolytic process can seriously damage foetal tissues, including those of the brain. Mental subnormality of variable degree can thus occur in survivors. Both mortality and morbidity rates have been reduced by the environmental alteration achieved by exchange transfusions undertaken soon after birth. This technique involves the removal of the infant's blood, containing harmful maternal antibodies, and its replacement by normal donor blood.

Without prejudice to the reservations made above, the conditions to be discussed in this chapter are subdivided into those of genetical and those of environmental origin. As Penrose (1963a) points out, the distinction between hereditary and environmental causes must be based upon temporal sequence; the former are determined prior to conception (in parental, or more remote ancestral, germ cells) and the latter subsequent to it (before, during or after birth). It is perhaps as well to add a reminder here that the terms hereditary and congenital are not synonymous. The latter term is more comprehensive in that it is applicable both to conditions which are inherited and to those which arise from events occurring during intra-uterine life. Thus, all hereditary conditions are congenital though some congenital ones are not hereditary. The point can be illustrated by reference to congenital cataract. One variety of this, described by Garland and Moorhouse (1953), occurs in association with subnormality and ataxia and is due to a recessive gene. Another variety is a well-known consequence, together with other abnormalities including mental defect, of foetal infection with the rubella virus during the early stages of pregnancy. A further point which emerges from this reference to congenital cataract is that genetical and environmental events can give rise to similar defects. Goitrous cretinism, discussed on page 147, provides another example of this.

I. MENTAL SUBNORMALITY OF SPECIFIC GENETICAL ORIGIN

Genetically determined conditions closely associated with pathological types of mental subnormality may be due to:

1. Harmful genes. Dominant, recessive and sex-linked abnormalities are the main ones in this category. The genes resulting in pathological types of subnormality are rare specific ones, in contrast to commoner non-specific genes which may be supposed to be operating to produce what Lewis (1933) called 'subcultural' variation.

2. Aberrant chromosomes. These aberrations may involve the autosomes or the sex chromosomes and, sometimes, both.

Each of these will be considered in turn. An understanding of the mechanisms involved in the production of these abnormalities presupposes some knowledge of the characteristics of chromosomes and of the genetical units, or genes, which are regarded as an essential part of their nature. Some aspects of this subject are referred to in the context of the data presented below, though a general account of it is beyond the scope of the main theme of this chapter. Among the most recently published introductions to the science of human genetics are those of Carter (1962) and of Penrose (1963b).

1. Conditions due to harmful genes

(a) Dominant abnormalities

Several conditions, in which mental subnormality is not uncommon, fulfil the criteria of dominant inheritance. Such conditions are due to a single gene transmitted by a parent to half his offspring, though actually, because human sibships are relatively small, frequently more or less than half the children are affected. The parent is capable of transmitting the gene either because it has arisen by fresh mutation in his germ cells or because he himself inherited it. In the former case, the parent will not himself suffer from the disease and, in the latter, he must be sufficiently mildly afflicted to be capable of reproduction even though his affected offspring may be so grossly diseased as to be infertile. Fresh gene mutations and variability in the manifestations of disease therefore play an important role in dominant conditions associated with severe abnormalities. These considerations can make the demonstration of dominant inheritance of such abnormalities very difficult in practice.

Epiloia illustrates these points. Bourneville (1880) was the first to recognize the pathological features of the condition which he called *sclérose tubéreuse* (tuberous or tuberose sclerosis) in view of the tuber-like nodules which are found in the brain. Feeling the need for a name based on clinical rather than neuropathological considerations, Sherlock (1911) coined the term epiloia for the disease. Three of its main features are mental subnormality, epilepsy, and various skin anomalies of which the most important is adenoma sebaceum, consisting of multiple papules in a mainly butterfly-shaped distribution on both cheeks (see Plate 1a). Mental subnormality is usually severe but can be absent. Epilepsy commonly begins in the first year of life and may be the first sign of abnormality noted. There is wide variability in the frequency of fits and remissions can occur, lasting for months or years, even without the use of anticonvulsants. Adenoma sebaceum, which is a most valuable diagnostic sign, does not usually appear till the child is a few years old though it may possibly be present at birth (Walsh *et al.*, 1938) and has been observed also, for the first time, at the age of 26 years (Finlayson, 1955). In addition to these variable manifestations, many internal tissues, apart from those of the brain, can be involved (for example, the kidneys, heart and lungs) with the production of a wide range of clinical signs. Various combinations of pathological and clinical findings occur in individual cases, even in the same family, making it difficult to obtain accurate data concerning the familial and overall incidence of the disease. Incomplete forms, with some of the more obvious features absent, add to the difficulty. Nevertheless, many pedigrees show a dominant mode of inheritance. A considerable number of cases, perhaps about half, seem to occur sporadically and many of these are thought to be due to new gene mutations. Penrose (1963a) estimated the frequency of epiloia due to a dominant gene to be one in 30,000 in the general population of England. The condition is not unusual in populations of severely subnormal persons; there were 10 instances of it among 800 consecutive admissions of idiot and imbecile children to the Fountain Hospital, London (Berg, 1963a).

Among other conditions which can reasonably be regarded as dominant, and which are not infrequently associated with mental subnormality, are neurofibromatosis, acrocephalosyndactyly and craniofacial dysostosis. As in epiloia, new gene mutations are thought to determine many instances of these conditions and they display considerable variation in symptomatology.

Neurofibromatosis (*von Recklinghausen's disease*) is characterized by nerve tumour formation which may involve many parts of the body (see Plate 1b). If there is cerebral involvement, mental subnormality can be one of the sequelae. Preiser and Davenport (1918) noted that 7·8 per cent. of 243 reported cases of neurofibromatosis were feeble-minded. However, the disease is rare among the severely subnormal.

In the Fountain Hospital series of 800 children referred to above, there were only two examples of it. Penrose (1963a) points out that many pedigrees are consistent with the hypothesis that an irregularly dominant gene is responsible for the disease.

Acrocephalosyndactyly (*Apert's syndrome*) is a condition in which, as the name indicates, a high, wide and short cranium is associated with malformation of the fingers and/or toes. According to Sirkin (1944), the intelligence of most reported cases is normal. However, Penrose (1963a) notes that mental defect, though not usually severe, is a common accompaniment. Blank (1960) distinguished two main clinical categories of acrocephalosyndactyly, 'typical' and 'atypical', interdigital osseous union being a conspicuous feature of the former and absent in the latter. He described the former as being commoner and estimated its incidence at birth to be about one in 160,000. Most cases are thought to be due to fresh gene mutations.

Craniofacial dysostosis (*Crouzon's disease*) is another condition in which cranial deformity can be associated with mental subnormality. The physical characteristics of the condition include a thin, acrocephalic skull, prognathism, exophthalmos and optic atrophy. These characteristics are variable and a considerable range of associated anomalies also are sometimes reported under the heading of Crouzon's disease. They may not all be examples of the same disease. The incidence of the condition in some families suggests a dominant mode of inheritance. According to Dodge *et al.* (1959), about one-quarter of reported cases have no history of other members of the family being affected.

(*b*) *Recessive abnormalities*

A larger number of recessive conditions are known to be closely associated with severe subnormality than is the case with dominant conditions. This is not surprising as the heterozygous carriers of genes responsible for recessive abnormalities are not themselves affected, in the sense of being diseased, and so are fertile despite the fact that the genes they transmit can produce, in the homozygous state, major defects resulting in infertility. It should be added that important advances have been made in recent years in the detection of heterozygous carriers of genes for recessive abnormalities by means of special examinations. Examples of such examinations are the chemical tolerance tests for the detection of carriers of the gene for phenylketonuria and that for galactosaemia.

Both parents must be carriers of the gene determining a recessive abnormality for that abnormality to occur in offspring. As this is more likely to happen if the parents are blood relations, there is a higher incidence of consanguinity among the parents of children with rare recessive defects than would be expected on the basis of chance alone. Parental consanguinity is thus a useful pointer to the presence of rare recessively inherited defects though, of course, many non-consanguineous parents have children with recessive abnormalities and many consanguineous parents have normal children only. The increased incidence of parental consanguinity in series of cases of severe subnormality indicates that rare recessive conditions are likely to be found in such series. Among 800 consecutive admissions of severely subnormal children to the Fountain Hospital, London, 10 (1·25 per cent.) had parents who were first cousins (Berg, 1963b), compared with a figure of 0·4 per cent. for children admitted to general hospitals in England (Bell, 1940).

When both parents are the carriers of a gene for any particular recessive abnormality, there is a one in four risk of any one child inheriting the gene in duplicate, one from each parent, and thus being affected. As with dominant conditions, however, small individual human sibships do not provide a statistically adequate sample for the precise Mendelian ratio of affected to unaffected children to occur often in practice, quite apart from the difficulty created by early death of some cases.

A brief account follows of some conditions, considered to be recessive, which are connected with mental subnormality. Each of these conditions is rare in the general population with frequencies of the order of one in 50,000 (Penrose, 1963a).

Phenylketonuria, a metabolic disease discovered by Fölling (1934), is characterized chemically by an inability to convert phenylalanine to tyrosine and this is thought to be due to the absence of an enzyme, phenylalaninehydroxylase. As a result, phenylpyruvic acid is excreted in the urine from a few weeks after birth onwards and this acid can be conveniently identified by the green colour reaction produced on the addition of ferric chloride solution to urine containing it. Mental subnormality, usually of a severe degree, is present in most cases though a number of persons with the disease have near normal, and even normal, intelligence. The latter fact must be borne in mind in considering the effect on mental level of a phenylalanine-free diet given as treatment. The basic reason for mental subnormality in phenylketonuria is obscure but post-mortem examinations of brains of affected cases show definite abnormalities, including reduction in size and fibrous gliosis (Crome and Pare, 1960). Other clinical features include dilution of hair and eye colour in comparison with unaffected sibs, a tendency to dermatitis, broad, widely spaced incisors, brisk reflexes and, as in many other types of severe subnormality, reduced stature and head size and, in early life, a liability to have fits. Gross physical deformities are uncommon.

In recent years, a number of new diseases have been discovered which, like phenylketonuria, appear to be recessively inherited, are characterized by the excretion of specific amino-acids in the urine and are associated with mental subnormality. They include *maple syrup urine disease* (Menkes *et al.*, 1954), *argininosuccinicaciduria* (Allan *et al.*, 1958), and *cystathioninuria* (Harris *et al.*, 1959). Few examples of these rare conditions are known as yet and available information about them is considerably more scanty than in the case of phenylketonuria. They illustrate, however, the progress being made in the differentiation of specific types of mental subnormality by the application of new techniques of investigation, in these instances mainly biochemical ones.

Galactosaemia is a disorder of carbohydrate metabolism in which the absence of a particular enzyme prevents the normal transformation of galactose to glucose. The symptomatology has been attributed by some authors to the toxic effects of galactose on various tissues (Donnell and Lann, 1951). Clinical features include failure to thrive, jaundice and liver enlargement in the early stages of the disease; subsequently, mental subnormality and cataract formation may be noted. Many reports testify to the value of early treatment with a galactose-free diet in preventing or ameliorating these abnormalities.

Amaurotic idiocy is a condition in which there is a disturbance of lipoid metabolism resulting in intracellular deposits of abnormal substances, mainly in the brain and retina. The disease is associated clinically, as the name implies, with visual defects and mental subnormality. Manifestations appear at different ages, the two most documented varieties being the infantile type (Tay–Sachs disease) and the juvenile type (Spielmeyer–Vogt disease). In the former, neurological and ophthalmological abnormalities develop within several months of birth and are rapidly progressive with gross mental defect, paralysis, epilepsy, a so-called 'cherry-red spot' in the macula, optic atrophy and blindness as common features, followed by death at the age of about 2 years. In the latter, symptoms are similar but onset is usually delayed till the child is several years old and the disease advances more slowly until death occurs about 5 to 10 years later.

Gargoylism (see Plate 1c), like amaurotic idiocy, is a disease in which abnormal substances accumulate within cells. Both lipoids and polysaccharides are concerned and many tissues are involved. The grotesque facies and deformed appearance, which produce a close resemblance between affected persons, led Ellis *et al.* (1936) to name the condition gargoylism, a term which has become widely accepted. Other terms which are sometimes used are lipochondrodystrophy, dysostosis multiplex, and Hunter's or Hurler's disease. Abnormalities can be observed in early infancy. The typical facies include coarse features, well-developed bony prominences, bushy eyebrows, corneal opacities, a broad nose and large mouth, lips and tongue. Among other clinical findings are hirsutes, a protuberant abdomen due to enlargement of the liver and spleen, dorso-lumbar kyphosis and limitation of extension of joints. Mental subnormality is usually of severe degree. A sex-linked form of the disease occurs which differs clinically from the commoner autosomal recessive variety in being associated with normal corneae.

Cretinism can conveniently be discussed here as there is considerable evidence that some cases, in which chemical defects in the synthesis of thyroid hormone occur, are recessively determined. Cretinism in these cases is associated with enlargement of the thyroid gland, a circumstance which also can be environmentally determined by insufficient iodine intake in the diet or by the ingestion of goitrogenic agents like thiouracil. Imperfect embryonic development of the thyroid gland, for whatever reason, can result in cretinism as well, in this instance without goitre. Recent data indicate that cretinism is less common than is often assumed. No more than two examples were noted among 800 (0·3 per cent.) consecutive admissions of severely subnormal children to the Fountain Hospital, London

(Berg, 1963a). At the larger children's hospitals in Scandinavia, only one or two cases of congenital cretinism are diagnosed annually (Åkerren, 1955). The clinical features can include mental subnormality, general sluggishness, anaemia, small stature, coarse skin, large tongue, low temperature, slow pulse and chronic constipation. If treatment with thyroid extract is started early, the prognosis as regards physical development is generally considered to be good but the effect on mental development is more variable (Hubble, 1953; Lawson, 1955).

Microcephaly literally means smallness of the head and, as such, can be used as a descriptive term for a physical sign that is noted in various different types of mental subnormality. Among these are, for instance, many cases of phenylketonuria and mongolism and children born to mothers who were exposed to irradiation or to the rubella virus early in pregnancy. When used in this way, the term is often restricted, rather arbitrarily, to persons with a head circumference below a certain size, for example less than 17 inches in adults or at least three standard deviations below the mean for age and sex in children. Microcephaly is considered in this section because there is convincing evidence that some mentally subnormal persons with small heads of a particular shape have recessively inherited their condition (Böök *et al.*, 1953; Komai *et al.*, 1955; van den Bosch, 1959). Penrose (1963a) points out that such individuals, sometimes referred to as 'true' microcephalics, have heads in which the height and width show relatively greater reduction than the length, and they tend to have a receding forehead and a face approaching the normal in size. Penrose regards these features, combined with a well-developed, though dwarfed, body and a tendency to a stooping posture and quick, furtive movements, as highly characteristic; some observers (for example, Kirman, 1957), however, dispute this.

(*c*) *Sex-linked abnormalities*

The abnormalities considered thus far are determined by genes located on the autosomes, consisting, in man, of 22 pairs of chromosomes. In addition to these abnormalities, there are a number, closely associated with mental subnormality, which are thought to be due to genes on the X chromosome. These abnormalities are referred to as sex-linked. As there are two X chromosomes in females and only one in males (the other sex chromosome in males being a Y), a gene for recessive defects on the X chromosome has different effects in the two sexes. Males with one such harmful gene on the X chromosome would be affected whereas females with the one gene on an X chromosome would be heterozygous carriers of the abnormality; females would be affected if they were homozygous for the gene in question (i.e. if it were located on each of their X chromosomes).

In general, males are affected by sex-linked recessive abnormalities and females are carriers, though it is possible for females to be affected also. An affected father, even if fertile, cannot transmit the abnormality to his sons though such a father's daughters would all be carriers despite the mother being normal. If the father is normal and the mother is a carrier, there is a one in two risk that a son will be affected and the same risk that a daughter will be a carrier. In the less likely circumstance of the father being affected and the mother being a carrier, sons will be normal or affected and daughters will be carriers or affected. If both parents were affected, and could have children, all of them would have the abnormality.

Because of its occurrence in royalty, one type of rare sex-linked condition, the bleeding disease haemophilia, has become especially well known. The disease has no particular association with mental subnormality. A sex-linked form of gargoylism, referred to on page 147, does have such an association and the following abnormalities are further examples.

Oculocerebrorenal syndrome is the name now most usually applied to a condition discovered by Lowe *et al.* (1952). The disease is so called because of the association of eye abnormalities (such as cataract and glaucoma) with mental subnormality and kidney defects (manifested by excess amino-acids in the urine and other changes). The disease affects boys and is transmitted by females. Abnormalities, particularly cataracts, may be noted at birth or soon after.

Nephrogenic diabetes insipidus is a disease in which excessive excretion of dilute urine is associated with undue thirst. Manifestations appear in early infancy. Unlike other varieties of diabetes insipidus, the condition does not respond to treatment with antidiuretic hormone. Mental subnormality, of variable degree, occurs in some cases. Unless adequate fluid intake is maintained, dehydration occurs and this can have an adverse effect on the mental level (Kirman *et al.*, 1956). The disease usually occurs in males, but females are sometimes affected (West and Kramer, 1955; Glaser, 1958). Heterozygous female carriers may be detected by a reduced ability to concentrate urine when fluids are withheld (Carter and Simpkiss, 1956).

Hydrocephaly (see Plate 1g), like microcephaly (see p. 148), can be looked upon as a physical sign which may be due to a variety of causes, both genetical and environmental ones. Among the latter causes are, for instance, tuberculous meningitis which is discussed on page 161. Genetical types of hydrocephaly include a variety which is characterized by narrowing of the aqueduct of Sylvius and demonstrates a sex-linked pattern of inheritance. Edwards *et al.* (1961) reported a family with a defect of this kind in which there were 15 affected males and no affected females in three generations. Whatever the cause of a particular case of hydrocephaly, cerebral pathology is present so that subnormality and neurological abnormalities, like spasticity and epilepsy, are common clinical consequences in survivors.

2. Conditions due to aberrant chromosomes

(*a*) *Autosomal aberrations*

The nuclei of somatic cells in normal humans contain 46 chromosomes, largely consisting of desoxyribonucleic acid (DNA), of which 44 are known as autosomes and 2 as sex chromosomes. Twenty-two autosomes and one sex chromosome are derived from each of the two germ cells (ovum and sperm) which unite to begin the formation of the new individual. The development, in the recent past, of cytological techniques which enable each of the chromosomes to be clearly seen under the microscope, in suitable preparations of dividing human cells (see Plate 1e), has led to the discovery of a substantial number of chromosomal aberrations which are closely connected with various abnormal clinical conditions. By an international agreement (the Denver nomenclature), individual chromosomes are identified and numbered according to their length and the position of a constriction called the centromere. It is thus possible to match the chromosomes in pairs and distinguish one pair from another. Abnormalities can occur both in the number and in the morphology

1 SOME PATHOLOGICAL TYPES OF MENTAL SUBNORMALITY
(Clinical photography by M. A. C. Ridler)

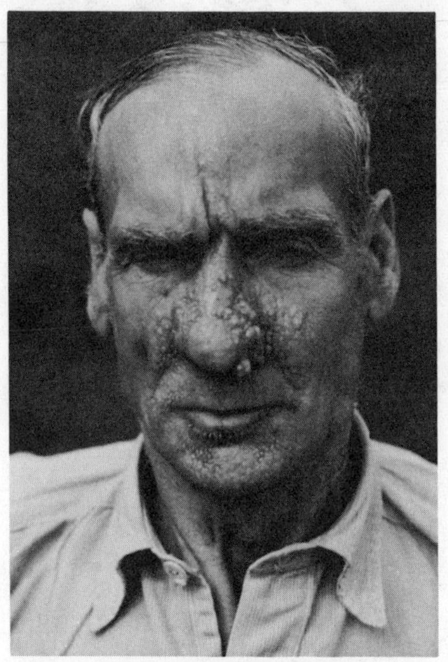

a. Epiloia: Severely subnormal man aged 64 years. Note adenoma sebaceum

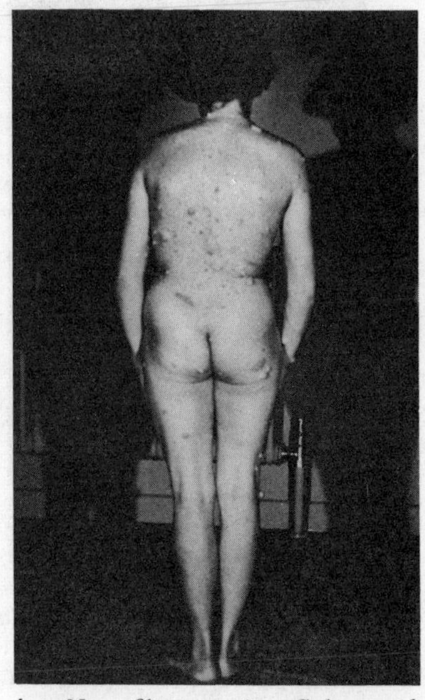

b. Neurofibromatosis: Subnormal woman aged 32 years. Note multiple tumours and pigmentation of skin

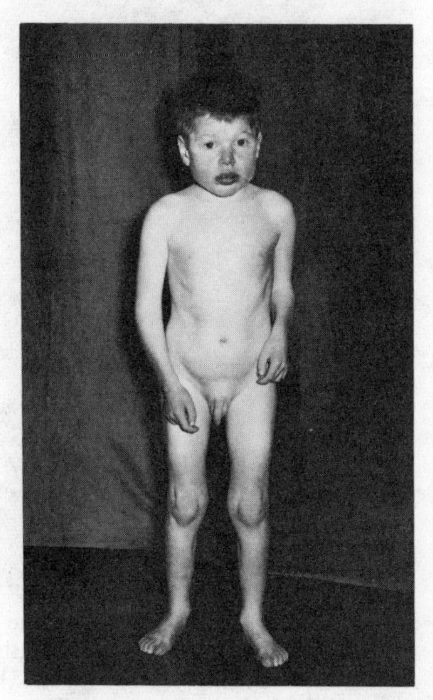

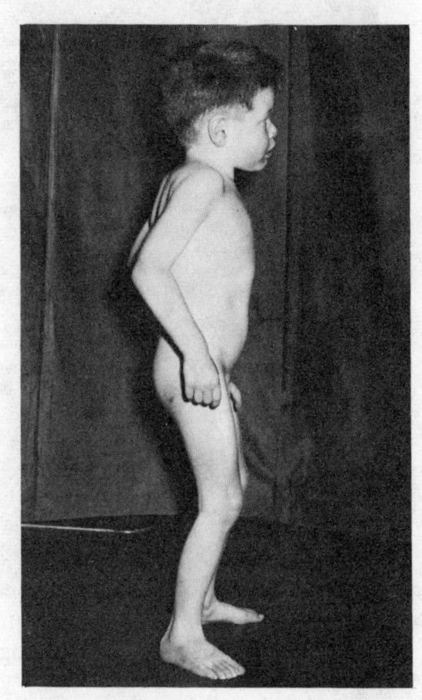

c. Gargoylism: Severely subnormal boy aged 9 years. Note coarse features and limitation of extension of joints

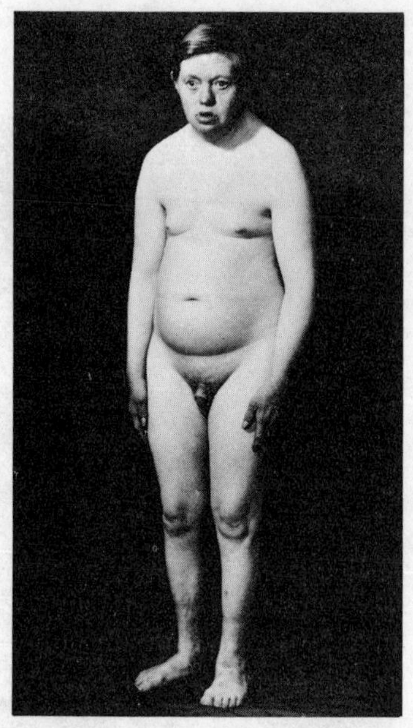

d. Association of Down's disease and Klinefelter syndrome: Severely subnormal man aged 49 years. Note slanting eyes and breast enlargement

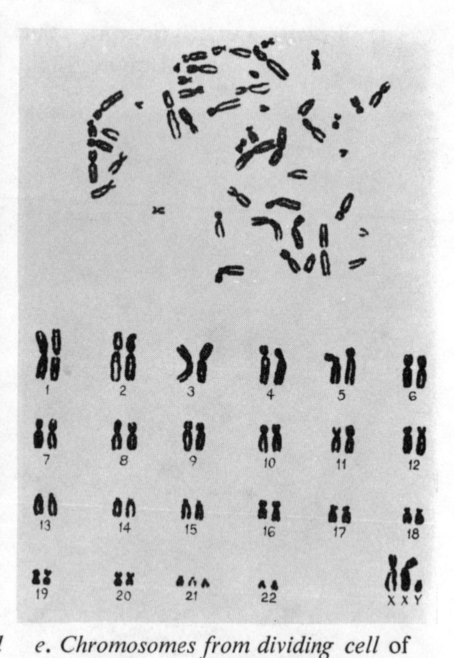

e. Chromosomes from dividing cell of patient on left with analysis (Denver classification). Note extra No. 21 and extra X chromosome

(*Published by permission of the Council of the Hunterian Society*)

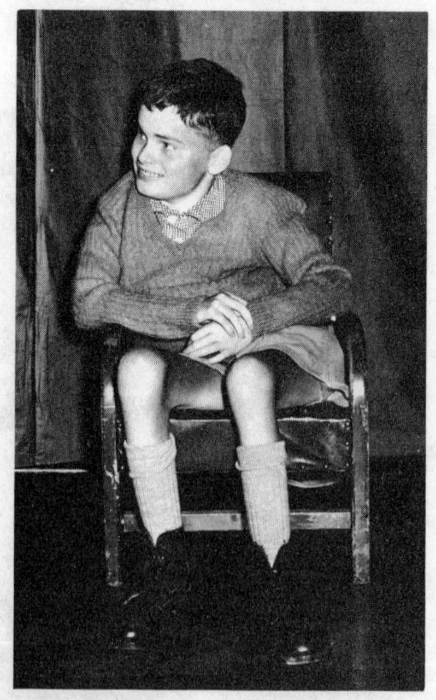

f. Tuberculous meningitis resulting in severe subnormality: Boy aged 15 years. He has also enlarged head and spastic diplegia

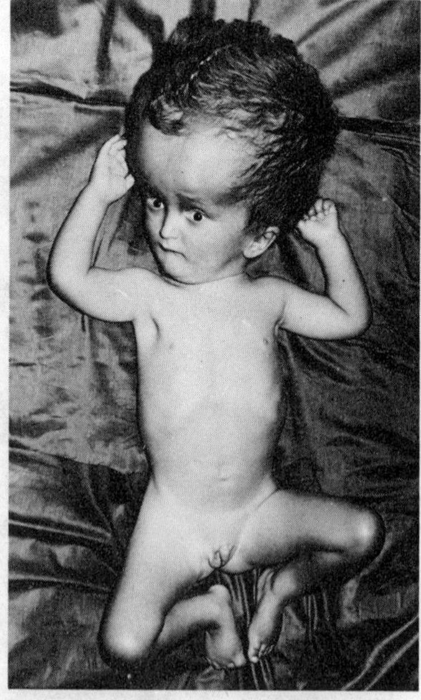

g. Congenital hydrocephaly of uncertain aetiology associated with severe subnormality: Boy aged $3\frac{1}{2}$ years. Head circumference = 79 cm. (norm = 51 cm.)

of human chromosomes. It is possible also for the same person to have some cells in his body showing a chromosomal abnormality and other cells which are normal, or he may have more than one type of chromosomal aberration in different cells. This phenomenon is known as mosaicism.

The first reports of human chromosomal aberrations began to appear in 1959 and it was evident, from the outset, that the aberrations were often associated with mental subnormality. New discoveries are comparatively frequent in this rapidly developing field and it can reasonably be expected that a good deal of new data will be forthcoming on hitherto obscure forms of subnormality and other defects. The following are examples of types of mental subnormality now known to be connected with autosomal aberrations. Much still remains uncertain as to the aetiological factors which determine these aberrations and as to how the latter operate to produce abnormal clinical states.

Mongolism (*Down's disease*) is by far the commonest disease entity detected in subnormal populations. Among 800 consecutive admissions of severely subnormal children to the Fountain Hospital, London, there were 175 (21·9 per cent.) cases of Down's disease (Berg, 1963a). By contrast, the next most common entity was mental defect due to meningitis with an incidence of 2·8 per cent. The incidence of Down's disease in hospital populations of subnormal persons of all ages and grades of defect is often about 10 per cent. Despite the possible implications in the name 'mongolism', the condition is not especially characteristic of, and is not limited to, any particular race.

The frequency of Down's disease at birth was found by Carter and MacCarthy (1951) to be one in 666 in London and the Home Counties and this figure agrees closely with other European surveys as well as with a recent large Australian one (Collmann and Stoller, 1962a). The well-known and striking variation in incidence that occurs at different maternal ages is shown in a table by Penrose (1963a); at birth, the incidence is less than 0·1 per cent. up to a maternal age of 34 years and then rises steeply to as much as 2·75 per cent. in the maternal age group of 45 years and over. Respiratory infections, heart defects and other causes result in a higher early mortality in cases of Down's disease than in the general population, so that the incidence of the condition falls in older age groups. In 1958, the incidence was about one in 1,000, at the age of 10 years, in and around London (Carter, 1958). The mortality rate of cases of Down's disease has decreased markedly in the past few decades as it has also in children in general.

The clinical features of Down's disease have been recorded many times since Langdon Down's original description in 1866 and they will not be considered in detail here. Many, though by no means all (Zappella and Cowie, 1962), cases are recognized at birth; the diagnosis is usually made in the first year of life. A wide range of abnormalities occur though manifestations vary and many are found individually in persons not suffering from the disease. Stature is reduced and the limbs are hypotonic. The head tends to be small with greater reduction in length than in breadth. The characteristic facies includes slanting eyes, epicanthic folds, squint, Brushfield's spots (white specks) in the iris, and small nose and ears. There is a tendency for the little finger to be curved inwards and for a wide gap to occur between the first and second toes. A single transverse palmar crease is often present and characteristic dermatoglyphic patterns occur in the palms and soles as they do also in some other conditions in which there are chromosomal aberrations (Penrose, 1963c). The incidence of leukaemia is increased in young children with Down's disease (Krivit and Good, 1957). Biochemical studies of the blood and urine have not shown abnormalities limited to the disease.

Marked neurological handicaps, like epilepsy and cerebral palsy, are unusual and nearly all cases learn to walk. They are often co-operative and friendly. These aspects of their personalities, as well as the traditional views that they are especially fond of music and better mimics than other children, deserve further study. Many cases have I.Q.s between 20 and 40; some, however, are gross idiots and others have I.Q.s above 45 and can benefit from attendance in schools for the educationally subnormal (Dunston *et al.*, 1960).

Abnormalities in the pelvic bones have been reported (Caffey and Ross, 1956; Kaufmann and Taillard, 1961) and many internal organs can be malformed. Heart malformations, of many kinds, are particularly frequent. Contrary to views expressed by some authors, Berg *et al.* (1960) have found no heart defect specific to Down's disease though some defects are particularly common. Malformation of the duodenum is also relatively frequent (Bodian *et al.*, 1952). The brain is reduced in weight and tends to be rounded with small frontal lobes, brain-stem and cerebellum, but it does not appear to show constant abnormalities on histological examination (Crome, 1957).

There is no known cure for Down's disease and claims for the efficacy of pituitary and thyroid preparations should be viewed with caution (Berg *et al.*, 1961). Recent advocacy of the value of siccacell treatment is also unconvincing.

An outstanding advance in knowledge about Down's disease was made with the discovery that persons with the disease have 47 chromosomes in somatic cells instead of the normal 46 (Lejeune *et al.*, 1959). In these cases there is an extra chromosome No. 21 and this circumstance is often referred to as trisomy 21. It is considered to arise as a result of non-disjunction whereby both, instead of one, members of the relevant pair of chromosomes enter the germ cell during the formation of the latter. The association in these cases of Down's disease with advancing maternal age implicates the ovum rather than the sperm.

A number of variations in the chromosomal findings can occur in Down's disease. In a small minority of cases, 46 chromosomes are found in somatic cells. The karyotype, however, is still unbalanced because, by a process known as translocation, a considerable portion of a No. 21 chromosome is fused with another autosome, which may be a No. 15 or a No. 22. These cases of Down's disease are not obviously different clinically from those with 47 chromosomes. However, in the 15 : 21 translocation type both maternal and paternal age is close to that in the general population, whereas in the 21 : 22 type advancing paternal (and not maternal) age may be aetiologically significant (Penrose, 1963d). Balanced translocations may be transmitted through several generations without producing clinical effects unless an extra amount of chromosome material is present. Another chromosomal variation in Down's disease is the occurrence of mosaicism, in which circumstance some cells can have a normal chromosome complement whereas others show trisomy 21. Such cases may have only limited signs of the disease. Down's disease can be associated also with the Klinefelter syndrome (see Plate 1d). This occurs in males with 48 chromosomes in their cells, one of which is an extra No. 21 and the other an extra X (see Plate 1e). Since the first case with this association was recorded (Ford *et al.*, 1959), a number of further instances have been reported.

Trisomy 13–15 occurs in persons who have a characteristic combination of congenital malformations including cerebral and heart defects, anophthalmos or microphthalmos, harelip, cleft palate, polydactyly and capillary haemangiomata. Mental retardation is noted even in early infancy and seizures usually occur (Patau *et al.*, 1960; Lubs *et al.*, 1961). The condition is referred to as trisomy 13–15 because there are 7 chromosomes in this group instead of the normal 6, and it is uncertain to which of the three pairs (13, 14, or 15) the extra chromosome should be designated. As in Down's disease, trisomy 13–15 is commoner among the offspring of older than of younger mothers.

Trisomy 17–18 is another syndrome in which an extra autosome (either a No. 17 or a No. 18) is associated with multiple congenital abnormalities. These include an abnormally shaped head, peculiar facies, webbing of the neck, syndactyly, chest deformity and heart malformation (Edwards *et al.*, 1960). In this condition also, delayed mental development is observed in infancy and, on the average, maternal age is increased.

Other autosomal aberrations have been found in humans and it is evident that more will be detected. Frequent new discoveries make systematic classification difficult at this stage. The main autosomal aberrations known to date are those described above. Trisomy may involve other autosomes also. For instance, Ellis *et al.* (1962) reported trisomy, probably of chromosome No. 22, in a subnormal person with epilepsy. It is also possible for cells to contain 69, 92, and even 184 chromosomes. Apart from abnormalities in the number of chromosomes, morphological aberrations can occur. Translocation has been referred to on page 153. Other rare abnormalities of chromosome structure include deletions and duplications resulting, respectively, in shortened and lengthened individual chromosomes. Mental subnormality is commonly associated with many of these chromosomal aberrations.

(*b*) *Sex chromosomal aberrations*

Of the two sex chromosomes normally present in humans, an X is derived from the mother and an X or Y from the father. Females have two X chromosomes in their cells and males have an X and a Y. As in the case of the autosomes, aberrations of the sex chromosomes can occur which are closely associated with various abnormal clinical states. The two conditions in this category most relevant to the field of mental subnormality are the Klinefelter syndrome and the triple-X condition.

The diagnosis of sex chromosome anomalies is facilitated by the discovery made by Barr and Bertram (1949) that cell nuclei of normal females contain a sex chromatin structure, known as the Barr body, which is visible under the microscope. Examination of buccal smears shows that some cells contain one Barr body less than the number of X chromosomes in the sex chromosome constitution of that individual. Thus, a normal male (XY sex chromosome constitution), a normal female (XX), a Klinefelter male (XXY), and a triple-X female (XXX) have 0, 1, 1, 2 Barr bodies, respectively, in their cell nuclei. The examination of buccal smears for Barr bodies is a comparatively simple procedure so that a valuable screening test is available for investigations of X chromosome aberrations.

Klinefelter syndrome is the name given to a combination of abnormalities described by Klinefelter *et al.* (1942). These abnormalities, which become apparent from puberty onwards, occur in males and include gynaecomastia, small testes, poor hair growth and increased excretion of follicle-stimulating hormone. Many cases are mentally subnormal, often mildly so. Manifestations can be variable and not all cases described as examples of the Klinefelter syndrome have the same features or necessarily suffer from the same disease. Some of these persons have a normal sex chromosome constitution whereas others have an extra X chromosome and so are of the type XXY. The latter is the usual finding when the chromosome constitution is abnormal but, occasionally, clinically similar cases have 3 or 4 X chromosomes with one Y, or 2 Xs and 2 Ys. Still others (mosaics) have an abnormal sex chromosome complement in some of their cells only. The association of Klinefelter syndrome and Down's disease in the same person has been referred to on page 153. Klinefelter syndrome is commoner among patients in hospitals for the mentally subnormal, and among those attending infertility clinics, than it is in the general population. The incidence of chromatin-positive cases (i.e. those showing Barr bodies) is of the order of 0·25 per cent. in new-born males (Moore, 1959) and of the order of 1 per cent. in several hospital series of subnormal males (Barr *et al.*, 1960).

The triple-X condition, which occurs in persons also referred to as 'superfemales', is, like the Klinefelter syndrome, a condition in which an extra X chromosome is present. These persons, who are females, thus have an XXX sex chromosome constitution. The clinical features are not strikingly abnormal (Johnston *et al.*, 1961). Subnormality is present in some cases and most of these are mildly retarded. Menstruation can be absent or irregular but some have regular periods, are fertile and can have normal children. The condition is not usually found as frequently as the Klinefelter syndrome in hospitals for the mentally subnormal and had an incidence of 0·4 per cent. in one large series of retarded females studied (Maclean *et al.*, 1962). Chromosomal variants of the condition occur and these include females with 4 X chromosomes and others who are mosaics of the type XXX/XX or XXX/XO.

Other sex chromosomal aberrations in humans are also now known and, as with autosomal aberrations, their number is likely to grow. One of these conditions, in which there is a total of 45 chromosomes in somatic cells (with one X and no Y), is known as Turner's syndrome. Physical abnormalities involving the ovaries, neck and heart occur but the condition does not appear to be associated particularly with mental subnormality. Still other rare aberrations consist of abnormalities in the form rather than in the number of X chromosomes. These chromosomes may be shortened, lengthened, or distorted in other ways. Aberrations of the Y chromosome have been found less frequently than those of the X chromosome. The occurrence of an XXYY sex chromosome constitution has been mentioned on page 155. Two Y chromosomes have been reported also in a mentally normal, fertile 44-year-old male, without serious physical defects, who was considered to have an XYY sex chromosome constitution (Hauschka *et al.*, 1962).

II. MENTAL SUBNORMALITY OF ENVIRONMENTAL ORIGIN

A large number of agents and events having their origin in the environment have been regarded as causes of pathological types of mental subnormality. Many of these circumstances have been convincingly established as being aetiologically significant whereas others have been postulated on more tenuous grounds. The occurrence of an abnormal environmental event or disease in a person subsequently noted to be subnormal is not, of itself, proof of a causal connexion. The likelihood of such a connexion is greatly increased if the particular abnormal event produces characteristic features which include signs of cerebral involvement and if other causes of subnormality can be reasonably excluded.

Environmental events leading to pathological types of mental subnormality can occur before, during, or after birth and they are considered below in each of these categories.

1. Prenatal causes

The causes of mental subnormality discussed under this heading are those which operate during intra-uterine life. The causes themselves can originate from events occurring before or after conception. Examples in each of these categories are, respectively, maternal infection with the spirochaete producing syphilis and with the virus producing rubella. A brief account follows of these, as well as of some other, prenatal agencies which can result in mental subnormality.

Congenital syphilis has long been recognized as a cause of mental subnormality in live-born offspring of infected mothers. The spirochaete responsible for syphilis can pass from the mother to the foetus and produce abortion, stillbirth, or mental and physical abnormalities in surviving children. Among the abnormalities which may be noted in childhood are mental defect, blindness, deafness, epilepsy, paralyses, and characteristic anomalies of the skull and teeth. In one variety, juvenile general paresis, manifestations often develop in late childhood or adolescence and include mental disturbance as well as defect and characteristic neurological signs. A general decline in the incidence of syphilis in this country has resulted in a marked reduction of cases of subnormality due to this infection. Compared to a 4 per cent. incidence of congenital syphilis found by Penrose (1938) in Colchester, and by Benda (1942) in Massachusetts, a recent survey in London (Berg and Kirman, 1959) revealed a history of syphilis in only 0·6 per cent. of 1,900 defectives.

Rubella in early pregnancy was first shown by Gregg (1941) to be a cause of congenital abnormalities in the offspring of infected mothers, and many reports on the subject have since been published. The most important structures involved are those of the brain, heart, eyes and ears with the production of a characteristic, though variable, symptomatology. The proportions of affected children reported among those at risk have varied greatly in different studies but have been of the order of 10 to 20 per cent. in some of the more recent prospective surveys. An important fact which emerged from the earlier studies was that the incidence of affected live-born children falls markedly when the mother develops rubella after the first three months of pregnancy. The risk appears to be particularly great if rubella occurs in the first month of pregnancy (Pitt, 1961). Data from the Fountain Hospital, London, indicate that rather less than 1 per cent. of cases of severe subnormality were due to maternal rubella (Kirman, 1955). The role of this infection in the production of minor degrees of subnormality is less clear.

Irradiation, in the form of *excessive* exposure to X-rays, in the early stages of pregnancy is now well established as a cause of abortion and of mental subnormality, reduced head size and other defects in surviving children. Early studies on the subject include those of Zappert (1926), Murphy (1928; 1929), and Goldstein (1930). Similar dangers to the foetus of radiation from other sources were demonstrated by Plummer (1952) and by Yamazaki *et al.* (1954) who investigated, respectively, effects of the Hiroshima and Nagasaki atomic explosions.

Rhesus incompatibility between mother and foetus has been referred to on page 140. In these circumstances, the basal ganglia and other portions of the brain can become pigmented and damaged, a pathological state to which the term kernicterus is frequently applied (Baar, 1959). Affected live-born children are jaundiced soon after birth and may subsequently suffer from mental subnormality, athetosis and deafness. The mental level varies from extreme idiocy to normality. Eleven out of 800 (1·4 per cent.) severely subnormal children admitted to the Fountain Hospital, London, were considered to owe their defect to Rhesus incompatibility (Berg, 1963a). Maternal-foetal incompatibility involving the ABO blood groups can produce similar effects and they are known to occur also in the absence of evidence of blood group incompatibility.

Other prenatal causes of subnormality have been implicated or postulated on many occasions. Space does not permit a discussion of each of them in turn so that a brief general account is given in this section of some agencies not specifically considered above.

Many infections, apart from syphilis and rubella, can be transmitted to the foetus but few of these have been convincingly shown to cause mental subnormality. Interest in maternal virus infections, from this point of view, was stimulated with the discovery of the hazards of rubella. Cytomegalic inclusion-body disease, transmitted through the placenta, can produce microgyria, among other defects in the brain and elsewhere (Crome, 1961), and so result in subnormality. Maternal Asian influenza was noted by Coffey and Jessop (1959; 1963) to be associated with an increased incidence of central nervous system abnormalities in offspring, but Doll *et al.* (1960) did not find such an association. Bacterial infection in pregnant women has not been proved to cause subnormality in their offspring but maternal toxoplasmosis, a protozoal infection, can do so. Other findings in congenital toxoplasmosis include abnormalities of head size, intracranial calcification and ocular defects (Couvreur and Desmonts, 1962). Malaria, another protozoal infection, can be transmitted to the foetus and was found by Archibald (1958) to be associated with a reduction in birth weight; follow-up studies of such children, compared with others, in regard to mental function would be interesting.

Teratogenic effects of various chemical agents have been demonstrated many times in experimental animals. The possibility of serious hazards to the human foetus of particular chemical substances is receiving increased attention following the recent thalidomide tragedy. The commonest malformations resulting from thalidomide, taken during pregnancy, are those involving the limbs (Smithells, 1962; Leck and Millar, 1962) and there appears to be no specific relationship of this drug with mental subnormality. Other drugs, however, may have such a relationship. Thiouracil (Elphinstone, 1953), for instance, and also large doses of insulin (Wickes, 1954), administered to pregnant women, have been occasionally associated with the birth of subnormal children. Apart from the question of therapeutic chemical agents, various deficiencies in the maternal diet may be harmful to the human foetus with the possibility of adverse effects on subsequent mental development.

Deleterious effects on the foetus have been attributed also, from time to time, to various other events occurring during pregnancy,

Few of these can be regarded as established causes of mental subnormality. Among ancient explanations of the origin of foetal defects are supernatural intervention, either by gods or devils, intercourse during menstruation, and unpleasant sights and frights during pregnancy (Pitt, 1962). Recent claims also have been made that acute maternal anxiety and emotional stress can result in foetal malformation, but evidence for this view is unconvincing. Physical trauma sometimes may cause damage to the foetal nervous system. So may anoxia and Courville (1959) has considered various circumstances where this could occur. Possibly harmful consequences of the unsuccessful use of chemical contraceptives and abortifacients deserve fuller study, as do a wide range of other factors.

2. Natal causes

The two events at birth which are especially relevant to the question of causation of cerebral damage, and hence of mental subnormality, are mechanical injury and anoxia or asphyxia. These events are closely associated and it is often difficult, in clinical practice, to distinguish the role of each. A further difficulty is that of trying to decide whether evidence of birth trauma or anoxia in a particular case represents the cause or the consequence of abnormality.

Birth injury is a term which is often used to cover the combined effects of mechanical trauma and of anoxia or hypoxia occurring in relation to the birth process. Birth injury has been blamed for anything from under 1 per cent. to over 50 per cent. of cases of subnormality. In general, the higher estimates have been based on retrospective evidence of obstetrical complications or of neonatal distress in subnormal persons and in many of these cases a causal connexion is not convincingly demonstrated. In a detailed study of 1,280 subnormal patients of all types, Penrose (1938) found only 11 cases (0·9 per cent.) whose defect could be regarded, with reasonable certainty, as due to birth injury. He added, however, that trauma may have been an unrecognized aetiological factor in a number of other cases. Drillien (1963) concluded, on the evidence from an extensive longitudinal survey of Edinburgh children, that obstetrical hazard is not a major factor in the causation of gross defect.

The risk of birth injury is increased in premature births and this could be a factor in the poorer mental development that has been noted in prematurely born children, as a group, when compared to children in general. A greater liability for twins to be injured at birth may account also for some of the excess of twins found in subnormal populations (Berg and Kirman, 1960). Other circumstances, often interrelated, which have been considered to have a bearing on the problem of birth injury include maternal age, complications of pregnancy such as toxaemia, birth order, and various abnormalities of presentation and delivery.

3. Post-natal causes

A large number of abnormal events and diseases having their origin in the post-natal environment can be responsible for mental subnormality. Though many of these events and diseases are themselves common, they often do not have an obvious effect on mental function. Variations between individuals in susceptibility to an illness, its severity, and the efficacy of treatment are among the factors which may influence the outcome. Mental retardation, when it does result, varies widely in degree from case to case.

The aetiological significance of post-natal agencies, particularly when they do not operate till a considerable time after birth, is frequently easier to assess than is the case with either prenatal or natal events. This is because there is the opportunity of observing the child's development before, as well as after, the post-natal hazard occurs. However, the possibility must be considered that some diseases which are determined earlier, for instance certain types of amaurotic idiocy (see p. 146), may show clinical manifestations only some time after the child is born.

Several examples of post-natal causes of subnormality are described individually below and others are referred to in a general section.

Tuberculous meningitis, which was nearly always fatal before modern drugs for the treatment of tuberculosis became available, is now periodically seen as a cause of mental subnormality (see Plate 1f). Many children with tuberculous meningitis are treated successfully but some, who would probably otherwise have died during the acute illness, now survive and show mental and physical abnormalities of varying degrees of severity. Among 800 children with I.Q.s below 50 admitted, from 1949 to 1960, to the Fountain Hospital, London, 11 (1·4 per cent.) were considered to owe their subnormality to tuberculous meningitis (Berg, 1962a). Other handicaps in these children included, in order of frequency, spastic paralysis of the limbs, blindness, hydrocephaly, epilepsy and deafness.

Whooping cough encephalopathy is a term which may be used to designate the cerebral involvement which sometimes complicates this infectious fever. As a consequence of such involvement, mental subnormality, behaviour disturbances, epilepsy, paralysis, and impairment of vision and hearing can occur (Berg, 1962b). Definite, though variable, abnormalities are found in the brains of children with neurological complications who do not survive the acute illness. These include haemorrhagic, inflammatory and degenerative changes. Levy and Perry (1948) considered that subnormality seemed to be due to whooping cough in 2 per cent. of 1,000 children with I.Q.s of 70 or less in a Washington State institution. By contrast, this cause of subnormality has only very occasionally been established among severely subnormal children in the Fountain Hospital, London. Byers and Rizzo (1950), in a follow-up for several years of 35 Boston children who had whooping cough before the age of 2 years, found that 6 (17 per cent.) suffered from intellectual or emotional difficulties of sufficient severity to 'compromise their competitive status'.

Lead poisoning in childhood is rarely reported in Great Britain but many cases have been recorded in some countries, notably the United States, Australia and Japan. Pica is a frequent precursor and painted woodwork is a particularly common source of the lead. The average toddler is said to take some three months to nibble away sufficient lead-containing paint to produce symptoms (Shrand, 1961). Cerebral involvement is relatively common in children; clinical manifestations can include changes of temperament, tremors, convulsions, coma and papilloedema. Patchy, widespread lesions are found in the soft, oedematous brains of children who die during the acute illness (Blackman, 1937). Among persisting abnormalities in survivors are subnormality, behaviour disturbances, paralyses of the limbs, and blindness associated with optic atrophy. Intellectual, emotional and sensori-motor handicaps have been found in cases followed up after apparent complete recovery from the original illness (Byers and Lord, 1943). A useful review has been published by Gibb and MacMahon (1955).

Head injury is not infrequently blamed by parents for subnormality in their offspring. In fact, it is rarely established as the cause of gross mental defect in childhood (Berg, 1960). Less severe post-traumatic effects are commoner. Behaviour disturbances and personality changes leading to poor scholastic achievement were noted by Newell (1937) in 5 out of 20 persons who had had head injuries. A lasting adverse influence on their school careers was thought by Rowbotham *et al.* (1954) to be likely in 8 out of 82 children with such injuries. It is often said that adults tolerate head injuries less well than children (Glaser and Shafer, 1932; Blau, 1936) so that harmful mental effects may be commoner following cerebral trauma in adulthood. In studies of subnormal patients of all grades and ages, post-natal cerebral trauma was thought to be aetiologically significant in 0·9 per cent. of 1,280 cases in Colchester (Penrose, 1938) and in 1·5 per cent. of 1,000 cases in New York State (Boldt, 1948).

Other post-natal causes also can be implicated, with a fair degree of certainty, in particular cases of pathological types of mental subnormality.

Various organisms can cause meningitis and lead to subnormality and physical defects similar to those due to the tubercle bacillus. Among these organisms are the pneumococcus, meningococcus, staphylococcus, and the influenza bacillus. Between them, they were responsible for the same percentage of cases of severe subnormality (1·4 per cent.) as was due to tuberculous meningitis in the Fountain Hospital series referred to above.

Besides whooping cough, other acute infectious fevers (for instance, measles, chicken pox and scarlet fever) can sometimes be followed by mental deterioration. Careful follow-up of cases which appear to recover completely at the time of the acute illness may show a higher incidence of harmful mental effects than is often assumed to occur. Gibbs *et al.* (1956) did electroencephalographic studies on children with whooping cough, measles and mumps who showed no clinical evidence of neurological involvement during, or immediately after, the acute illness. On the basis of these studies, they thought that in some cases a 'state of disorder' is established which might take months or years to run its full course and which might sometimes manifest itself in clinical disorder long after the acute illness. Immunization against whooping cough very occasionally produces neurological complications, including subnormality, similar to those which can occur with whooping cough itself. Mental subnormality has also been noted, though rarely, following vaccination against smallpox.

Many other infections and infestations can result in cerebral damage and thus lead to subnormality. Among the various encephalitides, encephalitis lethargica attracted especial attention because of widespread epidemics of the disease in the earlier part of this century. Manifestations of the condition include anti-social behaviour, intellectual retardation, a mask-like expression, and muscular tremors and rigidity. Cerebral involvement also can complicate disease due to certain parasitic worms, protozoa and fungi, so that these are potential, though rarely implicated, causes of subnormality. Subnormality has also been observed as a sequel to gastro-enteritis accompanied by marked dehydration (Crome, 1952).

The effect of psychological and social influences on mental function has attracted a great deal of attention in recent years. Adverse influences in this category can play a role in the production of maladjustment and intellectual impairment and thus can be crucial in regard to a diagnosis of mental subnormality in certain cases. This subject falls outside the scope of the present chapter which is concerned with pathological types of subnormality due to organic disease processes. It is dealt with extensively in other sections of this book.

CONCLUSIONS

Organic disease or pathology is responsible for nearly all cases of gross mental defect and for some cases in which the defect is relatively mild. The pathological types of mental subnormality determined in this way have been considered in this chapter and shown to be due to the operation of a large number of harmful physical agencies of both genetical and environmental origin.

Clinical evidence of cerebral abnormality, such as paralyses of the limbs and epilepsy, is found in many persons with severe mental subnormality. Cerebral pathology, often widespread and of various kinds, is demonstrable also at post-mortem examination in the great majority of gross defectives (Crome, 1960). Nevertheless, the causes of such pathology, and hence of the subnormality, can be established, in the present state of knowledge, in only a minority of these cases. In circumstances relatively favourable for diagnosis, because of the availability of a great deal of relevant data, definite causes of, and distinct syndromes closely connected with, subnormality were found in only one-third of 800 children with I.Q.s below 50 (Berg, 1963a). If the 175 cases of Down's disease in this series of 800 children are excluded, only 100 of the remaining 625 children (16 per cent.) are accounted for in terms of aetiology. These data give some impression of the great amount of knowledge that still needs to be accumulated before the causation of pathological types of mental subnormality can be regarded as being satisfactorily understood. Even when clear-cut syndromes closely associated with subnormality can be recognized, the exact aetiology and pathogenesis of the mental defect in these syndromes is not always altogether clear as yet. The precise reasons why subnormality occurs are still obscure in, for instance, conditions associated with chromosomal aberrations and in phenylketonuria.

The problem of the elucidation of the many different causes of pathological types of mental subnormality is deservedly receiving increasing attention from the viewpoint of a variety of scientific disciplines. This problem is, indeed, a fundamental one because understanding of causation is an essential basis for rational preventive and curative measures.

Chapter VII

INDIVIDUAL DIFFERENCES IN THE MENTALLY DEFICIENT

by J. Tizard

The outstanding psychological quality common to all 'true' mental defectives (by which is meant in this context idiots, imbeciles, and obvious simpletons) is gross subnormality of intelligence. But mere stupidity is not the only trait which is said to mark off the mental defective from the normal person. *On the average*, though not universally, they also differ from normal persons in height, weight, psycho-motor abilities, and some other traits. It has also been suggested that mental defectives differ qualitatively from normal persons of the same mental or chronological age in the way in which they think and in temperament. Though the questions raised by these suggestions are of great interest, the literature in many cases does not permit firm conclusions to be drawn. The following matters have been studied:

PHYSICAL CHARACTERISTICS

Many studies have been made contrasting the physical characteristics of the mentally defective with those of normal persons. A comparison of the growth of 800 mentally deficient males aged 5–25 years in two American institutions with that of normal males has been made by Flory (1936), who also reviews the considerable literature on the subject. Eleven physical measures, of height, weight, chest, and hip measurement, arm span and length, width and height of head, were made; Roentgenograms of the right wrist and hand of the subject enabled readings to be made of the degree of carpal ossification; and anomalies of development were recorded. Flory presents many tables showing that on the average the growth rate is slower among the mentally deficient than among normal children. The period of growth is, however, longer, indicating an extended period of immaturity. At all ages the mentally subnormal tend to be inferior physically to normal children, and according to Flory, the more severe the degree of mental defect, the greater the physical inferiority.

> Amentia [he says] is a condition which is accompanied by general organic deficiency. It appears that a feeble mind in a normally developed body is relatively rare. Mental deficiency does not appear to be confined to the central nervous system. A blighted mentality seems to be symptomatic of calamity which has affected the whole organism.

Though Flory's data were obtained from an institutional sample, his conclusions agree well with those of other writers reporting associations between mental and physical growth of children of average and superior ability (Paterson, 1930; Abernethy, 1936; Burt, 1946).

Head size and brain weight

Flory reports that the head dimensions of idiots and feeble-minded persons hardly differ at all on the average, though both groups fall slightly, but statistically very significantly below the average for normal children of the same age. Other literature summarized by Penrose (1949) and by Tyler (1956) indicates that the prediction of intelligence from head size is of little practical significance. A similarly low, though statistically significant, correlation is found between brain weight (itself closely related to head size) and intelligence. Both head size and brain weight may be affected by various specific diseases, for example, mongolism, or microcephaly. In the absence of disease they tell us little about mental functioning.

'Stigmata of degeneracy'

Investigations of Lombroso led him to the belief that criminal types were characterized by physical stigmata of degeneracy in the form of abnormalities of the ears, hands, palate, etc. Subsequent studies by Galton, using an ingenious method of composite photography, and by Goring, disprove this theory as applied to criminals. Stigmata are, however, found among defectives, and are still sometimes said to be of diagnostic importance. A. F. Tredgold (1949), for example, remarks that anomalies of anatomical development are found more frequently in psychopaths and aments than the general population, and that their number and severity are on the whole directly proportionate to the degree of defect. Burke (1931), however, making a careful examination of the case records of 1,000 idiots and 1,400 imbecile children, found little difference in frequency – the percentages showing 'stigmata' were 7·0 and 8·4 respectively. Flory (1936), on the other hand, reports much higher frequencies. Clearly much depends on definition and on the thoroughness of the examination. What can be said is that some clinical types, especially mongols, microcephalics, and cases suffering from endocrine disorders, show a concentration of physical peculiarities attributable to a retardation of growth at an early critical period (Penrose, 1949). But apart from physical signs associated with specific diseases, no useful correlation has been found between physical abnormalities and mental growth or development.

Electro-physiological responses in mental defectives

Reviews of the known relationships between E.E.G. phenomena and physiological and psychological processes have been made by Lindsley (1944, 1956); Ellingson (1956); and Netchine and Lairy (1962). Ostow (1950) has reviewed the literature on the relationships between E.E.G. variables and intelligence. There seems to be general agreement with Lindsley's 1944 statement that 'it appears very doubtful that there is any very high degree of relationship between intelligence as measured by tests and the E.E.G.' Ellingson concludes his review of recent literature by stating that

> the so-called higher mental processes still appear to be beyond reach. Present neuro-physiological techniques do not seem to be adequate to deal with them. Little practical assistance can be offered [by the electro-physiologist] to the psychologist investigating the processes of learning or thinking, or to the psychiatrist dealing with neuroses and psychoses,

though much research on these problems is going on. There is still no convincing evidence either of differences between mental defectives and normal persons, or between patients of the various clinical types.

Sensory handicaps

Before the development of intelligence testing, many efforts were made to assess mental abilities by means of sensory tests. Whipple (1924) and Anastasi and Foley (1956) summarize much of the early literature. The work of Binet and his successors led to a loss of interest in this topic, because intelligence tests were so much more efficient as indices of mental function.

Sensory deprivation as a cause of mental defect has frequently been remarked upon, but it is usually considered to be very rare. Tredgold lists 'isolation amentia' among his causes, including under this term both social and sensory deprivation; but he makes it responsible for only 0·2 per cent. of cases. However, though there is little evidence that mental defectives are necessarily inferior to normal persons in such sensory abilities as two-point space discrimination, visual and auditory acuity, and so on, the prevalence of sensory handicaps among the mentally subnormal is extremely high. Birch and Matthews (1951), for example, carried out an audiometric survey of patients in a mental deficiency institution, aged between 10 and 19 years, whose mental ages were approximately 5 years or more. They found that only 44 per cent. of subjects had no hearing loss in either ear, though two-thirds of the population had hearing which was within the normal range. One patient in 20 had a hearing loss which they regarded as probably sufficient to handicap them occasionally in ordinary life activities, and more than a quarter of those tested had losses sufficiently great to handicap them in many ordinary life activities. Reports by Foale and Paterson (1954) and Schunhoff and MacPherson (1951) confirm the conclusion of Birch and Matthews that the proportion of those with serious hearing losses is 'an alarmingly large figure by any standard'. More often than not, the handicaps of partially deaf children remain unrecognized until special studies are made to discover them. In the (1959) study made by Siegenthaler and Krzywicki of mentally defective women of child-bearing age, deafness occurred in 16 per cent. of cases as compared with 3–4 per cent. for a comparable group of normal women living in the community. Much more work is needed to separate out cortical from peripheral defects responsible for hearing losses, and to discover suitable methods of training deaf, mentally subnormal children.

Undiscovered partial deafness can lead to behaviour which is indistinguishable from imbecility. Two such cases are known to the writer. One child who was diagnosed as mentally deficient spent four years in a mental deficiency hospital before his handicap of severe deafness was discovered. Treated as a deaf child his behaviour improved rapidly. He first attended a school for educationally subnormal deaf children, then an ordinary junior school for the deaf. Later he won a scholarship to a technical school, and his intelligence is now well above average. In the second case the child had encephalitis in infancy. His subsequent behaviour was distractible and destructive, and he was thought to show a 'typical post-encephalitic syndrome'. He spent some time in hospital, and following this had several changes of foster home before being sent to an institution. There he was discovered to be partly deaf. Suitable measures to deal with his handicap were taken, following which both behaviour and I.Q. have shown a remarkable improvement.

No adequate study of visual handicaps among the mentally defective is known to the writer. Of 1,800 blind children of school age in England and Wales, about 400 are mentally deficient, but no one cause of blindness predominates. Ten per cent. of the blind children of normal intelligence and 25 per cent. of mentally deficient blind children suffer from other physical handicaps. Many other mentally defective children suffer from squint or myopia, and O'Connor (1957) has shown that colour blindness is more common among imbecile males than among the general male population. Further investigations are needed.

Sir Cyril Burt (1946), in studies of backward children carried out in London after the First World War, reported that 'on the average each backward child suffers from at least three adverse factors tending to retard his progress at school'. Minor defects of general health were found in 67 per cent. of 400 cases who were examined; defects of sight, hearing, and speech were found in 62 per cent. of cases, of whom one third suffered from severe handicap. He reports (1937) a correlation of marked hearing defect with backwardness (0·44) and of marked speech defect with backwardness (0·33). Sixty per cent. of backward children suffered from dullness of general intelligence, and smaller proportions were handicapped by poverty in the home, emotional instability, special intellectual defects, cultural deprivation, and irregular attendance at school. A valuable review of other studies summarizing the reported associations between mental and physical characteristics is to be found in H. E. Jones (1954).

Though recognizing the importance of sensory handicaps in aggravating mental subnormality, Burt does not regard them as of great causal significance, except in a tiny proportion of cases. This view is probably shared by the majority of clinicians today. It is none the less possible that the effect of sensory deprivation, like the effect of poverty, or of early emotional trauma, has been under-estimated. The importance of total handicap is universally recognized; but partial handicap, which gives a child sensory information in an inconstant and bewildering manner, may be more crippling to the intelligence, and a more potent cause of maladjustment, than an easily recognizable handicap such as total deafness. With the development of peepshow techniques, and, more recently, of the E.E.G. and of conditioning methods for testing hearing of babies and idiots, advances in our knowledge of this field should be rapid (Bordley, 1956). Since hearing aids able to be worn by babies as young as 6 months are now available (Whetnall, 1956), remedial measures to correct deficiencies in hearing, which is probably a more important sense than sight in fostering mental development in man, can now be undertaken from the earliest age.

Motor handicaps

Before and after the First World War the study of motor functions in the mentally deficient was investigated vigorously, but for the last 20–30 years few investigations have been carried out. It is a clinical commonplace that mental defectives tend to be clumsy, and that many are stiff and awkward in movement. The field is open for much more intensive research.

Most work has been done on the construction of age scales, modelled on intelligence test scales, of which the best known is the Oseretsky Scale (see Lassner, 1948, for bibliography). Oseretsky constructed his test to assist him to diagnose neurological and motor defects in children. Six aspects of motor function were studied, namely, 'general static co-ordination, dynamic manual co-ordination, general dynamic co-ordination, motor speed, simultaneous voluntary movements, and asynkinesia (i.e. lack of precision of movement)'. One test of each of these supposed functions was included for each age level from 4 to 16 years. The various categories were arrived at on an *a priori* basis. Despite a certain crudity in the construction of the scale – the shortcomings of which appear to have been recognized by Oseretsky himself – the test remains the most ingenious and widely used of those that have been so far devised. A promising attempt has been made by Sloan (1955) to re-standardize the scale and to eliminate ambiguities in the scoring. Sloan and his associates tested a representative sample of 380 boys and 369 girls in age groups 6–14 years. Approximately 40 boys and 40 girls were included in each age group. He gives detailed instructions for administering and scoring the test, and tentative norms based on his study for each age group. In his monograph he also gives a short bibliography of other motor scales, and has many suggestions for further research both with the Oseretsky Scale itself and into the development of motor abilities in children. His work provides a good basis for further research into psychomotor abilities of both normal and mentally defective children.

A number of earlier studies showed that feeble-minded persons tend to be inferior to normal persons, and imbeciles to feeble-minded persons, in motor proficiency. Correlations between scores on tests measuring motor abilities are in general higher when mentally subnormal subjects are tested than when normal persons are tested, even when I.Q. is partialled out. This was shown in a pioneer study by Attenborough and Farber (1934), who tested 80 educationally subnormal schoolboys aged 10–14 years, and with I.Q.s mostly between 60 and 80, attending a special school in Manchester. They report correlations between Binet, Otis, and Porteus Maze I.Q.s and test results on a pin board, a peg board, and an assembly test. The correlation between I.Q. (Binet) and summed manual dexterity score was 0·58. Attenborough and Farber quote earlier studies reporting much lower correlations between scores on manual dexterity and on intelligence tests given to normal children.

Later work has confirmed the findings of Attenborough and Farber. In a study carried out by the writer (Tizard, 1950) 104 young feeble-minded adults were tested on parts of the U.S.E.S. General Aptitude Test Battery. The mean score of the subjects was below average on all tests, and their factor scores on the four factors of Spatial Aptitude, Form Perception, Dexterity, and Motor Speed were all well below average. The mean score for motor speed was actually the poorest of their scores, being 2½ standard deviation units below the mean of the general population, whereas that for spatial ability was only one sigma below the mean, and that for intelligence about two sigma below. Whether this discrepancy arose because the subjects were really inferior in motor speed, because of faulty standardization of the tests, or because the subjects were unable to carry out the fine movements of picking up washers because most of them had nails bitten almost to the quick, was not determined.

Comparable findings have been obtained by Sloan (1951) and by Cantor and Stacey (1951). A pioneer study by Norsworthy (1906) should also be mentioned, and much other early work is summarized by Whipple (1924).

The work to date gives support to the commonsense view that 'true' mental defectives are not only deficient intellectually, but are subnormal in all respects. Alternatively, it is arguable that the factor composition of motor tests changes when subnormal groups are tested. Even an able-bodied, nimble-fingered dullard or simpleton might do badly on complex manual dexterity tests because he found it difficult to grasp the instructions quickly enough to do the test well. Given tests that were simple enough, or sufficient practice on more complex tests, he might not be inferior to a normal person. If this is true it would follow, first, that performance on motor tests would be inferior to the performance of normal persons in so far as scores correlated with scores on intelligence tests (i.e. were loaded with a general intellective factor defined by intelligence test scores). Secondly, those motor tests on which performance was highly correlated with intelligence test scores on a first occasion of testing might be expected to have lower correlations with I.Q. on retest, while correlations with other manual tests defining a general factor of motor ability might be expected to increase. No studies on these lines are known to the writer, but work by Holman (1933), Clarke and Hermelin (1955), and Loos and Tizard (1955) with mentally subnormal subjects, and by Woodrow (1940), Reynolds and Adams (1954), and others with normal subjects, lend indirect support to such an hypothesis. At present it seems almost certain that lower grade defectives are inferior to normal children in manual abilities; but higher grade cases may be little, if at all, inferior.

Among tests on single aspects of motor function the Heath Rail Walking Test has been used by a number of writers. The test material consists of three rails, 4 inches, 2 inches, and 1 inch wide respectively, along which the subject has to walk, heel to toe, as far as he can (details are given by Heath, 1942). The score is the number of feet walked on the rails, the scores for the 2-inch and 1-inch rails being weighted by factors of 2 and 4. The distribution of scores is markedly skewed, but the test discriminates well between those whom Heath calls motor morons and those with normal balance. No analysis has been made of the factors that go to make for good or poor scores but Heath (1946) claims that the test discriminates between 'brain injured' and endogenous defectives. As in so much recent work by psychologists on 'brain injury' the criteria of the condition are somewhat vague (see Chapter IX), and the theoretical basis of the testing procedure is flimsy. The rail walking test shows up clearly enough a motor defect in many mental defectives. To claim more for it seems unwarranted at present.

QUALITATIVE DIFFERENCES IN THOUGHT

Suggestions have been made that mental defectives as a group differ from those of higher intelligence not only in intellectual power, but also qualitatively in the way in which they think. A plausible hypothesis has been put forward by Kounin (1941) following Lewin (1935). Kounin points out that an adult has on the one hand more 'knowledge, abilities, skills, emotions, and needs' than a child; on the other hand, the older a person the greater the 'functional independence' of various parts of the personality. A young child who is thirsty will be 'cranky and ill tempered all over' while an adult may be pleasant and retain his normal perspective even though he is thirsty. Put into Lewinian or so-called topological terms it is said that whereas an adult has a greater number of 'psychological regions', the boundaries of these regions become more 'rigid' with age. The degree of rigidity in this context refers to 'the degree of the functional relationship between neighbouring regions of the person's structure. The more rigid the boundary the less one region affects neighbouring regions.' Kounin claims that whereas the degree of rigidity increases with chronological age, the number of psychological regions increases with mental age.

From these two assumptions it follows that mental defectives will differ from normal people of the same mental age – that is, having the same number of psychological regions – in being more rigid. The difference in the degree of rigidity will be proportionate to the age differences between the two groups. A number of tests of this hypothesis that rigidity increases with chronological age were devised, and groups of adult defectives aged 29–53 years, young defectives aged 10–17 years, and children of normal intelligence aged 6–8 years, were tested. The groups were matched for mental age. Results were held by Kounin to be consistent with his theory.

Kounin's theoretical formulations have been criticized by Goldstein (1942) and by Werner (1946) on account of their vagueness. Sarason (1949), who summarizes the literature, has also criticized the theory on clinical grounds. Osborn (1960) recently established that rigidity of conceptual organization of word association was not found to a greater extent in defectives, whether brain injured or not, than in normals. A study by Brand *et al.* (1953) has raised the question of length of institutional care as a confounding variable. Solomon (1954) in a small study was, however, able to show (*a*) that there was a highly significant correlation between age and 'rigidity', and (*b*) that there was no significant association between 'rigidity' and length of institutional care. The subject is clearly in need of further research, perhaps guided by a different theoretical model.

The concept of rigidity has also been applied by Strauss and his school to account for the differences between exogenous and endogenous defectives. These concepts are discussed in Chapter IX of this book. Other investigations into qualitative differences in intellectual functioning are discussed in Chapter VIII.

PERSONALITY[1]

A great deal has been written about qualities of personality found in mental defectives, but little empirical study has been made. The traditional dichotomy is between over-active and excitable defectives on the one hand, and apathetic or withdrawn defectives on the other. Tredgold (1949) gives the following description of the 'mental and nervous condition' of imbeciles, and makes similar comments about both idiots and feeble-minded persons:

> . . . the behaviour of many imbeciles is abnormal even in infancy, some being unusually placid and unresponsive, others being markedly restless and excitable. These abnormal reactions are constitutional; they persist throughout life, and they enable us to differentiate two clinical types which we may term the *stable or apathetic* and the *unstable or excitable*. We have seen that a

[1] The writer (1957) has reviewed the literature on this problem elsewhere, and this section follows closely his earlier treatment of the subject-matter.

similar difference exists in the idiots, and we shall see that this is also the case in the feeble-minded. The stable imbeciles are harmless, inoffensive, stolid, and well-behaved persons who give no trouble, and who are tolerably industrious within the limits of their capacity. The unstable imbeciles, on the other hand, are constantly chattering, running about, and generally interfering with everything and everybody. Their restlessness and defect of active attention make it quite impossible for them to be employed in any kind of work, and some of them are so destructive and troublesome as to need almost constant supervision.

Very similar descriptions are to be found in other textbooks. Some writers regard a dichotomous classification as being too rigid. Wallin, for example, comments as follows:

> Some defectives cannot be classified in either group. They are rather neutral or indifferent, being neither very unstable nor very phlegmatic. Some belong in a mixed group, being sometimes excitable and sometimes dull and listless. Many defectives are like many normals; they have their ups and downs, their episodes of sluggishness and impulsiveness. These contrasting emotional characteristics exist, in varying degree, in all kinds of individuals, normal and abnormal; but they are particularly characteristic of the neurotic, psychotic (mentally disordered), and mentally defective.

Much depends upon definitions. Typologists in general have not regarded psychological types as being discrete entities, but have tended rather to regard temperamental qualities as being on a continuum or 'dimension'. According to this way of looking at things, excitable and apathetic defectives would be extreme cases; many, perhaps the great majority, would be neither markedly sluggish nor very excitable. Most writers on mental deficiency who have used typological concepts have in fact taken a similar stand, saying that the majority of defectives fall somewhere along a scale characterized at one end by extreme excitability and at the other end by complete apathy.

Expressed in these terms, the traditional typology has a certain obviousness about it. What seems to be implied is that (*a*) if one counts up the number of outbursts of excitement or temper occurring in a given period of time, individuals will be found to differ in the frequency of attack; (*b*) that such manifestations tend to be fairly constant from week to week and month to month. A similar conclusion can no doubt be arrived at in regard to very many other traits.

The field of personality study in mental defect is a very promising one. Behavioural rating scales and observational techniques which have been used with normal children and with patients in mental hospitals (Lorr, 1954), and conditioning techniques, are suitable instruments to use in this field. Porteus (1941) summarizes some of the earlier work at Vineland on this subject, and Claridge (see Chapter XIII) has made a recent attempt to devise a behavioural rating scale for imbeciles. Investigations of single traits can easily be carried out; for example, one might follow Goodenough's (1931) procedure and study anger in young mentally deficient children both in institutions and at home, or compare a special group such as mongols, with other mental defectives, or with normal children. Secondly, measures of different qualities, or different measures of the same trait, could be compared by factor analysis or other appropriate techniques, to arrive at meaningful dimensions of the personality structure of mental defectives. It is possible that personality types would be more clearly revealed in mentally subnormal persons than among the normal. Again, institutional children are very suitable subjects for dynamic or longitudinal studies. Since we do not know how the emotional maturation of mentally subnormal children compares with that of normal children, to what extent clear temperamental differences are to be found in low-grade cases, and how they persist or are modified by experience, or even, in any but a crudely empirical way, how to control outbursts of excitement or periods of apathy socially or pharmacologically, such studies should be of more than purely theoretical interest. From the evidence available one concludes that mental defectives who are not also suffering from psychosis or behaviour disorders present the same range of temperamental qualities as do normal persons. They probably mature more slowly, and they tend, on the whole, to be more placid. Beyond this one cannot go.

It is often said that mental defectives belonging to different cinical types exhibit different patterns of personality. Mayer-Gross, Slater, and Roth (1954) maintain that

> certain types of central lesion are associated with certain types of

> personality. For instance, the friendly and sociable character of the athetotic child is well known; Bender (1940) described the 'clinging' personality of children with cerebellar lesions. Poliomyelitis, when it involves the brain-stem, may affect the personality; and this may partly explain the feeble reactions and resigned attitude of paralysed poliomyelitic patients. Finally any intellectual impairment, due to a cerebral lesion, will also affect the level of adaptation.

Again, microcephalics are often described as characteristically bird-like, quick and active in movement and highly distractible. The greatest claims are made about mongols, who are numerically by far the commonest among the clinical subgroups. Mongols are said by Tredgold to be attracted by everything around them, full of initiative, and very observant. They

> look bright and intelligent, are very fond of drill and dancing, and show aptness for mimicry and marked sense of rhythm, and a remarkable fondness for music. As they grow up they remain of a happy and cheerful disposition. They are affectionate and good-tempered and easily amused. They like to be taken notice of, and are usually a great favourite with all who have to do with them.

These claims appear to be without foundation. Careful investigation by Rollin (1946) and by Blacketer-Simmonds (1953) of institutional mongols show them to be no more homogeneous in personal qualities than is an unselected group of defectives of the same mental grade. They are not noticeably fond of music, nor do an undue proportion of them show the desirable qualities mentioned by Tredgold and others. A similar conclusion was arrived at by Dr J. C. Grad and the writer (1961) studying mongols and other imbeciles living at home. Blacketer-Simmonds in his paper reviews historically the description of mongols from the first description of the condition by Langdon Down in 1866 to the present day, showing how each later investigator has added to the list of desirable qualities mentioned by earlier writers. Since mongols resemble each other physically, one might expect to find corresponding resemblances in qualities of personality. If such similarities do exist it is a task for the future to establish the fact.

If it is true that mongols are not more alike than are other defectives, it seems unlikely that any close resemblance in temperament or personality will be found among members of other nosological groups. The rarity of other forms of clinically diagnosable mental defect makes such investigations difficult, and only gross differences are likely to be revealed by existing crude techniques for investigating qualities of personality.

As in the field of general personality study, such investigations have more than an academic interest. Lauretta Bender (1953), for example, believes that faulty methods of handling are in part responsible for the 'typical' post-encephalitic syndrome so often described and observed. Similar criticisms have been raised against the concept of the 'epileptic personality'. Such matters are of great practical importance, and further work is clearly needed to investigate them.

MENTAL DISORDER

Prevalence

Among lower grade defectives neuroses and functional psychoses are found, but it is difficult or impossible to diagnose them according to types of mental illness found among those of normal intelligence. Penrose (1949) has made the most detailed study of the prevalence of psychoses and neuroses in institutional defectives. Other studies have been made by Earl (1934), Kaplun (1935), and Humphreys, Watts, and Boldt (1937), while Wallin (1949) has much useful information on problems of mental disorder and mental defect.

A major problem is that of epilepsy. Penrose found 16 per cent. of his group suffered from epilepsy; a corresponding figure obtained in a survey of 12 mental deficiency hospitals in the Greater London area was 12 per cent. noted as having had fits within the previous year. Of these, a quarter were severe cases (major fits once a fortnight or more), a quarter were moderate, and the remainder mild (O'Connor and Tizard, 1956).

Of 627 patients classified as feeble-minded or dull, Penrose diagnosed 17 per cent. as neurotic and 6 per cent. as psychotic. O'Connor, on the basis of work done at Darenth Park, concluded that 6–12 per cent. of feeble-minded patients (mean I.Q. = 70) suffered from 'severe neurotic handicap' for which special treatment was needed, and that no less than 40 per cent. suffered from 'mild neurotic tendency' or 'instability', which tended to disappear as they grew older, or were placed in a more stimulating, emotionally warm environment. Psychotic defectives were not studied in this investigation, which included both the dull and feeble-minded groups of Penrose's nomenclature in about equal numbers.

O'Connor, in his review of the literature on emotional instability among the feeble-minded, gives many discrepant figures as to prevalence. In summary it may be said that only in cases where a trait can be objectively assessed, e.g. having fits, do we find agreement in different surveys, or between different observers. Where traits are ill defined, or are subjectively rated, disagreements may be very large. Accepting Penrose's statistics as the most complete there are, one can say that among low-grade defectives and simpletons in institutions, about 30 per cent. suffer from behaviour disorders. Among the higher grade cases the proportion rises to perhaps double this figure. The disabilities of many, and perhaps of the majority of the higher grade cases are, however, neither serious nor likely to be permanent (O'Connor and Tizard, 1956). The treatment and management of maladjusted defectives is discussed by Gunzburg in Chapter XV.

Habit disorders are not infrequently found. In the survey of 12 mental deficiency hospitals in the Greater London area, 13 per cent. of patients were found to be doubly incontinent, and a further 5 per cent. were enuretic. Though the great majority of these cases were either children or idiots, a small number of feeble-minded adults who are not obviously neurotic or maladjusted, still wet their beds at night. (Treatment by conditioning methods may be effective in such cases.)

No surveys of other habit disorders – thumb sucking, nail biting, head rolling, masturbation, and so on – are known to the writer. In institutional defectives such traits are common, partly because institutional children receive less individual attention than do those living at home. Rocking is often seen in idiots and imbeciles, but like catalepsy in schizophrenics, it is much less common in hospitals where the patients are given interesting things to do, than in those in which patients sit in idleness most of the time.

Childhood psychosis

Special problems arise over the differential diagnosis, treatment, and management of childhood psychosis. The condition, albeit difficult to define, is rare but is thought by Creak (1961) to be three times more common in boys than in girls. Its frequency among imbeciles in mental deficiency hospitals is much greater than in the normal population. In a group of 450 patients in the Fountain Hospital, Hermelin and O'Connor (personal communication) identified 12 cases.

C. J. C. Earl (1934) described what he called 'primitive catatonic psychosis in idiocy'. Earl refers to a previous paper by Critchley and Earl (1932) in which kinetic movements and catalepsy resembling catatonic schizophrenia were noted in cases of epiloia. Some movement stereotypies occur in all imbeciles but Earl talked about a symptom complex which may fairly be described by his phrase. This complex includes (1) signs of deterioration, (2) signs of catatonia, and (3) signs of emotional dissociation. The patient deteriorates and becomes either cataleptic or excited. Autism and finger play are characteristic. A useful clinical description has been given by Kirman (in Hilliard and Kirman, 1957). He points out that whereas schizophrenia arising in late childhood or adolescence is unlikely to be confused with mental defect if an adequate history is available, in young children the problem of differential diagnosis is much more difficult. Kirman lists the following characteristic features of psychoses of the autistic type found among patients classified as mentally deficient:

(i) There is an obvious contradiction between ability and the capacity to make effective social use of it. Some children will discriminate nicely between people, showing clearly that they recognize them and that they appreciate character differences in the adults with whom they come into contact, but they will use this discriminative capacity in order to take advantage of those adults who are frightened of them, to be noisy, difficult, unruly, to run away, or to annoy.

(ii) Very frequently such children will reject social contact. In some cases they will drape a cloth around themselves, peering from behind it as though it were a saree. In other cases they will adopt other measures to prevent interference, as by spitting into one's face if attention is forced upon them. Although in some instances well able to speak they will avoid doing so, using sign language, whilst if they do speak it is in a low mumble which is difficult to follow. If group activity is going on, e.g. dancing, the psychotic child will remain outside the group, engaged in some quite different pursuit.

(iii) They frequently exhibit negativism of which the asocial tendencies mentioned above are only one example. They may refuse food or accept only certain items such as biscuits and Swiss rolls. Other inborn behaviour forms may be reversed. They may bang their heads, pick their faces, and bite their hands, particularly if attention is given or the pattern of stereotyped behaviour is disrupted.

(iv) They are prone to manneristic and compulsive behaviour; that is, they form stable stereotypes which serve no useful function. These vary enormously from one patient to another but tend to be constant in the same patient and usually take well recognized forms. Examples are, a little clicking movement of the jaw with a suggestion of biting, a habit of smelling things which are unlikely to have any recognizable smell, a rapid side to side waving of the hands, or a constant shuffling from one foot to the other. Sometimes the mannerisms take a more elaborate form closer to those seen in adult schizophrenics. For example, any piece of paper may be shredded finely into hundreds of pieces which are thrown on to the table or floor and then collected into a definite pattern of little piles to the accompaniment of facial, digital, and bodily contortions. Vocal mannerisms are sometimes also a feature. Although these performances are accompanied by a blank, unsmiling expression or by meaningless grimaces, although the patient avoids meeting one's eye, although he is emotionally cold and never permits himself to smile a welcome or to wave good-bye, behaviour is in fact socially geared in a perverse and negative way. For example, noisy and irritating mannerisms are frequently abandoned when the patient is alone but reach a new pitch in intensity as soon as an audience is guaranteed. Similarly, although normal rapport is lacking they often show individual strong preferences for particular people in an indirect way. Thus, when a particular nurse appears, the patient just happens to be near her, looking the other way and apparently oblivious of her presence. Should she move to another part of the ward, however, he also happens to be going that way, though still appearing as unaware of his surroundings as previously so that she at once attracts and repels, excites and inhibits him. In some respects he is like a shy suitor who is so overwhelmed by the strength of his feelings that he is quite unable to behave like a normal person. Although apparently shunning all social contact these unfortunate children seem also to desire them, to gaze at them from afar like a beggar child at a feast enjoyed by the rich.

Other writers have drawn attention to the deterioration which takes place in children whose development may proceed normally for perhaps three or four years before the illness develops (Bender, 1955; Bradley, 1941; Creak, 1951; Kanner, 1945). Normal speech may be lost, or be confined to meaningless phrases repeated endlessly, habits of dressing or eating may deteriorate, and in a few years the child may be indistinguishable from other idiot or low-grade imbecile children.

The prognosis in childhood autism is poor. Bender (1955) gives the following information about 60 children for whom information was available out of 90 diagnosed between the ages of 2 and 6, between 1935 and 1951. Of these half were at home or in the community; the other half were in institutions. Of those at home,

> 20 are very much improved and appear as nearly normal children; six in institutions, some of them special institutions, are also much improved. However, seven at home are not improved, and 18 in institutions are under protective or custodial care, most of them (13) considered by us as 'pseudo-defective', while 6 are considered 'deteriorated'.

Other writers, perhaps because they diagnose childhood psychosis much less frequently, are even more pessimistic as to its outcome. Kanner (1945) reports a 20 per cent. recovery rate in one study. Mayer-Gross *et al.* (1954) regard the prognosis as 'almost hopeless'.

Cases which do not recover do not always regress to dementia. Richards (1951) has described 16 cases of childhood 'schizophrenia' without previous mental defect, who were seen in a mental deficiency institution. In a further 6 cases also discussed, the diagnosis of primary mental defect could not be ruled out. All of these cases had been observed over a period of several years. The case history material he presents differs little from that commonly found in other adult schizophrenics. The predominant type of disorder resembles simple schizophrenia, though paranoid delusions and obsessive ruminative tendencies are sometimes mildly evident. Somewhat less frequent are cases of medium severity which often have hebephrenic features. (In Richards' investigation cases functioning at an idiot level were not discussed in detail owing to the difficulty of diagnosis.) In the series as a whole no special tendency was shown to motility disorders, though the occurrence of motor symptoms in childhood schizophrenia is usually given special emphasis in the literature. Only one case was markedly restless, and five in all had catatonic features. It is of some interest that even when the onset of the disease was in infancy, intelligence as judged by mental tests was in some cases within normal limits at adulthood.

Anthony (1962) recently presented his views on psychosis in low-grade defectives. In brief he thought that it was easier to make the diagnosis than to talk about it, but that it comprised treating people as things, attaching oneself to objects and desire to keep the environment constant as well as bizarre ritualistic mannerisms and lack of speech. Anthony states that there are three main trends in the theories of psychotic autism. The first is an input theory, invoking lack of an adequate level of stimuli. The second is Bender's (1954, 1960) control theory of diffuse pathology. The third, an output theory, is based on types of response.

Dr Mildred Creak (1962, 1961) has recently laid down diagnostic criteria for psychotic children with the help of a working party, and has discussed child psychosis and mental deficiency (1961). In the former, the working party laid down nine criteria, the first of which was found in 67 out of 68 psychotic children and the last of which was held by many members to be an essential criterion. These were gross and sustained impairment of emotional relations, apparent unawareness of personal identity, pathological preoccupation with particular objects, sustained resistance to environmental changes, acute and excessive anxiety, speech lost or not acquired, distortions of motility, and a background of serious retardation with islets of normal function.

The differing outcomes of childhood psychosis described above – in some cases profound idiocy, in others imbecility with 'islands' of abilities of a much higher level, in others again adult schizophrenia without mental deterioration, and in some cases complete recovery – suggest the possibility that different diseases are involved. There is, however, little empirical support for any of the attempts that have been made to classify or subdivide the various conditions.

Epilepsy

A discussion of the general problem of epilepsy falls outside the scope of this book, and the reader is referred to Wallin (1949), and to textbooks of psychiatry or medicine. Jones (1953) has reviewed psychological studies.

A distinction is often made on clinical grounds between *idiopathic* and *symptomatic* epilepsy. The word 'idiopathic' merely indicates that the cause is unknown – the epilepsy is believed to be associated with an inborn tendency to disrhythmic cerebral activity without any detectable structural abnormality. In symptomatic epilepsy the convulsions usually arise from a known brain lesion. Epilepsy is thus a symptom which can be produced by different causes. When the site of disturbance in the brain can be found, epilepsy is termed *focal*.

Henderson (1955), who in 1948 carried out the best survey of the prevalence of the condition in schoolchildren in this country, says that: 'In every thousand children there are at least one or two who have, or have had, epileptic fits.' In regard to behaviour, he writes that the majority of epileptic children outside special schools and institutions are as well behaved as their non-epileptic fellows. He found that 12 per cent. of a group of 365 epileptic children of whom he made a special study suffered from emotional disturbances, or bad behaviour sufficient to cause complaints by parents or teachers, and he adds that bad behaviour is often a reason for sending some of these children to special schools. There they often settle down quickly, but a small minority are so disturbed that no special school will accept them. A few of these are eventually admitted to children's units in mental hospitals, where some do well. Speaking of intelligence, Henderson writes that:

> As a generalization it can be said that, excluding children in institutions, there are rather fewer children with epilepsy above, and rather more below, average intelligence than in the general population. A very small proportion deteriorate in intelligence due perhaps more to the lesion causing the fits than to the fits themselves. With prolonged and heavy drug treatment, some children undoubtedly become slower in cerebration and speech.

He goes on to stress that it is imperative that epileptic children should attend school. Most of them do well in ordinary schools, and in his group of 365 epileptic children only about 10 per cent. had ever had a fit in school. These general conclusions find quantitative support in a small but very well controlled study carried out by Halstead (1957) in Birmingham, using a control group of normal children matched for age and socio-economic level.

The prevalence of 'idiopathic' epilepsy in institutional defectives is high. Penrose (1949) found that of 1,280 patients examined in his Colchester survey 210 or 16 per cent. suffered from idiopathic epilepsy. A further 143 may have suffered from symptomatic epilepsy, though in half of these cases there was some doubt about the matter. Nearly half of his cases with neurological lesions had fits of some kind, as did nearly a quarter of those with abnormalities of the skeleton, including those with cranial malformations, microcephalics, hydrocephalics, and acrocephalics. Symptomatic epilepsy was, as might be expected, commoner among low-grade defectives.

Having convulsions is probably a reason for institutional care being sought in some cases. Dr Grad and the writer have found that of 150 cases of imbeciles and idiots living at home in London, only 22 have fits, and only 10 of these have more than one fit a month (Tizard and Grad, 1961).

A major fit is a frightening thing for an inexperienced onlooker to see. In consequence, epilepsy has tended to be regarded with fear by the general public. It is well known that mishandling, whether it be the rejection of the epileptic or parental over-solicitude, tends to exacerbate the condition, and that frankness and sincerity are essential for good management. It need hardly be added that the additional handicaps imposed by epilepsy upon a mentally subnormal child add enormously to his difficulties in adjustment, and need skilled handling and advice. Since epilepsy is so common among the mentally subnormal, those who work with them should be familiar with the relevant literature on the subject.

MENTAL DEFICIENCY, DELINQUENCY AND PSYCHOPATHY

Some mental defectives are criminals, and others are so irresponsible as to be classified as 'psychopaths'. It was mentioned in Chapter I that the investigations of the Goddard school greatly overestimated the prevalence of mental subnormality among criminals and delinquents, and exaggerated the criminal tendencies of the mentally backward. A review by Woodward (1955) suggests that any difference between the I.Q.s of delinquents and non-delinquents can be attributed to cultural factors which adversely affect test scores. Lowrey (1944), reviewing studies bearing on the relation between mental deficiency and crime, arrives at a very similar conclusion and other studies have been summarized elsewhere (O'Connor and

Tizard, 1956). The simpleton or imbecile who is also a delinquent presents different problems of management from the person of higher mental ability. The number of mentally subnormal delinquents is not, however, large, and the problems they present do not differ much from those of other non-delinquent defectives, as the follow-up studies described in Chapter XVII show.

At the present time much more interest is shown in emotional and temperamental abnormalities than in cognitive defect as a factor leading to crime. The change probably follows the greater interest now being taken in forensic psychiatry. Unfortunately, both the definitions and the estimate of the incidence of psychopathy differ enormously. Moreover, there is no agreement as to methods of treatment. Persons who are so unstable that they require institutional care 'for the protection of others' constitute a social problem which is so different from that posed by the simple-minded that discussion of it falls outside the scope of this chapter.

Chapter VIII

LEARNING AND MENTAL DEFECT

by N. O'Connor

INTRODUCTION

The work carried out by Itard and Seguin in the late eighteenth and the nineteenth centuries, in training imbeciles, was the first series of investigations of the learning capacity of defectives in modern times. After Binet's criticisms of the unconfirmed claims of these educational experiments, however, psychologists and educators have been only too ready to identify lack of intelligence with incapacity to learn. The two are not necessarily identical, as can be shown by reference to a number of studies of the retardation of intelligence due to such chance environmental forces as deprivation of experience (Hebb, 1949), but they are associated. Since intelligence is often defined in terms of poor performance of academic tasks, this association is to some extent inevitable. Thus if we accept Spearman's (1927) definition of intelligence as capacity to perceive relations and educe correlates, backwardness in the use of symbols will certainly be a correlate of low I.Q.

Presumably all cognitive abilities as judged by most tests depend on information acquired being either formal in the sense of knowledge of reasoning method, deduction, and induction, as well as the knowledge of the facts in the area of discourse. The acquisition of this information must in itself demand the presence of innate abilities. The origins of backwardness might thus lie in particular abilities or disabilities, or simply in one, the symbolic, or in some general capacity.

When learning ability is considered to be impaired in the mentally deficient, we must first ask both why, and in what way. This incapacity is loosely assumed to be associated with poor ability to form connexions between facts or events connected in space and time, or to retain such formed connexions in memory. However, the disability is scarcely ever formulated even so precisely as this. In considering learning we will be discussing just such notions. The process might be defined as the relatively permanent modification of reactions as a result of experience.

THE LEARNING PROCESSES

(a) Many processes are involved

If mental defect is defined as arrested or incomplete development of mind which includes subnormality of intelligence, such a description still leaves the area of handicap or incompleteness unexplored. That deficiency may exist in all abilities, in some only, or greatly in some and less in all others, is a logical possibility. The evidence for the extent and character of deficiency is by no means complete.

D. M. Johnson (1955, p. 117) lays out a system of functions related to learning. Retention and recall are mentioned, but acquisition is analysed in more detail. Other relevant processes are considered to be conditioning, trial and error, imitation, intuition, tuition, reaction formation, thought, reasoning, reorganization and insight, creative imagination, and judgment. Conceivably the list is not exhaustive; one might add taking for granted, entertaining propositions, understanding, and so on (Price, 1950), but it indicates the degree to which the process of learning can be broken down. It might be possible to elaborate the list by indicating activities in which the functions predominate. Thus conditioning and trial and error may play more part in the acquisition of motor skills than in the acquisition of general concepts, but experimental work would be necessary to verify such a view. In a chapter concerned with learning among defectives it is impossible to describe the recent investigations in such a relatively new field as the analysis of types of learning. As mentioned earlier, it may be noted that lack of intelligence is the assumed correlate of general disability, just as intelligence is defined as the presence of general ability ('*g*') or equivalent group factors. However, bearing in mind the range of types of learning which may exist, the fact that all might be affected by mental defect, if it is a fact, requires explanation. If such factors as motivation and other circumstances attendant on learning are also considered, an incapacity to learn must inevitably appear to be a complex phenomenon.

Although motivation is generally assumed to be constant we know so little about motivational factors that apparent similarity of drive may mask considerable differences. A disability might be shown in any one or more of a number of such functions, as imitation, curiosity, insight, imagination, retention, reasoning, or judgment.

(b) Backwardness can be subdivided

Burt (1946, p. 528) presents an interesting table in which he assesses the relevant degrees and types of handicap to be found in his sample of London and Birmingham children. This is still the most adequate estimate available, and is reproduced below.

Psychologically, we might say, the backward are characterized by the following defects, and that in the order stated.

Defects in –

Reasoning Long-distance mechanical memory Short-distance logical memory Short-distance mechanical memory Long-distance logical memory Duration of attention	(mental) ratios below 85
Speed of association Scope of attention Auditory perception Visual perception	(mental) ratios above 85

This is one of the earliest attempts to subdivide learning functions and show the association of each with backwardness. It of course applies to the upper levels of backwardness, and although no comparative scale is known for the more severe degrees of intellectual handicap, the same difficulties are likely to be found.

Causes of learning deficiency present an equally complex picture. Causal factors range from genetic impairment (e.g. phenylketonuria) and pathological damage, to the recently adumbrated concept of protophrenia (Bourne, 1955). Cultural and pathological factors have been considered to be the principal causes of defect, but the division of the field between them has appeared to change in recent years from a predominance of the concept of primary amentia associated with neuropathic diathesis to an extension of the notion of congenital and environmental causes. Such causes become factors relevant to learning success. Different aetiological factors may affect different aspects of learning. Thus Strauss and Lehtinen (1947) and others suggest that particular forms of brain injury affect learning ability by leading to unusual distractibility. For this condition they recommend instructional techniques similar to those originally developed by Itard between 1800 and 1806 (see translation, 1932, 1962), and Guggenbuel, such for example as the use of contrast and the elimination of distracting stimuli.

Another clear division of some importance in this field is that between practical and verbal intelligence. Some authors like Duncan (1942) have maintained that some defectives may have a practical ability which, if encouraged, can lead to a high level of performance. Duncan quotes figures showing the tendency of his school entrants to do better on the Alexander Performance test than on the Stanford–Binet. The range and mean of the former were 67–119 and 96 as compared with a Stanford range 54–76 and mean of 66. Supplementing his results with findings on Raven's Progressive Matrices, he suggests that (p. 47) 'inferiority of this group of F.M.' (feeble-minded) 'children, . . . is much more a verbal than a general inferiority'.

A somewhat different approach to the problem of low verbal level has been attempted in recent Russian research inspired by Luria (1957) and his colleagues such as Liublinskaia (1957) and others. The theory underlying this exploratory work is that verbal connexions with sensory experience have not been made adequately in the case of defectives, because of, e.g., faulty teaching, and that special attention must be given to such connexion-forming if proper development of concepts is to be achieved. Their tendency is to give emphasis to the study of methods of instruction, and some of their techniques are described in another part of this chapter.

(c) Inequalities of development of concept learning and motor skills

Apart from the effects of intellectual handicap, it is well known that different individuals have different rates of learning. There are also *intra-individual differences*. It is generally assumed that such variations are due to differences in problem-solving ability, itself part of learning ability, plus differences in information remembered. Johnson (1955) reviews some of the findings of studies of different learning abilities. A general factor related to intelligence and reasoning ability appears in the learning of organized material, mazes, matching, number discrimination, and memory span. However, for simpler matching tasks a close correlation was not found. The consensus of results is that learning tests involving abstraction correlate higher with intelligence tests than do other tests, but that learning follows a pattern determined by the nature of the material. Johnson (op. cit., p. 138) writes:

> In summary, the published correlations between learning achievements at the end of a standard practice period give little evidence for a general learning factor related to general intelligence. If such a factor operates throughout a variety of learning tests, it must be quite small and relatively unimportant.

He finds group factors for maze learning, cancellation, substitution, and simple association or memory. Generally intelligence test results correlate better with reasoning than with recall. It is not surprising that this should be the case when '*g*' loaded tests often measure what is called reasoning ability or inference.

Whereas tests of cognitive ability correlate highly, tests of manual dexterity generally do not. The reason for the difference is seldom considered but may conceivably be found in the role of language in the academic abilities. Whereas motor skills are acquired by a process akin to conditioning, problem solving may be mediated by grasping a principle of solution which depends on a verbal formulation of the problem. Work on semantic conditioning in Piaget's and Luria's laboratories indicate that a verbal formulation makes a considerable difference to the assurance with which a problem is approached and solved.

(d) The differential effects of motivation

Individual differences in the development of interest in a performance of or motivation for a task have also been noticed. Mowrer (1950), Eysenck (1955), and others have noted personality correlates of learning. In experiments carried out by Claridge and O'Connor (1957) differences were observed between excitable and inhibited imbecile patients. Acquisition differed from group to group according to different conditions of motivation or lack of motivation.

In experiments with animals, by Thompson and Heron (1954), dogs were deprived of kinaesthetic and visual experience during early life, in varying amounts. Although their performance was handicapped, their curiosity or inquisitiveness seemed to have suffered no permanent damage and exploratory activity was much increased. Similar experiments with children (Barker, Dembo, and Lewin, 1941) had a reverse effect. Children were given toys to play with in a playground, and subsequently a shutter was lowered, permitting the children to see the toys, but not to get them. Their behaviour is discussed in terms of the frustration and regression which appeared to result.

McClelland, Atkinson, *et al.* (1953) show that individual differences in curiosity do appear, sometimes as a result of different home disciplines, and others have shown how lack of curiosity may lead to failure to solve set problems. In addition, the trend of Harlow's (1949) work showing that curiosity rather than reward is often the chief motive in human learning, further underlines the importance of an adequate development of exploratory activity for the full growth of learning capacity. In view of these interesting investigations it is clear that individual differences in ability may owe more than we generally assume to this important aspect of learning. At present investigations with animals have not been verified to any extent with children.

(e) Summary

The general question of individual differences in learning ability is at present scarcely discussed in psychological literature. This section is therefore confined to indicating the complexity of the field. This complexity has been concealed to some extent because all differences in performance have in the past been assumed to be due to differences in innate capacity to acquire knowledge. Because of this assumption, many factors relevant to learning such as those mentioned here, memory, curiosity, capacity for imitation, optimum conditions for exploration, trial and error learning, imaginative play, and so on, have scarcely been explored. Learning investigations in recent years have in various ways turned attention to the effect of past experience on learning capacity. Experiments by N. R. F. Maier (1949) with rats, Katona (1940) and others with human subjects, show only some sides of this question, which needs to be widely extended. It is not surprising, therefore, that the failure of defectives to learn should not have been studied in more detail. None the less, studies exist which throw light on the failure of the mentally handicapped to gain knowledge. These are discussed in the two subsequent sections.

FACTORS AFFECTING LEARNING AMONG DEFECTIVES

(a) Deprivation of experience and emotional deprivation

The problem posed by the title of this section has seldom been raised in the literature. However, recent studies by workers such as Harlow (1949), Hebb (1949), and many others suggest the great likelihood that early restriction of environment means poorer subsequent performance in some animals. Another hypothesis, not quite the same but having points of similarity, has been advanced by Spitz (1945) and Goldfarb (1945, 1947) in America, and by Bowlby (1951) and Bowlby, Ainsworth, *et al.* (1956) in England, in explaining child development. The work of Lorenz (1952) and Tinbergen (1951) is too well known to need description.

The problem has sometimes been presented in such a fashion that a permanently damaging effect of early maternal deprivation has been inferred. Orlansky (1949), Lewis (1954), Beach and Jaynes (1954), and O'Connor (1956) have contested the necessarily permanent nature of damage done and questioned the legitimacy of applying the analogy of 'imprinting' in animals to human beings. Some of the work of Riesen (1947) and Senden (1932) in this connexion has been re-assessed by Wertheimer *et al.* (1951). Moreover, work such as that of Clarke, Clarke, and Reiman (1958) shows how children whose backwardness may be considered as partly due to deprivation, may make notable advances in performance, improving their learning facility during adolescence and early adult life. In reply to such criticisms, Bowlby *et al.* (1956) have recently admitted that extreme claims have sometimes been made for some aspects of the maternal deprivation hypothesis, which now need to be modified.

There is thus considerable criticism of the claims for the necessarily permanent nature of the effects of deprivation in children, whatever may happen with, for example, the failure of imprinting in animals. There is also uncertainty and confusion concerning the theory which underlies the claims made for maternal deprivation. If emotional deprivation is meant, i.e. loss of love and affection, it can be shown that this may be relevant to learning backwardness. Evidence also exists to show that limitation of experience may be the relevant factor, or unfamiliarity with the teacher's idiosyncrasies. Animal studies and the classical deprivation experiment of Barker,

Dembo, and Lewin (1941) make it clear that other factors than a direct person-to-person relationship may be involved. Investigations of this kind show that frustration can result in lack of curiosity, and in a loss of drive for one particular pursuit, and that this may affect acquisition. Each or all of these mechanisms may be involved in 'maternal deprivation'.

(b) Types of discipline, motivation, and learning

McClelland, Atkinson, Clark, and Lowell (1953) have explored a number of factors which may affect the 'achievement motive'. They show how output in successive periods of short trials can be affected by motivation. Improvement was related to motivation rather than to intelligence in an experiment (op. cit., p. 230) with successive two-minute scrambled word tasks. Holding intelligence constant did not significantly alter the relationship between motivation and improvement ($r = 0{\cdot}48$, $P = 0{\cdot}01$). Their findings concerning the family background of those with high motivation scores might conceivably apply with high-grade defectives, improvement in performance being dependent on motivation rather than on intelligence level. They find that some measure of severity in upbringing may correlate positively with achievement. Encouragement of independence in early training also seems relevant.

(c) Socio-economic factors affecting backwardness

The possibilities of forces of a more general kind affecting learning have been explored many times since Burt's first surveys in London and Birmingham (1946), carried out after the First World War. Most investigations have confirmed his views so far as basic facts are concerned. That high-grade defectives tend to be more frequently found among lower socio-economic groupings, receives confirmation from Burt's published correlations between backwardness in scholastic skills and indices of socio-economic levels. Burt's thesis is that in the main such backwardness and lack of intelligence are very closely related, and that its other associations are secondary. However, if this were to be a matter of definition, low intelligence commonly involving backwardness – then both can be seen as related to socio-economic and physical deficits.

Burt's quoted correlations for factors associated with backwardness ($N = 400$) include correlations of 0·73 with poverty and 0·57 with poor relief; 0·89 with overcrowding, and 0·93 with infant mortality. Subsequent work such as that of Allardyce (1939) in Glasgow has confirmed this type of finding and a survey of London boroughs today would not contradict his general conclusion.

He also shows a general correlation between physical and mental growth. Binet, Simon, and Vaney (1907) note the same connexion in Paris schoolchildren. Many studies have shown similar relationships, and some, such as that of Seymour and Whittaker (1938), have shown changes in physique to be related to changes in mental performance. Burt also quotes (p. 165) a number of physical conditions correlating with backwardness to varying degrees, among the more outstanding being marked hearing defect 0·44, marked defect of speech 0·33. Birch and Matthews (1951) have subsequently shown that backward children have a significantly higher percentage of physical defects than do normal children. This existence of physical defects, however, may be a concomitant event and not necessarily causally connected. The question therefore would seem to need further systematic investigation, but the material at present available has tended to turn the scales much more in favour of environmental causes of defect than would have been considered likely 20 years ago.

Burt observes that poverty cannot be inferred to be a cause of learning disability, but notes that it is a frequent concomitant. By an analysis of some of the data presented in conclusions it can be shown that if I.Q. is held constant, the correlation between sensory defects and backwardness is of the order of 0·4, and in similar calculations irregular attendance at school has a correlation of 0·45 to 0·58 with backwardness. Burt does not give great weight to these data in his original text. He remarks (op. cit., p. 572): 'In the majority the outstanding cause is general inferiority of intellectual capacity, presumably inborn and frequently hereditary.' However, the excellent and detailed studies which he has given us admit of alternative interpretations in so far as they can be shown to demonstrate the importance of such factors as regular school attendance and freedom from physical disabilities.

Examination of the tables collected in Burt's two investigations shows that the percentage of backward children with various physical defects is about three times greater than it is in a control group. Burt considers that physical defects may be secondary without a direct effect on backwardness (p. 573) and this may be the case, but examples are to be found where backwardness has been ameliorated by attention to specific sensory defects. Also the Allardyce

(1939)[1] study shows the general effect of attention to social conditions, and Burt has more recently written an introduction to Segal's (1949) study of backwardness in schools which takes full account of social features. In his introductory note Burt remarks,

> The health of the mother, the wages of the father, the conditions of housing, and the security and insecurity of the family as a whole, their daily experiences, the papers and books they read – these and other features of the child's home life are bound to affect, directly or indirectly, the success of the work in the classroom and will largely decide its success or failure.

This section has been largely concerned with the effect of deprivation on intelligence. Presuming that learning and intelligence are not completely distinct entities, but are seen as developing in relation to each other at all stages of growth, the remarks made about deprivation may be seen to be applicable to both learning and intelligence. Thus a dull child is one who fails to acquire a particular educational technique at a certain stage, possibly because of lack of adequate instruction, as well as for other reasons.

(d) Summary

It would be possible to extend any analysis of the literature on deprivation and backwardness to a considerable length. However, although research continues and definitive statements cannot yet be expected in this confused field, it is necessary to attempt some generalizations at this point in the interests of clarity. It seems likely from the evidence available that the necessarily permanent nature of backwardness resulting from emotional deprivation is questionable, and the effect of a change in environment can be shown to be therapeutic. In addition, a number of direct therapeutic procedures have had positive results. Thus re-education is possible in some cases in which deprivation of experience has resulted in backwardness as in the Iowa studies. Emotional deprivation, where a child is deprived of affection or rejected, and frustration, can also be shown to have damaging effects, but it cannot be said with certainty that such effects are necessarily permanent. See also Chapter V.

Deprivation of food and similar physical deprivations having an

[1] The Allardyce study showed the relationship between presumed undernourishment as shown by a free milk issue and lack of scholastic success in a number of Glasgow schools (see Fig. 1, Chapter II).

ultimately deleterious effect on sense organs and physique in general, also affect capacity to attend, to learn, and affect intelligence. The permanence of such effects is also in question. In both this case and the case of psychological deprivation, there is no doubt that the length of deprivation and the age at which it occurs are relevant to the extent and perhaps the permanence of resulting defects. (For further discussion of deprivation, see Chapters V and XVIII.)

Re-educative and therapeutic techniques relevant to backwardness are discussed in the last section. In the next, having shown how a tendency to 'explain' backwardness in terms of lack of intelligence has led to a failure to appreciate the complexity of the learning process, we turn to a description of the few studies of learning which have been made with defectives.

EXPERIMENTAL INVESTIGATIONS OF THE LEARNING ABILITIES OF MENTAL DEFECTIVES

(a) Conflicting conclusions of previous studies

Despite the fact that learning difficulties are the chief problem of mental defect, investigations until 1945 were sporadic. In a previous summary of experimental studies McPherson (1948) refers to some 16 investigations of learning among defectives. These range from the extensive studies of Kuhlmann (1904) to the equally extensive investigations of Gardner (1945). Both of these reach the conclusion that *motivation must be maximal for effective study of learning and performance*. In Kuhlmann's study variability of performance tends to confuse the shape of the curve at the upper levels when motivation was temporarily lost. Two other general conclusions can be discerned in this review. The first is *that starting level is not related to ultimate or final performance level*, and the second that *both may be independent of mental age within certain limits*. This view is supported by the experiments of Woodrow (1917, 1938, and 1940), Johnson (1919), and de Sanctis (1931). However, other investigators quoted by McPherson[1] present evidence tending to connect problem solving and mental age. Part of the reason for the difference in findings on this issue is due to methodological imperfections. Thus Woodrow's studies show a tendency for defectives to improve as much as normals only if we use percentage improvement as a score.

[1] e.g. Ordahl and Ordahl (1915) and Aldrich and Doll (1931).

This capitalizes on their low starting level. His later investigations (1938, 1940), not noted by McPherson, do not suffer from this shortcoming, however. He maintains that the factor constituents of competence in a particular task, and the rank order of subjects, tend to change notably in the course of training.

(b) Problem solving and motor learning

A more important possible reason for conflicting results is the fact that many investigations showing a relationship of success with mental age are studies of problem solving, whereas those showing lack of relationship frequently involve hand-eye co-ordination. Thus most of Kuhlmann's (1904) tasks were of a problem-solving kind (although some were not), and in this investigation the closest correlation between success and mental age was achieved with domino matching, the most complex task. Ordahl and Ordahl (1915) similarly showed the existence of a relationship in a task involving a principle similar to that now used at the Applied Psychology Unit at Cambridge, to study vigilance, and called the 5-choice apparatus. In the Ordahl study typewriter keys were coloured; pressing one produced a coloured disc instead of a letter. This colour indicated the colour of the next key to be pressed. Thus the task required the learning of a colour sequence. Aldrich and Doll's (1931) studies were based on comparative investigations of problem solving in animals as were also Gardner's (1945). On the other hand, the studies showing improvement unrelated to mental age were, apart from Woodrow's, to which other objections pertain, those of Johnson, studying ball throwing at a target, and de Sanctis's study with a maze task.

However, a third and more important reason for the conflict in findings may be that mentioned in the first section above, in which intelligence is defined in terms of capacity to learn. Binet's original definition from which the concept of intelligence arose took account of educability and was designed for this purpose. In Binet and Simon's (1914) discussions this origin of the concept of mental age and backwardness is underlined.

(c) Concept formation in problem-solving tasks

Whiteside's (1934) and Gardner's (1945) work, mentioned by McPherson, adds to the picture. In the first, a complex study of generalization of a concept was undertaken with verbalization of a principle of selection from geometrical figures as one criterion of success. Other criteria were accepted if this could not be met. One point of some importance emerged, and this was that above the mental age of 8 or 9 years neither mental nor chronological age was a factor in success at learning the tasks. Below these mental ages, neither normals nor subnormals used principles in problem solution. Gardner's (1945) article is longer, but like those of Doll and Aldrich (1932) and others such as Berry's (1933) Stoke Park studies, Gardner's work arose from comparative psychology in the study of discrimination capacity in horses, cows, and sheep. In common with some of the assumptions presumably made in connexion with animals, Gardner (1945) assumed that a sweet would be sufficient motivation for imbecile and idiot subjects of ages between 6 and 15 years. Thus she states (op. cit., pp. 62–5), 'Motivation was rather weak. . . . As a rule the children were apathetic; . . .' She required them to carry out a discrimination problem for small food rewards. Although her evidence in general shows a direct relation between learning efficiency and increasing intelligence, she remarks, 'However, there were some good learners and poor learners in each group. The range of average box errors per trial for the high-grade imbeciles was 1·12 to 0·09; for the low-grade imbeciles 1·33 to 0·00; and for the idiots 1·41 to 0·17.' As the means were: 0·42, 0·66, and 0·70 respectively, the much closer approximation of upper and lower range limits is a finding which needs explanation. Transfer effects were good and positions of the three groups tended if anything to approximate in this respect. Change to a new principle of solution of the problem, i.e. a new position of the signal, was a serious handicap for the idiot group. This study, then, appears to add to the others by suggesting that learning ability varies considerably within each I.Q. range, producing much overlapping (see also Chapter XIII).

Between 1945 and 1955 few problem-solving studies were carried out with imbeciles. Since 1955 there have been a very great number. Some of these have involved motor performance and some have not. They have been of differing levels of difficulty.[1]

[1] Sloan has recently made a comment (personal communication) which is of great importance in the study of learning among defectives. It is of such relevance to the work reported in this section that it is given in full:

> A general point, which I think needs to be made in most studies of learning and intelligence in defectives, is the question of the level of difficulty of the tasks, or the converse of this, the level of ability of the subject. Correlations may or may not be obtained as one approaches certain levels. For example, if a task is so simple that all 8-year-olds can solve it very quickly, then little or no correlation will be obtained when using individuals with 9-, 10-, or 11-year mental

(d) Recent studies of motor learning

Other investigations concerned with learning or systematic training in performance have been described by Gordon, O'Connor, and Tizard (1954), Clarke and Hermelin (1955), and Claridge (1956). This group of studies has been concerned with the performance, retention, and activation of feeble-minded and imbecile patients. The general picture presented by these investigations has been analysed in Chapters XIII and XIV so that its findings will be only briefly summarized here.

Essentially this work showed that defectives, whilst inferior to normals in speed of performance at the commencement of training, were capable of improvement exceeding expectations based on their intelligence level. Suitable motivation had a very great effect on performance, and this effect was of a relatively permanent nature. Many practical results stemmed from the initial training techniques developed at mental deficiency hospitals and a scheme for industrial placement developed from this. We are concerned in this chapter, however, with the theoretical questions involved. Findings may be summarized as follows:

(1) The order of improvement in repetitive motor work achieved by those of subnormal intelligence is greater than their intelligence quotient would suggest. Although related to intelligence, the relationship is not so great that considerable changes in rank order may not occur during the course of many trials.

(2) Considered as groups according to intelligence level, results with long practice periods with defectives show that the ultimate level reached by imbeciles and feeble-minded patients and normals all overlap considerably on a simple motor task.

(3) Age seems to be unrelated to performance on a simple manual dexterity task.

(4) Incentives make a considerable difference to the habitual performance level of any group with which they are used.

---

ages. On the other hand, if a subject has a 6-year mental age and the task requires at least a 7- or 8-year mental age, again no relationship between learning and intelligence will be apparent. This is true if the range of mental abilities of the subjects does not coincide with the range of mental abilities necessary for solution of the task. A corollary of this is when too narrow a range of abilities is involved, then no correlation will be obtained because of the restriction of range. Thus, if a study includes individuals with 6- and 7-year mental ages, and the task can spread over a range of, say, 3- to 10-year mental age, then little or no correlation will be found, because the sample of the subjects does not cover the range of the possible scores that can be obtained on the task.

(5) Incentives affect different personality groups differently. When patients are arranged on a scale of excitability as judged or reached on verbal or social behaviour, it is found that excitable male defectives improve less than inhibited or unexcitable defectives when no incentives are offered. However, when incentives are used, the response of the excitable group is greater than that of the comparatively inhibited group.

Female imbeciles in general seem to be more inhibited than males, so that when incentives are offered they do not improve notably because the standard of performance set by them is already very high.

Certain other conclusions have been arrived at more recently. The following summary is extracted from Claridge (1956):

(1) The rate at which improvement occurs in imbeciles on a simple repetitive task, as revealed in the slope of the practice curve during learning, is independent of the strength of motivation operating during learning, but the *level* at which this improvement occurs *is* dependent on the strength of motivation.

. . . .

(2) The result of introducing external incentives, after learning has occurred without them, is such as to cause, in one trial, an increase in performance level to a point *above* that of subjects who have received these incentives from the beginning of learning.

(3a) The comparable removal of incentives after experience of them results in little material decrease in performance level, but there are individual differences in this respect which are associated with factors of temperamental excitability.

(3b) The persistence of motivation due to external incentives is such that the superiority in performance level achieved originally under the incentive of self-competition will be retained after a period of at least one year without practice on the same task.

(4) While goal-getting may be an effective incentive in directing the motivation of imbeciles towards some achievable end, its maximum effect is dependent on the occasional re-arousal, by means of external encouragement, of the striving produced by a goal. Similarly, the reward value for imbeciles of the outcome of goal-striving is dependent on social approval of success and sympathetic observation of failure in goal-achievement.

(5) In experimental situations the 'uncontrolled' motivation of hospitalized defectives appears to be high and it seems possible that this may be tentatively linked with factors associated with institutionalization, such as range of alternative activities available, lack of individual attention, and so on.

Claridge notes that this situation is considered to have affected the results of experiments with imbeciles in the following ways:

(*a*) The level of 'uncontrolled' motivation in most institutionalized imbeciles is such that the effects of the incentive of Goal with Encouragement do not appear when relatively short periods of work are employed. This suggests further that,

(*b*) The function of incentives such as Goal with Encouragement is to sustain motivation throughout relatively long periods of work on monotonous repetitive tasks. This function is differentially associated with temperamental factors of excitability and distractability.

(*c*) Uncontrolled motivation in the female imbecile is higher than in the male imbecile under certain conditions, since the female imbecile appears to respond to the presence of a male supervisor as part of the total experimental situation, even when he is taking no active part in the situation.

(*d*) This sex difference is reflected in a difference in performance level between male and female imbeciles working under conditions of no incentive, a difference which is nullified when the experimenter takes an active part in the situation with males by giving explicit encouragement and approval of work.

(6) The temperament of imbeciles may be meaningfully differentiated in terms of excitability and these differences can be related to the ability to improve in experimental situations. It is concluded that:

(*a*) When no incentive is given imbeciles rated as apathetic will improve more than those who are rated as excitable.

(*b*) Males and females do not differ in this respect.

(*c*) Under conditions of Goal with Encouragement imbeciles rated as excitable will show some tendency to improve more than those rated as apathetic.

(*d*) The superiority of apathetic imbeciles with regard to improvement is more marked where the longer period of work is involved.

(*e*) When Goal with Encouragement is removed after experience of this incentive, excitable imbeciles will decline more than apathetic ones.

(e) Recent studies of problem solving and learning

Some recent work is reported by Hovland, who (1951) quotes the works of Werner (1944), Gardner (1945), and Kulcinski (1945) in support of the finding that poor learning is shown by the mentally retarded. He also quotes Simrall (1947), who, after experiments with high-school students in which perceptual learning correlated −0·079 with intelligence and 0·277 with spatial tests, concluded 'under no circumstances do these data support the hypothesis that the ability to learn these tests is related to mental age'. It must be observed, however, that the starting level on the test correlated 0·6 with mental age. The number tested was 95. In concluding his discussion of intelligence differences and learning, Hovland proceeds to devote another section to a learning factor, concluding that such work as Woodrow's indicates that learning is specific to particular task methods. The considerable and increasing literature in this field continously calls in question the association between intelligence and learning. The subject therefore needs further research and clarification. However, studies revealing poor correlation between I.Q. and gain must not be accepted as evidence that final performance will not be correlated with I.Q. Generally a positive correlation can be demonstrated.

More recently, several studies have appeared, such as those of Stevenson and Iscoe (1955) on transposition and McCulloch, Reswick, and Roy (1955) on word learning. These investigations have tackled the problem of abstract learning among mental defectives. Like their predecessors, these investigators remark on the conflicting findings of research on learning and mental age. Ellis and Sloan (1957) have been analysing the relationship between intelligence and reaction time, finding in general a correlation of about −0·54 which would be significant beyond the 0·001 level of confidence. They also found (op. cit.) a relationship between capacity to develop learning arts and Mental Age as well as finding that Mental Age determined efficiency in discrimination learning.

Cantor and Hottel (1955) have discussed various aspects of mental deficiency, including discrimination learning, in which they found that differences depending on I.Q. are significant at the 0·05 level. McCulloch, Reswick, and Weismann (1955) have studied word learning among defectives. They conclude that grasp, initial score, and gain (total score minus number of trials multiplied by first score) were related in a complex way. Score on one could be predicted only with great uncertainty on the basis of score on the other. They conclude (op. cit.):

> The results demonstrate distinctiveness of abilities for one trial learning and repetitive learning. They seem consonant with the hypothesis that intelligence tests directly measure apprehension or grasp rather than ability for repetitive learning; and carry implications that these tests are inadequate for prediction in a large segment of human behaviour.

Other studies of interest are those such as Stevenson and Iscoe (1955) as well as other researches by these authors and their colleagues on transposition and abstractive generalization. So far these data indicate that generalization is possible even where the principle involved cannot be verbalized. Annett (1957) has also applied information theory to learning among defectives. He concluded that jobs involving zero 'bits' or one 'bit' of information do not discriminate imbeciles, normals, and the feeble-minded, whereas tasks involving more 'bits' do.

An increase in interest in studies of imbecile learning seems to have commenced in about 1955. Following this year several different groups of workers began experimental studies in England and America and those in Russia continued with the work which Luria reported when he came to London in 1956. His lectures have since been published in English (1961). Among studies carried out in England, those of Clarke and Blakemore (1961) and Clarke and Cookson (1962) on transfer must be mentioned. Another group of workers in this field have recently summarized their work on speech and thought processes in imbeciles. This research of O'Connor and Hermelin (1962) refers to other studies by Mein and O'Connor (1960), Mein (1961), and unpublished studies on transfer by Bryant (1963) and Maier (1961). Lyle (1959, 1960a) in collaboration with Tizard also studied speech development in imbeciles, both mongol and non-mongol. Woodward (1960, 1961, and 1962a) has made a number of developmental studies showing how concept of number and space among others can be studied in imbeciles, making use of Piaget's methods. In America several groups of investigations are notable. Those of Cantor and Hottel (1955, 1957), House and Zeaman (1958a, b, c; 1960a and b) and Spitz and Hoats (1961) and Griffiths, Spitz, and Lipman (1959) deal with many aspects of transfer of training, concept formation, and verbal mediation of learning as well as perception. In addition, Gardner *et al.* (1959) and Spradlin *et al.* (1960) have made various studies of activity and arousal level in relation to attention in imbeciles. Another set of studies by Kirk (1962) and his colleagues are marked by their interest in patterns of performance within any one individual. Sievers (1959), in various researches, has developed an instrument called the Differential Language Facility test which aims at specifying the nature of verbal deficit in a more precise manner. In such a short section as this one can give only a brief indication of the extent of this new group of investigations.

Their general trend, however, has been to break away from the psychological tradition of the past which was to use psychometrics as a technique for classifying the defective in grades. Such studies have been far more interested in process and function and the scholastic structure of such processes which amounts to learning and problem solving. In more detail it can be said that the workers mentioned have begun to draw the outline of cognitive dysfunction in imbeciles. It is not a uniform level of handicap but shows a general structure as well as individual patterns. In the main the research seems to show that the nature of orientation to a display is important for imbecile learning rather than the process of learning itself, if the two can be separated. Transfer and recall are relatively unimpaired as processes. O'Connor and Hermelin (1962), summarizing their own and other experiments, say

> A set or expectancy of what is required by the task, may take a long time to build up, and without such a set many trials may be needed before attention is focussed on the relevant aspect of a situation or display. It is only then that proper learning commences . . . but . . . once the relevant information has been extracted from a display it is available for use in subsequent situations. Furthermore, such information, once it has been acquired, is relatively well remembered.

They point also to another deficit of the learning process in imbeciles. 'The singling out of relevant features of a stimulus display is helped by naming, labelling, and the use of verbal coding . . . such verbal coding does not frequently occur spontaneously with imbeciles.' In any motor task verbal self-instruction, to use one of Luria's terms, must be taught as carefully as the task itself.

As with other questions in this field, the ground has been cleared but the critical experiments are still awaited. See also Chapter XIII.

THE TRAINING, EDUCATION, AND TREATMENT OF DEFECTIVES

(a) Training 'intelligence' through the senses: Lockeian empiricism

Binet is often quoted to justify the view that attempts to instruct the backward and defective are wasted. Thus Kirk and Johnson (1954) quote him as criticizing his predecessors for their lack of critical faculty concerning the results of education with defectives. But Binet and Simon (1914) also believed that every effort should be made to find methods of teaching defectives. Unfortunately Binet's successors have remembered his strictures on empiricism but forgotten his injunction to teach.

Exceptions exist, however, and among them recent work by Russian (Simon, 1957) investigators is of interest. There have also been several systematic attempts to educate defectives quite apart from Seguin's early efforts at sense training. Historically these have followed the early sensationist view that sense training was training for the mind, and although sense training now has different connotations, habit training is thought of as having a direct effect on mental performance involving thinking and judgment. Binet's intelligence measures involving the discrimination of sensory points on the skin were never proved popular and do not appear in recent revisions of the test. Instead, emphasis has been placed in academic tasks in the measurement of I.Q. At this time the possibility of treatment by training began to be dropped. The influence of peripheral receptors on the central nervous system, which had been taken for granted, began to lose its importance in the eyes of educators. This meant presumably that the Nativists had triumphed over the Sensationists after more than a century of discussion.

This author does not know the exact way in which this alteration came about, but the role of Darwinism is clear in the concepts so widely accepted at the time. The manner in which the change came about is not explored in any historical survey of the psychology of the period. It has been reflected in the pages of the earlier numbers of the *Eugenics Review*, and in the genetic studies of Goddard (1912) in America. The attitude characteristic of this work was that of genetic inheritance, and the theory of inherited determination of ability. Such was the strength of this view that any possibility of an environmental influence on learning capacity or intelligence was automatically excluded.

In these circumstances the possibility of training sense and intelligence were excluded by pre-supposition. The most that could be accepted was the possibility of a connexion between intellectual dullness and sensory inefficiency. The studies of Norsworthy (1906) and a study by Pearson (1914) in the series 'Studies in National Deterioration' are examples of the way in which research at this time was directed towards showing how in mental defect all functions, both central and sensory, were affected. Thus, both Pearson and Norsworthy thought that they had found oral temperatures and intelligence to be directly correlated.

However, Norsworthy makes observations about the educability of defectives which have been forgotten (op. cit., p. 39): '. . . these figures . . . have a very definite intrinsic value. They show definitely that the feeble-minded do improve from year to year and that their improvement is no mean one.' Moreover, she argues that bodily development is not so very much worse than normal in many cases.

Thus the tendency to consider the defective trainable lost its appeal when people began to think that mental defect necessarily involved damage to the cortex or the central nervous system, which would make learning impossible or difficult. More recently, however, a point of view on the education of the backward has developed which, whilst taking account of possible neurological damage in some defectives, attempts to train them and also those in whom no damage is discernible. The basic presumption of those who follow this line of thought is that the effects of mental defect can be ameliorated, those suffering from specific disabilities alleviated, and that general education can be effective. This is clearly a sophisticated opinion compared with the naïve empiricism of the sensationists.

The techniques developed in recent years by those interested in the education of the backward take account of a number of disabilities such as 'brain injury' and specific forms of deafness and visual defect. These techniques have been dealt with by Strauss and Lehtinen (1947) so that in this section only brief reference will be made to some recent Russian work which may be unfamiliar to psychologists in the field of mental deficiency.

(b) Training in sensory deficiencies

One study of this kind is by Leontiev (1957), although similar work has also been done in America by Wyatt (1945) and others.

The author, in co-operation with Yu. B. Hippenreiter, undertook a special investigation of young people who were incapable of reproducing orally their aural perceptions (1954). For this purpose pupils were chosen who in the initial tests gave completely negative results. They not only could not reproduce orally a sound of a given pitch or short melody which they had heard, but could not even correctly 'attune' their voices to the note which was being sounded. Later experiments consisted of trying to create in these subjects a correct afferentation of the phonation of their vocal apparatus (according to pitch) by forming the essential aural-oral connexions. The given sound was produced by an electrical sound generator; the sound produced by the generator and the sound reproduced by the subject were recorded on an oscillograph.

The subject first had to attune his voice to the pitch of sounds which were fed as continuous notes into the earphones by the sound generator; after he had succeeded in consolidating this achievement, another series of experiments was begun. After the subject had begun to vocalize a sound of given pitch, the sound generator was switched off, and he continued to 'sing' independently. Finally, experiments were carried out in which the subject had to reproduce a sound of a certain pitch after an interval of up to 6 seconds after he had heard it, that is, to sing 'from memory'. The experiments concluded with attempts to train the subjects to reproduce very simple melodies. Apart from the experiments described, certain other experiments were done with the subjects which aimed at providing supplementary material for analysing the nature of the process being studied.

The authors believe that the failure to be able to reproduce pitch at the beginning of the experiment was due to the fact that a connexion had never been formed. In this respect their views closely resemble those of Lorenz (1952), Tinbergen (1951), and Thorpe (1956) concerning imprinting in animals. In other words, a skill not learned at a particular stage of development is acquired later only with difficulty or with the aid of special techniques.

(c) Filling gaps in learning techniques

Children's mastery of arithmetic is shown to depend on the 'mastering of external actions with objects'. Galperin, Davidov, and Morosova are quoted by Leontiev (1957). They worked with the handling of geometrical material by children. The children first moved geometrical masses, then followed such movements with their eyes. The process of increasing remoteness is then continued by giving the child the experience of describing perceived movements in words and finally in sub-vocal speech. Speeding up of external handling at this stage results in shortening of mental connexions and processes. This kind of training has been shown to involve a number of steps, no one of which may be excluded without resulting in a deficiency of competence in the activity concerned. Leontiev remarks that in a complex process, later stages may be carried out by more primitive methods, when a link in the developmental chain is omitted. In such cases re-learning or re-conditioning may be necessary. These examples emphasize, as might many others, the need for omitting no stage in a learning process and moreover of following a definite organized curriculum. The work shows also the developmental approach to objectivity which Piaget's work stresses.

(d) The role of words in learning

Luria, who did such interesting work with students, neurotics, murderers, aphasics, and imbeciles (1932) during the early years of the Soviet régime, has continued his experiments with backward and normal children. In a recent article (1957) he reports some work of Zaporozhets and also of Paramonova, showing the slow development of inhibition in children of 2 years of age. The children were asked to respond to a red light by pressing a button, but they were unable to inhibit a similar response to all other forms of light signal.

> It is characteristic that even the detailed verbal statement, 'Press the red light only, do not press the green one', does not produce any lasting effect, and even if the child gives one or two correct responses at the beginning, a series of positive signals will make him begin to react to all signals, and the inhibition evoked by the verbal instruction disappears. But if, on the other hand, we give the child one or two positive signals and then a series of inhibitory signals, irradiation of inhibition takes place; this temporarily destroys the reflex evoked by the instruction, and the child stops pressing for any signals at all, whether negative or positive.
>
> Characteristically, the verbal instruction is still retained by the child; even at the end of the experiment he finds no difficulty in repeating what he had to do; but he neither carries out the instruction nor even mentions in his report the mistakes he has admitted to making.
>
> In just a few cases irradiation of the stimulatory or inhibitory process is so great that towards the end of the experiment the child begins to misinterpret the instruction and, pressing the button to every signal one after the other, declares that that was what he had to do.

The quotation indicates the nature of the process and may also illustrate a difficulty of prime importance in the education of the backward, namely, the difficulty in establishing connexions between verbal instructions and the manipulation of concrete material.

If this difficulty of connexion forming is so important, the question arises in what way the connexion-forming process can be aided. Luria comments,

> The simplest method for these purposes . . . is to bring the spoken order nearer to the direct signal. . . . By continually accompanying every direct signal by the command 'Press' or 'Do not press', it is possible to dispense with the necessity of subjecting one's movements to connexions previously established in the verbal system.

Speech reinforcement of this kind can be made quite stable after 2 or 3 positive and 3 or 4 negative reinforcements.

Leontiev has this to say about pathological conditions of the cortex (1957):

> If in normal conditions this stable interaction is early established between the direct and verbal systems, and if it subsequently remains fairly stable, it may still collapse sharply in severe pathological conditions of the brain (as has been shown in the work of N. A. Filippichevaya, A. M. Meshcheriakov, and M. P. Ivanova); while in the abnormal development of a backward child it is established only with the greatest difficulty and by no means completely.
>
> This is why the anomalous or mentally retarded child, even though to all appearances possessing good speech, may manifest profound defects in his voluntary activity. It is also why the study of the breakdown conditions of the direct and verbal systems and of the means of bringing about their joint work, may become the key to the understanding of important mechanisms of anomalous development.

Leontiev is not hopeful that any easy solution will be found to the tendency of the defective to reduce spoken accounts to 'inert verbal stereotypes'. The tendency stands in the way of generalization which is basic to learning. However, any re-education must take account of the shortcomings outlined.

In most of the Russian work, the importance of speech is emphasized. Sometimes the very possibility of a process of voluntary organization is thought to depend on an intention or plan of action reflected in speech. Liublinskaia (1957) has stressed this in studies of children's capacity to discriminate between striped and spotted shapes. Discrimination was very imprecise before the patterns were characterized by such descriptive words as 'dots, spots, waves, etc.' When they were thus characterized accuracy increased immediately. Liublinskaia notes that 'Results obtained in experiments with the control group entirely confirm the dependence of this reorganization of perceptual differentiation on the introduction of language.' Liublinskaia proceeds to discuss material which adds considerably to the import of these findings, but which is not necessarily relevant to the backward child.

(e) Direction of attention and problem solution

One other example of an attempt to examine the function and role of different activities in defectives and backward children has been provided by Leontiev (1954). The experiment consisted simply of noting two things: the state of preparation for the solution of a problem, and the state of motivation for the solution of a problem.

For example, the problem might be the drawing of 3 continuous straight lines through 4 points set out in the corners of an imaginary square. The solution indicated in one possible form in the diagram was offered only when certain conditions were simultaneously fulfilled, i.e. when motivation was aroused but not either fatigued or satiated, and when practice on similar material had first been given.

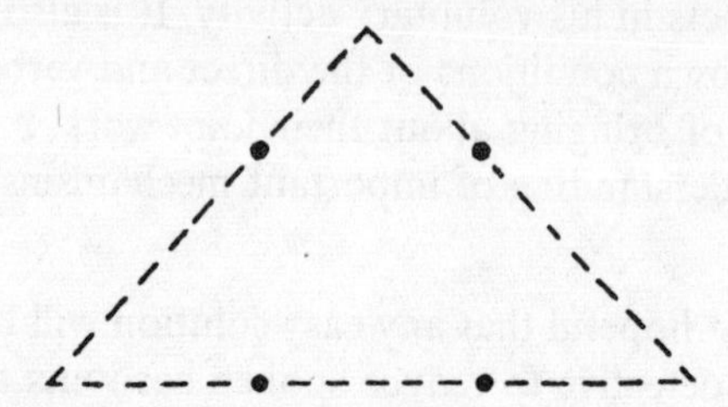

When motivation or preparatory training was absent or inadequate, solutions did not occur.

The above examples each provide an instance of the way in which attempts are being made to overcome the learning problems of the backward. No doubt many others could be adduced from other sources, but these seem to show a regard for theory and critical appraisal of results which is so valuable in a field where, in the past, pessimism has characterized the little research which has been undertaken. At present the return to such research gives hope that it will yield more fruitful results than are revealed by a survey of the literature in the first fifty years of this century.

A section on the education of the retarded may seem one-sided in referring only to Russian work. However, until the last year or so, very little strictly pedagogical research with defectives has been attempted in England, apart from well-known researches by Burt, Duncan and Schonell. This, and the rarity of acquaintance with the investigation, explains its presence here. Other investigations of great interest such as that of Inhelder (1943) in Switzerland, and the Iowa studies, are excellent descriptive studies which for the most part do not have a pedagogical aim. Some American research mentioned in the previous section is only in its early stages, and for this reason the very interesting and suggestive character of the studies described here determines their inclusion in a chapter concerned with learning among the backward.

Chapter IX

BRAIN DAMAGE AND MENTAL DEFECT

by N. O'Connor

INTRODUCTION

Interest in brain damage dates back to neurological concern with speech disturbance, following Broca's (1861) observation and Hughlings Jackson's (1932) attempt to order neurological functions theoretically. Both these workers, among others, were primarily interested in the location of lesions whether cortical or subcortical, and with their effects on mental and physical functioning.

From such early work grew concepts of localization and attempts to diagnose the site of injuries by neurological signs. However, even in such work as Head's (1926) which added considerably to neuroanatomical knowledge, some indications of a more general effect of lesions were apparent. More precisely, even the early investigations showed the development of two general lines of approach, that of Gall (1835) in favour of extreme localization of function, and that of Flourens (1824) in favour of localization of some functions, but making higher function independent of any particular part of the cerebrum.

A similar dichotomy has arisen in more recent psychological studies; in these, however, between the theories which take the same positions as the neurological theories, lies an intermediate one. Of these three viewpoints, the Associationist and the Field theories correspond to our earlier division and the intermediate position is taken by the so-called Regional Equipotentiality theory. These will be discussed more fully in the next section.

In the field of mental deficiency, research has tended to follow different lines. Thus investigators always attempted to localize lesions and describe the conditions associated with clinical symptoms, but as destruction was frequently gross, early descriptions tended to be general. More recently, psychologists examining defectives with milder forms of backwardness believed that they had found signs of cortical dysfunction corresponding to disturbance originally noticed by Field theory exponents such as Goldstein and Scheerer (1941). Strauss and Lehtinen (1947) therefore describe a condition which corresponds with Field theory, whilst the traditional pathological studies might with some looseness be described as localization theories. However, in mental deficiency practice, pathologists have not so far tried to associate location of lesion with specific dysfunction. The two disciplines, pathology and psychology, deal in general with two distinct classes of mental defect, imbecility and idiocy on the one hand, and feeble-mindedness on the other (with, of course, some overlap). In the latter, obvious damage is rare, in the former, i.e. in imbecility and idiocy, it is common. What is generally referred to as the problem of Brain Damage in Mental Defect is in fact the problem of some damage in the brain of a feeble-minded person which may result therefore in some anomalies of performance or behaviour. It is these anomalies for which special educational treatment has been recommended by the exponents of this concept of brain injury.

THEORIES OF BRAIN FUNCTION AND ORGANIZATION

B. Tizard (1957) and Meyer (1957) have discussed theories of brain functioning and organization. As these have been mentioned in the previous section, it may help to put later discussions in perspective if some more detailed consideration of these theories is given here. In addition, it is felt that every reader should be made aware of one important fact in this field. The concept of brain injury or brain damage as used by psychologists or neurologists working in mental deficiency is a term which suggests that some people are brain injured and others are not. If gross injury is meant, this is of course true, but pathologists would agree that most adult brains show minor abnormalities. This statement is based on autopsies on subjects who have not been diagnosed as abnormal during life, yet found to have some minor neuropathological anomaly. In some cases quite gross injuries have been found, which apparently had no discernible effect on behaviour. The inference from this observation might be that there is not *necessarily* a very close correspondence between neurological injury and higher nervous function.

The three main types of psychological theories of brain function are summarized by Meyer (1957). He describes '*Associationism or anatomical theory*' as a strict localization theory. Evidence arises from the study of aphasics and from electrical stimulation of the cortex. Connexionist theories of learning are associated with this neurological theory. Presumably some parts of Pavlovian theory would be considered Associationist.

The second, *Field theory or theory of equipotentiality*, has been advanced by Goldstein (1939) and Lashley. It holds that higher nervous function is not localized, although specific sensory input is localized. The study of aphasic patients led Goldstein to the view that their symptoms are a function of a general disorder, for example the inability to grasp abstract concepts. These views are held to correspond to Gestalt, pattern formation views of learning.

The third view, the *Regional equipotentiality or functional equivalence theory*, accepts limited localization with learning taking place by modification of synapses. However, it also assumes that complex processes involve the functioning of the brain as a whole. Evidence both for and against each of these general views can be presented and Meyer (1957) suggests that despite more sophisticated terminology the basic problem remains. In subsequent work, Meyer (1959) suggests that the results of surgery with 25 cases provides 'strong support for regional equipotentiality of brain functioning'. There was no clear relation between results and the extent of the operation.

However, current theory and test results are still indecisive. Before looking at studies of brain damage in mental deficiency let us therefore consider some of the more general investigations into the psychological effects of brain injury.

PSYCHOLOGICAL INVESTIGATIONS OF BRAIN INJURY

(a) Measures of brain damage

(i) *Some general tests*

So many of these tests exist that, as we are primarily concerned with investigations of mental defectives, it will be desirable to shorten our discussion of tests in general by referring to recent descriptive summaries such as those of Yates (1954b) and Shapiro (1951, 1952, 1953, 1954). A review of reported literature indicates that the tests are either qualitative or quantitative, involving higher functions such as learning and problem solving, or simpler forms of perception. Most of them are methodologically poor and many have inadequate and unstandardized scoring systems. Yates (1954b) observes 'It is doubtful whether any aspect of psychological testing has been more inadequately treated than the diagnostic assessment of brain damage.'

Goldstein and Scheerer (1941) developed a series of well-known tests involving the copying of block designs. As these were developed before methodology was far advanced, no subsequent standardization is available, although Shapiro (op. cit.) has provided detailed experimental material concerning one aspect. Moreover, as Yates indicates, Boyd (1949) has shown that intelligence may be as important in determining test scores as presence or absence of brain injury. Some studies have given contradictory results with comparison of brain-injured and other groups.

Experiments involving sorting of objects or blocks or the copying of blocks are those of Halstead (1947), who claims discrimination of normal and frontal lobe injury cases on an object-sorting test, and Grassi (1953), who discriminated organic and non-organic cases with no overlap on a simple and complex block copying task. Halstead's (1947) larger battery is considered later. These tests may appear to offer a satisfactory clinical instrument in themselves. However, they are subject to the criticisms which can be made of all measures of brain damage and which are given at the end of this section.

Assessments such as the Hunt–Minnesota (1943) involving a vocabulary test, a word-design test of brain damage as well as others, have not been validated on repetition by Armitage (1946), and others who have shown that normal-pathological overlap of scores is considerable. The Shipley-Hartford Retreat Scale (1940, 1941), with its two subsections, vocabulary and problem-solving, can be criticized for the same reason. Furthermore, both scales have in common the shortcoming that verbal tests cannot be guaranteed to give an infallible measure of native intelligence. Yates (1954b) refers to several studies which criticize the actual standardization of this test. Criticisms concerning tests of native intelligence have been thought to apply to the Wechsler Deterioration Index. Thus Gutman (1950), Allen (1947), Rogers (1950), and others on large numbers of subjects do not report favourably on this index, derived from subtests of the Wechsler test.

Among the earliest Rorschach workers to put forward criteria descriptive of intracranial organic pathology was Piotrowski (1937, 1938, and 1940), who described ten signs which he believed differentiated those with cortical and subcortical pathology from other patients:

1. Conceptual impoverishment: number of responses not more than 15.
2. A high percentage of poor form responses: F+ per cent. below 70 per cent.
3. An average response time of more than a minute.
4. Lack of human movement: not more than one M response.
5. Number of Popular responses below 25 per cent. if less than 25 responses.
6. Colour naming.
7. Repetition or perseveration: dominance of the stimulus object, rather than control from within.
8. Impotence: recognition by the patient of the inadequacy of his responses, but inability to withdraw them.
9. Perplexity: a constant need for reassurance from the examiner, sometimes leading to a dependence on his judgment.
10. Automatic phrases: frequent use of a pet phrase or expression in an indiscriminate fashion.

Ross (1941) investigated the diagnostic validity of these signs and found that while 55 per cent. of the patients with cortical and subcortical lesions showed five or more signs, these were also present in the records of patients in other clinical groups, including 30 per cent. of those with non-cortical lesions of the central nervous system, 20 per cent. of psychotics and 14 per cent. of neurotics.

Hughes (1948, 1950), on the basis of a factor analysis of 22 Rorschach signs of cerebral damage mentioned in the literature, evolved a scale of 14 to each of which he gave a weighted score. By using this system of scoring the signs, Hughes found that 82 per cent. of patients with intracranial organic pathology had an index of 7 or more, while only 1 per cent. of non-organic clinical cases were falsely classified as organics.

The work of Diers and Brown (1951) has, however, cast serious doubt on the validity of the Hughes signs in differential diagnosis, and Yates (1954) in a detailed summary of published work on some of the psychological tests of brain damage concludes: 'That the Rorschach offers distinct promise in this problem cannot be denied; that it has been shown to be a satisfactory test of brain damage is open to question.'

The majority of these studies have not included groups of mental defectives and it should be remembered that several of the signs said to be characteristic of brain-damaged patients are also commonly found in the records of the feeble-minded in whom organic pathology is not suspected.

Of well-known clinical tools, the Halstead Impairment Index (1947) must be mentioned. This battery is specialized in so far as it discriminates frontal lobe injury rather than brain damage in general. The most successful of the sub-tests is the Halstead Category test. Others in the battery are a flicker-fusion test, a modification of the Seguin formboard, Seashore's musical test, a simple mechanical speed test, a memory for time test, and a speech sound, perception test. The Category test measures capacity to 'abstract' or classify. This battery seems well validated. If the patient is known to be organic, the scale enables the clinician to say with some certainty whether or not the lesion is in the frontal lobes.

More recently other indices of organic impairment have been developed. A series of well-conducted investigations due to Shapiro (1951a, 1952, 1953, 1954) on perceptual anomalies of the rotation of copied block designs have led to the validation of this measure. The rotation effect has been studied in great detail by Shapiro and his colleagues and is thought to be diagnostic of brain injury. In its most recent form this instrument is objectively scored, and allowance is made for sex, age, and intelligence. With the Halstead Battery and Halstead's Category test it seems to provide a rare example of consistent results. It also fulfils stringent methodological criteria. Shapiro *et al.* (1962) have recently added further information on rotation and modified Shapiro's original interpretation. They say 'it was concluded that . . . visual field defects and "oculo-motor" defects' were 'sufficient causes of rotation' not 'a generalized increase in strength of inhibitory processes in brain damaged subjects'. These findings and new interpretation are consistent with Teuber's (1959) views on visual field defects.

Other measures recently developed are the Trail Making and Patch tests due to Armitage (1946), the Graham and Kendall (1946) Memory for Designs, the Symbol Arrangements of Kahn (1951, 1955) and the Price and Deabler (1955) Spiral After-effect. Evidence for the

Trail Making test, of ability to link up several points on a figure, suggests that it is capable of fair discrimination. Misclassifications are of the order of 21 per cent. The Patch test, a pattern-making test, appears to have somewhat poorer discrimination. The Graham and Kendall (1946) test seems to be subjective in its scoring, but none the less is relatively well validated. The Memory test of Kahn seems to need further study, although it gives discriminations significant at the 0·001 level. The Spiral After-effect is not yet developed to a stage where it could be regarded as a reliable clinical instrument, although some promising results on mental defectives have been reported.

In the last four years further tests have appeared often with ambiguous results. These new measures have tended to take account of cortical structure and function. Thus Heibrun (1956) has developed a test sensitive to lateralization of lesions. Left-sided lesions on this tend to show lower verbal scores. And whilst Werner and Weir (1956) and Wahler (1956) maintain the classical views about figure-ground confusion and visual retention, others like Walker (1956) criticize them. But 1956 seems to represent the high point of the undifferentiated 'brain injury' hypotheses. After this, tests changed in character. Bensberg and Cantor (1957) discussed the effect of brain injury on simple and complex reaction times. Siegel (1957) examined visual–verbal concept formations, and Sievers (1959) and Sievers and Rosenberg (1960) developed a differential language facility test.

This section would be incomplete without some reference to the work of Teuber and his colleagues. Weinstein and Teuber (1957) showed that lesions of the parietal and temporal areas of the left hemisphere affected intelligence test scores whereas lesions of the frontal and occipital lobes did not. In a discussion involving Holmes, Teuber, and Weinstein (1958), Holmes maintained that Teuber's and Weinstein's work established brain localization; Teuber and Weinstein, on the other hand, said their work showed consistently that brain injuries in man tend to produce both specific and general alterations. This point was further discussed by Teuber and Liebert (1958).

(ii) *Criticism of the tests*

Apart from the methodological shortcomings of the tests mentioned, such as inadequate diagnostic controls, controls for age and inadequate standardization, theoretical uncertainties affect them. Thus the theory of 'brain damage' as a unitary phenomenon with a common effect is found alongside theories of localization. An adequate explanatory theory of brain damage must therefore be formulated before tests can be developed to a more advanced stage. It would be fair to comment, whatever the merits of the measures discussed above, that rather few psychological tests of brain damage are yet at that stage of refinement where they provide an instrument which can assist the neurologist.

Other criticisms could be made concerning the localization of injury, the age at which it occurs, and the difference between damage due to diseases such as encephalitis and to injury, and the slight correspondence between site and extent of injury and behaviour. However, as this chapter is concerned primarily with brain injury in mental defectives, it is considered that this section should be confined to descriptions of some measures and the criticisms which apply to them. The level of development of research in this field is obviously unsatisfactory, and the phenomena are not well understood. As Meyer (1957) points out, individual differences in anatomical structure have been reported, as well as differences in brain size and brain weight. Functional impairment may therefore differ from person to person, even though, for example, surgical operations are apparently identical in nature and extent. Children and adults differ in their responses to damage, children showing more diffuse effects (Klebanoff, 1945) and also better recovery. Thus it seems likely that anatomical structure on the one hand and psychological structure on the other do not necessarily show a one-to-one correspondence in any simple way. Meyer (1957) analyses many other similar strictures on a simple interpretation of cortical localization of psychological function. The research concerning brain injury among mental defectives is in need of an equally strict appraisal.

(b) Tests of brain damage with mental defectives

(i) *Introduction*

Brain damage among defectives has come to mean not gross pathology but relatively slight damage in feeble-minded defectives which may have detectable consequences in behaviour. This usage which was mentioned above has been current largely in the last 20 years. The term frequently used has been Brain Injury, but in general the term means all kinds of damage to the brain. Strauss and Lehtinen (1947) define the brain-injured child as follows (op. cit., p. 4):

> A brain-injured child is a child who before, during, or after birth has received an injury to or suffered an infection of the brain. As a result of such organic impairment, defects of the neuromotor system may be present or absent; however, such a child may show disturbances in perception, thinking, or emotional behaviour, either separately or in combination. These disturbances can be demonstrated by specific tests. These disturbances prevent or impede a normal learning process.

This definition might appear to include imbeciles and in some experiments they are involved, but the emphasis is on those of feeble-minded grade. It is thus important to appreciate in evaluating the work of Strauss that it is mainly about the brain-injured child of relatively high I.Q. and not about the low-grade defective. He remarks (1951, op. cit., p. 116):

> We do not wish to conclude this chapter without answering some of the questions which often arise.
>
> One concerns the differential diagnosis between malformation of the brain, a developmental defect of brain substance, and the acquired defect of brain injury. Children with malformation of the brain usually show gross motor disturbances. They show definite brain defects on the pneumo-encephalogram, and they do not show the slight behaviour abnormalities of the brain-injured child either in regard to mental development (they belong quasi-exclusively to the group of imbeciles and idiots) or with respect to the slight deviations of emotional behaviour as described. . . .

It is thus apparent that Strauss's whole book is about patients above I.Q. 50, perhaps about those of normal I.Q., and an entirely different approach would appear to be indicated in the case of those defectives who are known to suffer from brain damage due to malformations. Many of these fall under one or another well-known clinical heading. They are thus not necessarily brain-injured in the sense in which it is used by Strauss and Lehtinen (1947) and Strauss and Kephart (1955). In their books, causes of brain injury are listed as follows: premature birth, caesarian birth, dry birth, precipitate delivery, eclampsia, pelvic malformation, antepartum haemorrhage, anomalies in presentation, twisting of umbilical cord, use of forceps, improper use of anaesthetic, infectious diseases during early months (e.g. whooping cough, measles, scarlet fever, pneumonia), encephalitis and meningitis, concussion, and finally the sequelae of Rh blood incompatibility. This is a very comprehensive list and it does not include the developmental abnormalities such as microgyria. But the neurological signs mentioned in connexion with this list are none the less found with such abnormalities.

To test the presence of brain damage associated with mental defect two main groups of studies have been carried out. These are studies of verbal-performance ratios on tests of intelligence and studies of the perception of patterning of figure and ground. In Strauss's experiments it is shown that brain injury involves a tendency to anomalies of attention. The studies of verbal versus nonverbal performance on intelligence tests appear as a somewhat separate group not necessarily explained in this way. This is also true of the isolated motor performance investigations of Heath (1944).

(ii) *Studies of verbal versus performance quotients*

These studies have been carried out extensively with the Wechsler–Bellevue Intelligence Scale, but also with other measures. Thus, in a paper by Strauss (1939) the relationship between Performance score and Binet Mental Age was shown to be related to supposed endogenous or exogenous origin of defect. Results showed that the endogenous pattern was to have performance scores higher than M.A. However, in a careful study by Sarason and Sarason (1946) a group of 'garden variety' mental defectives were given an E.E.G. examination and a neurological examination. Every attempt was made to exclude exogenous defect and yet the group was divided on the basis of Kohs versus Binet, performance versus verbal ability. Two groups were formed, one with Kohs results 18 months on test in advance of Binet and one with Binet 18 months in advance of Kohs. A third group consisted of the remainder. The first two groups were compared on Binet items and E.E.G. score and Rorschach. The Kohs-below-Binet group did worse on diamond drawing, paper cutting, and memory for designs. An abnormal E.E.G. was shown by 9 of the 15 members of this group (60 per cent.) and by 2 of the 11 in the Kohs-above-Binet group (18 per cent.). Sarason (1953) believes that this combination of findings may suggest that a verbal performance ratio could be diagnostic of brain injury even in cases of apparently endogenous mental deficiency when no clinical neurological signs are present. However, the same author is aware from his own work with Potter (1950) that the same kind of test pattern may be diagnostic of social maladjustment in the presumed absence of brain injury. A single diagnostic group may thus appear to be divided into two on the basis of verbal–non-verbal ratios. This is an example of the lack of correspondence between neurological tests and psychological tests. It is in fact an example of that lack of a one-to-one relationship between anatomical and psychological diagnosis which has been mentioned earlier. Such findings are complemented by those in which two groups, differentiated by neurological signs, none the less overlap on psychological tests.

Among work of this kind that of Hoakley and Frazeur (1945) may be mentioned. Their results, although presented tentatively, seem to justify the conclusion that scores on subtests of the Binet test or Arthur Point Scale show no differences between the brain-injured and the familial defective matched for age and I.Q. On only one test in the Arthur Point Scale did differences appear significant. This was on the Timed Score on the Mare and Foal subtest where great variability was found but mean scores were not sufficiently different to achieve really high levels of significance. In the case of the Binet test only the Diamond provided a significant difference between the groups, although of course the Binet includes a number of examples of visuo-motor tests. It is also interesting to note that in the many subtests involved so few differences could be found between brain-injured and non-brain-injured cases.

Among others who have examined this question have been Allen (1947) and Blake *et al.* (1948). These authors found that the index proposed by Allen and based on Verbal Performance ratios on the Bellevue–Wechsler, resulted in the brain-injured scoring higher on the verbal than on the performance scale. This is not the usual direction of results. However, Blake (1948), commenting on Allen's work, notes overlap despite a statistically significant difference between the groups. Allen (1947) also carried out a study which he claimed showed that the brain-injured and the brain-diseased were very similar in their verbal performance ratios, although the brain-injured showed slightly more marked discrepancies. This investigation is important because it is the only one which compares brain injury and more generalized damage such as that which often characterizes the lower grades of mental deficiency. It differs in its conclusions from Strauss's hypothesis outlined in the previous section.

One of the reasons why such test ratios do not provide good diagnostic differentials may be because of the composition of the subtests within them. The arrangement of such measures may overvalue speed of psycho-motor performance or alternatively overvalue the part verbal organization plays in the solution of 'performance' problems. In the chapter on learning among defectives (Chapter VIII) it was pointed out that defectives have been frequently found to have higher performance quotients than verbal quotients. However, so many variables enter into these comparisons that critical experiments have not yet been carried out. As Sarason (1953) suggests, defectives are a very heterogeneous group, differing in length of stay in hospital, in home background, and in many other psychological and social characteristics in such a way that failure to control such variables might be partly responsible for the failure to find clear-cut test patterns in exogenous and endogenous groups.

No doubt this problem can be seen in terms of the three theories set out in an earlier section. It would be surprising, for example, if damage to the cortex did not sometimes result in damage to speech areas rather than areas involved in some kinds of psycho-motor tasks, or in perception and vice versa. Either kind of damage could be concomitant with a general cortical effect or could take place independently of such an effect.

The relationship with theories of cortical function needs further discussion. However, it becomes clear from an examination of the material summarized in this section that it is impossible to state definitely that a syndrome of 'brain injury' has been isolated by the tests discussed. It seems unlikely that the variety of possible injuries would make it probable that any one test or symptom alone would be diagnostic.

(iii) *Tests of perceptual disturbance*

Although nearly all studies of brain damage, whether of perceptual disturbance, rigidity, or test pattern, are associated with ideas of disturbance of *gestalt*, this is most true of the studies conducted by Strauss. Many of these have been summarized in the two books written by Strauss and Lehtinen (1947) and Strauss and Kephart (1955). It will be convenient to refer to the first of these, which summarizes Strauss's theory and arguments in favour of his approach.

Strauss suggests that for historical reasons the problem of the brain-injured has arisen in the sphere of education following universal compulsory education. Binet and Simon (1914), Strauss observes, record the existence of three types of abnormality in children, mental defect, lack of mental balance, and a mixture of both. Strauss points out that research following Broca's discoveries and following neurosurgical advances in the First World War led to the identification of the syndrome of 'traumatic dementia'. This was thought to be marked by specific effects according to the area damaged, combined with disturbances suggesting attention to the concrete aspects of situation and disturbance of attention.

These changes, resulting from injury, obviously differed from senile dementia and some workers such as Strauss asked two questions. The first was whether injury in infancy might not give rise to a category of brain-injured children similar in some respects to brain-injured adults? The second was whether these children might differ from those classified as mentally defective in whom, at that time, defect was presumed to be due to 'familial' causes. It is to the definition of such a syndrome, the elaboration of diagnostic tests, and the delineation of an appropriate educational programme, that Strauss addresses himself.

There were of course antecedent studies. Tredgold (1952), the writer of one of the first comprehensive medical texts on mental deficiency, generally attributed a small percentage of mental deficiency to 'secondary' causes such as birth injury. Other categories such as cerebral palsy were also well known. However, brain injury in children as discussed by Strauss is primarily concerned with children who come under the definition quoted earlier in this chapter (op. cit., p. 207). The rest of his discussion is concerned either with test procedure, methodology, or education.

One of the definitive tests of brain injury used by Strauss and Lehtinen (1947) was the marble board test. As this is a characteristic test on which the psychological diagnosis of brain injury was supposed to be possible, the procedure is described here in some detail. The marble board is a set of two identical grey boards with depressions of a darker colour. The boards are 11 inches square and contain ten rows of ten holes each. The vertical distances between the centres of the holes is 1 inch and the diameters $\frac{3}{8}$ inch. Black and red marbles of about $\frac{1}{2}$-inch diameter may be placed in each hole. One board is the Experimenter's Board on which he sets up patterns with marbles which the subject is then asked to copy. The manner in which the designs are copied is regarded as discriminating between brain-injured and normal performances. Each subject's procedure can be recorded. Designs set out in Strauss and Lehtinen (op. cit.) are geometrical, involving triangles, squares, and one pattern of irregular figures. The authors think that three types of performance are possible, an outstandingly good visuo-motor performance which they call constructive, a second type which may characterize immature or incomplete development which they call global, and a type characteristic of brain injury which they call incoherent.

The supposed reason for the brain-injured performance is that those so handicapped become distracted by the background of the board and so cannot follow the pattern of the marbles. The argument was reinforced by carrying out an experiment in perception. Sketches drawn against a figured background were exposed tachistoscopically for one-fifth of a second. The brain-injured children saw background, defective non-brain-injured and normal children saw the imbedded figures and not the background.

This is the main phenomenon described by Strauss and Lehtinen (1947) and Strauss and Kephart (1955), but other workers have noted a variety of other phenomena which appeared to be connected with brain injury and its effect on perception.

Other tests are described in Strauss and Kephart (op. cit.) and in previously published articles. These, very briefly, are measures of flicker fusion threshold, Stanford–Binet Scale and Wechsler Intelligence Scale for children, Goodenough Draw a Man test and the Porteus Mazes. Other tests mentioned by them are the marble board and memory for designs, based on Kohs blocks. As we have mentioned all of these with the exception of the Goodenough and Porteus Mazes, it only remains to say that those tests are not yet adequately validated as diagnostic of brain injury. One other, the Ellis Vinel Designs, is described in Strauss and Kephart (op. cit.) This was designed by F. W. Ellis and described by Healy, Bronner, *et al.* (1932). It consists of ten geometric figures presented briefly for subsequent reproduction. According to S. Goldenberg in Strauss and Kephart, the misclassification is about 48 per cent. of the brain-injured and 4 per cent. of the normal on a cut-off chosen by Cassel (1949b). The figure does not justify a confident use of this measure.

Very few of the test instruments described above can be said to be capable of standing alone in cases of disputed diagnosis. Strauss and Lehtinen's (1947), however, contains the basic materials which, with the articles to which it refers, constitutes the findings on which their argument is based. One of these articles is of great interest because it contains Strauss's (1941) attempt to outline the essentials of a neurological examination of children of a feeble-minded level of intelligence. Similar material is also contained in the book. Strauss finds that neurological signs, mostly pyramidal, increase in proportion to the decrease in I.Q. by 10-point steps: 'If the group is distributed according to 10-point I.Q. classifications between 50 and 80, the higher the I.Q. classification the lower the incidence of neurological signs.'

Strauss is obliged to take the view that there are three main difficulties in the neurological examination of mentally defective children:

'1. Incompleteness of the child's history.
2. Imperfectness of our knowledge of development neurology.
3. Lack of a standardized short scheme for neurological examination in mentally defective children.'

He presents his own scheme, but this is, of course, subject to confirmation. It is important to notice that, in his imperfectly validated neurological criteria in a 'mixed' group of feeble-minded subjects, 84 per cent. had neurological signs as compared with 70 per cent. in those with a history of brain damage or disease. Both however had signs, whereas none of the endogenous showed signs. In this brief clinical investigation no methodological controls are mentioned. This is unfortunate because it is necessary to check on the possibility of contamination in such experiments where the nature of inference from such signs is uncertain because of the unreliability of the signs themselves.

In many instances of mental deficiency we are dealing with unknown causation which may be neurological or social, or both. In the case of idiots and many imbeciles there may be little doubt, but in the case of the feeble-minded there may be many uncertainties. Unlike the early research of Goldstein (1939), who was working with brain-injured normals after the First World War, there is no guarantee of pathology. For this reason it is desirable to be cautious in arriving at a designation of brain injury, lest thought disturbances and emotional disturbances, sometimes attributed to brain injury, may be due to other causes.

However, one fact, it has been claimed, has reached a reasonable level of certainty; this is the relationship between cortical damage and partial or more complete impairment. Thus Strauss and Lehtinen (1947) mention a negative correlation between intelligence and brain damage. O'Connor (1953) and O'Connor and Haritos (1953) carried out two controlled experiments. The first was with two feeble-minded groups matched for intelligence and varying from I.Q. 50 to I.Q. 105 in the Wechsler–Bellevue Scale. In this case, irrespective of known brain injury, the relationship between I.Q. and marble board performance was found to be 0·7 ($P = < 0{\cdot}01$) in the case of the brain-injured group and not significantly different in the case of the group in whom no known pathology existed. As a result of this investigation a further study was conducted with two groups; one imbecile ($N = 15$) and one a group of normal children ($N = 15$). The groups were matched for mental age, but naturally differed in chronological age. I.Q. was measured and performance on the marble board scored objectively. Strauss's patterns were used in the experiment and Binet I.Q.s. given to each.

It was decided to test the null hypothesis and three hypotheses were therefore considered:

(i) that there is no difference in 'jumping scores' between brain-injured and normal subjects. That is, the brain-injured do not stop and restart in different parts of the design more than do normals;
(ii) that differences in 'jumping scores' are due to intelligence levels rather than brain injury;
(iii) that difference in error scores are related to mental age.

Mental age ranged from 5 to 7 years in both groups, chronological age from 9 to 22 years in the case of the brain-injured group and from 5 years to 7 years with the normal group. Average errors and average restarts were analysed in a two-way analysis of variance to test the effects of mental age against brain injury. In the case of the restart score neither factor was significant but mental age approached significance. In the case of the error scores Mental Age was a significant contributor to the score differences, $F = 10{\cdot}09$, $P = 0{\cdot}001$, and brain injury was also relevant but to a lesser degree, $F = 4{\cdot}64$, $P = 0{\cdot}05$. On the basis of the first analysis of variance between groups for restart scores the null hypothesis was established in relation to brain injury and normality and over the mental age range used in the experiment. For error scores, mental level was shown to be considerably more relevant than the existence or absence of brain injury. Therefore in this experiment the peculiarities of brain injury do not stand out, although the patients had suffered severe damage.

So far as the effects of brain injury are concerned, therefore, the null hypothesis is indicated by these results.

Logically the inference might be drawn from these investigations, assuming the brain pathology of the imbecile groups (which in this case was guaranteed by the hospital pathologist on the basis of previous post-mortems in similar patients), that performance on this test is dependent on intelligence level rather than brain injury. In another study, Yates (1954) found correlations of −0·60 between intelligence and rotation of designs in Shapiro's data for brain-damaged groups, and a corresponding correlation of −0·55 for a control group of normal subjects. Tizard (1957), with brain-damaged patients, found an insignificant correlation of −0·39 between rotation and I.Q., but she proceeds to account for the statistical insignificance of her findings in terms of the attenuation of I.Q. range in her sample.

These results, amongst others, therefore suggest that no clear conclusions can be drawn in diagnosing brain injury by the use of figure ground tests of the kind used by Strauss. Obviously in cases where there are clear-cut neurological signs perceptual disturbances may occur. However, the phenomenon is not inevitable as Strauss and Lehtinen (op. cit., p. 104) say: 'We therefore conclude that, whereas the presence of a severe visuo-motor disturbance is strongly indicative of brain injury, the fact of brain injury does not guarantee a visuo-motor disturbance.'

Such a difficulty applies of course not only to one type of test but to any test in which specific receptor apparatus (which may be damaged) is involved. Some more recent studies such as those of Betty Hunt (1959) reflect the need for attention to localization of injury in trying to take account of its effects. Thus the copying of two-dimensional designs in three dimensions is more affected in children with visuo-motor brain injuries than in children with brain injuries affecting their auditory function.

(iv) *Miscellaneous tests of brain injury*

Tests of brain injury used with defectives apart from those already described, have been few. Most notable perhaps has been the Rail Walking Test of Heath (1944). Heath's purpose was to discriminate those in the army who could be trained to an adequate level of motor co-ordination. His test consists of 3 rails of different lengths and widths, i.e. 9 feet by 4 inches, 9 feet by 2 inches, and 6 feet by 1 inch, along which subjects are asked to walk heel and toe in their stockings. Heath claims that the exogenous cases are significantly more clumsy. However, the neurological status of his groups is not impeccable.

One other set of studies – those of Werner and Thuma (1942) on flicker fusion with endogenous and exogenous defectives – should be noted. They also carried out studies of the perception of apparent movement, with the two groups. The exogenous group saw the lines as separate in the apparent motion test at a speed sufficient to give the illusion of movement with the endogenous group. The exogenous group also had a lower fusion frequency than the endogenous group.

The results are explained in terms of a perseverative after-effect of stimuli when controlling cortical inhibition of lower centres is reduced as a result of injury.

METHODOLOGICAL CONSIDERATIONS AFFECTING TESTS OF BRAIN INJURY

Examination of the criteria set out in many studies of brain damage shows that these sometimes tend to be circular. When validating a diagnosis of brain injury in retrospect, for example, it may transpire that neurological signs, E.E.G., and pneumo-encephalogram are indecisive. In such circumstances, when histories are also of doubtful reliability, it is clearly methodologically unsound to base diagnoses on psychological tests. However, Strauss and Lehtinen seem to argue (op. cit., p. 112) that the presence of perceptual anomalies may be taken as evidence of damage even in the absence of the three primary criteria, neurological signs, a history of injury, and mental retardation. This seems unacceptable to this author in view of the poor discriminating capacity of most tests and because of their unreliability.

In addition, it is obvious that theoretical issues have not been clarified to the point where the effects of brain injuries of different locations and extents and at different ages of the patient can be assessed adequately. Mention has already been made of the failure to present results from control groups in describing Yates's (1954) observations. Such controls should be matched and account taken of a level of intelligence as well as age. These points have frequently been made by critics of brain injury studies and have been recently summarized by Meyer (1957) and Wortis (1956).

Another point made by Meyer is that if the cortex has several levels of function, injury may have different effects in so far as it alters functioning in one or more of these levels. This is, of course, the basic question of the organization of the cortex which was discussed in terms of these theories in the second section of this chapter. Meyer, returning to this question at the end of his article, suggests that, just as some writers consider that intelligence is hierarchically organized, so brain mechanism may be arranged on a similar pattern. Hughlings Jackson (1931) was, of course, of this opinion.

The point being raised is again the same question, namely, that of wholistic or departmental functioning. To solve it Meyer recommends the following procedure:

> Thus the first proper question to be answered is to what extent the brain functioning is 'unitary', and to what extent 'departmental'. This could be achieved by a study on a large scale which would include a representative sample of brain-damaged patients and a sample of the normal population. The total brain-damaged sample would have to be sub-divided according to the locus of lesion (anterior, central, posterior), by lobe injured (frontal, parietal, temporal, occipital), by involvement of one or both hemispheres (unilateral, bilateral), and by laterality of lesion (right, left). A large battery of tests should be selected including those tests which are known to be measures of well-defined orectic and cognitive factors. The results should be submitted for statistical analysis; the performance of each of these subgroups should be analysed in relation to those of the controls, and of a complementary subgroup consisting, in each case, of the remainder of the brain-damaged group. Such a study should provide a clear-cut answer to the problem of 'generality' versus 'specificity'.
>
> The next step would be to study extensively and intensively each significant association between factors and loci of injury, controlling for all the relevant variables, with the ultimate aim of clarifying the significance of each association, including the neurological mechanisms responsible for the positive and negative properties of functions.
>
> Similar studies should be conducted on children of various age levels with the purpose of defining the nature of developmental aspects of brain organization and functioning.

Most recent studies such as those of Meyer (1959) himself and Holmes, Teuber, and Weinstein (1958) would seem to suggest that steps have begun to be taken to implement this programme. Results indicate both local and general effects of cortical lesions.

Much research remains to be done, however, and individual differences in this area of research present so many problems that at the present juncture it is proper to advise caution. No adequate theory and no adequate test of the relationship between brain injuries and behavioural abnormalities exists. In fact, in evaluating the extensive wartime and post-war work on brain injury, and relating it to defect, we must conclude that much of the fairly elaborate edifice of brain injury has been erected on somewhat shaky foundations. It would be a most regrettable event if the contribution of psychology to mental defect should have to be judged by the methodological solidarity of the investigations into brain injury. As Wortis (1956) has commented, 'There is in short, I believe, no brain-injured child, but only a variety of brain-injured children whose problems are quite varied and whose condition calls for far more refined analysis than some current generalizations on the brain-injured child provide.' [1]

Recent studies show two trends, a tendency to emphasize right–left differences, for example, Zangwill's (1960) monograph, and a willingness to reconsider localization. The author considers that a further step is necessary. The nature of lesions which cause behavioural disturbances must be compared with those which do not. Such a question is highly relevant to the question of brain injury as opposed to severe subnormality.

Fortunately, the facts of figure-ground confusion, rotation, rigidity, and concreteness seem well attested as phenomena. It is to be hoped that the concomitants of these phenomena will receive systematic attention from psychologists concerned with mental defect. These problems bear directly on the central problem of all defect, inability to use symbols in thought; in a word, inability to abstract. They are therefore problems of prime importance not only to brain-injured, but to all backward children. Undoubtedly the most creditable aspect of this work is the attempt made by Strauss and Lehtinen to provide an educational system for the children they have studied. Gallagher (1960) has now developed a more systematic tutoring curriculum with brain-injured mentally retarded children.

[1] Chapter X deals with cerebral palsy, one aspect of brain damage.

Chapter X

CEREBRAL PALSY AND MENTAL DEFECT

by Elspeth Stephen

INTRODUCTION

Of recent years increasing interest has been shown in cerebral palsy both in this country and in America. Although Little first described a case of spastic paralysis (or Little's disease) in 1862, it is probably true that the intensive work in this field dates from the 1930's. Since then, there have been a large number of articles written on all aspects of the subject and a corresponding development of services for the cerebral palsied.

At first, the interest in cerebral palsy was mainly medical. In 1930, however, Lord published an account of her pioneer work and since then psychologists have given increased attention to the subject. It is, however, worth noting that in her original study, Lord asked some of the important questions which still remain largely unanswered. She was, for example, interested in discovering a psychological method of evaluating mental status in spite of motor handicap; this is still a main problem for the psychologist.

This chapter is an attempt to review the major studies on the psychological and educational aspects of cerebral palsy. Experiments in which cerebral palsied patients have been studied in order to investigate psychological dysfunction associated with brain injury, or maldevelopment, are reviewed by O'Connor in Chapter IX, and are not included here. No attempt has been made to cover the strictly medical aspects of cerebral palsy, or to consider the literature on the ancillary medical services, such as physiotherapy, occupational therapy, and speech therapy. It is true that co-operation between the different services exists in practice, possibly in varying degrees However, although the need for team work involving a galaxy of talent drawn from many disciplines is repeatedly mentioned in the literature, studies of the results of such team work are only now beginning to appear in the journals.

Yannet (1944) defines cerebral palsy as a 'motor defect present or appearing soon after birth and dependent on pathologic abnormalities in the brain'. This definition excludes motor defects due to lesions of the spinal cord or peripheral nerves or progressive neuromuscular disease. It appears that all writers on the subject would subscribe to this wide definition.

It is generally agreed that the primary motor and sensory functions are localized, whereas the localization of the 'higher mental functions' in specific areas of the cortex is not known, if indeed it exists. From this it follows that though the motor dysfunction, and possible concomitant sensory dysfunctions, in cerebral palsy may be localized, where the damage extends beyond this it cannot be localized. The position seems to be that although the presence of motor defect may indicate damage to the motor area of the brain, in many cases neither the neurologist nor the psychologist can be certain whether it extends further, and if so, what other parts of the cortex are involved.

According to Walshe (1952) there are four main categories of motor disorder:

1. Where the pyramidal system is acting defensively or not at all.
2. That resulting from loss or impairment of the extra-pyramidal mechanisms.
3. From cerebellar lesions.
4. Where the lower motor neurone is involved.

The prevalence of cerebral palsy in school-age children is estimated as 1–2 per 1,000. This is the figure given by Asher and Schonell (1950) and by Dunsdon (1952). The New Jersey Survey in 1938 gives the prevalence as 3·8–4·8 per 1,000. However, more recent studies, Hansen in Denmark (1960) and Henderson in eastern Scotland (1961), give prevalence rates which agree with Dunsdon's rate for school children. It seems possible that discrepancies between estimates of prevalence are due to the difficulty of defining the limits, perhaps particularly in the mild cases.

CLASSIFICATION OF CEREBRAL PALSY

The classification of the cerebral palsies seems still to be in considerable confusion. Clear descriptions of the present systems of classification are given by Illingworth (1958, Chapter I) and Mitchell (in Henderson, 1961, Chapter IV). The following section gives a comparative outline of the present forms of classification.

I. Classification according to type

The three main types of cerebral palsy are the spastic, the athetoid, and the ataxic. There is also a mixed type. These types are defined according to the locus of the injury in the motor areas of the brain.

1. In spasticity the pyramidal system is involved. Spasticity is characterized by a 'clasp-knife' rigidity of the muscles and exaggerated reflexes.

2. In athetosis the lesion involves the extra-pyramidal system and basal ganglia. Wyllie (1951) comments:

> consideration of a coronal section of the brain shows it to be highly improbable that a venous vascular lesion, the commonest type, due to asphyxia or anoxia at birth, affecting the basal ganglia, could spare the internal capsule of pyramidal fibres passing between and in close connexion with the various basal masses of grey matter. . . . Functionally, athetosis is an irregular movement of muscular tonus, a release phenomenon from damage to the old brain.

Athetosis is characterized by slow worm-like writhing movements.

3. Ataxia is characterized by disturbance of balance.

Some form of spasticity is the most frequently found type in all surveys, otherwise there seems to be considerable variation between the incidences of the main types as noted by the different workers. It seems possible that this is due to differences in diagnostic criteria. Sarason writes 'many cases show such diffuse lesions that they cannot be said to fall either entirely within or entirely outside the pyramidal tract. These diffuse cases are by far the majority and there are few which can definitely be described as pure spasticity or pure athetosis.' This is also Wallin's (1949) point of view. At present there seems no adequate explanation of the fact that there are apparently so many more athetoids in America than in Great Britain.

TABLE 14

Distribution of cerebral palsy by type
(adapted from Dunsdon, 1952)

Study	Date	Percentages			
		Athetoid	Spastic	Mixed athetoid and spastic	Ataxic rigidity, etc.
Brockway (U.S.A.)	1936	8		92	
McIntire (U.S.A.)	1938	36	36	5	23
Phelps (U.S.A.)	1940	40	40	3	17
Phelps (U.S.A.)	1942	40	40		20
Phelps (U.S.A.)	1942	45	40		15
Dunsdon (England and Wales)					
a. Diagnostic selection	1952	13		81	6
b. Special inquiry areas	1952	7·8		82·7	9·5

TABLE 15[1]

Incidence of cerebral palsy by type

	Athetoid	Spastic	Mixed athetoid and spastic	Other
Asher and Schonell (1950), 349 cases of congenital C.P. in children	10%	83%	5%	1·9%
New Jersey Survey, Hopkins, Bice, and Colton (1951), 1,406 cases	23·6%	45·1%	3·4%	26·9%
Hansen (1960), Denmark, 2,621 patients	9·3%	78·5%	4·6%	7·6%
Henderson, Eastern Scotland (1961), 240 cases	11·7%	77·1%	9·6%	1·6%
Crothers and Paine (1959), 406 cases		64·6%	13·1%	22%

[1] In a number of the quoted Tables it will be noted that the percentages given by the various authors do not always total 100.

The relative number of spastics and athetoids is important for psychologists and educationists if, as some writers seem to assume, they form separate groups with regard to certain psychological or educational characteristics.

II. Classification according to number of limbs involved

Some authorities apply this principle of classification mainly to spastics; others, for example Wyllie, Dunsdon, Bice, and Hopkins, apply it to all types of cerebral palsy. Wyllie (1951) suggests the following classification:

1. Congenital symmetrical diplegia (bilateral symmetrical paralysis, most common in lower limbs).
2. Congenital paraplegia; this is a mild form of 1. in which the legs only are involved.
3. Quadriplegia or bilateral hemiplegia, greater disturbance in arms than legs.
4. Triplegia, three limbs involved; a very rare condition.
5. Hemiplegia, both limbs on one side involved.
6. Monoplegia, one limb affected; very rare.

'With additional qualifications of (*a*) spasticity, (*b*) flaccidity, (*c*) mixed types, (*d*) athetosis, (*e*) ataxy.'

It seems to the writer that this implies a continuum of motor

TABLE 16

Percentage incidence found in main types of cerebral palsy

(from Dunsdon, 1952)

Area and sample	Quadri-plegia	Hemi-plegia	Para-plegia	Other	Total
I. Brockway (1936), California, 1,000 cases	32	41	26	1	100
II. McIntire, New Jersey (1938), 146 cases	67	17	14	2	100
III. England and Wales (1948–49), 3,701 cases (British Council for the Welfare of Spastics and National Foundation for Educational Research)	26	46	28		100
IV. England, special school candidates, Dunsdon, 474 cases	59	14	27		100

TABLE 16a

Three recent surveys

	Spastic mono-plegia	Para-plegia	Hemi-plegia	Di-plegia	Tetra-plegia
Hansen (1960), 2,057 spastic patients (78·5% of 2,621 C.P. patients)	4·3%	14·5%	41·9%	21·0%	18·3%
Henderson (1961), of 240 C.P. patients	5%	12·1%	37%	Tri-plegia 3·8%	19·2%
Crothers and Paines (1959), 406 patients	0·4%	2·8%	40·5%	1·9%	19·0%

disturbance, rather than clearly defined types. The concept of a continuum does offer a possible explanation for the apparent discrepancies between the incidence of each class quoted by different workers in Tables 16 and 17.

Dunsdon (op. cit.), in her review of the surveys, uses the terms hemiplegia, paraplegia, and quadriplegia.

Perlstein (1957) considers that hemiplegics comprise one-third of all cerebral palsies. Dunsdon thinks that the greater incidence of quadriplegics in the 1938 New Jersey Survey and among her special school candidates is due to necessarily biased sampling. In both groups the children referred were the more severely handicapped.

Table 16 gives the results of the 1951 New Jersey Survey, one of the most extensive made in America. In the two more recent European surveys, Hansen and Henderson were concerned with all the cerebral palsied patients in their areas within clearly defined age groups. Hansen's sample consisted of all patients with cerebral palsy in Denmark who were born in the years 1925–53. Henderson's sample included all patients with cerebral palsy under the age of 21 whose parents were domiciled in the Eastern Region of Scotland on 31 March 1955. In a third survey Crothers and Paine were concerned with patients referred to their clinic and therefore not necessarily representative of all cerebral palsy patients. The latter is particularly interesting as it is a follow-up study (Table 16a).

TABLE 17

Incidence by sub-types in the New Jersey Study, 1951

(after Cruickshank and Raus, 1955, Chapter I)

Sub-type	Spastic						Athetoid						Rigidity					
	Boys	%	Girls	%	Total	%	Boys	%	Girls	%	Total	%	Boys	%	Girls	%	Total	%
Quadriplegia	99	26·4	61	22·5	160	24·8	172	89·5	120	85·1	292	87·6	51	53·1	37	45·6	88	49·7
Triplegia	32	8·8	23	8·1	55	8·5	1	0·5	1	0·7	2	0·6	2	2·0	5	6·1	7	3·9
R. hemiplegia	94	25·1	63	23·2	157	24·3	8	4·1	12	8·5	20	6·0	26	27·0	17	20·9	43	24·2
L. hemiplegia	82	21·9	60	22·1	142	21·8	8	4·1	7	4·9	15	4·5	15	15·6	15	18·5	30	16·9
Paraplegia	63	16·8	61	22·1	124	19·2	2	1·0	1	0·7	3	0·9	2	2·0	7	8·6	9	5·0
Monoplegia	4	0·1	3	1·1	7	0·5	1	0·5			1	0·4						
Totals	374		271		645		192		141		333		96		81		177	

III. Classification according to time of onset (ante-natal, natal, or post-natal)

One would expect this to be an important area of research. Several workers, including Wallin (1949) and Wyllie (1951), have suggested that ante-natally acquired cerebral palsy is more likely to be associated with general mental defect than natally or post-natally acquired cerebral palsy. There seems to be little work reported on this subject, possibly because of the difficulty of distinguishing between ante-natal, natal, or early post-natal cerebral palsy. Perlstein (1957) states that only 10 per cent. of cerebral palsy is post-natally acquired, while nearly one-third of spastic hemiplegia is post-natal in origin. Wyllie (op. cit.) gives a clear account of this problem.

IV. Classification according to degree of involvement

Schonell (1956) classifies her sample of 340 cerebral palsied children as slightly handicapped, 87 (25 per cent.); moderately handicapped, 148 (44 per cent.); severely handicapped, 85 (25 per cent.); very severely handicapped, 20 (6 per cent.). Her descriptions of each category appear to involve subjective judgments of the severity of the total handicap for each child, involving sensory as well as motor dysfunction. Mitchell (Henderson, 1961) classified his sample of 227 patients under the age of 21 as mildly handicapped, 97 (42·7 per cent.); moderately handicapped, 79 (34·8 per cent.); and severely handicapped, 51 (22·5 per cent.). Mitchell makes the point that the large number of mildly handicapped cases in his series is mainly due to the fact that the majority of cases of hemiplegia, the commonest form of cerebral palsy, fall into this category. Hansen classifies his patients in terms of six grades relating to motor disability, but these grades are also defined in terms of self-help – approximately 64 per cent. of his sample were able to look after themselves with regard to daily living functions. What seems to emerge from these classifications is the need to assess total handicap in relation to placement. From these figures it appears that about 60 per cent. of cerebral palsy patients are probably independent for daily living functions. In Hansen's sample 3·6 per cent. were completely helpless.

V. Classification according to the extent and nature of the brain damage; or according to the presence and importance of concomitant sensory defects

Many workers have noted that in cerebral palsy the damage may be confined to the motor area or it may be more widespread, perhaps involving the sensory cortex or the higher centres. It seems impossible at present to discriminate between these groups with either psychological or neurological tests. It is, however, conceivable that from the point of view of brain damage, the cerebral palsied may not be a homogeneous group, or, in other words, there is as yet no clear evidence indicating how they are homogeneous. However, we know that patients with cerebral palsy are brain damaged, also that about 50 per cent. have I.Q.s below 70, and therefore it seems reasonable to infer that as a group they tend to be intellectually damaged, even allowing for the associated handicaps from which they tend to suffer. Now there is evidence, in a recent study (Wedell, 1960), indicating that two sub-groups of cerebral palsied children, the bilateral and the left-sided spastic groups, show a specific perceptual disability compared with other groups of cerebral palsied children, and to a group of non brain injured children, matched for all relevant variables. Another suggestive finding was that motor and visual handicap had slight effect on perceptual ability. Further investigation of sub-groups, such as this, seems one of the most fruitful lines to pursue at present.

Workers have noted the number of cerebral palsied children who have various sensory defects. This was a necessary first step, but now more detailed studies are being carried out on cerebral palsied children with associated sensory defects. Johnson Abercrombie (1960) has studied eye movements in relation to perception in a group of cerebral palsied children. These more detailed studies, by describing the particular concomitant disabilities, should lead to more effective treatment.

The impression left by this attempt to consider methods of classifying the cerebral palsied is one of some confusion, but the situation is becoming clearer as more information is added by further surveys of total populations (Hansen, 1960; Henderson, 1961; and Woods, 1957); studies of specific aspects (Wedell, 1960; Abercrombie, 1960), and follow-up studies (Crothers and Paine, 1959).

AETIOLOGY

Wyllie writes

> infantile cerebral palsy covers a wide variety of clinical forms and underlying them a far greater number of aetiological factors. There is no uniformity of gross anatomy of the brain or in histology for the different clinical types. The infantile brain in its response to abnormal growth has a limited range of expression (1951, p. 125).

He adds that a survey of causes contributory to infantile cerebral palsy must include pre-natal, natal, and post-natal factors. He makes the point that it is difficult, in some cases, to distinguish between natal and post-natal causation in early infancy. 'Most activities of the new born infant depend on reflex pathways in the brain-stem and spinal cord and signs of pyramidal involvement of a higher level take a variable time to appear' (op. cit., p. 151).

In this short chapter it is only possible to mention the views and findings mainly of the psychologists on this subject. Hansen (op. cit.), Mitchell (Henderson, op. cit.) give full and interesting analyses of the aetiological factors found in their samples, as does Ingram (1964).

Sarason (op. cit.) comments on the increasing tendency to discount factors of birth as primary in the causation of cerebral palsy, 'One reason being the increasing caution with which birth histories are evaluated.' He goes on to say that in many cases of cerebral palsy, where the motor defect is very severe, there have been no indications of a difficult or complicated birth, also 'the anatomical defects and malformations found in many cases of cerebral palsy are not of the type that one would expect as a result of birth injuries. Difficult labour may be the result of malformation rather than vice versa.' Sarason states that recent studies of cerebral palsy among the mentally deficient have indicated that:

1. the average age of the mother at the birth of the cerebral palsied child is significantly greater than that found in the general population;

2. there is no significant difference between the percentage af affected children who were first-born and the percentage expected on the basis of chance selection;

3. in families of cerebral palsied children where there is more than one child, there is a slight tendency for another sibling to have a similar condition;

4. the incidence of mental deficiency among the non-affected siblings seems to be greater than in the general population;

5. cerebral palsy cases in which a definite history compatible with the diagnosis of birth trauma is present comprise approximately 10 per cent. of institutionalized cerebral palsy cases.

It is important to note that these findings apply to mentally defective cerebral palsies and might not be found in a study of cerebral palsy amongst the non-defective. One might, for example, expect to find a larger birth trauma group among non-defectives.

Dunsdon (op cit.) found that 66 per cent. of 327 cerebral palsied children were first-born. She gives the birth order of the cerebral palsied types as follows:

	1st Pregnancy
Athetoid	75%
Spastic	64%
Others	64%

It has been argued that first pregnancies tend to be associated more often than succeeding ones with difficult labour and therefore possible birth injury. It seems interesting that although 66 per cent. of Dunsdon's group were first-born, in only 14 per cent. was there a history of birth injury. A possible difficulty in estimating the incidence of birth injuries may be that we have no reliable or valid measures, and slight cases may be missed. A continuum theory of brain damage implies that all brains are more or less 'damaged'.

Other abnormal features associated with the birth of 190 cerebral palsied children and noted by Dunsdon are:

Prematurity	39%
Instrumental delivery	30%
Birth injury	14%
Jaundice	19%
Asphyxia	40%
Convulsions	20%

Sarason sums up the present position –

> it has been recognized that no single aetiological factor accounts for all cases of cerebral palsy. . . . If one were to consider only those cases which all workers consider *not* to be due to birth injury, he would have to conclude, on the basis of the available evidence, that the aetiological factors are unknown.

On the aetiology of athetosis Asher and Schonell (1950) found that in their series of 400 cases of cerebral palsy among children, the evidence suggested that athetosis is usually the result of birth injury, asphyxia, or neo-natal jaundice. Wyllie (op. cit.) also believes that the commonest type of athetosis is due to a venous vascular lesion, caused by asphyxia or anoxia at birth, and affecting the basal ganglia. 'Uncomplicated cases of athetosis with extra pyramidal rigidity occasionally occur among cerebral palsies and may be due to rhesus incompatibility, rare survivors of kernicterus.' Cruickshank and Raus (1955), after discussing the 1951 New Jersey Survey, say 'the genetic component appears to be another variable in the galaxy of problems related to cerebral palsy'. The 1951 New Jersey Survey contains much valuable information on possible aetiological factors, and Cruickshank and Raus (op. cit.) give an excellent summary.

INTELLIGENCE AND CEREBRAL PALSY

Sarason (op. cit.) summarizes the earlier American researches as follows:

> In a study of 50 cases, Smith (1926) found 22 per cent. normal, 16 per cent. morons, 40 per cent. imbeciles, and 22 per cent. idiots. Schroeder (1929) reported that 66 per cent. of 146 children classified as cerebral palsied were mentally retarded. . . . McIntire (1938) reported that 26 per cent. of his series of 143 cases were mentally defective.

There is considerable variation in the incidence of mental deficiency reported in these studies. Greater reliance can perhaps be placed on the following figures from more comprehensive and recent surveys. It should be noted that in the 1951 New Jersey Survey (Table 18) 15 per cent. of the total group were found to be untestable; also that Hansen (op. cit.) based his classification of intelligence on 'a general evaluation, in which intelligence measurements have been of assistance in only a minor number of cases'.

These studies agree in indicating that approximately 48 per cent. of cerebral palsied children, who are testable, have I.Q.s below 70. This finding is in line with the conclusions of Bice and Cruickshank (1955) in their detailed comparison of the major American and English surveys.

The two facts which emerge are (1) that amongst cerebral palsied children, an unduly high proportion are mentally defective on

TABLE 18

Recent studies of the intelligence of patients with cerebral palsy

English reports

1. *Dunsdon* (1952): 916 children (selected areas and special school candidates)

I.Q.s	Under 55	55–69	70–84	85–99	100–114	115–129	130 plus
%	35	23·6	17·2	15·5	6·2	2·0	0·05

2. *Schonell* (1956): Of 354 cases over the age of 3 years, 51 per cent. had I.Q.s over 70, 23 per cent. had I.Q.s between 50 and 69.

3. *Floyer* (1955): Liverpool survey, 75·5 per cent. had I.Q.s below 85.

4. *Cockburn* (Henderson, 1961): 223 C.P. patients in eastern Scotland aged 14 months to 21 years.

I.Q.s	under 70	70.99	100 plus
%	48·4	33·7	17·9

American and Danish studies

1. *New Jersey:* 1,000 cases, 1951, taken from Cruickshank and Raus (1955)

I.Q.s	0–49	50–69	70–89	90–109	110–129	130 and above
%	28·4	20·4	22·7	21·6	5·3	1·6

2. *Denmark:* Hansen (1960): Classification of 2,621 patients according to intelligence.

Classification	%
Estimated normally intelligent	47·7%
Presumably retarded (observation for mental retardation)	9·4%
Retarded, hardly mentally defective	11·0%
Feeble-minded	9·8%
Imbecile	10·3%
Idiots	7·0%
Classification as to intelligence uncertain	4·8%

intelligence tests, usually the Binet, and (2) that 40–50 per cent. of cerebral palsied children are not mentally defective. This could suggest that in relation to general intelligence the cerebral palsied are a fairly heterogeneous group. Mental deficiency may occur more frequently among the cerebral palsied than among the normal population because cerebral palsy tends to be associated with damage to, or maldevelopment of, other parts of the brain than the motor cortex.

INCIDENCE OF MENTAL DEFICIENCY AND TYPES OF CEREBRAL PALSY

It has been stated by several authors that in athetosis, intelligence is relatively unaffected because the damage is to the basal ganglia and is therefore subcortical. This seems to have been a fairly widely held view in America. However, in England, Schonell, and in America, Hopkins, Bice, and Colton (1954) in their 1951 New Jersey Survey, found there was no difference between the mean I.Q.s of athetoids and spastics. Dunsdon supports this finding. Among 104 athetoid children, she found that 49·9 per cent. had I.Q.s below 70. The more recent surveys in Denmark and eastern Scotland are in line with this.

Schonell (1956) in the following useful Table (19) gives the means and standard deviations of the estimated I.Q.s of 340 children grouped according to the form of cerebral palsy.

TABLE 19

I.Q.s according to type of cerebral palsy

Type Schonell (1956)	Spastic	Athetoid	Ataxic	Mixed
Mean I.Q.	67·9	67·6	62·3	62·4
S.D.	27·7	25·5	19·3	21·5
N	277	41	4	18
Not yet assessable	9	4	—	1
Cockburn: Eastern Scotland (1961)	**All spastics**	**Spastic tetraplegias**	**Spastic except tetraplegias**	**Athetoids**
Number	177	51	126	19
Average I.Q.	66·7	35·4	78·9	77·4

TABLE 20*

Intelligence and extent of handicap (number of limbs involved)

(from Schonell, 1956)

	L. hemi-plegia	R. hemi-plegia	Paraplegia	Quadriplegia
Mean I.Q.	77·9	76·8	74·3	50·2
S.D	20·1	26·0	23·6	27·6
N	41	57	85	80
Not yet assessable	1	2	2	4

* This Table is confined to pure spastics

Schonell's Table (20) suggests that in terms of general intelligence, as measured by the Binet, there is no significant difference between the two main forms of cerebral palsy. The mean I.Q.s for all types seem to be significantly lower than that for the normal population. Cockburn's table is of interest because it illustrates a point, emphasized by the tables which follow. She writes 'the most clear-cut finding is that the spastic tetraplegics who were the most extensively handicapped among the spastics, tended to be of lower intelligence than any other sub-group of the cerebral palsied'.

Tables 20 and 21 both appear to indicate a highly significant tendency for the quadriplegics to be less intelligent than either the hemiplegics or paraplegics.

These tables also indicate a correlation between the extent of handicap and mental subnormality. The average I.Q. of all spastics may be the same as the average I.Q. of all athetoids in recent surveys because, as Hansen points out, the hemiplegics comprise one-third of the spastic group. In his sample 60·8 per cent. of the hemiplegics were normally intelligent.

Cerebral dominance and I.Q.

Assuming that the left hemisphere is the dominant one for most people, it has been hypothesized by several workers that right (R) hemiplegics and quadriplegics would tend to be less intelligent than left (L) hemiplegics. McIntire's (1947) findings in the New Jersey Survey, 1938, tend to support this hypothesis. From 800 cases, he

TABLE 21

Per cent. incidence (these are likely to be severely handicapped)
(from Dunsdon, special school applicants)

	I.Q. under 55	I.Q. 55–69	I.Q. 70–84	I.Q. 85–99	I.Q. 100–114	I.Q. 115–129	I.Q. 130 plus
Quadriplegia, %	30·3	10·7	9·6	5·6	1·5	1·3 Total 59·6	0·6
Hemiplegia, %	3·9	4·1	3·4	1·5	0·6	0·2 Total 13·7	0
Paraplegia, %	10·0	6·2	4·1	4·3	1·5	0·4 Total 26·7	0·2
All, %	44·2	21·0	17·1	11·4	3·6	1·9 Total 100	0·8

selected 287 who fulfilled the following conditions: (1) spastic hemiplegics or quadriplegics, (2) the result of cerebral lesion, (3) mental diagnosis being available. This resulted in a group of 97 (R) hemiplegics and 77 (L) hemiplegics. Of the former, 70 per cent., and of the latter, 29 per cent., were mentally defective. The difference between these (R) and (L) types seems significant but they may have been very severely handicapped spastics, and thus not truly representative of the spastic population. In the 1951 New Jersey Survey, the mean I.Q. of the (R) hemiplegics was significantly lower than that of the (L) hemiplegics. However, numbers were small (Cruickshank and Raus, op. cit.). Crothers and Paine (op. cit.) found that patients with (L) hemiplegia were slightly more intelligent than patients with right hemiplegia.

Conflicting evidence comes from Perlstein and Hood (1957), Woods (op. cit.), and Schonell. Perlstein from his study of 334 infantile spastic hemiplegics found that the laterality of involvement did not seem of much significance in relation to intelligence. He says himself that his sample was not representative of all spastics. Schonell's figures, Table 20, support Perlstein's findings. Woods comments that from her figures the (L) hemiplegics tend to show a lower I.Q. rating than the (R) hemiplegics.

It does not seem possible to draw any firm conclusions from these studies, and this is an area in which further work is needed.

INCIDENCE OF CEREBRAL PALSY AMONGST MENTAL DEFECTIVES

Although there appears to be a widespread belief that many of the cerebral palsied are wrongfully detained in hospitals for the mentally subnormal, there seems little, if any, published evidence to support this. Remarkably little research seems to have been undertaken on the incidence of cerebral palsy among defectives. Kirman (1960) writes:

> The proportion of cerebral palsied cases in mental deficiency institutions will be less than 9·5 per cent. of the whole or some 6,000 in England and Wales – even less information is available about mental defectives under supervision and/or in hospital. It may be that there are some 7,000 further cases of cerebral palsy among mental defectives in the community, making a total of 13,000. Further elucidation is very necessary as this estimate is little better than guess work.

In their excellent chapter on 'The Physically Handicapped Child', Hilliard and Kirman (1957) emphasize the frequent association between mental and physical handicap. They write 'The same anatomical abnormality of the brain which gives rise to mental defect may also produce cerebral palsy or epilepsy, two conditions which frequently complicate mental deficiency.' They stress the need to diagnose physical handicap in cases of mental defect only on very clear evidence, because of the 'special educational and occupational problems which it implies'. It is now recognized that patients with mental and physical handicap represent a long-term hard-core problem on the borderland between several branches of medicine, education, and social welfare. Hilliard and Kirman define the problem in relation to children and mental deficiency by describing three main groups of children:

1. Children in whom the physical defect is the main problem.
2. Trainable imbeciles with double defect.
3. Idiocy associated with other defects.

The first group they describe as wrongly diagnosed as mentally deficient. From the point of view of cerebral palsy it would include (*a*) children in whom the physical defect exaggerates the apparent mental defect, (*b*) children with an undetected sensory defect such as deafness in athetosis, masking an average intelligence, and (*c*) cases where the physical handicapping is so widespread that it makes education and training impossible even if intelligence is within the normal range, as in some spastic quadriplegics and athetoids with gross impairment of speech and manual ability.

The second group, the trainable imbeciles, they say is fairly common, and although the presence of a double defect makes training difficult 'it is sometimes possible to get gratifying results' (cf. Quibell, Stephen, and Whatley, 1961). In the third group, the idiots, the mental defect is the main deficit and the physical defect may merely complicate the nursing problem.

Hilliard and Kirman also make the important point that the larger group of educationally subnormal children tend to have more physical defects than normal children, and in relation to cerebral palsy this is confirmed by all the major surveys of intelligence. This is of great importance because it does seem that it is now being increasingly recognized that all methods of treatment have a useful part to play in the habilitation of educationally subnormal and imbecile children with cerebral palsy.

Of the cerebral palsied patients in a Mental Deficiency Hospital for children, Crome (in Hilliard and Kirman, 1957) writes:

> Experience at the Fountain Hospital suggests that in the majority of patients with cerebral palsy and mental deficiency, birth injury can be excluded by scrutiny of the history and the morphological findings.
>
> It is sometimes possible to relate the type of palsy to the distribution of lesions. Thus hemiplegia may be associated with hemiatrophy, lobar atrophy, porencephaly, or microgyria in the contralateral cerebral hemisphere. But the second hemispheres are seldom entirely spared in mental defectives. Usually they are also affected by similar, albeit slighter changes.

This is in line with the general findings in the surveys that quadriplegics tend to be the most severely mentally handicapped group amongst the cerebral palsied.

Hilliard and Kirman give the following useful table showing the incidence of cerebral palsy at the Fountain Hospital recorded over a five years' period.

TABLE 22

Form of palsy	Total		With epilepsy	
	No.	%	No.	%
Spastic diplegia	103	45	51	50
Hemiplegia	35	15	18	17
Athetosis	19	8	4	4
Ataxia	5	2	0	0
Unclassified	66	29	30	29
Total:	228		103	

From this table it appears again that spastic diplegia is the commonest form of cerebral palsy amongst mental defectives.

Doll (1933) considered that 6–10 per cent. of the mentally defective patients at Vineland had motor handicaps due to birth lesions. Kirman's (1956) figures for the Fountain Hospital in 1955 were 23 per cent. cerebral palsied. The apparent difference between these percentages may be due to differences in the intelligence level of patients, and in the implied diagnosis of cerebral palsy. Henderson (1961) points out the difficulties which may arise in connexion with cerebral palsy and mental deficiency. He writes,

> no fewer than 61 of the 301 children (20 per cent.) regarded as cases of cerebral palsy who were examined by the paediatrician were found not to have the condition. Most of these children had uncomplicated mental deficiency, their characteristic clumsiness being mistaken for cerebral palsy. No doubt the knowledge that the mentally normal child with cerebral palsy is often wrongly considered to be mentally defective and that mental deficiency is often associated with cerebral palsy had added to the confusion.

The Vineland training school probably contains a larger proportion of high-grade defectives than the Fountain, which is mainly a hospital for ineducable severely subnormal children. Kirman writes: 'in most cases the cerebral lesion is probably more gross and widespread than in those children with cerebral palsy who attend school'.

Perhaps as one goes down the scale of intelligence, brain damage becomes more diffuse and widespread and tends to be associated with general developmental anomalies, not relatively clear-cut lesions. This would seem to be supported by the general finding that spastic tetraplegics, where the lesion is presumably widespread, tend on the average to be of lower intelligence than other cerebral palsied patients.

Sarason (1953) quotes McIntire's (1938) figures of the incidence of the different types. McIntire's findings for defectives with cerebral palsy were: 29 per cent. borderline, 27 per cent. moron, 22 per cent. imbecile, and 21 per cent. idiot to the nearest per cent. There is a need for an up-to-date detailed study of mentally defective patients with cerebral palsy. Cockburn (1961) found that of 59 mentally handicapped children of school age 21 were ineducable, 11 were trainable, and 27 were educable.

ASSOCIATED DEFECTS

Sensory defects and cerebral palsy

Dunsdon (op. cit.) gives the following Table (23) of the incidence of articulatory defects amongst 500 cerebral palsied children aged 4½–14 years.

TABLE 23

Articulatory defects in cerebral palsied children

Type	No.	% Speech defects	% No speech	% Development delay
Athetoid	83	71	14	48
Ataxic	35	86	20	60
Quadriplegic	185	71	22	42
L. hemiplegic	30	37	3	30
R. hemiplegic	34	91	29	56
Paraplegic	133	39	6	26

This seems the most thorough analysis of speech defects amongst the cerebral palsied in this country. From these figures there appear to be significantly more speech anomalies amongst the (R) than the

(L) hemiplegics. On the question of delayed speech Perlstein's findings (op. cit.) appear to be different. Perlstein found that in his sample the (L) hemiplegics walked and talked slightly earlier than the (R) hemiplegics but the difference was not statistically reliable. Dunsdon attributes the greater incidence of speech anomalies amongst (R) hemiplegics to the localization of the speech areas mainly in the (L) hemisphere, the one damaged in (R) hemiplegia. It is relevant that Goodglass and Quadfasel (1954), in a review of the literature on language laterality, suggest that cerebral dominance for speech is not fully established in children up to the age of 9 years. Before this age a shift in laterality can take place easily, according to the present evidence. Therefore, it would seem that age at onset of hemiplegia must be taken into account in studies of the relationship between laterality and speech anomalies. Woods (1957) gives an interesting table of the Hearing and Speech Defects in her sample, but she was not concerned with this problem; like Dunsdon she found that athetoids and quadriplegics show a high frequency of speech defects. In this table Woods also gives the frequency of hearing defects, and this shows that while 30 out of 33 athetoids had speech defects, 12 had hearing defects.

The speech defects shown by the cerebral palsied obviously vary in severity, type and aetiology. Some may be due to the motor dysfunction itself, some may be central in origin associated with damage involving the speech areas, some may be associated with hearing loss. On the basis of the work summarized here, which is not a complete review, one can only say that many cerebral palsy cases show speech defects. The practical implications are that a large proportion may require speech therapy and, possibly, specially adapted teaching methods (see Chapter XVI). It is interesting that of 42 patients without speech in Cockburn's sample of 223 patients, 33 had I.Q.s under 50.

Visual defects

Dunsdon found that of 575 children nearly one-third had visual defects. In the 1951 New Jersey Survey 21·4 per cent. of 1,300 cases had visual defects. Douglas (Henderson, 1961, Chapter XII) gives a full account of the ophthalmological aspects of the Dundee survey. In relation to mental deficiency and cerebral palsy it is significant that he writes 'severe visual, physical, and mental handicaps are frequently found in association'.

Hearing disabilities

Mowat (Henderson, 1961, Chapter XIII) reviews the literature on hearing disabilities and cerebral palsy and gives a detailed analysis of hearing in the Dundee sample. He also writes 'the results suggest that the incidence of deafness, but not necessarily the severity varies directly with the degree of physical and mental handicap'. He believes the true incidence of deafness is probably between 20 per cent. and 25 per cent.

Epilepsy

Dunsdon found that 14 per cent. of 796 children with cerebral palsy had a history of convulsions or seizures, the greatest incidence being amongst children of low I.Q. Kirman (1956), in his study of certified defective children, reports a tendency for cases of cerebral palsy with epilepsy to be less intelligent than those without epilepsy. He found that in 265 cases of epilepsy, 37 per cent. had cerebral palsy. Floyer (1955), in her Liverpool Survey, found that 29 per cent. of children with cerebral palsy had a history of one or more seizures. In the 1951 New Jersey Survey, 29·2 per cent. had a history of seizures. Woods (op. cit., Chapter XVI) gives an interesting table showing the incidence of fits in the different types of cerebral palsy in her Bristol sample of children. The percentage incidence of fits in her whole sample was 38 per cent.

Manual defects

Manual ability is of prime importance in relation to all aspects of life, but it appears to have been somewhat neglected in the major surveys. There may be two reasons for this, (*a*) it is too obvious, (*b*) up to now the main interest has been in children rather than in adult patients; the vast majority of cerebral palsied patients have at least one hand which is normal enough to make them socially and educationally adequate as children. However, in adult life, particularly in employment, it may be that normal hand ability is more necessary, and that even a slight disability is an obstacle to full adult independence. Cockburn has studied this aspect and her findings are of considerable interest: (1) In her sample of 223 patients manual defects were more common than speech defects, only 32 patients were rated as having normal hands. (2) 179, or 80 per cent., of the patients had one hand at least that was normal or only slightly affected (they could use a pencil). (3) When severe speech and manual defects occurred together, gross mental deficiency was frequently present too.

Other defects

In cerebral palsy, it is implicitly assumed by some workers, and explicitly stated by others, that in some cases the damage extends beyond the motor areas of the brain. Therefore, in those cases, one might expect to find specific or generalized disabilities due to (1) damage to the higher centres, and (2) disabilities resulting from injury to the sensory cortex. Some hemiplegics, for example, show disturbances of sensation. Tizard *et al.* (1954) studied impairment of sensation and visual defects in 106 children with hemiplegia. Impairment of sensation was found in 50 per cent. of the cases, both in those with hemiplegia, presumably acquired at birth, and among those with brain injury, usually acquired later in childhood. The incidence of hemianopia was slightly less than 25 per cent. and hemianopia without sensory deficit was found to be very rare. The types of sensation most frequently affected were the cortically localized discriminatory faculties. The usual types of sensation tested were touch, pain, temperature, position sense, passive motion vibration, location sense, sharp-dull discrimination, two-point discrimination, and stereognosis. In his summary, Tizard says that sensory impairment is in some instances the major reason for disuse of the arm affected with hemiplegia; if present, it is important in constituting a limiting factor for the results that may be expected from physical therapy, apparatus or orthopaedic surgery. Woods (op. cit.) studied sensory defects in all the cases in her series of 301 children with cerebral palsy, except those who were too young or too backward to co-operate in testing. Sensory loss was detected in 47 cases and she writes that there was also evidence of a loss of body-image and a finger agnosia. She considers that the sensory defects were cortical in nature.

To sum up this section, undoubtedly there is a tendency for children with cerebral palsy to have more, and a wider variety of concomitant defects than one would expect to find in the general population. Although the cerebral palsied are not a homogeneous group, we are beginning to see how they can usefully be grouped for educational purposes. The first group are the severely subnormal or mentally deficient, and present evidence suggests that they will also be the most severely physically handicapped. Cockburn (op. cit.)

sums up the present position, with regard to children with cerebral palsy: 'within the group (the Dundee sample) the wide range of intelligence and of disability means that provision must be diverse and that the cerebral palsied form not one but several educational groups. On the basis of their educational needs, many can be classified with other broad categories recognized for educational purposes.' She gives the following table showing the educational classification of 133 children of school age in her sample.

TABLE 24

Educational classification (from Cockburn, 1961)

1	2	3	4	5	6	7	8
	Mentally handicapped			Blind	Deaf	Remainder	Total
	Imbecile	Trainable	Educable				
Number	21	11	27	3	1	70	133

From the point of view of mental deficiency, cerebral palsied patients will tend to be severely handicapped in other ways as well.

THE ASSESSMENT OF GENERAL INTELLIGENCE

Most authors assume the usefulness of assessing the I.Q.s of cerebral palsied children. Sarason (1953) quotes Strother (1945):

> The parent, the doctor or the teacher is interested in knowing the child's intelligence, not to satisfy idle curiosity, but to help them determine what to do for the child. The specific questions they have in mind are questions such as: Is the child able to profit from surgery or physiotherapy? Can he be taught to talk? Can he profit from education? Is he ready to enter school? . . . What special materials or methods of instruction does he need?

With the appearance of the follow-up studies the answers to some of these questions are beginning to emerge; Quibell, Stephen, and Whatley (1961), for example, have shown that some severely handicapped cerebral palsied children with I.Q.s 45–69 do respond to surgery and/or physiotherapy.

There are two questions involved in the assessment of general intelligence in the cerebral palsied. The first, with which Sarason was concerned, involves the uses of assessments of intelligence, which, in cases of severe and multiple handicap, is a matter for follow-up and experiment with treatment. The second question concerns the extent to which cerebral palsied patients can be validly tested with formal tests of intelligence, standardized on children and adults who are not cerebral palsied. It may be that, as Cockburn (op. cit.) suggests, the majority of cerebral palsied children can be adequately assessed by means of standard intelligence tests (three-quarters of her sample of children of school age were testable on a verbal intelligence test). The difficulties of applying formal intelligence tests, which follow, may occur, on the whole, in relation to a relatively small number who tend to be severely or multiply-handicapped. This is a matter for further detailed investigation, it may only be grossly true.

Since in addition to their motor handicaps, some cerebral palsied children have sensory defects, and in some cases the damage may extend to the higher thought centres, Meyer's (1957) comment on the problems involved in the testing of brain-damaged patients is relevant here. He writes:

> Psychological tests are not pure measures of abilities. . . . For this reason failure on such a test may result from the selective impairment of any one of those abilities following injuries in various regions of the brain at different levels of integration . . . The brain-damaged patient's peripheral or primary motor and sensory defects, and any behavioural aspects which might affect the performance, must be taken into account. It is just as illegitimate to give a patient a test of intelligence which is affected by his peripheral defects and conclude from low results that his intelligence has declined, as it would be to give a blind subject a visual test of intelligence and conclude that he is mentally defective from his lower score.

Lack of experience is another disability which may be associated with cerebral palsy and which may affect scores on standard intelligence tests. This lack of normal experience may be due to a necessarily restricted environment, lack of sensori-motor experience (e.g. where the hands are particularly affected), or other defects or combination of these.

Sarason (op. cit.), after commenting on the difficulty of administering standardized tests to cerebral palsy cases, makes an obvious but extremely important point. He writes, 'However, the unfeasibility of adhering to procedures standardized on normal individuals is not obviated by relying on impressions and unsystematic observations as a basis for evaluation.'

Present testing practice

Dunsdon's (1952) method was to use a standard intelligence test, the Terman–Merrill revision of the Stanford–Binet, supplemented by various performance tests. She used her own modifications of test items, where the test was obviously inappropriate. She explains this procedure:

> Thus in a discussion of only one small item of a test scale it should be clear that many factors are involved and that results based on substitution or modification of the standard form are liable to be most misleading unless they are made with full knowledge of the nature of the test, its aim as a whole, and the relative importance, for diagnostic purposes, of the various aspects of the test (op. cit., p. 37).

The assumption that even an experienced psychologist has this 'full knowledge' seems optimistic, unjustifiable at present, and likely to lead to undesirable testing practices in the opinion of the writer, but many workers in the field seem to agree with Dunsdon.

Sarason, in discussing the validity of test procedures used with cerebral palsy cases, considers McIntire's (1938) method the most valid. McIntire's study appears free of sampling errors; he made use of pre-test familiarization periods, flexible test procedures, and supplemental interviews with people knowing the patient well. The flexible test procedures, however, sound ominous.

Schonell (1956), in discussing intelligence testing, stresses the experience of the psychologist. 'Experience with the Terman–Merrill test suggests that if it is administered with understanding and interpreted with caution, a reliable estimate of intellectual potentiality may be obtained in the majority of cases' (op. cit., p. 45). No decisive evidence is offered to support this claim. In her survey, Schonell used the Terman–Merrill test, and obtained three I.Q.s; the tested I.Q. scored according to the test instructions, the modified I.Q. obtained by scoring as successes items which the psychologist judged the child would pass except for some special disability, and the estimated I.Q. She also had pre-test familiarization periods and took case histories.

Cockburn in the Dundee survey used intelligence tests with no modification to assess intellectual status and I.Q.s in working out group results though she used six broader categories for individual purposes. Woods, Hansen, Crothers, and Paine made use of intelligence tests to varying extents but this was not their only way of assessing intelligence and they grouped children in broad descriptive categories, not defined by exact I.Q. levels. In the writer's opinion the use of descriptive categories does not solve the problem of how to assess intelligence in patients with cerebral palsy. I.Q.s have the merit of being internationally understood and they apply only to intelligence. Descriptive categories, on the other hand, may vary between workers and some seem to measure education and social competence (which may depend on physical handicap) as well as intelligence. Another difficulty arises in regard to follow-up studies; then, in order to assess changes in status, it is necessary to use fine measures, such as I.Q.s, because changes in category status may mask or distort improvement.

Tests used in the assessment of general intelligence

Sarason (1953), Dunsdon (1952), Floyer (1955), and Schonell (1956) advocate the use of one of the revisions of the Stanford–Binet as the main instrument of assessing the general mental level of children with cerebral palsy, and this is the measure used in the major surveys both in England and in America. Cockburn used the Stanford–Binet with the Langan adaptation of this test for blind children; the Griffith Developmental Scale for infants and others unable to score on the Stanford–Binet; Raven's Progressive Matrices and Kohs Blocks for deaf children. In the Bristol study the psychologist tested the children on whatever test seemed appropriate. However, as they were concerned in educational placement rather than the assessment of intelligence for research purposes, they used trial periods in school to supplement intelligence testing in some cases.

It does seem that the Stanford–Binet remains the most frequently used test. Administering mainly the Terman–Merrill revision, Dunsdon believed that she could obtain reasonably accurate measures in all cases 'except one in many hundreds' (op. cit., p. 35). This is also Schonell's (1957) view. In her sample of 354 children between the ages of 3 and 15 years, she says that 340 were testable on the

Stanford–Binet. Cockburn found that verbal tests were applicable to the majority of her cases. The verbal test used for the children of school age was the Terman–Merrill revision of the Stanford–Binet. This finding may be approximately true, in relation to functioning intelligence. It seems to be one group of cerebral palsied patients, the severely mentally and physically handicapped, who tend to suffer from the clear-cut sensory and experiential defects, which make testing on the Stanford–Binet obviously invalid. However, as the distribution curve of intelligence in these patients is negatively skewed, whatever method of intellectual assessment is used, it may be that there are many patients assessed as intellectually normal, whose scores, and even their actual level of functioning, are depressed by minor degrees of handicap.

Various performance tests were used by Dunsdon and Cockburn to supplement their procedures. Holden (1952) quotes studies in which Raven's Progressive Matrices and the Ammon Full-Range Picture Vocabulary test were used. So far the results do not seem to have been very satisfactory.

It is worth noting that the assessment of intelligence in patients with cerebral palsy is dependent upon the tests available at the time, just as theories of the intellectual development and brain function of the cerebral palsied are dependent upon general theories of intelligence and brain function. One reason for using the Stanford–Binet for cerebral palsied children has been that, until the advent of the Wechsler Intelligence Scale for Children, it has been the best test. The other measures which have been used are, on the whole, of lower validity and/or reliability when used with normals.

It seems possible that, because of their many and varied concomitant handicaps, no one test will ever be the most suitable for the cerebral palsied as a group. It may be that from the point of view of intelligence testing a number of cerebral palsied children will belong to other atypical groups, such as the deaf and the blind, for whom these are appropriate tests already. Dunsdon's argument that it is legitimate to use standard tests, provided they are not obviously inappropriate, seems sound if limited to estimates of present status. She believes that tests give the measure of what is left of a child's assets, although they may not give a measure of his defects. A possible difficulty here is that one is not sure how far the impairment, whether central, peripheral, or environmental, has had a general as well as a limited effect. Therefore, although it may be possible to assess present level of functioning with sufficient accuracy for practical purposes, it may not always be possible to predict future level. For example, it would be expected that, as with other deprived groups, continued lack of experience would have a cumulatively depressing effect on intellectual status. O'Brien and Hewson (1948) found that of 20 moderately and severely handicapped children, one athetoid showed an increase of 10 points of I.Q. after intensive physiotherapy and speech therapy, but there was a general trend towards lower I.Q.s on retest among the others. Crothers and Paine (op. cit.) found that changes in estimates of intelligence on follow-up were small except in the extra-pyramidal group, where gross underestimates were made: 'This is in large measure due to the fact that five of the children were victims of kernicterus, and in the early days covered by this study we did not adequately study the hearing of these children.' Using the same data Meyer Taylor (1959) found that of a total of 214 cases, 73 per cent. were in the same category in both examinations, 15 per cent. were in a lower category and 11 per cent. were in a higher one. She also notes that 'The greatest number of cases that are higher at follow-up than at original examination occur in the group with extrapyramidal involvement.' As the method of reporting changes was in terms of categories over inevitably varying periods of time, this study cannot provide definitive information on long-term changes in intellectual level amongst cerebral palsied patients; for this carefully planned prospective studies are needed.

So far no one has shown how the cerebral palsied as a group are homogeneous with regard to intellectual functioning. Sarason (op. cit., p. 182) writes: 'In regard to the test functioning of the cerebral palsied, there does not appear to be a characteristic test pattern which differentiates them sharply from all other diagnostic or aetiological groups in which brain abnormality is present.' Two further points should be added: (1) at present psychologists have no tests which discriminate perfectly between brain-damaged and other groups, or more accurately, which measure degrees of brain damage, and (2) it seems even possible that some cerebral palsied children, when the impairment is confined to the motor areas, may be so slightly brain damaged that they are normal on this continuum. A more promising line of inquiry now seems to lie in the careful prospective studies of specifically defined defects in sub-groups of cerebral palsied patients, such as Wedell's work on perceptual ability among different types of patients (Wedell, 1960).

In the assessment of general intelligence the only procedure possible in the meantime is to consider each case in relation to the test, or tests, which seem most appropriate; to administer and score these strictly according to the instructions; and then to check the findings against the case history and school report, if available. The degree of confidence one places in the results will depend on the appropriateness of the measures used and on all the information available.

In some cases, when the test is not entirely appropriate, it may be possible to establish a useful minimum estimate of general level. The assessment of children with multiple handicaps does present, in some cases, insuperable difficulties at present. However, it seems important to recognize that when children cannot respond to standard intelligence tests because of communication difficulties of physical origin, they are unlikely to respond to standard educational methods either. This is an area calling for inventiveness and ingenuity on the part of everyone concerned with the management of cerebral palsied patients.

Specific cognitive disabilities amongst the cerebral palsied

Most workers have assumed that children with cerebral palsy will tend to show specific cognitive disabilities. O'Connor has reviewed the work in this field as it is related to theories of brain damage or dysfunction (Chapter IX). It is proposed in this section to mention briefly some of the more empirical studies, which appear to be less clearly linked to psychological theory. It should be pointed out that these studies relate to cerebral palsied children within the normal range of intelligence and not to mentally deficient children.

Floyer (1955) carried out a controlled study of the visuo-spatial ability of children with cerebral palsy. Her experimental group consisted of 36 cerebral palsied boys and 36 cerebral palsied girls. Her normal controls were matched for age, sex, and I.Q. The tests used as measures of visuo-spatial ability were form boards, block building from memory, copying simple designs from memory, and Raven's Progressive Matrices. She found that a visuo-spatial disability, as defined by a low score on these tests, was significant at the 1 per cent. level among the girls, 'less so among the boys'.

Dunsdon (op. cit.), from the work of Lord (1930) and Bender (1938), expected to find that the visuo-spatial ability of children with cerebral palsy tended to be impaired. She gave the circle drawing test and the Bender Visual Gestalt test to 35 children with cerebral palsy. Approximately 60 per cent. of these children made below normal scores as compared with the standardization groups.

Floyer (op. cit.) makes an obvious but important point in relation to visuo-spatial disabilities, which has wider application. She believes that no one knows the implications for education of specific visuo-spatial disabilities. Williams (1961) has begun to investigate the effect of emotional factors on perception and concept formation in cerebral palsied children.

Dunsdon (op. cit.) assessed verbal ability by using measures of vocabulary, verbal memory, and verbal reasoning. Two hundred cerebral palsied children were inferior on all three types of test as compared with the norms of the Terman-Merrill test (1937).

Dunsdon and Floyer showed that cerebral palsied children as a group showed visuo-spatial disabilities and verbal disabilities compared to the general population of children. Sarason summed up this situation as follows: 'Some cases have inordinate difficulty with tasks involving visuo-motor activity and others do not, some cases have a relatively high vocabulary relative to mental age and others do not' (op. cit., p. 182). However, a start has now been made in the elucidation of the problem suggested by these earlier workers: namely, which cerebral palsied children show which specific disabilities. Wedell (1960) carried out a study in which he compared four groups of cerebral palsied children and a control group of non-handicapped children, matched for age and I.Q., on several visual perceptual tests. He found that the scores of the bilateral and left spastic groups on these tests were consistently lower than those of the athetoid, right spastic, and control group. He also found that levels of performance in the visual perceptual tests increased with chronological and mental age in all groups, and motor and visual handicaps were found to have a slight effect on perceptual ability. In this study, in order to fulfil the condition of his experimental plan, Wedell selected 20 athetoids and 53 spastics from a total population of 2,000 cerebral palsied children. In a follow-up study of 36 cerebral palsied children Wedell (1961) found clear evidence of improved visual perceptual ability in all the children, and also that a large proportion of children, predominantly from the left-sided and bilateral spastic groups, did not seem to improve at the same rate as normal children. He points out that the evidence that perceptual impairment is associated with left-sided rather than right-sided spasticity is still not conclusive.

Williams (1960) carried out a small pilot study of 20 cerebral palsied children and their parents. Her findings suggested that adverse parental attitudes may interfere with the development of perceptual ability in children with cerebral palsy. Cruickshank, Bice, and Wallen (1957) in a study involving 325 cerebral palsied children and a control group of non-handicapped children, found consistently poorer responses on the part of the cerebral palsied children on certain perceptual tests; they also found that athetoids performed significantly better than spastics on certain tests, and they found developmental trends. They end their monograph: 'Thus although this study indicates impaired perception in the cerebral palsied children, there appear to be more variables involved than forced responsiveness resulting in the observed figure–ground disturbances. Further research is needed to clarify this latter issue.' A useful survey of the literature on perceptual disabilities is given by Abercrombie (1964).

Specific motor and sensory disabilities and intellectual functioning

The assessment of motor and concomitant sensory disabilities is of importance for education and training. It may indicate weakness, where special training is needed, or the need to develop other avenues of learning. Lord (1930) stated one aspect of the problem:

> If kinaesthesia is impaired, can the association areas and the silent areas be stimulated primarily through vision and audition? If the silent area is intact, can it function by means of a minimum response of sufficient stability to be recorded as an index of mental maturity?

One aspect of motor development has been studied by Dunsdon. She writes: 'Whether in later years, general intellectual backwardness is equally apparent among cerebral palsied children, whose delayed progress in early years has often been attributed solely to the effects of their motor incapacities, is a matter requiring investigation.' In 425 cases of children with cerebral palsy, whose 'sitting age' was known, she found a general positive relationship between delay in sitting and intellectual retardation. This is expressed in percentages. However, 'approximately 40 per cent. of these who later demonstrated reasonably average or better capacity were two years or more retarded in sitting balance' (op. cit., p. 22).

The concomitant handicaps shown by some cerebral palsied children, such as deafness, might also be expected to retard intellectual growth, or to affect personality development; however, at this stage, it might be more useful to investigate these disabilities in groups of children where they represent the primary dysfunction.

There do not appear to be any definitive studies entirely concerned with the relationship between manual disability and intellectual development. One would expect lack or impairment of sensorimotor experience, due to manual disability, to have a retarding or distorting effect on intellectual growth. Wedell (op. cit.) suggests that this may be so; he writes: 'Motor and visual handicap appeared to have a contributory rather than a determining effect.' One possible approach to this problem would be to follow-up children who improve in manual ability after physiotherapy. Floyer says there is no improvement in intellectual status after physiotherapy, but gives no data.

PERSONALITY DEFECTS AND CEREBRAL PALSY

Many workers stress the importance of personality factors in the study of cerebral palsy, and research has been directed mainly towards two aspects of this subject, the emotional adjustment of cerebral palsied children and the emotional adjustments of their parents. This last reflects an increased concern with parents' difficulties in the whole field of work with handicapped children. The need to study the relations between parental attitude and children's adjustment is commented on by Sarason (op. cit.) when he points out the need for a large-scale follow-up study in which it would be necessary for the psychologist to study parent–child relationships. The findings of Shere (1954) in a twin study and of Schonell (1956) emphasize this need. The pilot study by Williams, referred to earlier, is concerned with one effect of parental attitudes on one group of cerebral palsied children, i.e. that adverse parental attitudes may impede the perceptual development of children with a weakness in this area.

Emotional adjustment among cerebral palsied children

Dunsdon (op. cit.) assessed the prevalence of instability among children with cerebral palsy, using school reports as a basis. One of the difficulties for psychologists is the lack of standardized objective measures of personality traits; the use of teachers' judgments seems one of the most useful procedures at present. In a special school for cerebral palsied children, Dunsdon found that of 16 with I.Q.s below 70, only 2 seemed reasonably stable; of 50 children with I.Q.s over 70 instability was noted in 38 per cent.

Floyer (1955) also considered the frequency of instability. The characteristics of instability which she describes resemble those defined by Straus and Lehtinen (1947) as typical of the 'brain-injured' child. The criticisms made of this concept are also applicable when it is related to cerebral palsy. Floyer found that 42 per cent. of a group of 100 cerebral palsied children showed excessive emotionality, this being defined in terms of distractibility, lack of drive, tension, disinhibition, fluctuation in performance, history of fits, and perseveration. However, her procedure is not very clear. She notes that 58 per cent. did not show excessive emotionality and had apparently equal environmental strain and additional handicaps. This, she says, suggests innate factors predetermining emotionality, an interesting point of view which requires further investigation.

In contrast to Floyer, Schonell (1956) quotes Gesell (1947): 'In general temperamental characteristics are the least affected by cerebral injury. The child has an underlying individuality which makes itself manifest.' One would expect, from studies of brain-damaged adults, that the latter part of this statement at least is likely to be true. It does, however, require to be made more precise. Schonell believed that her research findings tended to confirm Gesell's point of view. Her study of the pupils at a special school for cerebral palsied children revealed that they had no innate limitations on the temperamental side, but 'it was on the acquired side of personality that there was need for help'. This is an important suggestion of the need for research on personality changes in cerebral palsied children. It may be that we are not yet ready to investigate innate and acquired characteristics; it might be more fruitful to carry out a prospective long-term study of adjustment changes in a group of cerebral palsied children. In a small unpublished study, Quibell and Stephen's findings suggest that some dull cerebral palsied boys become more maladjusted in adolescence. In their small series, adjustment did not appear to be related to response to treatment or to family background – but this requires further study; it is merely suggestive of the need for more precise research in this area. The work of O'Connor and Tizard (1956) on the employability of defectives also suggests that one might expect personality changes to occur among the cerebral palsied. They found that the selection of high-grade defectives for employment by means of psychometric tests was not practicable, one reason being that evidently changes do take place in qualities of personality. Crothers and Paine (op. cit.) describe some cases illustrative of the reactions of cerebral palsied patients and their parents to the changing demands of their environment. These authors distinguish two groups of patients, in terms of their manner of dealing with emotional problems. The first consisted of all those who developed difficulties comparable to the catastrophic reaction described by Goldstein. They were thought to have lesions in the cerebral hemisphere. The second group, those with extrapyramidal lesions, 'never, as far as we know, had disorders which resembled the catastrophic reaction. They were frequently very much disturbed, often resentful, but they never retreated into helplessness.' Schonell, like Phelps (1948), found that the following characteristics were shown by spastics: fearfulness, timidity, dislike of loud noises, fear of falling or being left alone. Athetoids tended to be extraverted, friendly, and affectionate. However, their findings appear to be based on impression, rather than systematic inquiry.

Cruickshank and Bice (1955) describe a study in which the Bender Visual Gestalt test (1938) was administered to 216 children with cerebral palsy, to determine whether the use of tests (involving different types of perceptual or conceptual abilities) could contribute to an understanding of their personality or adjustment problems. This is a promising and interesting line of inquiry, but so far they appear to be still concerned with the exploration of differences in perception between the various diagnostic groups.

Emotional adjustment amongst parents of children with cerebral palsy

Boles (1959) and Thurston (1960) have investigated the attitudes and emotional reactions of parents of cerebral palsied children. Boles in New York City compared the parental attitudes of 60 mothers of cerebral palsied children with a control group of 60 mothers of normal unhandicapped children. The two groups were carefully matched and were given a questionnaire to elicit their attitudes in relation to anxiety, guilt, protection, rejection, lack of realism towards their children, marital conflict, and social withdrawal. The results were broken down in terms of the age of the child and the religious affiliation of the mother. The only significant differences between the two groups, irrespective of religion or age of child, were that the mothers of the cerebral palsied children were more overprotective and had more marital conflict than the mothers of the normal children. An interesting finding was that the scores for anxiety, measured by the Taylor Manifest Anxiety Scale, were equally high for both groups. Their results also showed that personal, social, and cultural factors influenced maternal attitudes and that these changed with the age of the child. This is a careful, well-planned study. Thurston's work is directly relevant to this chapter, because he was concerned with the attitudes and emotional reactions of parents of institutionalized cerebral palsied retarded patients. He studied the effects of long-term institutionalization of these children on the parents by sending the Thurston Sentence Completion form to 610 parents and relatives. This form explores such areas as:

(i) personal reactions and concerns
(ii) attitudes about comfort and discomfort of patient in the institution
(iii) reactions of brothers and sisters
(iv) reactions of community, friends, and neighbours
(v) attitudes to institution and its staff
(vi) hopes and expectations for the handicapped child
(vii) general attitudes.

Of the total sample, 255, or 41·4 per cent., returned the questionnaire. The results are given in order of frequency for each area and are interesting and suggestive. One of the important findings was that on average considerable emotional disturbance remained for parents even ten years after the birth of the child and placement in an institution. This study has important implications, suggesting the need for long-term social work supporting the parents of institutionalized mentally retarded cerebral palsied patients.

Cockburn (op. cit.) studied the homes in her sample of cerebral palsied patients. She writes:

> about one quarter of the cases studied came from homes deemed unsatisfactory or unsuitable, though in most cases these homes would have been unsuitable for any child. . . . the handicap of cerebral palsy was better understood in homes of good intellectual status, and in cases where the handicapped person was older, and the handicap more severe, but acceptance of the handicap bore

little relation to the intellectual status of the home, or to the age or the degree of handicap, of the cerebral palsied person. . . . One home in five was considered to provide an unstimulating background. . . . Only 48, 31 per cent., of the cerebral palsied over 7 years of age were considered to be persons with interests.

Tizard and Grad (1961), in a sample of 60 adult defectives living at home, found that 8 had slight motor impairment and 6 severe motor impairment. They present an illustrative case of severe motor impairment in an adult defective with spastic diplegia, 'he was heavy and had to be carried to bed, washed, dressed, and kept in napkins like a baby'. He could not speak but understood speech. This indicates the total problem which the parents of severely handicapped cerebral palsied defective patients have to deal with.

EDUCATIONAL ATTAINMENTS OF CEREBRAL PALSIED CHILDREN

The findings in general indicate that cerebral palsied children tend to be educationally retarded. Dunsdon found that her group of 35 special school children were retarded in either one or both of the basic subjects, usually in both. Floyer (1955) studied educational attainment in half her sample. She found that in 38 per cent. reading attainment and mental age were nearly equivalent: 62 per cent. showed an average retardation of nearly 2 years. In arithmetic 88 per cent. showed retardation relative to mental age of 3 years on the average.

Schonell gives an interesting Table (25, below) of the reading level of 213 children, over 7 years of age, with different forms of cerebral palsy.

In a study of the attainments of left hemiplegics, right hemiplegics, paraplegics, and quadriplegics, Schonell found no statistical differences between the means of the reading ages. She also found that in her severely handicapped group 75 per cent. were non-readers. Cockburn (op. cit.) considered the educational attainments of her series in relation to their mental ability. She found that of 153 cases, aged 7 years and over, 41 had no measurable educational attainments but all these had I.Q.s of 70 and under; the remaining 112, 73 per cent., made some score on reading attainment tests but almost two-thirds, 71, scored below the level expected in relation to their ability. Cockburn says that a very small percentage of the cerebral palsied children in her series had educational attainments which would have been considered good for the average child, and that better attainment tended to be associated with higher intelligence and milder handicap.

TABLE 25

Reading level and different types of cerebral palsy

N = 213

Readers	Spastic		Athetoid		Ataxic		Mixed	
Mean reading quotient	88·7		94·5		78·0		89·5	
Standard deviation	15·7		20·46		—		15·0	
	No.	%	No.	%	No.	%	No.	%
Readers	98	56	12	43	1	50	2	25
Non-readers	77	44	16	57	1	50	6	75

What emerges is the wide range of attainment in the cerebral palsied group and the high incidence of educational retardation. Like Cockburn, Schonell found the highest incidence of non-readers came in the severely handicapped group.

Recommendations on the education and training of children with cerebral palsy

Dunsdon's recommendations are based on her study of the children in a dual-purpose school for the cerebral palsied and an estimated population of 5,300 school-age children with cerebral palsy in England and Wales. As this estimate was based on a prevalence rate of one per 1,000 and the school age population in 1948, it is likely to under-estimate the size of the present problem.

Cockburn's findings are based on a recent survey of one region of Scotland but she agrees on several important points with Dunsdon.

Both suggest that the majority of cerebral palsied children can be adequately catered for within the present system, without the provision of separate units for the cerebral palsied, which will only be needed for a relatively small number of children.

Dunsdon estimated that of the 5,300 children of school age, 50 per cent. would be able to attend ordinary schools because they were slightly handicapped. A further 20 per cent. could be absorbed in special schools either for the physically handicapped, or the educationally subnormal. This would leave 30 per cent., but many of these would be severely subnormal mentally, possibly a further 20 per cent.

Dunsdon's recommendations are worth careful study. She was concerned with the educability of cerebral palsied children, therefore she was not primarily interested in the trainability of ineducable children with cerebral palsy. In her study of the highly selected children in a dual-purpose school for the cerebral palsied, she found that the children who made a 50 per cent. rate of progress educationally were almost without exception children with I.Q.s over 85.

On the basis of her survey and of this finding she made the following recommendations: (1) Children aged 5–10 years who by reason of cerebral palsy could not be suitably placed in either ordinary or special schools, and who were not clearly mentally deficient, should attend dual-purpose schools for the cerebral palsied. In these the emphasis should be on social and motor training rather than on formal education. (2) At ten years there should be a break. She envisaged that some children would then be able to go to existing schools, others would go to training centres, and only a few with I.Q.s over 85, but unsuitable for special schools for physically handicapped children, would go to special schools for the cerebral palsied. In these schools for children aged 10–16, the emphasis would be on education rather than physical treatment. Interestingly, although her main concern was with educable children, Dunsdon points out that it is the group of children who are not formally educable, because of their combination of mental and physical handicap, but whose needs may not be met in Training Centres for the severely subnormal, who require special attention. The needs of this group of children are again emphasized by Cockburn (op. cit.). She found that of 26 children with cerebral palsy unsatisfactorily placed, out of a total of 133, 16 were mentally handicapped. She writes 'the greatest need encountered amongst those unsatisfactorily placed in this group was for education suitable for mentally handicapped children'.

Dunsdon based her recommendation that I.Q. 85 was the base line for formal education on the reasonable assumption that cerebral palsied children tend to have so many handicaps that they require a relatively high I.Q. and chronological age in order to make worthwhile educational progress, and on the evidence of the group of children in a special school, quoted above. Schonell's (1956) recommendations differ, in some ways, from those of Dunsdon. Schonell suggested that special schools for spastics might function in three different ways for three groups of children, all with I.Q.s over 70. The first group would comprise the intelligent, less handicapped children who were retarded educationally. For this group, the special school would provide remedial education and return them to ordinary schools. The second group would consist of children with moderate physical handicap, who would attend special schools mainly for physical treatment. The third group would be children with severe physical handicap who would attend special schools for the whole of their school life.

Schonell envisaged schools as dual-purpose centres for all ages, unlike Dunsdon, who considered that the main emphasis should be on a social and motor training up to 9–10 years and then on education from 10–16 years. Schonell's recommendations appear to stem from one study of the reading attainments of children attending the Carlson House Special School for cerebral palsied children. The experimental group consisted of 17 special school children; the control group comprised 17 children with cerebral palsy from special schools for the physically handicapped, ordinary schools, and no schools at all. The two groups were paired for mental age, chronological age, physical, sensory, and speech handicaps within an age range of 7–10. She found that the mean reading age of the experiment group was significantly higher than that of the control group.

There seems general agreement that the majority of educable cerebral palsied children can attend existing ordinary and special schools, but most workers would also agree that a small number might benefit from special schooling as cerebral palsied children. The size and identity of this group and the efficacy of the special teaching methods advocated are matters for further research.

The great need of the mentally handicapped child with cerebral palsy for special consideration is mentioned by both Dunsdon and Cockburn.

Special methods of education

Up to the present, there has been little detailed description, or scientific evaluation, of specific methods of education used with children with cerebral palsy. There are statements in the literature that special training is necessary for teachers of spastic children; although this may be true, there is little evidence to substantiate the claim. The lack of published evidence on the efficacy and nature of special methods of teaching may be due to the fact that the special schools in England have not been in existence for very long.

In considering the literature on the education of the cerebral palsied, the following points emerge. Commonsense techniques to obviate physical handicaps are widely used. Some authorities, Schonell and Orville Johnson (1955) among them, advocate the use of modern teaching methods, such as centres of interest, modern textbooks, and reading-readiness programmes. Orville Johnson (op. cit.), in discussing the education of mentally retarded cerebral palsied children, suggests that they require ordinary methods of teaching but that each stage will take much longer than with normal children. There seems to be a fairly widely held belief that cerebral palsied children learn slowly, even if they are of at least average intelligence, and that therefore they require three or four years of extra schooling. This seems a reasonable hypothesis which could be usefully tested.

In America, teaching techniques based on the work of Strauss and Lehtinen (1947) and their concept of the 'brain-injured child' have been used in the teaching of the cerebral palsied. Their method consists of the avoidance of all irrelevant stimuli and the clear simple presentation of the material to be learned. An empirical criticism is that Strauss and Lehtinen have not shown that this method is more effective than others. They describe various devices to aid in the teaching of reading, writing, and arithmetic; these are related to their concept of brain injury and are, therefore, intended to overcome the dysfunctions which they ascribe to brain injury. Many of their suggestions are in apparent conflict with current teaching practice with normal children; for example, they advocate an analytical phonic method for teaching reading. Their detailed recommendations are too piecemeal and unsystematic, however, to provide a comprehensive method of teaching. The evidence of the success of their methods, as applied to the 'brain-injured child', depends entirely on individual case histories. Strauss and Lehtinen's work is interesting and seems worth developing and testing, but this critical work has yet to be done.

The evidence on the education of cerebral palsied children is most unsatisfactory. It may be that there are some cerebral palsied children who are best educated as a group, but even this has not been clearly shown. It may be that the main advantage of a special school, or centre, for the cerebral palsied is the availability, on the premises, of physiotherapy and speech therapy. A consideration of some of the current assumptions about the education of cerebral palsied children suggests that there may be many untested theories underlying the educational provisions made for other categories of children.

At present cerebral palsied children are educated and receive physical treatment in a wide range of hospitals, schools, and institutions. It would seem an excellent time to carry out prospective research into the efficacy of different methods of education and treatment for comparable groups of children. This should be carried out in conjunction with research work in the assessment centres which are developing for young and/or multiply and severely handicapped children. One sometimes gets the impression from the published studies that the medical and educational placement of the cerebral palsied tends to be dealt with separately although this may not be so in practice.

Follow-up studies of patients with cerebral palsy

Although there has been little long-term study of educational methods with cerebral palsied children, there are follow-up studies of patients with cerebral palsy. Crothers and Paine (op. cit.) in their classic study were concerned with the natural history of cerebral palsy, and not with assessing the results of any specific treatments. However, they do provide much useful information on the adult status of the patients in their sample.

Wallin (1949) reports two studies of the response to treatment of mental defectives with cerebral palsy. The first was of 18 subjects, age range 8–50 years and Stanford–Binet I.Q. 20–62. The treatment consisted of 3–12 months muscle re-education, formal education, and occupational work. Seventeen of the patients showed large increases in Stanford–Binet I.Q., 6 showed marked physical improvement, 3 moderate improvement, and 9 no appreciable improvement. In the second group, there were 46 defectives, I.Q.s 29–71. After five years of muscle, speech and educational training 37·5 per cent. improved in walking, using hands, dressing and feeding themselves. Improvement depended more on effort and co-operation than on Stanford–Binet I.Q. Most were classed as mentally normal after treatment.

Quibell, Stephen, and Whatley (1961) carried out a retrospective study of the progress in daily living functions of 40 physically handicapped children I.Q. 48–70, age 2–16 years; 30 of these children were cerebral palsied. All had been treated in a long stay children's hospital and school for at least one year, and improvement was assessed on a scale of activities essential for daily living. Thirty-one of them made demonstrable gains in functional independence, including 2 children of imbecile level. They comment: 'It appears that the minimum I.Q. or mental age, necessary in order to make useful progress in daily living functions, is much lower than may sometimes have been assumed. Our survey suggests that the children who did not show improvement, could not, because of the severity of the physical handicap, rather than because of mental dullness.' From these studies it appears that some mental defectives with cerebral palsy show marked improvement after treatment.

Placement and employment of adult patients with cerebral palsy

Most surveys of patients with cerebral palsy have been concerned with children, and there are no firm figures on the prevalence rate of adults with cerebral palsy.

Crothers and Paine (op. cit.) found a death rate of 14 per cent. among their sample of 847 patients born in 1915–55 and concluded that 'the majority of cerebral palsied patients have a considerable life expectancy'.

Henderson (op. cit.) in his sample found a prevalence rate of 1·54 for ages 15–19 per 1,000.

Tizard and Grad (op. cit.) in their London sample of 150 mentally defective children and 100 mentally defective adults found that

> cerebral palsy and various types of paralysis were the most common of the special disabilities. These conditions, or unsteadiness of gait or muscular weakness, were seen in nearly one-third of the children and more than one-fifth of the adults. Of the children 15 per cent. were rated as suffering from slight and 15 per cent. from severe motor impairment. Among the adults 14 per cent. showed slight and 8 per cent. severe motor impairments.

6 per cent. of the adults with severe motor impairment were living at home.

There is some information on the frequency of mental deficiency amongst adults with cerebral palsy. Holoran (1955) in a survey of young adult cerebral palsied patients in Leeds found that out of a total of 78, 15 had been notified to the mental deficiency authority before the age of 15 and 2 were in occupation centres, i.e. 22 per cent. were mentally deficient. Hansen (op. cit.) reports that 27 per cent. of 1,127 adult patients with cerebral palsy 'were fit to be dealt with as mentally defective'. In both these surveys the mentally deficient adult patients were among the unemployed. In discussing the placement of young adults in her sample Cockburn (op. cit., p. 324) writes: 'Almost half of those over school age were unemployable and in the majority of cases this was due to serious mental handicap.'

Stephen (1961) gives the following summary of the findings in the major studies of adult patients with cerebral palsy, including the mentally handicapped:

1. About 25 per cent. of adults with cerebral palsy are in open employment, but there are wide variations in the published figures, implying that different degrees of handicap are included in the different samples, and/or that there are considerable variations in the facilities and conditions of employment in different areas.

2. Monoplegics and hemiplegics are the types most frequently employed, followed by paraplegics. Quadriplegics and athetoids have the poorest chance of employment at present. When cerebral palsy is associated with low intelligence or other handicaps these constitute a further bar to employment.

3. There is little published evidence so far on the results of vocational guidance and training in this country. The American and Danish surveys indicate a large wastage in training (at least 50 per cent.). This may now be unavoidable but suggests that new methods should be inquired into.

There is clearly a need for increased facilities for training and vocational advice. She also pointed out the need to give particular attention to the severely handicapped adult patients and to their families.

Ingram (1964) has followed up the patients surveyed by himself (1955, 1964) and Henderson (1961). This is a fascinating study of all aspects of the lives of adult patients with cerebral palsy in two areas of Scotland. One of his interesting recommendations is that, 'because of the low prevalence rate of cerebral palsy, services for cerebral palsied patients must be planned at a national level'.

The work of a cerebral palsy unit

An interesting account of the work of a Cerebral Palsy Unit is given by Collis *et al.* (1956). They emphasize the importance of early diagnosis and the role of the mother in the management of the condition under the long-term guidance of a specialist staff. Results are documented by quoting follow-up studies of cases illustrating the main types of cerebral palsy. In a further article on the work of this unit, Lawson (1958) analysed the 206 cases referred between 1954 and 1956. He found that 34 per cent. of these patients had mental defect only. This figure is not statistically different from the 20 per cent. suffering from 'mental defect only' found by Henderson in his Scottish sample. Lawson's findings in relation to intelligence and educability in his sample are in line with those in other studies. Like Cockburn and Dunsdon he points out that relatively few children with cerebral palsy require education in special schools for the cerebral palsied; he argues that this number will be further reduced if these children are sorted out and trained for a few years before school age, and that there is a limited place for looking at the education of cerebral palsied children as a special problem apart from all other handicapped children. This would seem to apply not only to education but also to training and work placement. Lawson does, however, make two further interesting and related points. The first is that only 10 per cent. of the children were referred in the first 18 months of life and 34 per cent. were already of school age at referral. In view of the increasing emphasis on the importance of early diagnosis it is noteworthy that in practice so few children were referred during the first 18 months of life to a cerebral palsy unit. The second is that 'it was estimated that nearly one-third should eventually be capable of leading a completely independent life in society, while just over a half will always be fully dependent'. Again this finding highlights the long-term nature of the problems involved in cerebral palsy, the need for more provision for adults and for more research into the present training schemes and placement of these patients.

SUMMARY AND CONCLUSIONS

In the psychological and educational field, perhaps the most important work so far has been in the study of the incidence of cerebral palsy in the general population, the incidence of concomitant sensory defects amongst the cerebral palsied, and the establishment of the range of test intelligence of the cerebral palsied. Most of the major studies have been carried out on children and the most widely used intelligence test has been one of the revisions of the Binet. Studies have also been carried out on the range of intelligence of various subgroups of cerebral palsied children. From this work, it has been reasonably established that between 40 and 50 per cent. of children with cerebral palsy have I.Q.s under 70. There is a great deal of useful information on these points in the major surveys.

During the past five years there has been a marked increase in our knowledge of cerebral palsy. Recent studies have confirmed the earlier finding on its prevalence and on the range of intelligence amongst children of school age (Henderson, 1961). More detailed information is now available on certain aspects of the subject; an interesting and important example is the reports on patients with cerebral palsy and mental subnormality from which it is now becoming clear that there is a tendency for severity of physical handicap and frequency of sensory handicap to be associated with severity of mental retardation (Hilliard and Kirman, 1957; Henderson, 1961).

Five years ago it seemed that there were many more specific problems which had been studied with little success because of the difficulty of defining and studying specific problems in such a heterogeneous group as that of children with cerebral palsy, where the only factor they are known to have in common, and which distinguishes them from other children, is a recognizable motor dysfunction of cerebral origin. Now the picture is becoming clearer; some subgroups have been described and shown to be associated with specific disabilities by such workers as Cruickshank *et al.* (1957) and Wedell (1960).

New areas have been explored, among them the attitudes of parents of children with cerebral palsy (Boles, 1959), and information on the outcome of treatment and management, and on the placement of adult patients, has been provided by follow-up studies (Crothers and Paine, 1959). A beginning has been made in the study of the interrelationship between disabilities and emotional problems (Williams, 1960). Increasing interest is being shown in patients with minimal brain damage. In this context it is worth noting that from the 'continuum' theory of brain damage (Meyer, 1957) one would expect to find in the community a number of very mild cerebral palsy cases who are undiagnosed as such and regarded as normal children. These may well be the ones who show symptoms such as clumsiness, awkwardness, or mild behaviour disorder, the organic basis of which is not recognized and therefore not allowed for.

There is still much to be learned about cerebral palsy, but there is now a body of well-established knowledge.

Part III

PRACTICAL PROBLEMS

Chapter XI

PSYCHOLOGICAL ASSESSMENT IN MENTAL DEFICIENCY

by H. C. Gunzburg

INTRODUCTION

The clinical investigation of the mentally deficient by means of psychological tests is concerned mainly with assessing their attainments, the factors affecting efficiency, their personalities, their potential mental resources, and their present mental functioning. The investigation serves not only diagnostic purposes but has a direct bearing on the problems of rehabilitation, on the need for and the accessibility to psychotherapy, on vocational guidance, and educational assistance. The assessment procedure is thus a constructive step with a definite aim rather than a mere labelling process for statistical or research purposes. It will often have to provide answers to certain practical questions such as whether the psychological examination can:

(*a*) indicate the most practicable way of utilizing the more positive aspects of a given personality to overcome his deficiencies?
(*b*) predict how a particular patient will react to strains of a life situation?
(*c*) predict and measure the relative success and failure of various treatment methods in an individual case?

These questions are very relevant and urgent ones and decisions relating to them have to be taken daily by those responsible for the care of the mentally deficient. It seems reasonable that any organization charged with the welfare of defectives in its widest sense, should enlist the assistance of comparatively novel psychological methods if they can contribute to a fuller and more reliable assessment and prediction than the traditional clinical approaches. A full understanding of a person's personality structure is not achieved – as is sometimes assumed – by obtaining a score from a psychometric test. It is the purpose of a full psychological examination to put test scores in their proper context and to relate them to the person tested rather than to the test used. The test situation is assumed to provide a sample of behaviour which is representative of a person's habitual mode of acting, his intellectual grasp, and his mode of tackling new situations. The test can, of course, give only tentative leads to a full estimate of the interaction of individual and environment since many variables, such as the motivational factors of interest, zeal, financial reward, or even the effect of mere chance, cannot be directly assessed in the test procedure. The ensuing comparative scantiness of observational data, and the difficulty of evaluating their relevance, makes it imperative to proceed with great caution when interpreting a person's test scores. Determination of the aetiology, the assessment of personality and the prediction of behaviour are based on inference and deduction, and, though the observational clues obtained in the test may be reliable and valid, it will depend on the skill, knowledge, and experience of the clinician to give the test the weight and proportion appropriate to the individual under consideration.

ASSESSMENT AND PREDICTION

The use of tests in a clinical situation involves an assessment of present status and, very often, an attempt to predict future status. To this end interest is focused on the distribution and inter-relations of *many* variables in *one* person; this situation is essentially different from the use of psychometrics in many research projects or screening procedures, where the emphasis may be laid on the measurement of size and distribution of *one* or more variables in a *group* of persons. In general, accurate prediction of group trends tends to be more easily achieved than a detailed forecast of the status of an individual, since in the group those who diverge from the expected trend in one direction may be counterbalanced by divergences in the other. Moreover, since behaviour is a function of the interaction of the individual and his environment, for accurate diagnosis and prediction we need, therefore, to know the patient's social history and to forecast his future environment. This latter is by no means always impossible, although it may often be difficult, because of the multitude of factors of unknown weight and the consequent unknown impact that they may have on the person. Accurate and reliable knowledge about an individual in certain defined situations, however, and about other persons in comparable situations, may so add to our understanding that no one can afford to do without the information derived from tests if faced with decisions regarding a patient's future. Implicit in the foregoing is the assumption, not always explicitly recognized, that, within limits, individuals may be flexible, particularly when fairly young.

It must be pointed out that, in general, test scores establish the person's status with respect to the standardization sample (see Chapter IV), which ideally should be constituted of persons of similar age, and should have included persons of similar educational and social status. In assessing the degree of a person's subnormality or abnormality, it is essential to compare his score with the central tendency of a representative sample of the total population. Without such objective assessments, diagnoses of abnormality must rely on subjective opinion, notoriously unreliable, particularly in 'borderline' cases.

Finally, two common misconceptions, which have bedevilled both research and clinical work in the field of deficiency, must be mentioned. These are: (1) the assumption that there is a psychological entity termed mental deficiency, whereas in reality the term tends to be a socio-legal one covering a wide variety of people; (2) the assumption that a given combination of defective traits coexisting in one person practically ensures a certain type of behaviour, irrespective of changing environmental conditions.

TYPES OF TEST AND THEIR INTERPRETATION

Tests used in clinical work in mental deficiency can conveniently be grouped under four headings: (*a*) Intelligence Tests, (*b*) Personality Tests, (*c*) Educational and Social Attainment Tests, and (*d*) Tests of specific aptitudes and '*ad hoc*' tests for experimental work. In practice none of these can avoid investigating incidentally some other aspects; e.g. an intelligence test may reveal many aspects of personality, whilst a personality test may permit an estimate of intelligence level. It is obvious, for example, that the opportunity of being able to watch a 'subject thinking' when executing a manipulative test is of great value to the clinician. The degree of planning and the reaction to failure give important clues and Earl (1937) has described three types of adult mental defectives on the basis of their performance test behaviour – the excitable, the integrated, and the inhibited mental defective. Earl's later work (1961) enlarges on this subject and gives a large number of examples for the influence of personality on test behaviour.

Most assessments rely on a battery of tests, and a few of those frequently mentioned in the literature on mental deficiency will be discussed in some detail in the following pages. Many other well-known diagnostic tools have proved inadequate because of the limitations of our subjects.

In view of the fact that a person's readiness to express himself may depend not only on the presence, or absence, of mental ability, but also on the manner and type of question, and considering also how much an observer's judgment may be influenced by his own personal idiosyncrasies and the chance element of asking the 'right', or the 'wrong', question, the advantages of putting a systematic, finely graded, series of questions, or tasks, of increasing difficulty to each successive person in the same way cannot be denied. In fact, the advantage of a psychological test examination over a psychiatric interview is its relative objectivity which permits comparison of numerical test results between examiners. Yet this very objectivity and apparent simplicity in obtaining 'scores' leads to the common mistake of comparing directly I.Q.s derived from differently standardized scales and the tendency of regarding the I.Q. as a direct index of innate intellectual ability without considering the influence of motivation, temperament, and environment in each individual case. The test provides *some* information which must be evaluated in the light of *all* information available.

The rigidity of test procedure has often induced would-be testers to sacrifice the advantages of standardization and precise administration instructions to a 'flexibility' aimed at giving the subject more opportunity for displaying his abilities. The dangers of this approach have already been discussed (Chapter IV) and this attitude appears moreover to put rather too much emphasis on the importance of achieving a high quantitative score.

A test *must* be given exactly as specified in the standardization instructions, otherwise new variables are introduced which change the situation and the norms are no longer applicable. After the test, the examiner may use the flexible approach to clarify particular points and enlarge in his comments on the 'underfunctioning' shown in the test; otherwise the examination would be, clinically, rather pointless (see Volle, 1957).

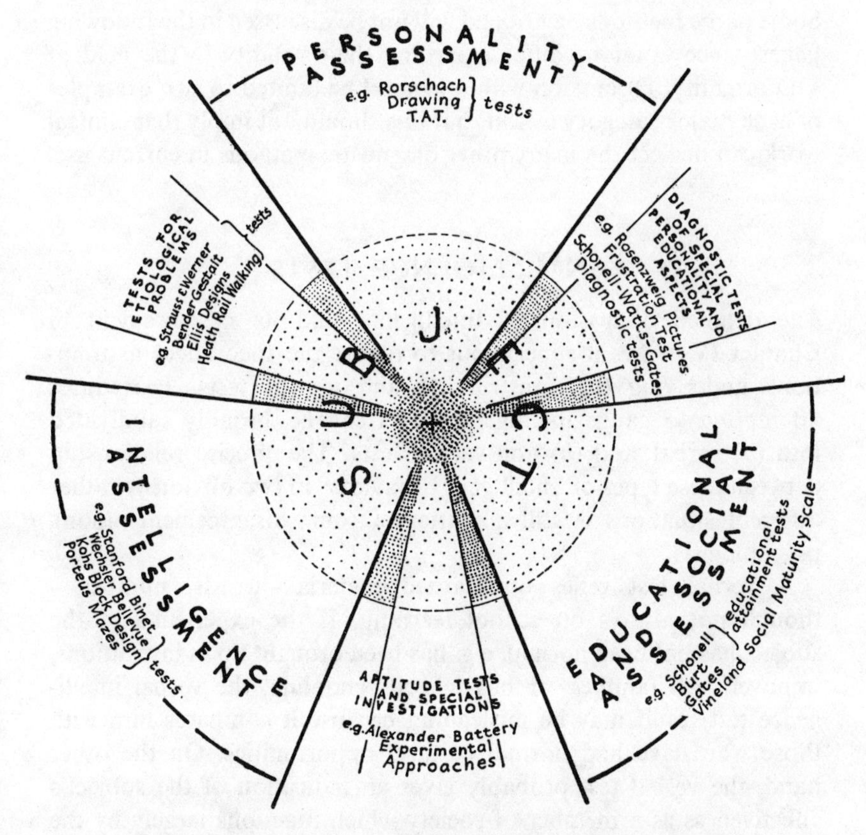

Fig. 3. Psychological investigation in mental deficiency. Primary and secondary assessment

The above diagram, Fig. 3, suggests an assessment programme[1] which gauges different and relevant aspects of the subject. Test results refer, of course, primarily to a subject's status at the time of testing, but they permit also interpretation referring to the

[1] Different test assessments can only throw light on one or the other aspect of the subject's individuality. Large sections will remain unexplored and their existence adds to our difficulties in prediction.

pre-admission time when, for example, the question of deterioration has to be decided, and to the future; for example, evidence of psychosis before it becomes overt. The use of this selection of tests indicates whether a second examination should clarify various points and could help to fill usefully the gaps left by the first examination. Some of the methods mentioned will not be discussed in the following pages, since opinions differ regarding their validity in the field of subnormality. Discussion will in general be limited to two examples of each major category of test, but this should not imply that clinical work can neglect the many other diagnostic methods in current use.

INTELLIGENCE TESTS

The detailed discussion of Intelligence and its measurement in Chapter IV makes it superfluous to repeat the theoretical assumptions underlying the construction and use of tests. Procedures attempting to gauge intelligence level can be broadly subdivided into (*a*) verbal and (*b*) non-verbal tests. The precise relationship between these types of 'intelligent behaviour' in two obviously rather different situations is still a matter of some disagreement among psychologists.

A verbal test relies on learned material – words, numbers – though not always on school learning. If the experience of the subject has not been normal, e.g. has been brought up in institutions, impoverished families, or has missed schooling, the verbal intelligence test result may be misleading because it compares him with those who have had normal cultural opportunities. On the other hand, the verbal test probably gives an indication of the subject's effectiveness as a member of society which functions largely by the effective use of words and symbols.

A non-verbal, or performance test avoids as far as possible the use of words and requires either selecting from abstract, geometrical designs and pictures or the handling of material like blocks, beads, or pieces of wood. Such tests are invaluable in the assessment of the intelligence of people with verbal or sensory handicaps, with abnormal schooling, or with unusual social backgrounds. In normal populations the non-verbal tests are equivalent to the verbal tests, but in abnormal and subnormal cases, where the verbal ability or the ability to handle concrete material intelligently has been affected, the difference in efficiency is often quite marked and has been assumed to be of great diagnostic import.

A useful subdivision of these tests differentiates between the non-verbal tests proper, mostly of the paper and pencil type (e.g. Raven's Matrices, Cattell's tests), and the manipulative or performance tests (Alexander Battery, Kohs Block Design test). The distinction is important because they may gauge different aspects of intelligent behaviour. Manipulative tests introduce quite markedly factors of persistence, zest, and desire to succeed (Alexander, 1935) in the face of often clearly recognized increasingly more difficult tasks.

Many people from subcultural environments, including mental defectives, do fairly well on performance tasks with a score often strikingly above their verbal test result (Kinder and Hamlin, 1937; Bijou, 1942a, b). It is possible that the ability to do well on performance tasks gives an indication of potential resources which have not been utilized educationally in a culture which places a premium on verbal efficiency.[1]

Results of some performance tests tend to fluctuate, often quite considerably, which may provide valuable diagnostic clues, as the uneven performance is often due to a subject's reactions to difficulties and not to the difficulties themselves. On the other hand, these fluctuations decrease the reliability coefficient and affect psychometric measurements.

(*a*) *The Stanford–Binet scale* (Terman, 1916, 1917)
The Revised Stanford–Binet test (Terman and Merrill, 1937; McNemar, 1942). Third Revision, Form L–M (Terman and Merrill, 1960)

These revisions and extensions of the original Binet scale are the most widely known intelligence scales and have been used for children and adults alike. The original 1916 and the 1937 version of the Binet scales have been reported to correlate with each other

[1] Sarason (1949) suggests that performance tests are solved by self-verbalization – by a process of 'talking to yourself' – and poses the very pertinent question 'why may talking over a problem *to yourself and in your own words* result in a more or less adequate solution than when one is required to respond orally to *someone* else?' Is it possible that the defective's well-known inability to handle verbal concepts originates in the conditioning by unhappy interpersonal relationships, which make verbalization only effective in a situation where he has not to respond to people but to materials?

well, but the I.Q.s obtained on the new revision seem often considerably lower than those on the old scale (Hoakley, 1940; Allen, 1942; Cruickshank and Qualtere, 1950). The test shows

> marked reliance on what has been learned, including arithmetic, language, information, and the like, and on tasks quite similar to those which occur constantly in school studies. . . . It is worked out in terms of a set of age norms which have a remarkable analogy to the steps of the 'educational ladder' and which probably put a good deal more significance on one year of development than would be the case if one were thinking simply of mental growth in and of itself, for a year is after all a calendar unit and has no intrinsic developmental significance however important it may be in pedagogical organization (Mursell, 1949).

It is well to keep in mind the bias of this test which thus seems to measure primarily the mental abilities necessary for success in academic school subjects. While it cannot be denied that achievement in academic work is indicative of intelligence, it is a broader survey of a person's mental functioning which is of value in the assessment of mental defectives.

Although the Binet scale[1] must be given pride of place as the first intelligence test, and while it may be useful in assessments in child guidance clinics, it is now increasingly recognized as unsuitable for use with the mentally deficient and, of course, quite inappropriate for testing adults. The reader is referred to Chapter IV (pp. 86–9) for discussion of some of the disadvantages of using the concept of Mental Age in assessing intelligence. In addition, the following must be noted as serious drawbacks to the 1937 revision:

(1) The lower end of the age scale has a performance bias, and the upper end a strong verbal weighting. Thus, different abilities are assessed at different ages, and the dull child from subcultural conditions is markedly penalized from about M.A. 7 onwards.

(2) The standard deviation of test scores varies at different ages (from 12 to 20 points) and, unless corrected, error will result, particularly at the extremes of low or high ability (pp. 81–2).

(3) Distributions of scores overlap more and more as age increases so that mean Mental Age will always be higher than mean

[1] This critique of Stanford–Binet, and some of the criticisms of the Wechsler Scale, were contributed by A. D. B. Clarke.

Chronological Age. Thus, the standardization mean I.Q.s vary between 101 and 109, this leading to further error.

(4) Mental Age units do not have the same meaning at different ages; for example, while a Mental Age of 5 may represent what the majority of 5-year-olds can score, a Mental Age of 20 does not represent what the majority of persons aged 20 can do (pp. 86–7).

(5) In standardizing the test, the percentage passing a given mental year varies considerably; between ages 2 and 6 the passing level varies from 64 to 87 per cent. while between 7 and 15 it ranges from 50 to 70 per cent. Thus the linear growth curve for averages must be primarily a function of varying the passing percentage by manipulating the test items and their order of difficulty.

(6) The standardization sample was poorly selected, and indeed Terman and Merrill give insufficient details of it. There appears to be an urban and higher socio-economic bias in the selection of the sample.

(7) The test is unsuitable for use with adults, for a number of reasons, including sampling.

(8) Finally, it should be mentioned that, as in most tests, the younger the child the lower the reliability, and the higher the I.Q. the lower the reliability.

The 1960 Revision was constructed from the better items of Forms L and M in the 1937 Revision. There have in effect been changes both in content and structure of the test. Less satisfactory items have been eliminated, there has been some re-location, and, in other cases, re-scoring of constituent items. Equally important, built-in corrections for different I.Q. variabilities at different ages have been incorporated, so that given I.Q.s at different ages can be legitimately compared. Secondly, there has been an extension of the I.Q. tables to 17 and 18, because recent work (see Chapter IV) has shown that mental growth on the Binet extends beyond 16. The I.Q.s now obtainable are basically standard scores with a mean of 100 and standard deviation of 16 points. These changes certainly help to overcome some of the standardization inadequacies of the 1937 Revision, which have nevertheless been mentioned in full because so much assessment and research has used this scale.

In general, therefore, and because the main structure and approach of the 1937 scale has been retained in the new, it still seems inappropriate for assessment of the mentally deficient except, perhaps, at the pre-school age where other tests may be even more inadequate, or at later stages of life where the person is so subnormal that he is likely to fall below norms on other tests.

(*b*) *The Wechsler–Bellevue Scale of Intelligence:* W.B. (Wechsler, 1939). *The Wechsler Adult Intelligence Scale:* W.A.I.S. (Wechsler, 1955). *The Wechsler Intelligence Scale for Children:* W.I.S.C. (Wechsler, 1949)

Wechsler considers intelligence as an aspect of the total personality. It is to be regarded as 'an effect rather than a cause' and is the resultant of interacting abilities – non-intellective included. This means that an intelligence test should consider also the ability to utilize and exercise 'intelligence' in particular situations which are meaningful. Wechsler makes it clear that his test does *not* measure 'all that goes to make up general intelligence' but assesses 'sufficient portions of intelligence to enable us to use it as a fairly reliable index of the individual's global capacity'. This global capacity is defined as an individual's ability 'to act purposefully, to think rationally and to deal effectively with his environment' (Wechsler, 1958).

The W.A.I.S. attempts to measure this global capacity by administering eleven different subtests, 6 of them verbal and 5 non-verbal. This 'shot gun technique' gauges diverse aspects of functioning such as general comprehension, range of information, or arithmetical reasoning on the verbal scale; the non-verbal tests are assumed to measure synthetic and analytic ability, basic perceptual abilities, and the subject's ability to comprehend and assess a total situation. This approach does not presume that there are different kinds of intelligence (verbal, non-verbal) but only that there are different ways in which intelligence may be shown. The subtests are 'different measurements of intelligence not measures of different kinds of intelligence'.

As has been pointed out in Chapter IV, the term I.Q. in the Wechsler scale is an index of brightness and compares the individual with others of the same age. A man, 60 years old, will be compared with the test performance of people of his age and not with that of young people aged 16. His intelligence is defined by his relative standing among his age peers which will not change under ordinary circumstances, though his absolute capacity may change. Some test items may be more difficult for people of advanced age than for young people and comparing them with their own age group may give little information regarding their actual efficiency in relation to situations outside the test room. Older people may obtain a higher I.Q. than is actually warranted on the basis of their actual life performance because the scale does not take into account such intangible factors as life experience. In such cases, it is suggested that an individual's performance should be compared with that of a reference group at the prime of their mental ability, namely between the ages of 20 and 34 (Fry, 1956).

Wechsler defines as mentally defective that segment of the population which includes approximately the lowest 2 per cent. He suggests that people with I.Q. of 69 and less should be classified as mentally defective on statistical grounds. He is, however, at pains to point out that 'there is no precise mental age or I.Q. which specifically classifies an individual as a mental defective' and stresses that there are many individuals with I.Q.s above 70 whose behaviour is definitely defective and others below 60 whose whole life history is that of a non-defective.[1]

The W.A.I.S. has more or less replaced the Wechsler–Bellevue test and many of the defects discovered in the earlier version have now been overcome. This refers particularly to the standardization sample which was mostly urban from the City and State of New York. In the W.A.I.S. subjects from all parts of the country were tested and the author claims that the norms of the W.A.I.S. 'represent a fair cross section of what may be called "American intelligence" as of the time of standardization'.

Some faults and drawbacks have, however, not been overcome even in the new W.A.I.S.

(1) The subtests have been chosen subjectively and there is little or no evidence that they in fact assess those aspects of intelligent behaviour they are supposed to measure;

(2) The reliability of some of the subtests is low. This has direct implications on the use of subtests for providing specific diagnostic clues on clinical groups;

(3) The claims which have been made for the clinical significance of the subtest patterns (Wechsler, 1944; Rapaport, 1946) have been

[1] Jastak used a multiple criterion for defining mental retardation in his survey of the State of Delaware and only persons who rated on test *and* life history measures below the scores of 25 per cent. of the population were regarded as retarded. Thus a person with an I.Q. of 65 who reaches average status in other aspects of adjustment as measured may not be retarded but a person with a low average I.Q. of 85 will be regarded as retarded if his ratings on the other criteria are significantly below average (Jastak, MacPhee & Whiteman, 1963).

repeatedly checked and found wanting. The mentally deficient person is said to display a typical pattern of successes and failures in the various subtests which should assist in differentiating the defective from other conditions showing a low I.Q. Some of the investigations have proved negative (Boehm and Sarason, 1947; Peixotto, 1950; Alderdice and Butler, 1952; Beck and Lam, 1955) while others confirmed the occurrence of test patterns (Cutts and Sloan, 1945; Cotzin and Gallagher, 1949), though others added that they depend on additional factors (Hays, 1950; Cutts and O'Kelly, 1947). Similarly, the value of Wechsler's Mental Deterioration Index is questionable (Sloan, 1947b; Bensberg and Sloan, 1950).

(4) The test shows poor differentiation at the lower end of the scale and the I.Q.s of older mentally defective people are inflated.

(5) In this country the order of difficulty of items in some of the subtests (e.g. vocabulary) appears to be different, which has implications on the test administration.

(6) The phrasing of some test questions appears to be confusing and incomprehensible and some test pictures are relatively difficult for English mental defectives.

The last mentioned drawbacks have led to many translations of, or substitutions for, American items in this country, which is highly unsatisfactory, yet the W.A.I.S. is nevertheless the best available individual scale of adult intelligence and should always be employed when assessing older mental defectives.

The Wechsler Verbal Scale results agree quite well with the Binet test scores (Sloan and Schneider, 1951), and the full Wechsler Scale has been shown to correlate much better with psychiatric diagnosis of mental deficiency (*r* ranging from 0·72 to 0·79) than the Binet (*r* ranging from 0·27 to 0·66). The same investigation assesses the Bellevue test's forecasting efficiency as about 40 per cent. against 5 per cent. of the Stanford–Binet (Balinsky, Israel, and Wechsler, 1939).

The W.I.S.C. is similar to the Wechsler–Bellevue and suitable for children between the ages of 7 and 15. Wechsler mentions that the W.I.S.C. should be used for adults testing below 50 I.Q. and suggests methods of equating scores and obtaining I.Q.s for adult performance (Wechsler, 1951).

(*c*) *Raven's Progressive Matrices test* (1938, 1956)
Coloured Progressive Matrices (1947)

Though Raven, the originator of the 'Progressive Matrices Test', states quite clearly that this 'is not a test of "general intelligence" and it is always a mistake to describe it as such' (Raven, 1938), it has been widely regarded as a test of non-verbal intelligence. Designed specifically to measure Spearman's '*g*' – Raven (1938) quotes a '*g*' saturation of +0·82, Slater (1948) +0·8 – it is held to be a test of general cognitive ability and Raven's Percentile Scores have been converted into the I.Q.s of other tests (Gwynne Jones, 1956; Orme, 1961).

The test consists of a booklet containing five sets of designs. One part of each design problem is missing and the subject is asked to complete the design by choosing from two rows of alternative parts, printed below the design problem. The test can be administered individually or in group form but Walton (1955) draws attention to the closer agreement between the Matrices and the Terman–Merrill when administered individually than in group form.

The Matrices results correlate generally well with other tests. Clarke, Clarke, and Reiman (1958) found $r = +0{\cdot}81$ with the Wechsler Full Scale I.Q. in 50 high-grade mental defectives. The Matrices results were on the average 2·6 points lower than the Wechsler. Stacey and Gill (1954) found $r = +0{\cdot}68$ with the Wechsler Full Scale I.Q. in 172 adult mental defectives, but $r = +0{\cdot}86$ with the Stanford–Binet in the same group of patients. Martin and Weichers (1954) obtain $r = +0{\cdot}91$ and Orme (1961) $r = +0{\cdot}93$ between the W.I.S.C. and the coloured Matrices.

Many workers are not happy with the results of the Matrices when used with low-grade patients. Mental defectives are liable to make snap decisions, to get bored and to exert themselves much less than in a test with a change of tasks. Disinterest and lack of application may invalidate the results in individual cases.

One of the major objections to the test is the fact that it seems to give hardly more than a quantitative percentile score, useful enough for screening and classification purposes, but not revealing information about the quality of the thinking processes underlying the execution of the test. Some investigators have made an attempt to widen the scope of the test by analysing the reasons for incorrect responses. Miller and Raven (1939), Bromley (1953), Crawford (1955), Maher (1960) have investigated the errors connected with 'position-preference'. The suggestion made was that answers tended to be selected because they were either positioned in the top row of alternatives or at the right hand of the page. Bromley (1953) tried to associate the 'top-line error' with 'boundedness to outer world stimuli' characteristic of deteriorated and immature individuals 'which is however a less primitive approach than the "right-hand error" denoting "egocentricity of thinking"'. Maher (1960) investigated these claims by comparing mentally retarded children with college students and found no support for the hypothesis that differences in intelligence lead to differential position preferences – nor even for the existence of position preferences.

Comparisons with other tests have suggested diagnostic and prognostic possibilities. Urmer *et al.* (1960) studied the performance of brain-damaged patients on the Matrices and notes their consistency in responding to item difficulty and in making figure-ground reversal errors. Johnson (1952; 1953a, c) suggested that a higher Matrices score than Binet level is shown by mentally defective children who improve in play therapy.

The children's version is coloured, and uses Sets *A* and *B* of the Adult Matrices, with another Set, A_B, of 12 problems intermediate in difficulty between *A* and *B*. This is useful with children from about age 7 to 12, and, if justified, it is easy to go on to Set *C* in the 1938 Matrices and disregard A_B in final scoring.

The reliability of results is easy to establish by checking the 'scatter' of success against norms. Where speech handicaps exist, the test is invaluable.

(*d*) *The Porteus Maze test*

The Porteus Maze test, consisting of 9 mazes of increasing difficulty, has been in use for over 40 years and has enjoyed much popularity, partly on account of the ease of administration. The test does not aim to measure school capacity like the Binet and cannot fairly be compared with, and validated against, that type of test. Correlations with other tests have been summarized by Porteus (1950) and by Tizard (1951) who quoted from the published literature correlations ranging from 0·54 to 0·69 between the Stanford–Binet and the Maze Test. Correlation of 0·69 for the full W.A.I.S., 0·41 for the Verbal and 0·67 for the Performance with the Maze are reported by Tobias and Gorelick (1962) on a population of retarded adults. According to Porteus, intelligence is the 'capacity for making planned responses to an increasing range of relevant stimuli' and the test has been so designed as to measure an individual's 'ability for a continued effort in a *single* mental task involving sustained effort'.

Since the feeble-minded 'lack foresight to anticipate a situation, mental alertness to recognize its significance and common prudence to deal with it' (Porteus, 1950), a test measuring these aspects of social adaptation can become extremely useful in the field of mental deficiency.

Published reports indicate that well-adjusted individuals tend to make significantly higher scores on the Maze test than on the Binet, whilst the maladjusted group, including thieves, truants, sex offenders, and other behaviour problems, tend to obtain low Maze scores compared with the Binet I.Q. (Poull and Montgomery, 1929; Karpeles, 1932). Institutional adjustment ratings (Porteus, 1950) of feeble-minded patients correlated higher with the Maze than with the Binet or other intelligence tests. Tobias and Gorelick (1962) showed that a cut-off score of 8·5 on the Maze was more accurate in identifying successfully employed ex-trainees of a workshop than was the Performance I.Q. of the W.A.I.S.

Low scores may be due to low intelligence, or to maladjustment, but maladjustment does not exclude high scores, and differential diagnosis calls for a qualitative analysis of the performance.

Analysis of this kind assumes that a person's habitual style of reaction is reflected in the manner of tackling and executing the Maze, which thus becomes a projective test. Attention must be paid to the subject's 'reactions' in the face of failure, particularly his ability to improve his approach with experience, or conversely to become 'rattled' or confused when the problem becomes more complex (Porteus, 1950). Thus, observation will soon tell the experienced observer whether the inefficient performance is due to intellectual limitations, or temperamental shortcomings which interfere with efficiency.

An attempt to quantify objectively the qualitative features of the Maze record has been made by Porteus when introducing his qualitative score (Porteus, 1942) where various aspects of the execution were penalized relatively independently from the level of performance. This refinement of technique showed remarkable differences between delinquents and non-delinquents (Porteus, 1950; Wright, 1944; Grajales, 1948; Docter and Winder, 1954), resulting in the establishment of a 'critical score' which was thought to 'be useful in differentiating that group of cases who become delinquent mainly because of environmental stresses and strain and therefore may be better prospects for reformative measures' (Porteus, 1950). Whether that critical score is equally valid in the feeble-minded population has not as yet been demonstrated. In a later work, Porteus (1959) drew attention to the 'projective-expressive aspects of the maze' and also offered an extension series of mazes to supplement the main series.

The test appears to be particularly sensitive to temperamental factors which may account for its low reliability. Retesting leads usually to markedly different scores which may indicate a subject's ability, or inability, to profit by experience. The test is also very short and apprehension or insecurity leading to momentary loss of efficiency are penalized heavily whilst chance success may result in an inflated test level. There have been many different editions, changes of instructions, and new norms published by Porteus quite often without the desirable mathematical basis. Many of these confusing and irritating changes appear to be adjustments resulting from clinical work with the test rather than the outcome of scientific computations. There is no doubt that this test has far more in common with the techniques of personality assessment which have been clinically accepted despite their weak scientific grounding, than with well standardized, validated, and reliable intelligence tests. Being a measure of a single mental task, the test can obviously not do justice by itself to such a complex problem as social adaptation which requires many capacities and abilities. There is also no evidence that the test indicates the capacity for adjustment rather than the presence, or absence, of planning ability at the time of testing. In the absence of follow-up studies, it is difficult to judge the Maze's value as a measure of existing, but not utilized, social intelligence. It may prove to be a particularly useful test in mental deficiency because the concrete apparently easy task appeals to the defective, but the test provides a situation primarily to form a clinical judgment and, only secondarily, to obtain a test score.

(*e*) *Kohs Block Design test*

The Kohs is probably of all manipulative tests the deservedly most popular single measure of intelligence and offers ample opportunity for qualitative assessment. It consists of a number of cubes with sides of different colours, and the subject is required to manipulate the blocks in such a way as to reproduce enlarged copies of designs of increasing complexity. The successful solutions require only adherence to a single principle: analysing the design into small square units – and we are thus able to study the application of this principle at different levels of difficulty, the subject's ability to learn, his logical procedures, and various personality factors.

Kohs regards intelligence as the ability to analyse and synthesize, and his test gives a fair opportunity to display this ability, though attention, adaptation, and autocriticism are also involved. Feeble-minded subjects often do better on the Block Design than on the Binet and it appears that the test is 'a fairer index of their functional efficiency in various occupations than the Binet' (Kohs, 1923). The good Kohs performer tends to show some personal stability and social adjustment (Sarason and Potter, 1947; Wile and Davis, 1930; Gunzburg, 1956b) whilst poor performance in the Block Design may be due to maladjustment, brain injury, confusion of visual organization, etc. (Goldstein and Scheerer, 1941; Wile and Davis, 1936; Shapiro, 1951a, 1954).

It may be that very large and striking discrepancies between the Kohs performance and the efficiency on other tests are indicative of disordered cerebral functioning, whilst a less dramatic lowering of Kohs performance may suggest emotional disturbance. The qualitative features of the performance have been remarked upon and they will afford the experienced observer further clues (Wile and Davis, 1930; Earl, 1937, 1940).

The evaluation of intelligence test scores

The overall score on any intelligence test, an I.Q., an M.A., indicates *how much* has been achieved and only approximately *how well* the task has been performed. There may be considerable scatter among subtests; or failure due to hesitancy, constant misunderstanding, and hastiness; or, rarely, success due to an exploitation of chance openings instead of systematic reasoning. This indicates that the *quantity* of the test score, so popularized as a measuring device, may be far less useful and often even misleading in estimating mental functioning, unless it is accompanied by a discussion of its *quality*. A low test result which is at disparity with other tests results, or clinical impression, is evidence which has to be used and explained in the clinical assessment, but must not necessarily be taken at its face value.

Analysis of the quality of performance supplements the information obtained from the quantity. This score is the necessary basis for objective recording and general classification. The qualitative aspects enable the experienced observer to decide on the validity of the quantitative results. The combined evidence is structured into a working hypothesis, a diagnosis.

An uncritical acceptance of the I.Q., particularly of low I.Q.s, as an explanation for all individual shortcomings, and therefore as a justification for inaction in the field of rehabilitation, has been responsible for much needless unhappiness. It appears, therefore, imperative that those who make the assessments should be familiar with the advantages and disadvantages, with the effectiveness and validity of the various tests, and should be able to evaluate the relevance of the performance of a person in respect to a given situation. Furthermore, a comparison of intelligence tests results with material derived from investigations of other spheres of the personality is often of crucial importance.

PERSONALITY TESTS

Personality assessment obtains its data, of course, not only from testing in an objectified situation, but from interviews, reports of behaviour, and observation of the person himself. Yet the relationship between the character of the defective and his physique, for instance, has not been adequately explored despite the work of Kretschmer (1936) and Sheldon. Sheldon's Varieties of Temperament (1942) and Varieties of Delinquent Youth (1949) give many examples of defective youth and though there is some controversy about this work much more understanding could probably be gained of the personality shortcomings of mental defectives if attention were paid to the inter-relatedness of mind and body. In this connexion the studies by Ch. Wolff (1942), who developed the psycho-physiological theory of hand-interpretation on objective and statistical lines, must be mentioned. Her investigations with Rollin of the hands of Mongolian imbeciles (1942) and of mental defectives (1944) suggest a new scientific approach to the investigation of temperament and character.

A survey of personality tests (Vernon, 1953) reflects the two main approaches used in this particular field, which can be described as (1) the objective study of separate traits or factors, and (2) the clinical, subjective study of the whole personality. There is no need to oppose these two viewpoints and the objective approach can do much to support, to validate, and to make meaningful to the clinician, the wealth of diagnostic material obtained by the clinical 'wholistic' approach.

The literature on personality testing in mental deficiency indicates that on the whole the clinical wholistic approach has been preferred and little work has been published using factorial analysis (Tizard, 1950; Alderdice and Butler, 1952; Satter, 1955).

Test profiles

The realization that intellectual functioning is closely associated with emotional adjustment has led to many investigations attempting to discover in the quantitative test scores a reflection of overt behaviour. The usual approaches to this problem rely either on the scatter, or variability of subtest scores within one particular test, or on the relationship among different types of tests, and have been referred to as test profile, or psychograph when graphically plotted (Rapaport, 1945, 1946; Jastak, 1949b).

The theory behind the choice of tests and the comparison of tests with widely different standardization, are open to much criticism. Though there have been many publications with 'positive' findings, which are accepted by clinical psychologists, the psychometric pattern has not found general acceptance like the I.Q. and M.A. and has, on the contrary, been referred to as 'intriguing but deceptive wishful thinking' (Wallin and Hultsch, 1944).

The main assumption, underlying the exploration of scatter, is the belief that mental dysfunctioning would show in significant and extreme fluctuations of efficiency on various tests, or test items, whilst the ordinary, normally functioning person would tend to score on comparatively the same level in various properly standardized and selected tests. It has been shown that psychosis, anxiety, and neurosis affect performance on certain tests while leaving unimpaired others, but the fact that subjects suffering from one particular state of mind show a particular test pattern need not necessarily mean that other people displaying the same pattern will also have the same illness. Various investigations have suggested that the mentally deficient show a very marked variability in the test performance (Satter, 1955; Zazzo, 1960a, b), not further surprising in a group of extremely heterogeneous character and with subtests of often very low reliability (Butler. 1954). (See also p. 294, point (4).)

(*a*) *Verbal and performance bias*

It has been held widely that mental defectives perform generally better on non-verbal than verbal tests. Wechsler (1944) found 74 per cent. of his subjects below I.Q. 80 to have a higher performance I.Q. compared with the verbal I.Q. Subsequent work on the W–B test tended to support this (Sloan and Cutts, 1945; Cutts and Sloan, 1945; Cutts and Lane, 1947; Hays, 1950/1; McKenzie, 1951; Vanderhost *et al.*, 1953; Mundy and Maxwell, 1958) and the same tendency was observed on the W.I.S.C. (Sloan and Schneider, 1951; Sandercock and Butler, 1952; Vanderhost *et al.*, 1953; Newman and Loos, 1955; Beck and Lam, 1955). Other investigations suggest, however, that the presence or absence of performance bias may well be the result of a particular I.Q. level (Stacey and Levine, 1951; Warren and Kraus, 1961; Manne *et al.*, 1962), sex (Miller *et al.*, 1961), or aetiology. It has, for example, been pointed out that brain-damaged defectives tend to have higher verbal I.Q.s (Allen, 1947; Andersen, 1951; Newman and Loos, 1955; Morrow and Mark, 1955), that the location and spread of lesion are important (Reitan, 1955; Milner, 1958), and that the verbal bias is found in C.N.S. infection and other organic nervous diseases but not in epilepsy (Fisher, 1960b).

Wechsler (1958) was unable to confirm the existence of performance bias in the subnormal on the W.A.I.S. despite his previous findings with the Wechsler–Bellevue, Form I, and this was corroborated by Fisher (1960b) who was also unable to establish a bias on the W.A.I.S. in a group of undifferentiated and familial 'garden variety' defectives. An interesting study of a severely criminal population in an institution showed that 'higher Performance than Verbal scores occurred throughout the Full Scale I.Q. range *except* in the case of mental defectives. In the latter group it appeared to be a matter of chance whether the Performance or Verbal Score was higher.' It was concluded 'that the frequency of sociopaths showing higher Performance than Verbal scores tended to *decrease* as Full Scale I.Q. decreased from normal to subnormal range' (Manne *et al.*, 1962). Warren and Kraus (1961) found, however, a performance bias on the W.A.I.S. in over 75 per cent. of their subjects with I.Q.s below 79.

It must, however, be borne in mind that practically all these studies are based on populations of institutionalized patients. A great proportion of mental defectives become hospitalized because of psychopathic behaviour and delinquency. Studies by the Gluecks (1950), Clarke (1949), Peixotto (1950), Diller (1952), Wiens *et al.* (1959), Fisher (1961), tend to indicate that a performance bias is typical for the adolescent psychopath as pointed out by Wechsler. On the other hand these findings are not fully corroborated (Strother, 1944; Clarke and Moore, 1950; Gurvitz, 1950; Foster, 1959; Panton, 1960; Field, 1960a). Much of the conflicting evidence can be ascribed to faulty experimental designs and to the difficulties of agreeing on the definition of 'sociopath' or psychopath (Rabin and Guertin, 1951; McCord and McCord, 1956).

Many clinicians hold the view that a performance bias carries a favourable prognosis. Besides studies using other tests than the Wechsler (Earl, 1937, 1940; Bijou, 1942a, b, 1944; Bijou and McCandless, 1944; Roberts, 1945a) there are now a few researches available based on the Wechsler patterns. Fitzpatrick (1956) pointed out that patients with a performance bias on the W–B were more likely to be placed on daily employment but she also suggested an extreme performance bias was not a favourable sign. Windle (1962) using data by Fry (1956) found some support for the 'predictive utility of pattern scores' but not in a second investigation. Other investigators were also unable to differentiate between adjusted and maladjusted cases on the basis of subtest patterning (Brill, 1936; Wallin and Hultsch, 1944; Sloan and Cutts, 1945; Cutts and Sloan, 1945).

The clinical significance of 'verbal bias' in mental deficiency has received far less attention. Verbal bias does not occur as frequently as performance bias, but there is much inclination to ascribe to it an unfavourable prognosis (Earl, 1940), and Hamlin (1938) found it frequently in behaviour problem cases. The idea of unfavourable prognosis is partly supported by Wechsler's observation that schizophrenic and brain-damaged cases tend to show a verbal bias, and it is reasonable to assume that brain-damaged and schizophrenic mental defectives have a poor social prognosis. There is, however, very little research available on this subject and some of it contradicts the unfavourable diagnosis attributed to verbal bias (Miller *et al.*, 1961).

As far as the prognostic value of performance bias is concerned, Windle's suggestion (1962) that 'performance patterns may be prognostic only for release and not for adjustment after release' offers a reasonable explanation for the consistency with which clinicians adhere to this favourable prognosis. It must be remembered that the sociopaths and delinquents, who tend to have a performance bias, are usually patients with some 'drive' and ability, who are more capable of impressing the institution authorities with their potential social adequacy than the undistinguished, driveless 'garden variety' patient. Until further research has established exact and reliable criteria of social failure and success, it is probably safer to associate 'performance bias' with the ability of making a 'good impression' and therefore getting a certain measure of priority and attention leading to early consideration for release rather than with actual social success.

Those clinicians who use test patterns for prognostic and diagnostic purposes should bear in mind that it is important to have some knowledge about the distribution and frequency of subtest scores on different age and I.Q. levels. Suitable techniques have been developed (Payne and Gwynne Jones, 1957; Field, 1960b; Fisher, 1960c) which offer a certain safeguard against drawing clinical inferences from occurrences which are only due to chance. An excellent discussion of prognostic methods can be found in Windle's (1962) monograph.

(*b*) *Moron battery*

As an example of the use of the psychogram in clinical and prognostic work, Earl's Moron Battery (1940, 1961) is illustrative. Based on the performance on the Terman Vocabulary and a verbal absurdities test on the one hand, and the Kohs Block Design and Dearborn Formboard test on the other, he constructed a psychogram, scored in deciles, and used it in the prognosis of social adaptability of young adult feeble-minded patients. Comparing the graphs with an evaluation of the subjects' behaviour and their psychiatric record, he found that patients who had unbiased curves had the best social prognosis. Irregular curves and those with verbal bias were of bad prognostic import. Performance bias had a fairly good social prognosis. The interpretation of the psychogram is not, however, exclusively based on verbal and performance bias but pays attention to inconsistent behaviour in the verbal and non-verbal areas.

The Moron Battery has been designed to obtain psychometrically an assessment of certain important personality factors which have otherwise to be judged and assessed purely clinically. In view of the great influence of environmental factors, prediction based on clinical assessments alone deals only with one group of factors determining success and failure. All that a 'good' prognosis means is that the mentally defective person is 'less vulnerable' to unfavourable circumstances than if he had a 'poor' prognosis. Indeed, it may be that the battery's best clinical use lies in drawing attention to the fact that patients with a 'poor' prognosis require more support and guidance than those with a 'good' prognosis, if social adjustment is to be effected. If the environmental support happens to be good, the 'poor' prognosis may actually be contradicted by facts – yet the essential vulnerability still remains.

In these circumstances, validation of this battery (or of any other similar type of test pattern approach) remains extremely difficult. Earl's small sample of 66 patients (1940) showed nevertheless on purely quantitative evidence valid social prognoses and Windle (1962) computed a $P < 0{\cdot}001$ for it. Gunzburg (1959) applied the battery to 44 patients, not contained in the original sample, and checked the prognoses six to nine years after test administration. He found great difficulties in establishing the 'consistency' of the prognosis with the final outcome, partly because it was nearly impossible to assess the degree of extra assistance given by the environment, partly because changes in legislation, public opinion, and hospital administration made it in many cases even more difficult to determine what was a genuine failure in social adjustment or merely a failure to comply with rules and regulations. Moreover, it was difficult to see what time limit was to be attached to a prognosis, since, for example, 'failure' ten years after discharge could scarcely be regarded as equivalent to failure one year thereafter. The results of the survey must be assessed in light of the observation made in the preceding section on performance bias and were consistent with Windle's (1962) suggestion that patients 'with favourable test psychographs are more likely to be released than those with unfavourable psychographs'.

The battery has not been used by other investigators, mainly because it is unwieldy, taking a fairly long time to administer. Until recently neither administration nor scoring procedure was available in print, but now there is a full manual in Earl's *Subnormal Personalities* (1961). There is also little doubt that some of the tests are probably of doubtful validity and that the battery is poorly and inadequately standardized. Yet, as a clinical tool, the Moron Battery with all its technical shortcomings, and considering the complexity of the task it is tackling, has value in providing a systematic approach to the exploration of cognitive and non-cognitive aspects which have a bearing on social adjustment. Earl points out that the psychogram must not be used purely quantitatively, but that the result 'must be interpreted in the light of the qualities of behaviour observed during the test, and eventually in the light of all the available data' (Earl, 1940).

(*c*) *Jastak's psychogram*

Another method which uses diagnostically the difference of levels of various tests has been advocated by J. Jastak. Rejecting the global concept of I.Q.s as often misrepresenting a subject's efficiency because I.Q.s 'are nearly always averages of widely disparate measures and thus bear a stigma of psychological irrelevance' (1949a) he points out how often certified defectives show in later life a surprising capacity for personal, scholastic, social, and occupational adjustment. This inconsistency between diagnosis and later life performance can be avoided by paying initially more attention to the pattern of success and failure. Only a person who has been examined on a large number of tests representing many different functions or abilities, and who has failed to pass the lowest two or three percentiles *on any* of the tests, can be called a genuine feeble-minded person. If there is average achievement on any test regardless of the ability tested, as indicated by the Altitude Quotient, intellectual defect can be automatically excluded despite a defective global I.Q.[1] This psychometric pattern indicates personality defects and suggests definite possibilities of rehabilitation whilst the truly feeble-minded is and will always be a failure.

Jastak gives an example of three cases, each with a global I.Q. 62.

[1] Jastak (1963) points out that 25 per cent. of the population have I.Q.s below 90 and would have to be regarded as mentally retarded if the I.Q. were used as the sole index. If this criterion is, however, combined with other measures of ability (schooling, occupational achievement, and altitude quotient) the multiple criterion selects only 5 per cent. as genuinely retarded. This 'implies that for every 25 individuals diagnosed as retarded solely upon the basis of I.Q., 20 of them (80 per cent.) would subsequently be found to be misclassified' if other aspects were also considered.

Jastak uses the concept of the *altitude* of intelligence which had been introduced by Thorndike. Altitude refers to the difficulty level of a task and in theory a person should be able to execute tasks of all kinds if of the same, or a lower, level of difficulty.

Even if it were possible to rank all tasks in order of intellectual difficulty, one would still have to consider how far lack of opportunity, motivation, reward, interest, etc., influence the efficiency of execution of tasks well up to the level indicated by 'altitude'. Yet the concept of altitude as an indication of a possible existing, but unrealized, potential, is useful for the clinical-therapeutic work in mental deficiency, if over-interpretation is avoided (Brown and Bryan, 1957).

The results of twelve different tests expressed in standard scores are plotted on the radii in Fig. 3. The middle circle represents average achievement or a standard score of 100, the two other circles indicate two standard deviations above and below the average achievement. The charted points of test levels yield a psychometric pattern showing visually at once whether a case is an all-round failure on all

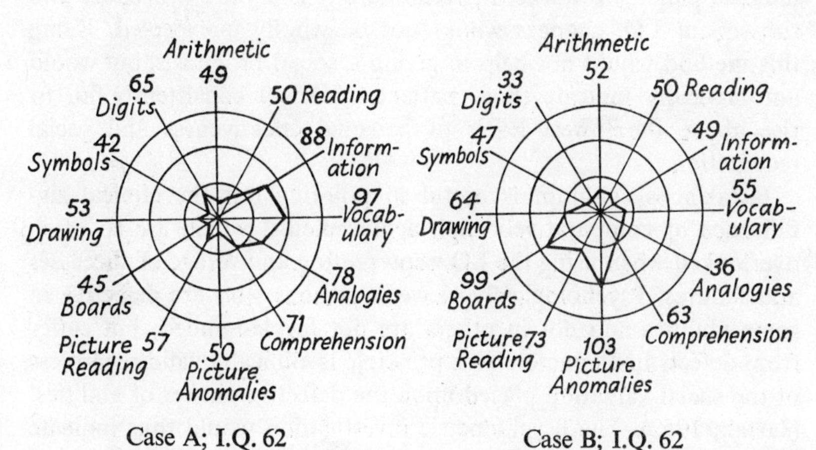

Case A; I.Q. 62

Psychiatric Diagnosis:
Schizoid personality in person of average intelligence

Case B; I.Q. 62

Psychiatric Diagnosis:
Psychopathic personality in person of average intelligence.

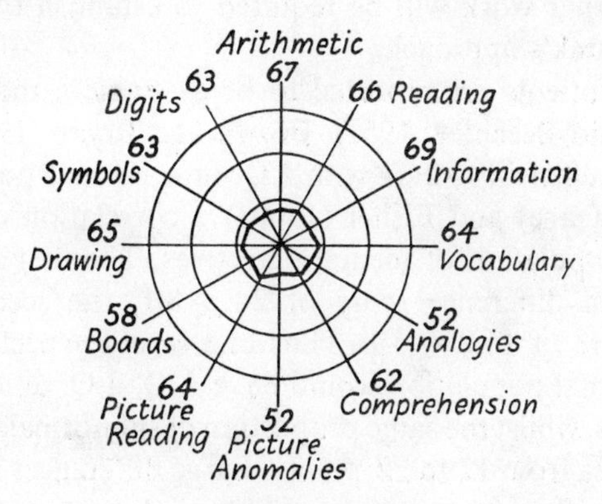

Case C; I.Q. 62

Psychiatric Diagnosis:
Inherent mental deficiency moron level, in person of adequate personality.

Fig. 4 (after Jastak)

tested abilities, or whether outstanding features indicate potentials and personality defects (Jastak, 1949a).

Such a rigid criterion of mental deficiency would separate psychometrically a very homogeneous group of patients with a genuine all-round lack of ability from those functioning on a low level despite existing abilities. This psychometric procedure would thus indicate patients for whom psychotherapy is a valid procedure and subsequent I.Q. changes would not be wholly unexpected. Using this method would not help in giving a social prognosis, but would automatically indicate those patients who will consistently fail to rise above the lowest levels of personal effectiveness and social recognition.

Jastak's psychogram is useful in pointing out the clinical significance of comparatively high achievements, which are so often overlooked when using the I.Q. representing an average of successes and failures. Psychologically viewed, 'persons who are defective in some abilities and not in others are not feeble-minded, but suffer from defects in character. This principle is clinically valid regardless of the social valuation placed upon the defective cluster of abilities' (Jastak, 1952). The psychometric investigation would thus indicate the need for further intensive treatment and Jastak states that this usually results in improvement; some experimental support for Jastak's views has come forth (Purcell *et al.*, 1952; Whiteman, 1950), but much further work will be required to establish the diagnostic validity of Jastak's approach.

Altitude quotients are reported to be as stable a measure as the I.Q. (Diller and Beechley, 1951). Brown and Bryan (1957) report a correlation coefficient +0·87 with I.Q. in a normal population (10 to 29 years of age) and Fisher (1960a) a correlation coefficient of +0·90 in a population of mental defectives. The first investigation found a mean difference score of 24 ± 8·1, the second a mean difference score of 16·9 ± 5·1. Thus one would expect that 68 per cent. in a normal population would have A.Q.–I.Q. differences from 16 to 33 points, whilst the same proportion of subnormals would show I.Q. differences from 12 to 22 points. Large differences between I.Q. and A.Q. are therefore quite common and are, in the mentally deficient, mostly due to those subtests on the Wechsler which have been found to be 'easy' for them (e.g. Object Assembly, Picture Completion, Comprehension – Fisher, 1960a, b; Baroff, 1959).

(d) Zazzo's Heterochronia

Impressed by the fact that the global I.Q. bears little relationship to social competency and adequacy in adult life, Zazzo and his co-workers have used the concept of Heterochronia for diagnostic and prognostic purposes (Hurtig, 1962; Zazzo, 1962a). A battery of tests measuring psychomotor efficiency, spatial organization, and educational achievement produces a number of developmental quotients (calculated in relation to the chronological age) which, together with the I.Q. (also regarded as a D.Q.), results in a psychogram. Zazzo confirmed the findings of previous workers that mental defectives show better non-verbal than verbal abilities, but he also showed that typically the mentally deficient child succeeds better in tests of psychomotor efficiency (cancellation and dotting) than in tests of spatial organization (Bender Gestalt). Zazzo gives the example of a mentally deficient boy aged 14, with Binet–Simon Mental Age 10. His performance expressed in terms of D.Q.s is 71 for the Binet, 57 for the Bender, and 86 for the cancellation test (Zazzo, 1962, b). The important point for Zazzo is the fact that it is normal for a mentally defective child to have different scores on different types of tests and that, compared with the normal child, he develops at different rates depending on the sector of development concerned.

This has important repercussions on prognosis. If unevenness of performance is characteristic of the genuine mental defective child, then the atypical even performance on the tests suggests 'pseudo-deficiency' and thus a good prognosis. Evidence quoted by Zazzo (1962a) appears to support this by demonstrating that children with uniformly poor test results tended to show greater improvement than others of the same mental level but showing uneven patterns.

Generally Zazzo's findings confirm those of his predecessors. The mental defectives' comparatively good performance ability is again underlined by his work and, like Earl, he finds that those defectives with an 'even' performance showed the best improvement. On the other hand, Zazzo maintains that the differential diagnosis between mental deficiency and pseudo-mental deficiency is established because of the typical unevenness of the psychogram in the first case and the evenness of performance in the second. Jastak holds the opposite view by asserting that the very unevenness of the performance suggests that there is no mental deficiency present, which is characterized by a poor even performance in all spheres.

These completely contradictory viewpoints cannot be reconciled.

As in Jastak's case, no work is available which corroborates Zazzo's predictions on the basis of the psychogram by actual follow-up in community adaptation.

Test patterns appear to offer the clinical psychologist support for his 'hunches' and indicate personality traits. He has to use his clinical experience, acumen, and insight to evaluate each individual performance and draws his conclusions by considering *all* available evidence. The judgment of the clinician based on, and incorporating, these test indications may be of high validity, but it is unavoidable that the clinical usefulness of test patterns is more than ever dependent on the craftsmanship of the user.

Projective testing

Techniques of this type use generally the same principle: the subject is faced with stimulus material as unstructured and amorphous as the test constructor thinks advisable for his particular purpose, and is thus able to respond freely, comparatively little guided by the stimulus. The responses reveal to the observer much suppressed and repressed material, often yield a better understanding of the subject, and lighten up his conflicts, wishes, and needs.

Projective techniques have been widely assailed because of their lack of objectivity and validity; however, clinicians who have been using these tests have, on the whole, been content with stating 'but it works' without troubling about scientific 'proof'.

The evidence obtained with the help of personality tests like the Rorschach and the drawing test, has often helped to confirm clinical observations in mental deficiency. Other tests, though not widely used in mental deficiency work, may produce in time valuable material: T.A.T. (Masserman and Balken, 1938; Sarason, 1943; Gothberg, 1947; Bergman *et al.*, 1951; Bergman and Fisher, 1953; Lubin, 1955); Lowenfeld Mosaic test (Kerr, 1939; Wertham and Golden, 1941; Diamond and Schmale, 1944; Himmelweit and Eysenck, 1945; McCulloch and Girdner, 1949; Shotwell and Lawrence, 1951; Lowenfeld, 1954; Carr, 1958); Lowenfeld World test (Lowenfeld, 1939; Michael and Buhler, 1945; Buhler, 1951; Lumry, 1951; Buhler *et al.*, 1951; Bowyer, 1958); Rosenzweig Picture Frustration test (Foulds, 1945a, b; Portnoy and Stacey, 1954; Lipman, 1959; Foreman, 1962).

The existence of adjustment problems, of emotional conflicts, of severely depressed intellectual functioning despite normal potential, of guilt feelings, of inferiority feelings, in short the existence of a 'personality' in the mental defective – which had been overlooked very often in the eagerness of measuring I.Q.s – has been shown in these tests.

(a) The Rorschach test

Klopfer and Kelley (1942) state quite categorically that the test is

> of particular value in its application to problems of the mentally deficient because, as seems obvious, such patients are not of importance merely because they have I.Q.s of a certain value; they are definite clinical problems. The detection of the nature and magnitude of their personality trends is perhaps the most valuable function of the Rorschach method. . . . The Rorschach method, indicating as it does the existence of certain potentialities or trends in addition to a certain intelligence level, may justly be applied to problems of investigation of the mentally deficient.

A perusal of the literature relating to the special field of mental deficiency (Kelley and Barrera, 1941) suggests that much effort has been spent on comparing Rorschach signs and intelligence quotients (Altus and Thompson, 1949; Tucker, 1950; Arbitman, 1953; Rosenblatt and Solomon, 1954; Zubin *et al.*, 1956; Ogdon and Allee, 1959) but little time on the study of the personality dynamics of the mentally defective functioning in the lower range of intelligence. Researches have been mainly concerned with checking the original hypothesis advanced by Rorschach regarding the prevalence of certain scoring categories (Kelley and Barerra, 1941). The occurrence of a pathognomonic response described by Rorschach as Do (oligophrenic detail) was not corroborated by later research workers (Pfister, 1926; Beck, 1930, 1932; Arbitman, 1953). Since mental deficiency is not an entity, it is not surprising that no characteristic test pattern has been demonstrated for the mentally deficient, except perhaps the well-known 'flat' record which gives little or no lead to the interpreter. It was, however, shown that certain types of responses tended to increase with mental age (Arbitman, 1953) though the quality of the responses still differentiates normal children from mentally defective adults of the same mental age (Rosenblatt and Solomon, 1954).

The Rorschach method seems not only to suffer from the usual handicaps of researches (small groups, inadequate control of variables, etc.), but even more because so many of those classified psychometrically and socially as mentally deficient, are, according to Rorschach findings, far from being so. The score diagnosis on the Rorschach appears to apply therefore only to the low-grade defective, whilst the presence of even a single 'good response' would strongly counter-indicate mental deficiency – an approach which is comparable to Jastak's rigid psychometric criterion (Hackbusch and Klopfer, 1946).

The Rorschach evidence – considering and weighing each response in its context and giving it relevance and significance beyond its categorical and numerical value – evolves in the case of the feeble-minded defective very often a picture at variance with accepted opinions and findings. Jolles (1947b) selected a group of 66 children with a Mean Full Scale Wechsler I.Q. 66·85 (all children had an I.Q. below 80) who had been considered mentally defective because of their serious educational retardation, their failure to respond to various teaching techniques, their emotional and social immaturity, and their apparent mental retardation as indicated by psychological tests. Though none of these children had shown overt behaviour problems, Jolles found in each case that the Rorschach revealed severe emotional disturbance. There were cases of anxiety neurosis, schizoid trends, feelings of inferiority, depression, compulsions, and he came to the conclusion that 'there is, perhaps, a greater incidence of normals functioning mentally defective than clinicians have believed to be true' and ends with the statement that 'a low I.Q. is only a symptom of a severe emotional disturbance in all cases except where an organic factor is present. Hackbusch and Klopfer (1946), Sarason and Sarason (1946), and Ruess (1958) discuss evidence of a similar nature where the Rorschach and T.A.T. tests helped to rule out a diagnosis of mental deficiency despite the results of traditional intelligence testing.

Several investigations suggest that the use of the Rorschach test highlights personality disturbances (Patterson and Magaw, 1936; Sloan, 1947a; Font, 1950) and assists in prognosis (Day *et al.*, 1940; Clarke, 1946; Sloan 1948; Solomon, 1955). Feeble-minded girls, who did fairly well in academic work, were shown to have a good integrated personality on the Rorschach, whilst girls with confused and scattered Rorschach responses did not do well at school (Abel, 1945).

The Rorschach test has also been used for diagnosing brain injury among the mentally deficient (Werner, 1945a, b; Eckhardt,

1961) and for differential diagnosis between schizophrenia and mental deficiency (Piotrowski, 1937; Clarke, 1946).

It is disappointing that Rorschach records revealing severe mental under-functioning have not led to follow-up studies to validate the diagnosis. Case studies of individuals, giving no opportunity of checking the validity of diagnosis and prognosis, are not so convincing (Font, 1950).

(*b*) *Drawing of a person* (*D.A.P. test*)

This test has been used mostly in the form introduced by F. Goodenough (1926) as the 'Draw-a-Man test'. In this original form it gave a good measure of intelligence, correlating well with other intelligence tests in populations of normal children on whom the test was standardized. An extension and revision of the original scale has been published by Harris (1963) who also reviews the work on human figure drawings. The popularity of the test on account of the ease of administration and scoring, and its appeal to the unsophisticated mind, has led to many other applications in populations for which the test had not been standardized. In populations of mental defectives there was found on the whole a significant, and at times high correlation with other tests, e.g. the Stanford–Binet: $r = 0{\cdot}72$ (McElwee, 1932), $r = 0{\cdot}60$ (Yepsen, 1929), $r = 0{\cdot}45$ (McHugh, 1945a), $r = 0{\cdot}48$ (Earl, 1933), $r = 0{\cdot}78$ (Murphy, 1956), $r = 0{\cdot}69$ (Birch, 1949). Evidence from other sources suggested that the drawing was affected by factors like maturity, environment, and pathological conditions ranging from psychopathy to organic damage (Hinrichs, 1935; McHugh, 1945b; Berrien, 1935; Earl, 1933). A wealth of literature dealing with art production in general and with the human figure in particular has made the conclusion inevitable that the D.A.P. becomes less valid as a measure of intelligence the more the subject deviates from 'normality'. This rule does obviously not apply to the subcultural person, the endogenous, uncomplicated feeble-minded whose mental deficiency is as normal, statistically seen, as are short and tall men in an unselected population. It applies, however, to people who function as mental defectives below their potential, to defectives whose efficiency is affected by emotional disturbances, to defectives with superimposed psychosis, and to those with organic involvement.

This was demonstrated by Gunzburg (1955a) when he compared two groups of 40 adult defectives, matched for sex, age, and the

Wechsler I.Q.s, but differentiated by psychiatric diagnosis. One 'pathological' group consisted of cases diagnosed as epileptics, neurotics, organics, psychotics, etc., who produced drawings correlating with the Wechsler Full Scale I.Q., $r = 0{\cdot}52 \pm 0{\cdot}08$. The other group composed of uncomplicated feeble-minded men created drawings correlating with the Wechsler Full Scale I.Q., $r = 0{\cdot}72 \pm 0{\cdot}05$. Murphy (1956) found similarly $r = 0{\cdot}78$ with the Stanford–Binet in a group of 30 adjusted mentally deficient adults. In another investigation (Bliss and Berger, 1954) the rank order correlation coefficient between standard intelligence tests and the drawing test was 0·27 in organic cases but 0·66 in familiar and 0·87 in 'unexplained' cases. Greene (1945) reports that the Goodenough drawings of mentally deficient 'problem' girls were nearly a year and a half retarded as compared with the adjusted group, though neither intelligence tests nor school achievement tests reflected this disparity.

It appears that the 'Draw-a-Person' technique for the purpose of obtaining quickly an intelligence estimate can be used only in cases where factors like cerebral injuries, psychosis, or neurosis can be ruled out. These are not always easily ascertainable although the drawing itself may often indicate the presence of factors interfering with its 'level'. This approach, comparable to the scatter analysis of psychometry, has been investigated in the cases of maladjusted and adjusted children (Brill, 1937; Springer, 1941), in disturbed educationally subnormal children (Gunzburg, 1950a, 1952), and in adult defectives (Earl, 1933; Gunzburg, 1955a).

Gunzburg enumerates some criteria in drawings which make it possible to differentiate between the normal productions of the uncomplicated feeble-minded and the abnormal drawings of the 'pathological' cases. On the basis of statistical findings he lists certain inconsistencies and 'pathological' signs in the drawings which indicate that the drawing level as measured on the Goodenough scale is affected by extraneous factors and need not be in agreement with intelligence test findings. The absence of these signs suggests that the level of the drawing has not been interfered with and can reasonably be assumed to correspond with the intellectual level established by an intelligence test. In a sample of 344 adult defectives he reports that in the 'pathological group' the Goodenough I.Q. correlated only $r = 0{\cdot}36$ with the Wechsler Performance Scale, but the non-pathological group correlated $r = 0{\cdot}73$ with the same scale. He gives a table of tentative norms applicable to non-pathological drawings.

Gunzburg's technique is in many ways unsatisfactory. Some of the criteria are rather subjective and many of them occur only in the more primitive type of drawing. The method requires further investigation of the high-scoring drawings and extension of the norms to older and female defectives; the present data refer only to young feeble-minded men.

Many of the inconsistencies and pathological signs utilized by Gunzburg have been interpreted by other investigators as indicating possible maladjustment. Light has been thrown on the aetiology of these features by the recent clinical approaches to the drawing of the human figure, connected with the names of Machover (1949), J. Buck (1948) and Hammer (1958). These authors and their collaborators assume that the 'artist' projects many unconscious wishes, needs, desires, and feelings into his concept of a person formulated on paper.

The stimulating, intriguing, and challenging hypotheses of these authors have so far been seldom supported by evidence of a more objective kind (Popplestone, 1954). A few case studies have appeared but most investigators have selected a few isolated points and submitted them to experimental verification. As far as the field of mental deficiency is concerned some difficulties arise by applying the clinical experiences obtained in work with intellectually normal people to intellectual subnormals, whose expressive powers are diminished and follow perhaps different rules. This means that the drawing test interpretation has to pay great attention to the 'artist's' intellectual level. The intellectually subnormal person, being little capable of adapting quickly to an emotionally disturbing situation, and of choosing a socially acceptable reaction, will show this inability far more strikingly in the drawing than the intelligent person faced with the same disturbing situation. An intelligent person, for example, drawing the crotch area with its sexual associations may betray his sexual tensions only by a heightened pressure of the pencil, or by a weaker uncertain pencil line; the subnormal may panic and omit closing the lines in the disturbing area. The intelligent normal, associating the drawing of hands with guilt feelings on account of masturbation, or stealing, may unconsciously express his feelings by hiding the hands in the pockets, or behind the back; the unintelligent, unable to find a rational way out of his dilemma, may simply cut off the hands, leaving the stumps to tell the tale.

There is a danger of indiscriminate over-interpretation by the enthusiastic clinician. Yet the wide range of often crude, but nevertheless expressive, drawings produced by the mentally deficient indicates in many cases far more than mere intellectual subnormality. Many of the 'abnormalities' in their drawings must be considered simply as signs of disturbed functioning expressed by primitive techniques. The drawings appear to point very often to areas of conflict, anxiety situations, and potential 'trouble spots' which require attention.[1]

An example will help to illustrate this test's potentialities:

Norman, who had attended a special school, was admitted to a mental deficiency institution at the age of 16, largely because it was felt that he was incapable of independent survival in the open community; nor had he relatives to take care of him. Soon after admission – which was a great shock to him – he became a constant absconder apparently with the aim of making 'outsiders' interested in him. These energetic escapades were brought to a sudden stop when he had to be hospitalized and operated on for a left maxillary and a large mandibular cyst. He then developed sciatic paralysis in the left leg and was extremely poorly for some time. The stay in hospital represented an eye-opening turning point in his life making him realize, probably for the first time, how lonely and deserted he was. After recovery the absconding was pursued rather half-heartedly and in the end he requested transfer to another smaller hospital where he settled surprisingly well for a few years.

Norman (Wechsler Full I.Q. 66, Verbal I.Q. 67, Perfomance I.Q. 71 at C.A. 18) has been given the Draw-a-Man test at varying intervals since admission to the special school. The first drawing obtained when he was 13 (Plate 2, A), after admission to the residential school, shows probably the after-effects of a disturbed childhood with many abscondings – perhaps in search for parents who had actually deserted him when only a few months old. The missing arms might be associated in this case with his fruitless search and the rejection by his parents.

The settling atmosphere of the school brought some happiness (B), but the abscondings, which had completely ceased during this school time, were resumed after admission to the M.D. Institution. The drawings of the after-school period (C and D) show at first no disturbance: Norman was too convinced of his ultimate success. Three months after the return from his stay in hospital the deep impression of this traumatic event was reflected in the drawing (E); mouth drawn excessively large – operation for the cysts; heel shaded – physical discomfort of wearing leg irons; no arms – rejection by others and/or fruitless appeal. The last theme of the missing arms recurs invariably in the subsequent drawings over the years (F, G, H, I, and K). But this same young man had not 'forgotten' the arms previous to the operation – except in the first unsettled period at school.

When he was 21 he produced an extraordinary drawing. His abscondings had at that time been considerably interfered with by his weak leg and had always ended in failure, as had his search for 'love'. He not only omitted the arms again – which had not obtained the realization of his desires – but he also 'forgot' the legs – which had failed constantly to carry him to

[1] Excellent illustrations of this aspect are given by Abel and Kinder (1942), pp. 40–1.

A: C.A. 13–3

B: C.A. 14–11

C: C.A. 17–2

D: C.A. 17–8

E: C.A. 18–9

F: C.A. 19–3

2a PROJECTION IN THE D.A.P. TEST: A CASE STUDY

G: C.A. 20–5

H: C.A. 20–5

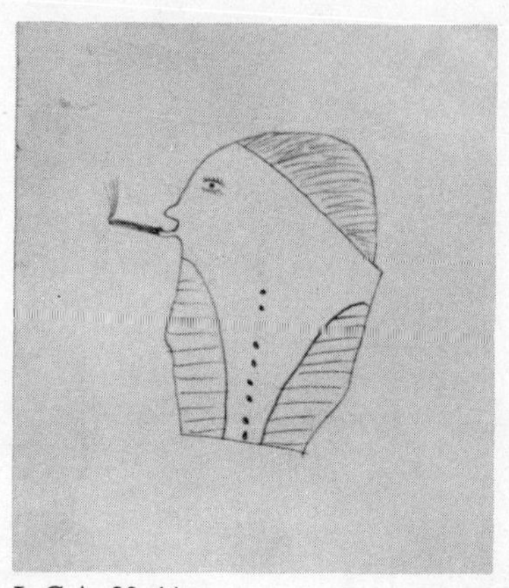

I: C.A. 20–11

K: C.A. 20–11

L: C.A. 22–4

M: C.A. 22–4

2b PROJECTION IN THE D.A.P. TEST: A CASE STUDY

freedom (I). The woman drawn at the same occasion had legs (K) but she (mother?) was still without arms (no love?), and though Norman was shown his drawing of the legless man again he did not spot the so obvious omission.

Soon after he was transferred to the small institution and his absconding ceased. He adjusted to the institution and became satisfied with his situation; see K and L which have become 'normal' and undisturbed again, rather similar to the drawings of his school time (Gunzburg, 1955b).

After some time Norman began again to abscond and consequently spoilt his chances of going on leave (see p. 409). This in turn produced a depression and the 'man' drawn during that time was again without arms. Later, Norman succeeded to keep out of trouble for two years and did not abscond once during that time. He also went on Daily Work (see p. 407) and the drawing obtained soon after the beginning of this new stage seems to reflect his newly found self-assurance. Yet, when licence did not materialize quickly enough for him he began again to abscond, became more depressed and asked repeatedly and with great insistence for a transfer to another hospital. The drawing obtained during that time seems to indicate the return to his feelings of dejection and loneliness – the arms are missing once again.

This short case study illustrates the destructiveness of maladjustment in the drawing, but also its eloquence which is not even hindered by unsophisticated approach and primitive form of expression. The dangers of over-interpretation, particularly in a single example, are very real – but nevertheless this appears to be not an adequate reason for rejecting the additional and supportive information which can be gained from this test.

In summary it can be said that the drawing test as used in mental deficiency directs attention to tension areas in a person, but it must not be expected to reflect automatically conditions which have no emotional significance in a particular case, e.g. the test will not show the *fact* of a homosexual experience unless it has given rise to a *feeling* of emotional disturbance. Though the presence of pathological features suggests abnormality, absence of these clues provides no guidance. Moreover, so far no evidence has been forthcoming which would permit an estimation of the degree and severity of a pathological condition from the degree of abnormality in the drawing, or indicate how much control it exercised over the emotional life.

The test reflects primarily personality, but yields also in many instances a valid estimate of intelligence. It will also often indicate the presence of pathological factors like cerebral damage and superimposed psychosis.

EDUCATIONAL AND SOCIAL ASSESSMENT

Assessment of educational level

No psychometric examination is complete without the administration of tests measuring educational attainment levels. A variety of useful and rapidly scored scales are available (Burt, 1924; Schonell, 1942; Watts, 1944) which will give an indication of the patient's status in relation to the normal school population, and yield valuable information on the extent to which his intellectual potential differs from his attainments. It is, for example, not unusual in any institution for the unstable or delinquent to find young people of normal or above average intellect who are semi-literate or occasionally completely illiterate. As indicated in Chapter XII, a long history of educational failure by no means necessarily connotes poor intellect, and, furthermore, may be directly linked with social maladjustment.

The extent to which educational testing should be applied will depend much on the use made of the findings. Several methods of detailed diagnostic testing of faulty reading and arithmetic habits have been developed in this country for remedial education, and would be applicable to mental defectives if intensive remedial work is planned.[1] A most important aspect of such investigations is to ascertain the degree to which the person is capable of using his attainments. Obtaining a certain fluency in 'barking at print' does not in itself imply adequate comprehension and use of the printed word. Even mastery of the 'four rules' does not guarantee that the defective is able to check his change at Woolworths. More profitable from the point of view of assessing capacity for social functioning is an investigation of how far an individual is able to make use of meagre school knowledge and how far, and in what way, he has been able to overcome his educational shortcomings.

The examination should, therefore, include both a standard test of reading comprehension and practical arithmetic, and expand into a prolonged systematic interview which should explore the use made of these skills as well as the command of 'civic knowledge'. It will be

[1] A careful individual diagnosis can be made even if no standardized tests are available. Bartlet and Shapiro (1956) describe the investigation of a 9-year-old non-reader with an I.Q. of 75, who had failed to benefit from special coaching at a school for maladjusted children. It was found that his difficulties were due to an inability to form associations within and across certain sensory modalities. If the work was in the visual sphere learning was unhampered, but if the work required the use of tactile and visual cues together, great difficulties arose. This analysis suggested the lines along which remedial teaching could successfully be carried out.

valuable to know whether he reads the newspapers, whether he has some inkling of what is going on in the world, whether he looks up advertisements and whether he can account for a day's shopping, or write a letter home. The use of the telephone, his realization of statutory deductions, his ability to obtain information, the manner of spending wages, and planning leisure time activities, will give a fuller picture of his educational standing than a mere reading or arithmetic attainments test.

Literature pertaining to this aspect of educational testing is sparse and suggests that rehabilitation programmes have not considered the effect of meagre educational knowledge. An exact mapping out of the vast blank spaces in a defective's educational knowledge will help to pinpoint many sources of insecurity, escape mechanisms and evasion tactics, and provide the basis for a wider educational approach than simply arranging for instruction in the '3 Rs'. The educational assessment results will then contribute to the therapeutic and rehabilitation aims in the same way as psychometric and personality testing.

A promising and interesting development is a diagnostic test of communication which encourages the design of an individualized remedial training programme to overcome specific weaknesses. The 'Illinois Test of Psycholinguistic Abilities' (McCarthy and Kirk, 1961) was developed from a theory of communication put forward by Osgood (1957). The model from which the test was derived postulates two channels of communication: (*a*) auditory and visual input and (*b*) vocal and motor output. It involves two levels of organization, (*a*) representational or meaning level, and (*b*) automatic-sequential level. Three processes are needed: (*a*) decoding which refers to those abilities required to obtain meaning from visual and auditory linguistic stimuli, (*b*) association refers to the ability to manipulate linguistic symbols internally, (*c*) encoding is the sum of all abilities required to express ideas in words or gestures. A battery of nine tests permits the exploration of each level or process through one of the channels of communication, thus pin-pointing the location of weakness in communication.

The test does not attempt to serve as a classification instrument and avoids a global diagnosis. It does not make

any assumptions with respect to neurological and neurophysiological correlates of behaviour. Its emphasis is on assessing behaviour manifestations in the psycholinguistic field, in relating the assets and deficits to a behavioural (not a neurological) model, and in extending this type of behaviour diagnosis to a remedial teaching situation (Kirk and McCarthy, 1961).

The test in its present form and in an earlier version known as a Differential Language Facility test (Sievers, 1959; Sievers and Rosenberg, 1960; Sievers and Essa, 1961) has produced some interesting work. The reliability correlation coefficients on test–retest reported so far, 0·82 for over 3 months (Smith, 1962), 0·94 over 9 months (Muller and Smith, 1964) and 0·83 over an average interval of 4 months with adult mental defectives (Gunzburg, 1964), suggest that the battery is reliable as a diagnostic instrument. The last-named investigator reports also test–retest coefficients relating to the 9 subtests which range from 0·38 to 0·79 but points out that the test was used for adults though it was standardized on young children.

Kirk's and McCarthy's intention in presenting the I.T.P.A. scale is to provide a diagnostic instrument which would make it possible to plan tutorial remediation in the weak areas by developing a programme starting on the level of actual functioning. Kirk and his associates present various case studies which illustrate the effect of tutorial remediation in those aspects which had been diagnosed as comparatively poorly developed (Kirk and Bateman, 1962; Kirk, Kass and Bateman, 1962).

There has, however, been other work suggesting that a general language programme also improves significantly the language abilities of the children without paying particular attention to specific areas (Smith, 1962). It is too early yet to assess the validity of the diagnostic procedure or even lasting usefulness of a language programme by itself not reinforced by environmental support. Mueller and Smith (1964) show that the gains observed on the I.T.P.A. battery over a period of 3 months were not maintained after approximately 9 months later. (See also pp. 85–6.)

Assessment of social maturity

Dealing with the complex problem of the subnormal has led to the conviction that an adequate sizing up of the defective can be done neither in terms of intelligence, nor personality alone. These aspects, important as they are, receive their relevance only from their influence on the individual's social relationships and, even though their correct assessment is indispensable for problems of treatment and guidance, they are of less help if a person's status in society is to be estimated. The competence with which an individual makes use of his innate abilities, and of his aptitudes, is thought to be measurable on a scale of social competence which reflects the maturation process.

It is no accident that the best known of these scales – the Vineland Social Maturity scale – originated in mental deficiency as it had become clear that the elusive concept of mental deficiency defied very often neat labelling in either intellectual, or personality, terms. Once a subject was rated near that indefinite border area between feeble-mindedness and normality, the final diagnosis depended, not so much on the capacities of the individual himself, but on the use he made of them in the interaction between him and the environment.

Doll set out to develop a serviceable instrument for appraising an individual's social competence which is defined 'as the sum total purposive effect of correlated aptitudes and integrated experiences'. He emphasizes that 'the person as a social unit stands above the mere quantitative synthesis of his distinctive characteristics' and postulates 'a relation between constitutional aptitude and environmental activity'. Thus 'deviation or variation from the normal in these respects, whether arising from physical, mental, or social causes, is ultimately mirrored in some measurable increase, decrease, or other modification of social competence' (Doll, 1953).

The scale which measures and describes in operational terms a subject's competence in defined spheres of behaviour is in fact a standardized interview of people who are in close contact with the subject. It thus does not require the subject's collaboration and is not affected by temporary emotional disturbances. The scale records observed habitual behaviour in areas like self-help, locomotion, occupation, self-direction, communication, and socialization. The inventory of performances is based on a statistical evaluation of their frequency for successive age periods. 'The items are conceived as integrative composites of such specific "trait" qualities as personality, habit, motivation, memory, judgment, emotion, special skills.' The scale is not 'a direct measure of intelligence, skill, personality, or the like, but only of their conative capitalization for social effectiveness' (Doll, 1953).

There have been so many studies of the use of this particular scale among mental defectives that a short reference would be wholly inadequate and the interested reader is referred to the full review in Doll's *Manual* (1953).

In conclusion it must be pointed out that many items of the scale are typically American and refer to that culture. It would require a new standardization in England to make the scale a basis for adequate comparison, though it has been used here occasionally for research work (Bodman, 1946; Rudolf, 1949a, b; Pringle, 1951, 1960). The scale purports to evaluate 'social maturity' and this is not necessarily equivalent to social competence and adequacy. The latter term, though related to, and mostly dependent on, 'maturity', is also a consequence of environment which may have prevented expression and mastery. Social maturity is also relatively independent of social adjustment and the Vineland scale does not seem for example to differentiate between favourable licence and unfavourable licence prospects (Whitcomb, 1945). From the prognostic point of view this latter study illustrates the limitation of a scale which neglects the important factors of personality make-up and emotional maturity and over-emphasizes a person's ability to exist independently rather than his ability to live together with others.

The scale attempts to assign a social standing to a person, just as an intelligence test assigns an intellectual standing to him. But, it should be noted, this rank is again only describing a facet, an acquired reaction pattern, and in itself gives little understanding of why he functions as he does.

Diagnostic testing must pay particular attention to the special needs of the mental defective and many of the tools developed for normal children and norms applying to normal children are not always as helpful as they should be. Recently various assessment procedures relating to social competence have been developed which pay particular attention to the social competence of the mental defective (Cain and Levine, 1961; Gunzburg, 1960, 1963; Katz, 1961; Matthew, 1964). The basis of these techniques is a simple inventory of skills relating to social competence. The choice of the skills is of necessity arbitrary and depends very much on experience and on research findings available. Diagnosing specific weaknesses in social competence should draw attention to individual needs and initiate a 'tailor-made' remedial programme (Cain and Levine, 1961). Comparisons with the standards prevailing in 'normal populations' are not very useful for actual remedial work and it is often more helpful to relate an individual subnormal person's performance to those of other subnormal persons with a similar intellectual handicap rather than judging him on the 'average performance' of a normal person. This method results in establishing the comparative standing of an individual mental defective in relation to a group of the same age and with comparable intellectual deficit, and indicates how much better or worse he is in relation to that particular group (Gunzburg, 1964c).

Since social competence depends partly on adequate training, education facilities, local conditions, and last but not least on the courage of parents and educators, the development of general norms appears to be inadvisable. On the other hand local and temporary norms can provide useful guidance and short-term teaching targets which would help to establish realistic and obtainable objectives. Norms of this kind have been published (Gunzburg, 1964a, b) but are of a temporary and local nature and cannot be used generally.

There is a somewhat astounding dearth of tests of social ability (Hegge, 1942). Porteus (1920) offered a Social Rating scale which rates each individual on a five-point scale on seven aspects of behaviour: lack of planning capacity, impulsiveness, irresolution, suggestibility, obtrusiveness, excitability, and instability of moods. It correlated with General Social Estimate in two small samples to the extent of 0·88 and 0·89, but has not been validated against actual life performance.

It would seem that the field where the crucial encounter between the defective and society takes place has been left largely unexplored from the point of view of psychological assessment. Intelligence and personality tests offer a large amount of useful information regarding the individual's resources and the dynamics of his personality make-up, but there is for the mental defective no adequate measure of what is sometimes called 'social intelligence'.

VARIOUS TESTS[1]

Aptitude tests

Little use has been made so far of aptitude testing in mental deficiency. Generally speaking the defective's abilities permit little

[1] *Editors' Note.* The work of the clinical or educational psychologist is by no means limited to the application of standard tests; Shapiro (1951b) and his colleagues have been responsible for a new and healthy trend in psychology in pointing out the value of the experimental approach with individual problems.

more than unskilled work and it appears hardly worth while to search for particular specialized abilities, the full exploitation of which is severely hindered by educational and intellectual shortcomings and by the defective's inadequate personality. Tizard (1950) applied a battery of tests aiming to measure spatial aptitude, form perception, eye–hand co-ordination, motor speed, finger dexterity, and manual dexterity. Though he found that apparently 'motor co-ordination and precision of movement are more difficult for defectives than are tasks demanding form and space perception', he was hesitant about the reliability and validity of his findings on statistical grounds. He also pointed out that a good deal more research needs to be done before such tests can be used for vocational purposes.

Summing up their researches on the use of batteries of various selected tests for the prediction of occupational success, O'Connor and Tizard (1956) concluded that so far 'ratings have been more successful predictors than were objective tests'.

Motor co-ordination

It has been held by many authorities (e.g. Tredgold, Doll) that mental defectives display marked degrees of motor retardation, showing often not so much in manual dexterity as in body balance and body movement. It has been suggested that there is a close relationship between motor co-ordination and the general maturation process and experimental work has tried to develop scales for

---

This procedure requires the designing of special tests to investigate a particular hypothesis. The use of control groups, and the careful step-by-step elimination of variables, demands experimentation which must be undertaken when practical questions of treatment are at stake which cannot be resolved by other means. Thus, Bartlet and Shapiro (1956) state that 'The problems of clinical and educational psychology are often discussed as if rigorously objective psychological work is limited to the use of tests of established standardization and validity. As there are very few such tests, the psychologist often thinks that he is forced into the use of subjective and intuitional methods.' This paper, concerning the investigation and successful treatment of a reading difficulty in a dull child with severe psychiatric disturbances, gives outstanding support to the authors' claim that an alternative method, the experimental investigation of the individual, with the use of *ad hoc* rather than standardized test material, is not only possible but fruitful. It may be objected that such an approach is exceedingly time-consuming; nevertheless the investigation of *individual* problems is likely to have implications for *general* theory, and advances in our understanding of *processes* can only come in this manner. This is by no means to deny the value of well standardized and validated clinical and educational tests but these in the main must be regarded as descriptive rather than explanatory. Description by itself is unlikely to identify the appropriate methods of treatment in difficult cases, although it lays the foundation for intensive inquiry. It cannot be urged too strongly, therefore, that investigation of *processes* must in future be given priority in the field of mental deficiency. See also Shapiro (1957).

measuring motor proficiency in general (Oseretzky), or in particular tasks (Heath, 1942). The use of these tests has not been widespread and no reliable norms or validation data are available for this country.

Using the Oseretzky Test of Motor Proficiency (Doll, 1946) in a small but well-controlled experiment Sloan (1951) found that 'mental defectives are significantly inferior to children of average intelligence in motor proficiency'. He concludes that motor proficiency is related to intelligence and not 'a distinct aspect of functioning which can be isolated from general behaviour but is rather another aspect of the total functioning of the organism'.

The rail-walking test (Heath, 1942), measuring the ability to balance across three wooden rails of standardized design, has been used on mental defectives in America (Heath, 1946), for differential diagnosis of endogenous and exogenous aetiology (Heath, 1942), and in England (Tizard, 1950), as well as on normal people (Heath, 1943). The test showed marked different levels in locomotor co-ordination.

Special tests

In some cases standard test procedures are inadvisable because of a suspected, or apparent, sensory handicap. In the first case a few special diagnostic tests will have to be applied, e.g. colour blindness (Ishihara), whilst in the second case some of the usual routine tests may have to be replaced by less well standardized tests which are, however, not so affected by sensori-motor handicaps. Abandoning a familiar and well-liked test because of the patient's deafness, which interferes with his understanding of test instructions, or because of his right-sided hemiplegia which affects his speed in performance tests, is unavoidable and the results of new untried methods have to be interpreted with more than usual caution. The dangers of the indiscriminate application of test norms to mental defectives, though they have been derived from different populations, have already been discussed in the chapter on brain injury and this applies to many other specialized tests. Low intelligence may easily produce test results which in the intellectually normal population would be held to be pathognomonic of psychosis, or cerebral damage.

The Bender Gestalt test is mainly used in differential diagnostic work. It consists of copying figures (Gestalten) and the quality of reproduction indicates the maturation level in the visual motor gestalt function. This is a function said to be associated with language ability and closely associated with various functions of intelligence (Keller, 1955; Munstberger Koppitz, 1958).

With the mentally deficient the test does not simply evoke

> a lower level of the integrated gestalt production commensurate with the mental level determined by the other standard tests. There is a much greater variety of productions among mentally defectives of a given mental age than among normal children of the same mental age. . . . Motor control is usually better than in normal children of the same mental age. Small energy-conserving figures are the rule. The primitive loop is freely used with less motor-play or experimentation. Perseverative tendencies tend to destroy the configuration. Fragmentation or dissociation may occur suggesting a schizophrenic-like process. Hyperkinetic features may be detected, but usually in cases where hyperkinesis is part of the general behaviour (Bender, 1933).

Keller (1955) points out the close relationship of the Bender Gestalt test to other test performances and behaviour, particularly when studying the scatter of failures and successes. His particular scoring system has been developed on a population of institutionalized mentally retarded boys and it is noteworthy as recognizing the possible influence of personality variables on the reproduction of simple geometric figures and attempting to avoid penalizing the child for it when establishing the level of maturation.

The test has been reported as differentiating between familial and brain-injured defectives (Bensberg, 1952), between schizophrenics and normals (Goldberg, 1957), delinquents and non-delinquents (Zolik, 1958), and the introduction of an objective scoring system (Pascal and Suttell, 1951) has renewed interest in this method, and in an attempt at establishing norms for mental deficiency (Baroff, 1957).

CONCLUDING REMARKS

An over-confident reliance on tests has led in mental deficiency, as well as in other fields of clinical work, to a great mass of significant and not so significant work which, one feels, has so far only touched on the fringe of the problem and has mapped out only some of the landmarks.

Psychological assessment is a craft and a successful plying of tools depends on the skill and experience of the user. His is the intuitive, selective grasp of essentials and the ability to weave into a valid picture the information obtained from psychometric and personality tests, from interviews, personal history and other sources. Examination of the situation, the comparing with and relating to standards and norms obtained by strictly scientific methods provides the firm basis for the evaluation of the single case – the subjective judgment which considers all available evidence. This judgment has high validity because a good part of it rests on comparisons with experimental findings, the use of laws of probability, and because it avoids systematically and effectively rushing to speculative conclusions. It is true that this scientifically obtained evidence is restricted because it has been obtained under experimental conditions. The need for strict objectivity and for reducing a problem to manageable dimensions requires exclusion of as many variables as possible and thus the laboratory test situation becomes so specific that the results relate, strictly speaking, only to this one, specific, narrowly circumscribed situation. Nevertheless, these laboratory findings of psychological testing provide – as generally in science – the building stones for erecting the structure of a valid and significant personality assessment.

The methods of clinical assessment can, in the hands of the expert, give a good understanding of the personality of the individual, an estimate of his mental resources, a measure of his abilities. Yet this is not sufficient to predict the actions of an individual in a particular situation. We have little or no knowledge of the motivational factors and the interplay of the innumerable environmental and personality forces which continually create unique situations. But although predictions of the actions of an individual amount to no more than an assessment of probabilities with our present methods, the knowledge obtained from the systematic psychological exploration of the individual is of considerable help in providing assistance, in avoiding glaring mistakes, and in shouldering considered risks for the benefit of the mentally deficient person.

Chapter XII

EDUCATIONAL PROBLEMS IN MENTAL DEFICIENCY

by H. C. Gunzburg

I. OBJECTIVES

When discussing educational problems in mental deficiency it is customary to differentiate between those relating to the so-called educationally subnormal child and those referring to the imbecile or trainable child. It is also customary and traditional to apply the term 'education' in this field almost entirely to pupils under 16 years old, and to exclude automatically the adult. Such distinctions are only defensible as being administratively convenient; they have no basis in theory and in research. It is impossible to draw a reliable and valid differential line between the educable and the trainable child and all that can be said is that certain children show lesser degrees of educability than others. It is an arbitrary decision to determine the exact point where a child ceases to be 'educable' and is to be called 'trainable' or referred to as 'unsuitable for schooling'. Similarly it is an arbitrary administrative decision to discontinue formal educational efforts when the chronological age of 16 has been reached, even though the mental age level is still well below that mark and can increase after the age of 16.

Historically seen, the contributions of the early pioneers in mental deficiency were concerned almost entirely with the severely handicapped child (see Chapter I). It is also interesting and significant that the rehabilitative work of these physicians, Itard, Seguin, Montessori, Decroly, was mostly of an educational character, influenced by the prevailing philosophical views of the early nineteenth century.

Itard and Seguin believed with many of their contemporaries that education and knowledge were obtained through the senses and concentrated, therefore, on developing sensory training. Though Itard's efforts, reported in the classic *The Wild Boy of Aveyron* (1932), did not lead to much success, he demonstrated the possibilities of sensory training achieving some improvement, even in apparently hopeless cases. Seguin's physiological approach considered the qualitative differences which may result from damage to, or defect of, the peripheral and the central nervous system, yet his educational method was the same for both types. He advocated specific muscle and sense training and pointed out the value of a good relationship between teacher and child, the importance of starting with the pupil's needs and desires, and the necessity to consider the child's individuality. Most of his practical work and techniques can still be regarded as sound today.

During the latter half of the nineteenth century the emphasis shifted to the less handicapped child, and from that time onwards the severely handicapped child – the imbecile – was comparatively neglected. The educational methods developed by Maria Montessori and Decroly were concerned mainly with the learning problems of the dull, educationally subnormal, and little attention was devoted to methods particularly suitable for the more handicapped child. Montessori's approach had much in common with Seguin's ideas concerning sense and muscle training, but she placed a new emphasis on self-teaching. She devised apparatus which provided autodidactic ways of training most senses with the teacher acting merely as a supervisor in the background. Montessori's methods, which were not limited to mentally deficient children, have been much criticized, particularly because of the artificiality of her system, the lack of opportunity for self-expression and the difficulties encountered in transfer of training. Systems like those of Decroly and Descœudres (1928) have attempted to be more realistic, encouraging the child to learn through practical concrete experiences.

The place of education in the treatment and training programme for the mentally defective cannot be defined, nor methods and curricula developed, unless there is a clear appreciation of the educational objectives. De Prospo (1962) put this very forcefully and clearly when he stated:

> the hue and cry has been for a new gimmick. Well-meaning teachers ask for new methods – new tricks. The *how* of teaching

has become the prime concern. But the main problem – the *what*, or the curriculum – does not get the attention it must receive if we are to succeed in preparing children for some eventual life placement. Methodology, important as it is, is the last step on the thorny road in the education of the children.

The contrast between the attitude of the first generation of workers to the question of objectives and present-day approach is striking. Descœudres (1928), one of the pioneers, mentioned among other objectives that instruction should be given relating to 'the child and the animal world, the child and the vegetable world, the child and the mineral world, to moral and aesthetic needs, their existence and their inevitableness'. Ingram (1953), a modern educationist, mentions among others: 'worthy home and community life, worthy use of leisure time, adjustment in industry'. Whilst Descœudres' generation approached the problem by adapting the normal school child's curriculum to the limitations of the mentally handicapped, the modern tendency is to study the needs of the defective and to create a programme which is based on actual requirements. The early generation designed a programme by deciding what, in their opinion, was good for the child. Nowadays, many educationists of the mentally handicapped child see in him the future adult and consider what skills and knowledge will be beneficial to him in his adult life. This modern approach is based on investigations, researches, and follow-up studies which make it possible to judge retrospectively how much education has contributed to success in the life situation and how far lack of a certain type of education may have contributed to failure. Whilst it is obvious that failure in adjustment is mostly due to inadequate personality make-up and unsatisfactory environmental support, it is thought that lack of educational knowledge can accelerate and trigger-off social breakdowns.

A careful consideration of the role of education in the social rehabilitation of the subnormal indicates that objectives have to be formulated not as 'subjects', e.g. reading, writing, arithmetic, but rather as areas of competence. Most modern workers have come to broadly similar conclusions, even though individual preferences add often a quaint note. Generally they have stressed (Kirk and Johnson, 1951; Ingram, 1953; Wallin, 1955; Stevens, 1958; Gunzburg, 1960) that the subnormal should be taught among other skills:

(*a*) how to get on with other people

(*b*) how to accept the work situation and give reasonable satisfaction
(*c*) how to manage money
(*d*) how to get about and make use of public services
(*e*) how to manage leisure time.

Within these areas of social, vocational, and personal competence, the subject approach and the tool subjects tend to be reduced to a minor role. It is realized that the mastery of reading or spelling results very often in the acquisition of a meaningless skill which cannot be put to good use because of the trainee's mental limitations and that teaching time is out of proportion to results. Very often this would leave very little time for the teaching of those social skills which have a direct bearing on the subnormal's problems in adjusting to the world around him.

Whilst teaching objectives of the kind mentioned above are realistic and feasible because they are essential for tackling life situations and can be taught within the limits imposed by time and school-structure, other educational aims mentioned in the literature appear to be so ambitious as to be unrealistic. 'Acquiring knowledge of, practice in, and zeal for democratic processes; becoming sensitive to the importance of group action in the attainment of social goals; developing meaning for life' (Nickell, 1951) are statements of aims which seem rather out of place when dealing with mental defectives.

The general training programme for the mentally defective aims at achieving a reasonable and acceptable minimum of occupational, social, and personal competence, which will enable adjustment to community demands on varying levels. It is increasingly being realized that education can contribute considerably towards these aims, but that the methods as well as the contents of the educational syllabus have to be drastically adjusted and pruned, if something worthwhile and usable is to be achieved. This results not only in a more effective deployment of educational resources but also in a sound therapeutic contribution. Remedial education which concentrates visibly and energetically on those areas of social malfunctioning which are felt and experienced by the defective as being weak and inferior, can achieve a strengthening of self-confidence and an amelioration of educational inferiority feeling which are of strong therapeutic import. Since the whole personality make-up of the defective is characterized by his inability to see far ahead and his proneness to strive only for short-term goals, special education which is obviously to the point and realistic is far more likely to catch his attention and interest than education of a broader type which deals with educational fundamentals rather than specific issues.

The fact that the mental defective's limitations prevent him from achieving normal standards, must not prevent the educationist from striving towards a relative competence within each individual's capability. The administrative classification 'trainable' or 'educable' indicates, at most, the maximum level of achievement expected at the time of classification, but not a difference in educational aims. In both cases only relative degrees of social, personal, and economic adequacy can be expected, yet even these limited skills will help the defective to live in the world – in many cases limited to his immediate surroundings – with some confidence and feeling of security (Hudson, 1955a, b; Rosenzweig, 1959).

II. THE TRAINING (OCCUPATION) CENTRE

It is often the practice nowadays to refer to the imbecile child by a number of apparently less 'degrading' names, e.g. the ineducable, the trainable, the severely subnormal, the severely handicapped child who is 'unsuitable for schooling', to differentiate him from the less handicapped child also known as the backward, retarded, slow learning, or educationally subnormal child. These children are generally regarded as being unable to benefit adequately even from the modified teaching given to the educationally subnormal child. In I.Q. terms the dividing line is somewhere around I.Q. 50, but it must be realized that factors like test reliability, delayed maturation, unfavourable environment, etc. make it imperative to reassess the individual child from time to time because such classification may be in fact most arbitrary and temporary.

Whilst no special arrangements are usually made for the ambulant imbecile child under 5 and many of them are admitted to ordinary day nurseries, the non-ambulant child requiring nursing care will usually be cared for in hospital or in special care-units attached to day-centres, if for one reason or the other home care is not available.

Mentally defective children between 5 and 16, who are ambulant but of too low an intelligence level to benefit from special school education, are admitted in England to day-centres, called in the past occupation centres and now junior training centres. Owing to the low level of intelligence of these children, often no concerted effort is made to achieve a defined level of competence. As the name 'occupation centre' suggests, there has often been a tendency to regard the centre merely as a place where the imbecile child is kept happily occupied as a relief for the parents. There has, however, been some urge in recent years to evolve far more positive and ambitious targets, and specialized training and the practice in some places indicate that efforts are being made to reach certain educational objectives.

Most programmes (Hafemeister, 1951; Rosenzweig, 1954; Cleverdon and Rosenzweig, 1955; Gunzburg, 1963) point out the need to teach and train

(*a*) care for self (feeding, washing, dressing self)
(*b*) occupation
(*c*) communication
(*d*) social relationships.

The day-centre where many children of approximately the same level are trained together – where they work, play, and live together – provides a most valuable extension of the training given at home, but must not be regarded as a substitute for or equivalent of the home training. It has different tasks by providing remedial education of a kind which cannot be made available at home – particularly in the area of living and working in a group.

It is not often clearly recognized that the task of the junior centre is not to occupy the imbecile child in a manner reminiscent of the school approach designed for more mature and intelligent children. If on the one hand the aim is to learn how to live together, and on the other hand how to find out (learning by doing), then the infant school approach often found in junior centres will fail entirely. The regular time-table approach, sitting in desks with a piece of sense-training apparatus in front (Cain and Levine, 1961; Norris, 1961), has little to recommend it. As has been shown in recent work (Tizard, 1960; Brandon and Stern, 1962) the most natural and successful approach is that employed in the nursery school (Hudson, 1955) where experimenting, make-believe, play-acting, singing, talking, taking turns, sharing, teaches in a natural, informal way those experiences which are best learnt by doing and finding out (Kirk *et al.*, 1958; Neale and Campbell, 1963).

Few junior centres are cognizant either of the nature of the task or of the means of achieving a solution (Tizard, 1960; Norris, 1961; Cain and Levine, 1961). They cannot entirely be blamed for this because this particular area has been singularly devoid of constructive leadership in recent years. Whilst the aims mentioned at the beginning of this section provide some sort of guidance and short-term goals, the evolvement of a detailed programme depends obviously to a great extent on the final goals of education and a clear grasp of the potentialities of the 'pupil'. It is important to know what possibilities and opportunities will be available to the adult imbecile, and how far training and education in childhood can help towards later realization. Considering the imbecile's very limited capacities, it may well be advisable to arrange his childhood programme in such a way as to give training and education in those areas which will be of special relevance to him in later life. As nowadays evidence is accumulating that a proportion of those children with I.Q. below 50 become in adult life relatively self-supporting (Delp and Lorenz, 1953; Craft, 1962a) it seems reasonable to give intensive and early training in those skills that matter in adult life. On the other hand, it must also be clearly recognized that early 'training' may in itself interfere with the slow growth and development of abilities which need the stimulation and encouragement of teaching. The child is then 'set' by successful training on a stage which represents by no means the limit of his potential and is thus deprived of further growth and functioning on a higher level of achievement.

This is a problem of education and training which has not yet been tackled and the work in the junior and senior departments has therefore not been adequately dovetailed. It may well be that in view of the slow maturation process the junior nursery school stage should be extended to give much experience by doing and finding out, that formal schooling should start later with a view to preparing for adult life, and that the occupational work training should start much later than at age 16. There is little justification for keeping to a timetable which is no longer related to modern thinking. Research regarding these problems is unfortunately very scanty so far and is urgently needed.

A survey of the literature suggests that relevant publications dealing with methods and curricula regarding the imbecile child scarcely exceed a dozen a year. To this scarcity of useful work is added the very real failure to correlate method and curriculum with the basic dictum: 'Teach them what they can learn and what is for them worth learning' (Dawe, 1959).

Principles underlying curriculum development for the imbecile child are often neglected. This refers particularly to 'developmental sequence'. Arithmetical, spatial, linguistic concepts grow in definable ways, each step following the other in a natural sequential order. A disregard in teaching of this developmental sequence leads to failure and frustration and to the pupil's inability to grasp and understand certain basic principles even though knowledge and skill can camouflage at a later stage the lack of real understanding.

The work of Piaget has recently been applied with great enthusiasm to problems in the mental deficiency field. It has been pointed out that Piaget's approach offers not only a possiblity of placing a child on a developmental scale even in cases which were regarded as untestable by the more orthodox test procedures, but that it also provides direct guidance to the teaching appropriate to a particular child's level. It is after all most important that teaching targets should not be set so low as to be unstimulating and resulting in sterile activities, or too high as to be disheartening in their remoteness. Since the sequence of stages in the process of intellectual development is known, it is possible to provide tuition which is adjusted to encourage the natural emergence of the various stages without setting up undue pressure. Piaget (1950, 1953, 1955) suggested that the level of thinking, typical for a particular child, will be used in intellectual activities of different types (Lovell, 1959; Peel, 1959; Lovell, 1961). Woodward (1959, 1960) has pointed out that this applies for example at the sensori-motor stage to most subnormal children who are stable, but not to emotionally disturbed children. In the latter case spontaneous manipulating of toys tends to be done at a level two or three stages below the problem-solving stage, and this may make the children appear more backward than they are. Older imbecile children and adults tend to use both intuitive and concrete operational thinking (Woodward, 1962a, b) for different concepts, like number and space, but the concrete operational approach is used from a full-scale I.Q. 60 upwards.

Attention has been drawn to the fact that a good number of children found in the junior centres are mongols and brain-injured, and the question has arisen whether special educational programmes and methods should be developed for them. As far as the brain-injured child is concerned, much work has been done by Strauss and

Werner in the U.S.A., but it has not been widely applied and corroborated by adequate research, though the work of Piaget and Bender without a doubt illustrates quite clearly the role of faulty perception in learning difficulties. Gibson *et al.* (1959), who made a careful study of the academic performance and its relation to aetiology, suggested that the exogenous learner finds particular difficulties in arithmetic (and language) whilst writing, reading, and social studies were comparatively unaffected by aetiology.

Methods of teaching the brain-injured child (Strauss and Lehtinen, 1947; Strauss and Kephart, 1955; Jolles, 1958; Kaliski, 1959) endeavour to overcome disturbances in perception, thinking, and behaviour which may be concomitants of brain injury. Ingenious teaching methods and aids, many of them self-correcting, are designed to control behaviour patterns, such as perseverative tendencies, distractibility, and hyperactivity, and to overcome special perceptual handicaps such as disturbed figure-ground relationships (Kaliski, 1955).

The educational methods of Strauss and his collaborators are based on clinical investigation and, since they take account of the aetiological differences found among children of comparable overall intellectual level, this approach represents a definite advance towards the ideal of remedial methods based on an analysis of the special needs of particular patients. (For further discussion of the techniques advocated by Strauss and Lehtinen, see Chapter X, pp. 274–5.)

Need for detailed assessment

In the imbecile child there is a marked discrepancy between chronological and mental age. The low mental age suggests only that on an intelligence test the mentally defective child does as well as a normal child of a much younger age group, but this does not mean that he should always be treated like a much younger child. This attitude may well lead to a perpetuation of this stage, because he is never encouraged to develop interests, self-reliance, control of emotions more in keeping with his age and his experience. There is a great danger that the child (and later on the adult) is kept on an 'easy' level of functioning without an attempt being made to encourage him to better efficiency on a more complex level of performance. Much confusion in curriculum building and development of methods can be traced back to the different implications of mental age, chronological age, emotional age, social age which make it impossible to apply always ordinary educational methods developed for younger children.

Before embarking on an educational programme for children of this type, it will be necessary, as in all other aspects of education, to investigate their level of attainments and capabilities and to become clear about the precise nature of the skills which we wish to teach.

The assessment of the level of attainment in various spheres can be done systematically by following the suggestions found in social development scales (Gesell and Amatruda, 1947; Doll, 1953; Kirk *et al.*, 1958; Gunzburg, 1963*b*, 1964). Most attention will naturally be devoted to the field of 'self-care': to train the child in the appropriate habits of dressing, eating, elimination, and so on. He will also have to learn to relate himself to others, to share in play and work, and to help the adults and other children. Adequate training will make it possible for many a family to accept more fully a severely handicapped child and will contribute quite considerably to a reduction of tensions and anxieties in a family group, avoiding in later years to a great extent the parent's maladjustment in relation to the handicapped child (Price, 1947).

A careful investigation of the position of each child in respect of simple social skills permits not only an assessment of achievements; it indicates also precisely the areas requiring further intensive attention and helps in planning future training programmes for a population of a far more heterogeneous character than the labels 'idiots' and 'imbeciles' imply.

In those cases where there are severe intellectual limitations, present-day opinion appears to be that it is not expedient to spend time and effort on teaching of isolated skills, e.g. recognizing the letters of the alphabet, which cannot be developed to practical use. As it is most unlikely that emotional disturbance will accrue from an imbecile child's realization of his educational shortcomings, fruitless attempts at formal education could be replaced by training and developing techniques and abilities which are meaningful within the child's own limited world and which may be of use for the likewise limited world of the imbecile adult. It is possible however, and often useful, to teach such children certain words, which they are likely to meet frequently, and also to make them familiar with coins in common use (see also Chapter XVII, pp. 486–7).

The recognition of one's own name, and those of other children, is a useful achievement and can be widened by a generous labelling of many familiar articles. It is surprising how many adults, even of feeble-minded grade, are unable to write their names and encounter difficulties whenever asked for a signature, and writing one's own name in script appears just as important as recognition of names spelt in block letters. Since the imbecile is likely to be restricted in his movements, it is often practicable to teach him to recognize printed words denoting landmarks in the area which he frequents. Bus destinations and street names are of some limited help in orientation to those imbeciles who can be allowed out without supervision. In the same way recognition of common warning words like: Danger – Poison – Wet Paint – Keep Out – No Smoking – Stop – has definite use (Gunzburg, 1964).

There is, however, no doubt that individual devoted and concentrated work can aim at far more and achieve far more than suggested in the remarks above. Various case studies have reported remarkable results. Thus Riese (1956) has described in detail the methods used in teaching reading, writing, and spelling to a child with an I.Q. of 41.

Despite the fact that most educationists agree that children with I.Q. less than 50 cannot learn to read, some investigations suggest a more optimistic view (Martinson and Strauss, 1940; Jones, 1945). Hermelin and O'Connor (1960) point out that in their experiment they were able to teach reading to imbecile patients with I.Q.s between 35 and 50, but also that there was no significant correlation between the number of words read and the I.Q. As far as comprehension of the words read was concerned, they observe 'that severely subnormal children are able to read only as long as the words to be read are familiar and meaningful to them through their speech'. Since the speech of imbeciles is limited, it has some very pronounced influence on the ability to remember and to learn.

Very little work indeed has been done in the field of practical arithmetic. Piaget's work on number (1952) is of particular relevance in this field. The recognition of coins, the realization that a number of small coins is equivalent to a coin of a larger denomination – simple skills of that level – should be taught and this is probably all that can be expected. There is much need for research and unprejudiced teaching.

III. THE SPECIAL SCHOOL

The so-called educationally subnormal or educable child in an approximate I.Q. range between 50 to 75 is too vast and specialized a subject to be properly dealt with here. Detailed discussions will be found in a variety of books, particularly in Kirk and Johnson (1951); Ingram (1953); Tansley and Gulliford (1960).

It must, however, be pointed out that the curriculum of the special school could benefit greatly by incorporating the experiences of those ex-special school pupils, who, at a later stage, are admitted to hospitals, institutions, and adult day-centres. Though it has not been demonstrated that generally educational shortcomings such as failure in reading and arithmetic, contribute markedly to the social incompetence which leads to institutionalization, it can be readily seen that feelings of insecurity are reinforced by a realization of educational inadequacy.

There seems also a marked need for introducing into the school curriculum those 'social skills' which a normal child gathers informally in course of growing up and which have often to be taught formally to the handicapped child. The teaching of social knowledge and social arithmetic etc. becomes increasingly more important (Tansley and Gulliford, 1960).

IV. ADULT EDUCATION

The problem

Adolescents and adults admitted to a mental deficiency institution have, in many cases, been special school pupils and very often school failures. Few have reached an academic efficiency corresponding to their mental capacity, and nearly all are conscious of their backwardness. Their reactions to their handicaps vary and men often seem more concerned than women. Some are grateful for every opportunity offered to improve, others are discouraged and ambivalent in their attitude, others again are frankly frightened and become neurotically aggressive when again faced with a formal learning situation.

Educational work at this late stage aims not only at supplying academic and social knowledge, but is also a conscious attempt to heal some of the damage the patient has suffered in his past unsuccessful encounters with school and learning. From this point of view educational work has a direct therapeutic aim, and should if possible be linked with other therapeutic measures.

The fact that many mentally deficient patients fail to achieve a level of academic success commensurate with their intellectual level has been ascribed by various authorities to a variety of factors. Since a large number of people falling in the range of subnormal intelligence have acquired the necessary educational skills, the mere fact of a feeble-minded intellect cannot alone explain academic failure. It is nowadays widely agreed that it is due to a combination of various factors with varying weights which have to be assessed in the individual case. Perceptual difficulties, incorrect teaching and unstimulating environment – these handicaps have been overcome by most children of ordinary abilities. It seems that it is the unfortunate combination of these handicaps of extraneous origin with the drivelessness, the insecurity, and the slow and limited grasp of the subnormal child which is responsible for school failure, despite comparatively adequate mental resources. The dispirited and despondent attitude, consequent upon failure both in reading and writing, reinforces feelings of insecurity developing from an inability to hold a job and to keep out of trouble, and it is difficult to assess in the end how much educational failure and disappointment have contributed to, or even been responsible for, general behaviour disturbances.

An excellent example of the therapeutic use of a carefully planned curriculum comes from the special school. Duncan (1942) based his approach on the well-known observation, supported by much research, that mental defectives generally obtain higher I.Q.s in non-verbal tests (see p. 302). Alexander (1935) had expressed 'concrete intelligence' by the sum of $g + F$ (where F represents a special factor dealing with *things* as opposed to gV, the ability to deal with *words* and *abstractions*). Duncan sees in the fact that the results on non-verbal tests are often well above those of verbal tests that

> the abilities of these children are far higher than many of us have suspected. That their attainments have been low is due to an educational approach through the medium of words, their weakest factor. If the abilities of duller children are to be matched by their attainments, we must set their feet on the gF pathway (Duncan, op. cit., p. 48).

In pursuance of this idea Duncan developed a practical method carried out at his school at Lankhills with planned exercises to develop children's thinking by observing visual and concrete relationships. Discarding chiefly manipulative and repetitive handwork, he retained those crafts which were suitable for developing a graded scheme of exercises stimulating intellectual activity: planning, thinking in sequence, grasping relationships.

Duncan is specific that 'just working with the hands will not do' (p. 61) and that the craft is primarily a means of education to be considered and justified on grounds of educational value. The subjects used in his education scheme (paper and cardboard work, woodwork, needlework, housewifery, cooking, laundry work) are graded in exercises and correlated with such academic subjects as reading, arithmetic, history, geography, and story lessons. Instruction is usually given on special assignment cards which permit each child to work at his own individual rate. According to Duncan, the effect of these practical concrete exercises resulted in considerable improvement in academic work. He argued that 'it appears as if the good intellectual habits that are set up in other activities (habits which cannot be developed by emotional stimulus only) are transferred' (p. 188). Duncan also added that much of the success of his scheme may be due to having been able to arouse a keen desire to learn to read because the children 'will not be able to do cookery work or handwork unless they can read written instructions' (p. 189).

Duncan's presentation, though not wholly convincing, and requiring much more support for his claim of transfer of learning and the stimulation of intellectual activities than he actually gives, is a significant step in modern educational practice with intellectually handicapped children. The emphasis on first making the child familiar with the concrete manipulative task for which he has a better understanding, before approaching him with abstract problems, and the close integration and use of concrete with abstract aspects should help a good deal in developing a practicable method of teaching more formal academic subjects. The method is moreover based on sound psychological practice by increasing the child's confidence through giving him success where he is most likely to gain it. Subsequently he is perhaps readier and more accessible to do work in those areas which are weak.

Educational work becomes therapy as soon as it is able to restore the defective's shaken confidence in his own abilities in that wide field where he has first met failure. It is clear that it needs a careful and sensitive approach if renewed educational efforts are not to upset a perhaps only precariously maintained equilibrium. Many young adults have, by evasion and skilful camouflage, avoided the most embarrassing consequences of their educational ignorance. They dimly feel the drawback of illiteracy and inability to handle their monetary affairs, but do not always take kindly and enthusiastically to a resumption of 'academic' work.

The situation is aggravated because neither adequate teaching methods nor suitable materials have been developed for the subnormal adult, nor is it usual for qualified teachers to be employed by institutions. Educational failure is commonly only one of a number of difficulties exhibited by the mentally deficient patient, and the requirements of general rehabilitation and social training may result in only a relatively limited amount of time being available for general academic work. Nevertheless, it is of vital importance to attempt to increase social competence by concentrating on those academic aspects which have a direct bearing on occupational and social adjustment.

An educational scheme applied to adult women (Buchan, 1943) states that systematic school training resulted in marked improvements.

> On the whole the girls . . . average about half a grade a year. . . . Most of the girls have gone far beyond the limits usually set by mental level and, in turn, their I.Q.s have risen on retests. However, there are gains along many lines which do not show up on tests. Girls who have been paroled and discharged have testified to the fact that their academic training was perhaps the most important factor in their general improvement.

The chronological average age of this group was approximately 21 years and included many women over 30.

An educational programme for the adult subnormal must be based on his interests and, where possible, on his recognition of his educational shortcomings which have presented, or will present, difficulties in his working and social life. It will have to be specifically related to his experiences, give him more information about different jobs and how to obtain them, about health and medical treatment, about unemployment, and about ways of planning expenditure and saving money. The basic subjects of reading, writing, and arithmetic will have to be integrated with practical and general knowledge.

Programmes of this kind have been developed for the adult in some American communities (see Salvatore di Michael (Ed.), 1952), but not on a comparable size in this country (Gunzburg, 1960, 1963c). Hungerford *et al.* (1952) point out that:

> the retarded, if they are to realize their potentialities, must be given a different developmental programme rather than a remedial or impractical adaptation of a normal programme. Such education must give to each child a competency in the following:
> (1) The technique of self-measurement, self-knowledge.
> (2) A knowledge of suitable job families, and social requirements.
> (3) The technique of meshing abilities with vocational and social requirements.
> (4) The 'drive' or desire for social contribution.

In those cases where the school has been able to lay an adequate foundation in the '3 Rs', much of the educational work will consist of keeping this knowledge from deteriorating and applying it practically. In others – and by no means the most unintelligent adults – formal academic knowledge is often practically non-existent and the educationist has to decide what is desirable and what is practicable to teach. He will most likely have to design a realistic and eclectic programme which gives the adult pupil security and confidence when faced with the ordinary day-to-day demands. It must be realistic because the importance and usefulness of the knowledge to be conquered must be grasped immediately by the adult, because it must appeal to his concrete type of intelligence and because it needs a constant reinforcement by day-to-day occurrences. It must be eclectic because of the impossibility of developing a systematically organized and integrated syllabus as at school, because the knowledge of practical experience has to be utilized and because each step should be a 'whole' in view of the inadvisability of long-term planning.

The first essential step in planning an educational programme, of a therapeutic and utilitarian character, which takes account of the limitations set by time, institutional practices, resources in staff, material and opportunities inside and outside the hospital, will have to be a survey of the extremely patchy knowledge the defective has been able to acquire (Williams, 1956b; Buchan, 1943; Londt, 1960, 1961). The syllabus will have to be built on these findings.

An educational programme for adults, related closely to the work done in the vocational sphere and supporting the psychotherapeutic approach, has been developed by Gunzburg (1960) in some detail. He describes it as 'An Educational First Aid Scheme' where relevant educational assistance is given as quickly and effectively as possible. Since vocational and psychotherapeutic considerations may very often set a premature end to a more traditional educational programme, he outlines a scheme which takes into account the fact that education is a desirable, sometimes even an important, factor in rehabilitation, but cannot be regarded as a generally decisive factor in the treatment and training of the mental defective. Education of the adult cannot rely on having the 'pupil' available for an exactly specified length of time as at school, and the programme must therefore be shaped in such a way as to give *at any stage* of the teaching some worthwhile practical educational knowledge which can be put into use.

The disadvantage of the approach developed by Gunzburg is that it is primarily 'training' rather than education in the real sense of the word. Pupils are not taught principles and they do not learn to grasp the elementary stages before tackling the more complex operations. No real understanding is elicited by careful teaching, and 'developmental sequence' (see p. 335) is completely neglected. Gunzburg defends his approach by pointing out that there is simply not enough time to teach the adult at this late stage, when he is essentially concerned with the problems of maturity, employment, girl-friends, entertainment, etc. The only objectives that can be reached through formal education are certain skills relevant in the social and personal spheres. Using the telephone does not require understanding of its operation – totalling up small money sums does not need the ability to do the 'sums' on paper.

Gunzburg expresses the belief that such an educational programme, although it cannot provide for the numerous contingencies that are bound to occur in the unintelligent person's life, will nevertheless help in overcoming many frustrations and embarrassments which lead often to friction and subsequent social failure. Gunzburg's 'Educational First Aid Scheme' is limited to a patching-up operation, conceived as therapeutic assistance in concrete terms, rather than as a curriculum and method to remedy once and for all the very marked educational weaknesses of mental defectives.

V. SPECIAL PROBLEMS

Reading

Surveys of mechanical reading ability among feeble-minded patients have shown not only consistently the great gap between actual achievement and mental ability – if mental age is taken as an index of at least minimum potential for reading skill – but also a wide scatter of reading attainments regardless of I.Q. Some low-grade feeble-minded patients obtain very high reading ages, considering their mental age level (Bennett, 1929); on the other hand, many people of mildly subnormal or even normal intellect are completely illiterate. Even people with I.Q.s well below 50 have been reported as being able to 'bark at print'; thus a low intelligence test result cannot be used as an adequate and complete explanation for illiteracy, unless additional factors aggravate the situation.

It appears that failure to learn to read mechanically is, in most cases, more dependent on the lack of motivation, drive, persistence, adequate teaching, etc., than on intelligence once a minimal I.Q. of, say, 50 has been established. A study of the reading processes of the subnormal reader should throw some additional light on the problem, but has seldom been attempted (Dunn, 1954).

It may be asked whether there is much point in the teaching of mechanical reading, unless a corresponding level of comprehension can be reached. It may, however, be argued that it is useful to be able to read such things as labels, notices, announcements, warnings, notifications, and inquiries, and that a certain level of competence in this respect will militate against feelings of inferiority and social insecurity. Furthermore, an adequate technical reading skill would make accessible much of the juvenile fiction which the subnormal enjoys as keenly as his normal contemporaries (Huber, 1928; Gunzburg, 1948b) and would help in overcoming the problem of leisure time (see p. 404), even though at present only a few defectives may have been sufficiently stimulated to read voluntarily in their spare time.

The question of the most suitable and practicable method of teaching reading to the adult non-reader has scarcely received sufficient attention. Most schemes, like the army educational methods, are based on the word recognition approach, which gives the illiterate the feeling of success by acquiring by sight a vocabulary of prearranged extent. The words are related to social and vocational needs and are adjusted to the experience, maturity, and academic standard of the illiterate and semi-literate reader. They represent the core of an interesting and, to the adult, evidently useful vocabulary (Goldstein and Mann, 1949; Borreca *et al.*, 1953; Williams, 1956a; Gunzburg, 1960, 1964).

The efficacy of the various methods of teaching reading – phonic, look and say, sentence method – will depend much on the illiterates' previous unhappy experiences with a particular method, the inclination and predilection of the teacher and the fact that the illiterates' difficulties stem from many causes. The basic principle for adopting a particular method appears to be its suitability to satisfy the need for success (Vaughn, 1941).

Gunzburg (1948a, c) investigated the learning of 'syllables' and their fusion rather than of a definite vocabulary, and achieved good results in improvement of reading skill over six months with daily drills. (Range of improvement: 6 months to 3 years 4 months; average 1 year 8 months.) He emphasized that the success was probably not so much due to the inherent merits of the method, but because he was able to instil in the poor readers confidence in the success of the reading scheme. This confidence led to persistence, overcame aversion to the monotonous drills, and strengthened the motivational factor of achieving competence equal to that of the normal population.

The same method and two others were used by Champness (quoted by O'Connor and Tizard, 1956, p. 109) for feeble-minded adults. He agreed that there were no significant differences between different methods of instruction. The results confirmed that substantial improvements in reading could be effected by a comparatively short intensive and motivated period of instruction.

The comprehesion of reading material is of course not entirely dependent on acquiring the requisite reading skill and vocabulary. Though understanding is obviously inseparable from the intelligence level, there are certain skills which can be taught to increase comprehension of reading matter. Gates (1935) published a diagnostic battery to measure four different aspects of comprehension: A. to appreciate general significance, B. to predict the outcome of given events, C. to understand precise directions, D. to note details. Other authors (Sangren, 1927; Watts, 1944) followed similar lines, and exercises based on the analysis of the poorly developed aspects of an individual's reading comprehension have been shown to be of considerable help (Duncan, 1942; Limb and Parker, 1932; Gates, 1935; Gunzburg, 1948a, c).

The smooth acquisition of reading skills is often retarded by specific personality factors. Gann (1945), who made a careful analysis of the personality of backward, good, and average readers on the basis of projective tests, came to the conclusion that the poor readers are 'emotionally less well adjusted and less stable. They are insecure and fearful in relation to emotionally challenging situations and they are socially less adaptable to the group.' She suggested that 'the building of reading adequacy in those who have experienced difficulty with the process would involve, therefore, the resolutions of inhibiting personality forces and negative attitudes, as well as increased interest and skill in reading itself'. It may also happen in some cases, as Burt (1922) has suggested, that the reading matter may be associated with emotionally disturbing memories and thus create a blank leading to miscomprehension and inability to follow the thread of the story. Burt compared these blanks 'to those lapses of speech and memory, the slips of the pen and the trippings of the tongue, which in adults have been shown by psychoanalysis to be so richly symptomatic of the profounder secrets of the individual's mental attitude'.

Though the relationship between emotional maladjustment and reading disability is by now widely accepted, opinions differ whether therapy should precede reading instruction (Axline, 1947; Ewerhardt, 1938), or whether the improvement in reading in itself will lead to better adjustment (Kirk, 1934).

Special techniques for the teaching of reading to the brain-injured person have been suggested by Strauss and Lehtinen (1947). The patient's inability to focus attention and his perceptual disturbances require carefully designed teaching methods (Dinsmore, 1954). On the other hand Bensberg (1953) found no differences in academic achievements in matched groups of brain-injured and familial defectives of either sex.

Arithmetic

Published work dealing with the arithmetical difficulties of defectives is largely limited to analysis of the processes involved, or to the influence of aetiological factors on arithmetical efficiency, and little agreement regarding an appropriate curriculum has been reached (Thresher, 1962). Cruickshank (1946, 1948a, b) compared carefully the techniques used by mentally retarded and normal children and pointed out certain inadequate habits like primitive and immature procedures, as counting on fingers and making marks on paper, carelessness and guessing, misreading of conventional signs and lack of comprehension for abstract concepts. Aetiology of defect appears to play some significant part in arithmetical difficulties (Strauss and Werner, 1938, 1939; Fouracre, 1958) requiring often special apparatus (Carrison and Werner, 1943; Rasmus, 1946), but these findings were not always corroborated by other investigators (Benton *et al.*, 1951; Capobianco, 1954).

Kirk and Johnson (1951) point to the necessity of acquiring a working vocabulary of arithmetical terms encountered in everyday life. It is quite surprising and a cause of needless misunderstanding how vague many defectives are with regard to the meaning of terms concerned with length and distance (inch, foot, yard, etc.), to measurements (quarter, half, dozen, etc.), to amounts (pair, twice, increase, decrease, etc.), to time (day, week, month, etc.), and others. Though they know how to count, the meaning of ordinal figures (first, second, third, etc.) is often unknown.

The limitations imposed by the mental abilities of the pupil, time and educational organization make it imperative to develop a curriculum which deals primarily and perhaps solely with those skills which are of direct use to the defective. As Burns (1961) points out, the introduction of each new arithmetical skill and operation should depend on questions like: 'Is it important enough to teach? If it is to be taught, how can it be introduced in a concrete way? How can the abilities connected with the topic be practised enough to assure real learning?'

The same author presents the outline of a suggested arithmetic programme which, while concrete and to the point in the initial stages, is strangely removed from reality when outlining the final stages. There the mental defective is expected to learn about overheads, dividends, money invested, promissory notes, etc., which appears to be a rather over-ambitious programme.

An important but largely overlooked aspect of the mental defective's arithmetical knowledge is the fact that he may have acquired such skills in the same way as mechanical reading. In neither case is the acquisition of 'barking at print' or 'doing sums' supported by an understanding of the processes and underlying relationships. Piaget's work on number (1952) may prove of great help in understanding the difficulties encountered in arithmetical reasoning. He points out – supported by the results of ingenious experiments – how little the ability to count, to add up, and the knowledge of the tables, ensures that the child has grasped the idea of number. Despite the apparent mastery of counting, the understanding of concepts like 'more', 'greater', 'less', 'as many', 'alike', etc., depends on maturational development; number in the earliest stages is related to size, shape, arrangements, it is *perceived* and not *understood*.

Piaget's ideas have not as yet been applied to the teaching of defectives, yet it would appear in view of the concrete nature of the subnormal intellect that many of the arithmetical difficulties they encounter may be due to inadequate number concepts, camouflaged by arithmetical skills which serve only in familiar and easy situations. Many of the devices used in number work may become real obstacles in the development of logical number thinking if the child becomes impressed with spatial, visual relations and carries those misleading, concrete examples into a later stage, relying on 'visual' rather than logical evidence. Piaget's experiments in 'conservation of quantity', 'ordination', and 'cardination' point to the need to lay far more systematically the foundation for an understanding of number before beginning the more formal tasks of teaching number work (Woodward, 1961, 1962a, b).

The ability to add and subtract correctly on paper the formal arithmetical exercises seems not to be sufficient to aid the dull adult in his ordinary financial dealings. The difference between the decimal system of his 'sums' and the complex monetary system of pounds, shillings, and pence, is so confusing that he has of necessity to entrust others with his change and bills. The defective's hazy ideas regarding money, in combination with his lack of planning ability, result in inadequate budget arrangements, an absence of savings, and the exploitation by others of higher intelligence. This combination of circumstances may lead to delinquency when he attempts to restore financial solvency by illegal means. He is liable to become involved in hire-purchase and often undertakes financial commitments, the consequences of which he is unable to grasp.

It thus becomes incumbent upon the teacher to provide a programme of utilitarian and social arithmetic. The emphasis must be put on the major task of how to handle money, how to estimate its purchase value and how to account for its spending. Financial operations of a concrete type, such as shopping outside the hospital for self and staff, saving for clothing and selecting sensibly, keeping a detailed account of amounts earned and spent, are of greater value and more immediate interest than pages of correctly ticked 'sums' (Williams, 1956a; Brown and Dyer, 1963).

Concept of time

It has been shown that there is generally a fairly good correlation between a short time test, relying on what might be called 'time vocabulary', and intelligence (Buck, 1946; Cofer and Biegel, 1948; Engle and Hamlett, 1954). A time test assesses not only the ability to tell the time but also to attach a conventional meaning to time words. There are, however, many defectives who have never learnt to tell the time and who find themselves in difficulties when time words are used by other people. This is a very obvious weakness which can and should be remedied in an educational programme, though the level of competence which can be finally achieved may be very modest.

The ability to tell the time from a clock face does not necessarily imply that this knowledge can be put to practical use, nor that there is an understanding of time terms or concepts. Some very careful research (Oakden and Stuart, 1922; Sturt, 1925; Gunn, 1929; Piaget, 1948; Brower and Brower, 1947; Bradley, 1941; Gothberg, 1949; Lovell and Slater, 1960) has shown the great part maturation plays in understanding of time concepts, but there has been no major research dealing with the problem of how to encourage their development.

Time tests, such as those of Buck (1946) and Engle and Hamlett (1954), are useful for drawing attention to the many gaps in time vocabulary, but even success on these tests may easily camouflage a very far-reaching inability to comprehend time situations. Though there is at present no adequate exposition of how to encourage the development of time concepts (Lovell, 1961) in the mentally defective, this should not discourage the teaching of a time vocabulary, which is a very useful social asset and which may lead indirectly to a better appreciation of time. The mere fact of drawing the defective's attention to time and to what is meant by it, may help him to develop time concepts. In this area too, one cannot be sure how far under-stimulation from the environment has discouraged the development of an ability which is, after all, closely interrelated with an appreciation and acceptance of the world around. Lack of social and emotional adjustment, lack of interest in people and surroundings, lack of experience, may contribute just as much to the stunting of this particular ability, as low intelligence and lack of maturation.

Language

Not only do the results of verbal and non-verbal intelligence tests suggest poor verbal functioning (see p. 302) but specific investigations point to the mental defective's difficulties in verbal expression and understanding. Earl (1961) discussed 'subnormal language' from the clinical point of view. He pointed out that low intelligence is only partly responsible for the defectives' difficulties in dealing with verbal symbols as abstractions. 'The selective interests of their minds differ from the normal' and in consequence the 'outer, generally agreed conventional meaning' will often be sacrificed to the subnormal's 'inner, private and individual meaning'.

Various investigations have confirmed the mental defective's difficulties in thinking abstractedly and in manipulating concepts and it has been pointed out that institutionalization (Papania, 1954; Badt, 1958; Mein and O'Connor, 1960) was in many ways responsible for the low level of abstractness, when compared with children of the same ability but receiving home training (Schlanger, 1954; Lyle, 1959). Mein and O'Connor (1960) studied the oral vocabulary of severely subnormal hospital patients and compared it with that of normal children of approximately the same mental level. The patients used about 1,000 fewer words than did the normal children. Sampson (1964) studied carefully the conversation of severely subnormal children living at home, following up her earlier work (1962) on language development of this type of child. The problems of language and communication have been ably summarized by Spradlin (1963) in the case of the mentally handicapped and by Renfrew and Murphy (1964) for handicapped children in general.

Since language is of utmost importance in making generalizations in acting and communicating (Luria, 1957), teaching the mother tongue (Gulliford, 1960) formally and directly is of major importance. Not much work has yet been reported whether from the classroom (Rittmanic, 1958) or in the form of sociodrama, but it is obvious that the development of personal and social competence is seriously interfered with if the coinage of words with their conventional, generally agreed meaning, remains unusable to the defective, because he has not learnt how to handle it. There is little doubt that learning to use language symbols in the generally accepted way would be of the utmost importance to the defective's ability to adjust more efficiently to the world around him, yet, so far, practically nothing has been done to strengthen this well-known weak area. Some of this neglect is due to the idea that this weakness is probably constitutional and some of it to the understandable emphasis put on the strengthening of those practical non-verbal abilities which are manifestly of considerable importance in work of a non-academic character. Yet the need for understanding verbal instructions, obeying directions, responding to verbal cues and learning in general, demonstrates that a programme of socialization and rehabilitation will have to devote far more attention to language and communication than in the past.

A potentially very valuable and promising approach to the problems posed by linguistic disabilities is that of McCarthy, Sievers, and Kirk already discussed in Chapter XI under the heading of the 'Illinois Test of Psycholinguistic abilities'. Here a definite attempt is made to throw light on the quality of a person's language ability and his skill in using channels of communication. Kirk (1962), and Kirk and Bateman (1962) give several examples of the use of this test, not only for diagnosis but for suggesting in each individual case a remedial programme to correct the linguistic disability.

Social skills

Another most important aspect of general education is to help the mental defective to become familiar with those arrangements of community life which are often so self-evident to the ordinary person that one hardly realizes that they may present sizeable obstacles to the feeble-minded. The fact that houses are numbered odd and even on the opposite sides of the street, that a return ticket may be cheaper than two single tickets, that a post office offers facilities for saving, that one has to register with a doctor, are only a few instances where a mental defective, particularly one who has been institutionalized for a long period, might find himself in as embarrassing a situation as a foreigner in a country with an unfamiliar culture. The defective, who may be too shy to request information and vaguely conscious of making a fool of himself, attempts to hide his ignorance and shortcomings by various subterfuges.

Neither institutional life, whether in a residential school or hospital, nor the culturally impoverished upbringing in the defective's home is able to offer opportunities for an unconscious absorption of these useful, but unconnected, pieces of social knowledge and information, and it thus occurs that a systematic effort has to be made to teach them at this late stage.

It will be helpful, and ease the defective's adjustment, to stage for him interview situations which make him familiar with the usual questions and to let him practise filling in forms of application with the usual headings: Surname, Christian Name, Address, Age, Sex, Nationality, Signature.

Similarly to learn to find one's way about an unknown district, to select appropriate public transport, to locate a given address and to follow verbal directions ('Take first turn to the left, till you come to the church, then turn right'), is an acquisition of great importance, quite literally widening the defective's horizon and creating in him a feeling of confidence in his abilities.

Social activities, such as buying clothes, putting money into the Savings Bank, obtaining tickets for a variety theatre performance, etc., have, of course, to be practised in the community itself and should not merely be discussed in the classroom (Williams, 1956a, b). Similarly insistence on the acquisition of the 'social graces', which will assist in making the defective less conspicuous in small groups (youth clubs, cycling clubs, etc.), as well as instruction in attending to personal needs (preparing a simple meal, or attending to personal clothing) will contribute in many cases to a smoother adjustment to society (Kirk and Johnson, 1951; Wallin, 1924; Gunzburg, 1960, 1963b). Only in this way may we hope to build up familiarity and knowledge with social practices which may assist the patient later on in independent life. (See also Chapter XIV, pp. 385–416.)

CONCLUSIONS

This brief survey of educational problems in mental deficiency has indicated a pronounced lack of direction and methodology. Whilst the so-called educationally subnormal child has received a fair amount of attention in recent years and is the responsibility of the educational authorities, the 'trainable' child is, in England, handed over to the Ministry of Health and Local Health Authorities. Qualified educationists are not taking part in the education of severely handicapped children, who are taught and trained by educationally unqualified staff. As a result this field is, in many ways, a stagnant backwater of mental deficiency, with no clearly defined objectives, approaches, and methods. Research into the various problems of teaching is almost completely absent and whilst many of those who work in this particular field realize the undeveloped potentialities of their pupils, they have neither the knowledge nor the skills to encourage and stimulate their growth.

Adult education, too, has never received adequate attention. As far as the adolescent imbecile is concerned, who has left the junior training (occupation) centre, the pretence at schooling has been dropped in favour of realistic practical vocational training. The possibility of further educational work commensurate with his mental level, rather than his chronological age, is scarcely considered. Very often there is a sharp dividing line between junior and senior departments with no transition or continuity of approach.

Adult education for the adolescent ex-special school pupil is little practised. Some authorities regard it simply as a belated attempt at formal school work, yet it represents an important therapeutic factor in the resocialization of the mentally defective. Simply relying on teaching academic skills and subjects in isolation, is a sterile and limited approach though often adopted when some form of adult education is carried out. Far too often the demands of 'school' in terms of time and staff are in conflict with the demands of the institution regarding vocational training and rehabilitation policy, and as a result nothing really useful is achieved in the end. One may seriously question whether it is defensible to teach the 'tool subjects' at a late stage in view of the fact that no great gains can be envisaged, and it is doubtful whether generally practical use is made of the skills so artificially fostered. In fact even the literate mental defective makes little use of his skills and many illiterates succeed in adopting a mode of life which successfully by-passes all needs for the applied 3 R's. On the other hand the mental defective's ignorance of the community's pattern of life, work, and leisure; his inability to communicate adequately or to understand communications from others; his lack of grasp of social conventions; the absence of tact and manners; all represent very real and sizeable obstacles to his adequate functioning. It is curious that educationists who stress so much in the initial stages the need for personal and social adequacy, requiring the development of detailed curricula, lose sight of these requirements in the later stages when emphasizing the importance of academic skills which, in their incompleteness, have very often little practical value.

A consistent approach to education in mental deficiency, based on research, and carried out by people fully qualified in the special requirements of this type of work, is obviously very much needed. Now that interest in the possibilities of vocational training for the defective has been awakened, and it has been seen that he is accessible to psychotherapeutic treatment, it is not too much to hope that the direct practical contribution that could be made by suitable education will at last be adequately recognized.

Chapter XIII

THE ABILITIES AND TRAINABILITY OF IMBECILES

by A. D. B. Clarke and A. M. Clarke[1]

INTRODUCTION

The study of psychological processes in imbeciles is important for two reasons. First, until recently this form of severe handicap has attracted little attention, and indeed such persons have been greatly neglected. Any light that can be thrown upon methods of consolidating or creating assets, and overcoming deficits, is bound to alleviate the burden imposed upon their families and upon society. Second, it seems likely that a study of man at the simplest (albeit damaged) level should have relevance to an understanding of normal psychological processes. At all events, these assumptions underlie the theme of the present chapter and the reader will be able to estimate the degree to which they are justified.

When the first edition of this book was published in 1958, some fifteen studies were discussed in this chapter. There was then no problem of selecting some researches for report while omitting others; it was concluded that

> in this neglected field of imbecile learning, it is clear that much more research is needed and that the investigations reported have merely laid a basis for later work. Even so, there is little doubt that already some traditional concepts of imbecile abilities and trainability are in need of qualification or revision; consequently this must also apply to our methods of helping and training the low-grade patient.

[1] The revision of this chapter formed part of a research project on human learning, generously financed by the Nuffield Foundation.

The writers are faced with a very different prospect in 1964 than in 1958. There has indeed been something of an explosion of interest in this field, for reasons which are briefly considered in the Preface. No longer can every study be reported within the compass of one chapter; rather, it has been necessary to seek out only those articles which seem to the writers to represent either entirely new research trends or to sample important areas for investigation. During this period the first book on the psychology of severe subnormality has appeared (O'Connor and Hermelin, 1963) representing a number of studies in such varied fields as visual perception, thought and language, recall and recognition. Since it would obviously be impossible to summarize this work in one chapter, the reader is referred to the original text.

The changing pattern of incidence and prevalence of imbecility, and the general principles in causation, have been discussed in earlier Chapters (II and VI). Suffice it to say that we define imbeciles as those with I.Q.s in the 20–49 range, and, both on the grounds of the Gaussian distribution and of post-mortem findings (Crome, 1954), they must be considered as *abnormal subnormals*. The probable differences in nature existing between 'pathological' and sub-cultural (or garden variety) defectives do not seem to be sufficiently examined by some experimenters. A number of studies have been excluded from mention here because the subjects used appeared to span an I.Q. range encompassing members of both populations. For example, Berkson's (1961) excellent review of psycho-physiological studies of the mentally deficient is marred by not differentiating or indeed defining levels of populations used.

The work to be reviewed includes studies from applied fields and also areas of pure research. Since the attack on the subject came initially from research on industrial training and special education, reports from these spheres will be presented first. Final sections will deal with more theoretical problems.

EXPERIMENTAL STUDIES OF ADULT IMBECILES IN WORKSHOPS

Studies of incentives

Interest in the psychology of imbeciles hardly existed until about 1950, and it was initially due to the work of Tizard and O'Connor that this situation began to change in England from that time onwards. Indeed, all that was available in the textbooks was the typical clinical description of imbecile behaviour which consisted in the main of general statements outlining obvious inadequacies. The early laboratory experiments were specifically designed to test the validity of such views, and it soon became obvious that these were in need of modification.

Gordon (1953), and Gordon, O'Connor, and Tizard (1954, 1955) studied some effects of incentives on the behaviour of imbeciles. Using an unpleasant test of muscular persistence, it was shown that the introduction of incentives effected striking differences between three matched groups working under different conditions. The mean *percentage* improvement over starting point was only 2·22 for the *Control* Group; 46·44 for those receiving *Encouragement*; and 115·0 for those working under *Goal* conditions. The results were orderly and predictable, and the mode of response was similar to that of normals. A further study by Walton and Begg (1955) confirmed this point. The shifting of subjects from one experimental condition to another was also used to elucidate the findings. In brief, it seemed clear that both (*a*) the type of incentive and (*b*) prior experience influenced the results.

Gordon, O'Connor, and Tizard (op. cit.) carried out a further experiment to provide data on the effect of incentives on subsequent performance. The test was repeated after an eight-week interval, and it emerged that it was the incentive conditions under which the subjects worked in the very first experiment which determined the degree of retention, rather than the more recent experiences of other incentives. These researches, then, gave an unexpected picture of what the adult imbecile could do in terms of intensity of effort and differential response to varying conditions.

Gordon (1953), and Gordon, O'Connor, and Tizard (1955) reported an additional set of laboratory investigations. With 40 young male imbeciles of average I.Q. 36 points (S.D. 5), they used a visuo-motor task in which the subjects had to place small nails in perforated zinc sheeting, under *Goal*, *Competition*, *Co-operation*, and *Control* conditions. Highly significant differences in outcome were found between the groups, in the order of success given above. After a six-week interval, the fall-off in performance was very small, indicating surprising retention of learning, a point which has been subsequently corroborated again and again. Indeed, the subjects 'achieved within three trials to equivalent performance which originally required at least thirty trials to reach' (Gordon, 1953).

A study by Tizard and Loos (1954) concerned the learning of the four form-boards of the Minnesota Spatial Relations test by six young adult imbeciles. This was chosen for its relative complexity, and for use in measuring transfer of training from one board to another. With two trials per day, and eight per board, all subjects showed rapid improvement and considerable transfer of training.

Loos and Tizard (1955) now transferred these subjects to a sheltered workshop where industrial work involving the folding of cardboard boxes was to be carried out. This task involved nine different bimanual movements in the correct order; and after initial difficulties it was achieved within two weeks. By this time the subjects were working deftly and at speed. It was found that in this simple type of industrial job, the ability of the imbeciles was not, in fact, markedly inferior to that of feeble-minded persons averaging an I.Q. of 71. Before long, however, it had surpassed the level of the brighter patients, and all that has occurred in this workshop over the last ten years has underlined the excellence of these imbeciles at industrial work.

O'Connor and Claridge (1955) have followed up some of the work reported by Gordon (op. cit.). In these earlier studies, it is possible that the success of the *Goal* Group depended to some extent on his personal approach and not merely on their self-competition. The present study aimed to make a more clear-cut distinction between encouragement and goal-striving and to discover their relative importance. The same subjects, after a gap of almost a year, were used on one of the earlier tasks, namely the Nail Frame test. The first point of interest was that there had been considerable retention of the methods and technique by the subjects, all of whom remembered what they had to do. There were three groups: (1) Goal with Encouragement; (2) Goal with Indifference; and (3) Control Group. These groups were matched with respect to their performance on two trials. For the first of these groups, experimental conditions were as follows: a marker was inserted in the frame at a point 2 per cent. higher than the subject's previous best score; this indicated his goal for the day. Later this was found to be too high and modified to a point 1 per cent. higher than the best score over the previous three trials. Throughout each session, encouragement was given.

The second group worked under exactly the same conditions, except that no comment was made at any time about success or failure, and as far as possible complete indifference was shown to the results of each subject. The third group was told to work as hard as possible, but given no goal and no encouragement. The results indicated that goal striving in itself did not increase the performance level significantly, unless accompanied by encouragement and social approval. A further point of considerable interest was that on the first trials of the experiment, the original members of Gordon's Goal Group retained their superiority of performance over the interval of one year, which gives somewhat unusual evidence of the long-term effects of an incentive, and may demonstrate the importance of good incentive conditions in the early stages of training.

Incentives and personality type

Claridge (1956) and Claridge and O'Connor (1957) point out that individual differences in improvement on learning tasks did not appear to be associated consistently with the tested intelligence of imbeciles, and raised the question whether personality differences might not be involved. They quoted Tredgold's division of imbeciles into apathetic and excitable types and developed a rating scale for the measurement of various aspects of excitability. Their procedure for scaling each item was initially to draw up concrete descriptions of typical behaviour in five graduated steps from one extreme of the activity to the other. A pilot experiment enabled an item analysis to be made and a final version consisted of nine items, seven of which were graded on a four-point scale and two on a five-point scale.

Each of 155 imbecile subjects was rated independently by two persons who knew them well. There seemed to be surprising agreement in terms of mean score and distributions among the samples from different hospitals, despite the fact that a number of raters had been involved. The scale appeared to represent a reliable estimate of the subject's excitability. The correlation with intelligence was positive but insignificant. All subjects had taken part in one or more of the group learning experiments already described in this chapter.

The authors first considered the relationship between excitability and improvement in learning under non-incentive conditions. It was found that apathetic imbeciles had improved during the first ten trials of a learning task more than those who were excitable; the correlation between the two scores was −0·56, and a further check confirmed this result. On the other hand, the correlation between excitability score and starting level was not significant.

Under incentive conditions there appeared to be a slight but consistent tendency for the relationship noted above to be reversed, excitable imbeciles improving rather more than apathetic ones. These results were, however, less clear-cut but at least it could be concluded that the inferior ability for improvement of excitable imbeciles could be offset by special incentives. The authors then considered the possibility that excitable and apathetic subjects might differ in their reaction to the removal of incentives after they had experienced them. The conditions of a group of imbeciles had been changed in this way after 12 incentive trials, and it appeared that most excitable imbeciles showed a tendency to decline, while apathetic subjects continued to improve following the removal of the incentive. The authors concluded that (*a*) differences in personality of imbeciles may be meaningfully discriminated in terms of excitability, and (*b*) these differences may be usefully related to corresponding differences in their improvement on a repetitive motor task as well as to their responses to incentives. They believed that the work of Eysenck (1955), following Pavlov, provides a possible theoretical basis for explaining the behaviour of subnormal individuals of different personality types in learning situations of this kind. The two correlated phenomena of motivational 'fading' and performance decreases, which both in the normal and the mentally deficient appear to be associated with personality factors, might ultimately be related more meaningfully to learning variables such as inhibition.

Claridge (1956) and O'Connor and Claridge (1958) considered the applicability to human subjects of Crespi's (1942) report about experimental work with animals. He had found that when a larger amount of food was introduced as an incentive after previous training under a smaller amount, performance level increased to a point *above* that of animals who had received the larger amount from the beginning of training. Crespi termed this excess increase an 'elation' effect and also recorded a corresponding 'depression' effect in animals shifted from larger to smaller amounts of food incentive. Claridge and O'Connor divided forty male imbeciles into four equal matched groups on the basis of two initial trials on

Gordon's (1953) Nail Frame task. For a further ten trials two of the groups worked under non-incentive conditions and two under incentives (Goal Encouragement). Subsequently one non-incentive group and one incentive group worked under reversed conditions, while the other two continued as before. The earlier work, which showed the superiority of incentives to non-incentives, was again confirmed, but when one non-incentive group was changed to incentive, the increase in performance showed a typical Crespi 'elation' effect. The subjects reached and maintained scores higher than that of those who had received the incentive from the beginning. A comparable decrease in incentive, occurring when the incentive group was changed to non-incentive conditions, was found to have little marked effect on performance level which established itself at a point intermediate between the scores of subjects who continued to receive incentives and those who had received no incentive at all. This confirmed the earlier finding that incentives have relatively permanent effects on the performance level of imbeciles.

Imbeciles as industrial workers

Clarke and Hermelin (1955) pointed out that to the unfortunate families into which imbeciles are born, such cases represent a formidable social, emotional, and economic problem, particularly since, in later life, they have seldom been able to contribute materially to their own support. They mentioned that most previous researches had employed laboratory tasks, and they set themselves four questions: (1) Can imbeciles do a full day's work on industrial tasks; (2) Can they acquire comparatively difficult skills; (3) To what extent does initial ability relate to final achievement; and (4) What, indeed, are the limits to imbecile trainability, and what practical and theoretical implications emerge?

They reported that their subjects were the same six typical imbeciles first studied by Tizard and Loos (1954) and that they had been under observation for a period of two and a half years doing simple industrial work efficiently. Supervision had been minimal, indeed on one occasion they did a morning's work voluntarily in the absence of any supervisor. Their age range was by now 20–30 (mean 24); their Stanford–Binet I.Q.s ranged from 24 to 41 (mean 33); and their period of stay in the hospital ranged from 6 to 14 years with, in most cases, long periods in other institutions. In view of subsequent results, it may be appropriate to amplify these bare

3 MONGOL, AGED 24, I.Q. 34, SOLDERING TELEVISION COMPONENTS

(*Clarke and Hermelin*, 1955)

4 REHABILITATION UNIT FOR HIGH-GRADE FEMALE PATIENTS. These girls are shown working at cracker-making, box-making and packing chocolates at the Manor Hospital, Epsom

(*Clarke and Clarke*, 1954, 1957)

5 FEEBLE-MINDED GIRL, I.Q. 66, LEARNING TO PREPARE ELECTRICAL WIRE FOR SOLDERING
(*Clarke and Clarke*, 1954, 1957)

figures by describing some of their behaviour. Two of the six can hardly talk at all; three cannot name colours correctly, though all can match them; two hoard rubbish; two are unstable, one of these showing apparently psychotic traits. Four of them do not know their ages, only one can count above ten, and two cannot really count at all.

The first experiment investigated the abilities of the subjects to use a simple guillotine and to cut insulated wire to exact lengths – in this case 10 inches. Though simple, this task requires both dexterity and co-ordination, qualities in which imbeciles are commonly regarded to be lacking. There were two sessions of one hour each, separated by a week of non-practice. Initial and final scores for each subject per 5-minute period were as follows: 35–46, 23–33, 40–52, 36–56, 16–48, 15–57. At the end of the second session, the level attained by most of the subjects was little different from that attained by individuals whose average I.Q. was 40 points higher and who had been well practised in the task. It was suggested that five out of the six subjects could earn between £2 and £3 per week on this task. The second experiment was a relatively complex soldering task – the soldering of four different coloured wires to the correct terminals of an 8-pin television plug. This is far from being a mechanical job, involving as it did the distinction of colours (and some of the subjects could not even name colours) and spatial relationships and the handling of a soldering iron in a relatively dexterous way. (See Plate 3.)

Initial scores, with assistance, ranged from 4 to 19 minutes per plug, with an average of about 8 minutes. At the completion of the experiment, after 34 trials, the time per plug, without any assistance, had been reduced to a range of from 1 min. 42 secs. to 3 mins. 30 secs. (average 2 mins. 37 secs.), and errors had become uncommon. It is of interest that from very different initial abilities on the testing after training, they reach very similar end-points. For imbeciles, the learning of this skill is very difficult indeed, and it appears to be somewhere near their limits; nevertheless, it was estimated that average earnings would be about £3 each per week, and there is no doubt that simple soldering processes are well within their powers.

In the third experiment, an attempt was made to teach a simple assembly task, involving a sequence of different operations. Bicycle-pump assembly was chosen, because nine operations have to be performed in the correct order, including the use of screws and washers. Initial scores ranged from 4 mins. 20 secs. to 10 mins. 45 secs., with assistance from the experimenter. By the 30th trial, the time per assembly ranged from 54 secs. to 1 min. 50 secs. without any assistance. Accuracy had become perfect; and indeed this seemed to be an ideal assembly task for imbeciles. In the fourth experiment, the subjects were unable to learn a more abstract series of operations, namely the construction of the first three designs of the Wechsler Block Design test. They were able, with difficulty, to learn to copy each design individually, but quite unable to learn to construct three designs as a sequence in the time available.

From these experiments, the authors deduce three descriptive principles: (1) the initial ability of imbeciles on industrial as on other tasks tends to be exceedingly low; (2) their initial ability has little relationship with the level achieved with training; and (3) the main distinction between the performance of imbeciles and others on simple tasks is not so much the end level as the time taken to achieve it. Nevertheless, the time needed is within practical possibilities for the trainer.

It is clear that traditional clinical opinions of imbeciles are reasonably accurate descriptions of their abilities *before training*, but to take them at face-value is to ignore their potentialities. Many could perform useful tasks and contribute in some cases substantially to their own support, in national conditions of full employment, provided that their physical handicap is not severe. Finally, the authors, while conceding the value of occupation centres, which keep the patient happily occupied, aid his social adjustment, and give some relief to parents and relatives, call for a more positive approach.

It is of interest that this small group, now supplemented by others, has been working happily and usefully for a decade. Increasingly, too, local health authorities in England have been setting up sheltered workshops and turning away from the earlier concept of mere 'occupation'. Although these industrial studies have been in many ways rather crude, it may be of use to summarize the principles of training of adult imbeciles for industrial work:

(1) *Incentives*. The imbecile, like the normal, is very much affected in the learning situation by the presence or absence of suitable incentives. The most effective seems to be to set him a realistic goal to work to, a little above performance on the previous occasion. This goal can be indicated visually by, for example, having yesterday's pile of

work in front of the person, or a simple scale and pointer. Needless to say, verbal encouragement and competition also reinforce his learning.

(2) *Break-down of work.* The task to be learned needs to be broken down to its basic constituents; e.g. to screw two pieces of perforated metal together it is necessary (1) to pick up a screw and screw-driver; (2) to place the pieces in some securing device which will hold them steady; (3) to see that the two holes are opposite each other; (4) to push the screw into the hole and (5) to commence screwing. Each has to be taught separately but in the right sequence so that the whole job from start to finish is tried at each attempt.

(3) *Correct movements.* It is essential that the correct movements should be insisted on from the very start, because by definition the correct ones are the easiest. Thus, following our example, if the imbecile fails to hold the screw-driver correctly he should repeatedly be shown how, no matter whether this takes five or twenty-five minutes.

(4) *Learning should be spaced.* It is much more economical if learning is spaced rather than massed. Thus, three separate 20-minute periods will produce more learning than a 1-hour session.

(5) *Need for 'over-learning'.* The learning process should be taken well beyond the amount at which correct responses are made, so that it becomes deeply ingrained. This is familiar enough to us all in school-days when, to our great advantage later, we have to 'over-learn' our 'twice times' and other tables.

(6) *Verbal reinforcement.* With normal subjects the acquisition of skills is made easier if the learner uses words almost as a commentary on his own actions. This is very apparent with young children, whose learning may be greatly facilitated if they use words at the same time. Thus two chains of events are learned: first, the actual movement needed for the task, and second, a parallel verbal chain in the simplest language, describing the actions. It is, however, not entirely clear how far this applies to the severely subnormal who are often severely retarded verbally. Opinions differ on this subject and further research is needed to clarify the problem. This is the basis of verbal

conditioning which is particularly difficult to achieve in the low-grade defective.

(7) At first, accuracy rather than speed should be stressed.

(8) Material should be arranged in such a way that muddle or fumbling can be minimized.

In general, the teacher must remind himself that initial level is a very inadequate predictor of response to training, and that even if no progress is made for a very considerable time, it is likely to occur if training is considerably prolonged. Finally, it is wise when teaching a new technique to keep the group small, and limited to two or three individuals at a time.

In England there has been a rapid development of Training Centres run by Local Health Authorities for adult imbeciles. As yet there appears to be a diversity of practice, ranging from sheltered work, from which no one graduates to simple outside employment, to prolonged education, recreation and craft activities. In other Centres, industrial work comes first, and successful attempts are made to place the better trainees in the community. Perhaps the most interesting experiment has been carried out by Dr Wigley of Middlesex who has placed a group of imbeciles in a factory, supervised by his own staff, but who play a normal industrial role.

SPECIAL CLASS OPPORTUNITIES

In recent years a number of researchers have studied the imbecile's responsiveness to special class opportunities. In reviewing the literature (Reynolds and Kiland, 1953; Goldstein, 1956; Guenther, 1956; Johnson and Capobianco, 1957; Hottel, 1958; and Peck, 1960), Kirk (1964) points out that most studies have been of short duration, and that it has been difficult to establish the benefits of special class training for this group; results have on the whole been negative.

> Although we have tended to attribute these negative results to the lack of adequate measuring instruments, lack of controlled experimentation, lack of experienced teachers and short-term research, it might be necessary to find new approaches to the educational programs for these children. It might be necessary to evolve new

> theories and new instructional approaches to the problem – possibly intensive case studies on a longitudinal basis, similar to Itard's classic experiment with a sample of one. . . .

Hermelin and O'Connor (1960) studied the reading ability of 32 institutionalized children with I.Q.s between 35 and 50, and ages between 11 and 19. These children had been taught for an unspecified time in a hospital occupation centre. Using a 'core vocabulary list' evolved by Mein and O'Connor (1960) they selected 200 words used by between 50 and 100 per cent. of imbeciles in experimental conditions. Each word was printed separately in one-inch letters on a white card. The average number of words read was 45, with an S.D. of 50 – a markedly skewed distribution. An association between reading ability and frequency of word use was claimed; 'those words which occur in the speech of 74–100 per cent. of imbeciles are read by 68 per cent. of the children while words which are used in speech by 50–73 per cent. are read by only 24 per cent.' Significant correlations between reading score and mental and chronological ages were also found.

It should be noted that the criterion group for word use was of a different age range (10–30) than the reading group. Moreover, the authors do not appear to have considered the fact that there are a larger number of bisyllabic words in the less familiar (50 to 73 per cent. range) than in the more familiar. Hence part of the less efficient reading might be due to the rather greater difficulty of these words. Nevertheless it would be surprising if the authors were not correct in their belief. Whether the teaching of reading to children of this type is justified remains, however, an open question. The Hermelin and O'Connor data on reading ability are hardly impressive from the practical viewpoint; the reading list was extremely simple, the physical size of the word was large and the average score low.

Gunzburg (p. 337) believes that 'it is possible, however, and often useful, to teach such children certain words, which they are likely to meet frequently, and also to make them familiar with coins in common use'.

He goes on to say:

> The recognition of one's own name, and those of other children, is a useful achievement, and can be widened by a generous labelling of many familiar articles. It is surprising how many adults, even of feeble-minded grade, are unable to write their names and

encounter difficulties whenever asked for a signature, and writing one's own name in script appears just as important as recognition of names spelt in block letters. Since the imbecile is likely to be restricted in his movements, it is often practicable to teach him to recognize printed words denoting landmarks in the area which he frequents. Bus destinations and street names are of some limited help in orientation to those imbeciles who can be allowed out without supervision. In the same way recognition of common warning words like: Danger – Poison – Wet Paint – Keep out – No Smoking – Stop – has definite use.

There is, however, no doubt that individual devoted and concentrated work can aim at far more and achieve far more than suggested in the remarks above. Various case studies have reported remarkable results. Thus Riese (1956) has described in detail the methods used in teaching reading, writing, and spelling to a child with an I.Q. of 41.

Very simple addition and subtraction, the recognition and handling of pennies, sixpences, and shillings, a realization of the equivalence of a threepenny bit and three individual pennies, is probably all one can expect from most children at this level. It is a useful social link by providing an appreciation of the value of pocket-money in relation to buying sweets, etc.

Charney (in Kirk and Weiner, 1963) gives a useful over-view of research upon trainable children. He points out that, so far as evaluations of school programmes are concerned, the Hottel study (op. cit.) is the only one using proper controls, and this indicated that children in the upper ranges of imbecility, I.Q. 40–50, made significantly greater gains in mental age than either those who remained at home or who attended the day class programmes but were of lower ability. In brief, then, one is confronted with a similar situation both in the United States and in Great Britain. Public funds are rightly being employed on an increasing scale, wonderful new facilities and modern buildings are being erected, but the basic research into the most appropriate means of aiding the severely mentally handicapped is not being carried out. Indeed, in English Junior Training Centres there is a marked contrast between the enrichment of the surroundings and the impoverishment of the training methods. These include learning thresholds that seem to be too high, learning steps that appear to be too far apart, and the fashionable but sentimental belief that unlike the normal child, learning pressures must not be imposed upon the severely retarded. It is to be hoped that research upon child imbeciles will soon begin to make the impact upon training procedures that research upon imbecile adults has already made upon their handling.

Schucman (1960) carried out a detailed study to evaluate the educability of the imbecile child, and the large sample involved the age range 5–12. Her basic hypothesis was that 'the child's educability can be inferred from his responses to learning situations which require abilities on which education depends, namely, to learn from instruction, to transfer the training, and to retain the learning'.

A battery of tests was administered to each child individually. After the first attempt at each, the subject was then trained to the correct responses, and retested to evaluate the gains following training. Different forms were also used to evaluate transfer, and retention was measured by retesting at various later dates. Five tests were eventually chosen after pilot experiments: a test of initiative ability and memory, size discrimination, brightness discrimination, shape discrimination, and another test of brightness discrimination. Teachers' ratings of learning ability, on a five-point scale, were used as an external criterion. I.Q.s and social quotients were also used.

The test battery was administered on nine occasions, the first three yielding pre-training, post-training, and transfer scores, respectively. The fourth and fifth measured retention under different conditions, and at different times, and the last four administrations were repetitions of the first four, given after an interval of seven weeks. It was found that the group as a whole learned, transferred, and retained learning to a highly significant extent on all tests. Intelligence was correlated with all test scores, and exerted a highly differential influence on pre-training. Transfer and retention scores were the most sensitive measures of differences in ability. This longitudinal approach to learning capacity is of great significance, and in contrast to the rather limited studies where preliminary performance on some variable is related to subsequent outcome. Other researches in this field, as will be indicated in a later section, have emphasized the inadequacy of initial level as a predictor of trainability.

LANGUAGE

The general proposition that language development in the mentally deficient tends to fall below the level of other abilities has commanded universal support for many years, and so far as the imbecile group is concerned, there is little doubt that this is so. Soviet psychologists, in particular, have stressed the role of speech in the regulation and integration of early behaviour, and have emphasized its function as externalized thinking in the normal child. Luria (1959), for example, considers that the imbecile shows pathological inertia of the nervous processes, particularly evident in the speech system. Moreover, unlike the situation for the undamaged child, there is said to be dissociation between speech and motor signalling systems. Both the general neural inertia and the dissociation combine as the gravest defects, and determine 'the extreme difficulties with which their training is connected'. The child is thus prevented from undertaking any creative, intellectual activity. It should at this point be noted that Luria's method of experimentation involves an attempt at linkage of speech and motor reaction under conditions of short stimulus duration.

As O'Connor and Hermelin (1963) point out in a useful chapter reviewing this area, the Soviet view raises two problems in connexion with speech. The first is the meaning of words for the imbecile, and the second, the connexion between words and motor behaviour. On the first point, the well-known experiment of Luria and Vinogradova (1959) is relevant. The subjects were adolescents of varying degrees of retardation, and their responses were compared with those of normals. They were required to press a button in response to a signal word and were also tested with words of similar sound and with words of similar meaning. Degree of motor response was measured by the pressure exerted on the button. In this way, an experimental method for eliciting objectively the synonym connexions with the stimulus word was evolved. While normals generalized almost exclusively to synonyms, the imbeciles generalized very considerably to homonyms. This research is of interest but is limited because of lack of precise description of the subjects, and because it is unclear whether the words to which generalization was possible were of a different level of familiarity or difficulty for the imbeciles.

In an endeavour to explore word familiarity in imbeciles, Mein and

O'Connor (1960) studied the oral vocabulary of 80 severely subnormal patients, with mental ages between 3 and 7, and chronological ages between 10 and 30 years. The results were compared with those of another study of 330 normal children whose average mental age was about one year higher. It was indicated that routine hospital existence resulted in the limitation of vocabulary concerned with individual interests and personal experiences, which tends to lead to the frequent use of a small number of 'heavy duty' words. Thus mental age had a more significant association ($r = 0{\cdot}72$) than chronological age ($r = 0{\cdot}31$) with vocabulary size. An appendix lists core words in the oral vocabulary of severely subnormal patients. Following the earlier study, Mein (1961) examined the grammatical structure of imbeciles' responses during interviews. A progressive drop in percentage of nouns paralleled this change in maturing normal children. In addition significant differences were found between mongol and non-mongol patients matched for sex, M.A., and C.A.

Lyle (1960a) has reported a study which was one of a series giving data on a group of imbecile children in an institution and a group living at home, attending day schools. A number of objective *ad hoc* scales were devised to measure various aspects of speech and language, and the verbal subtest of the Minnesota Preschool Scale was given. Results indicated a high intercorrelation of measure of speech and language, accounted for by one common factor of verbal ability. Lower verbal ability was found in mongols than in non-mongols, whether at day school or in the institution, and there was comparative verbal retardation among the institution group. The same author (Lyle, 1960b) tested the effect of a stimulating environment on the verbal ability of 16 imbecile children age 5–10 (excluding sensory or physical handicaps and the untestable), moved from an institution to a residential family unit. For a full account of special environmental situation, the reader is referred to Tizard (1962). A matched control group was used, and the experimental effects assessed by the differential improvement over a period of time on a series of *ad hoc* verbal tests, the Minnesota Preschool Scale or the Merrill–Palmer test. The experimental group developed verbally at a significantly greater rate than their controls who remained in the institution; positive changes in social and emotional maturity, affective relationships, and social participation were apparent in the experimental group. These changes were believed to be due to the creation of a *child-centred* social organization with no special training programme, where the social and emotional needs of the children were the focus of concern.

O'Connor and Hermelin (1963) showed that the structure of the language of the imbecile resembles that of normal children of similar mental age, and that words have the same semantic characteristics. Moreover, semantic generalization does occur in an experimental situation closely similar to that used in Soviet research. The authors believe, therefore, that 'Luria's theory that "meaningful verbal systems" can rarely be built up in such children might be too pessimistic a view' (op. cit., p. 50). Furthermore, it is possible to build-up learning sets which 'favour the meaningful verbal connections rather than random or "clang" associations' (op. cit., p. 55).

O'Connor and Hermelin's experiments were short term in nature but support Lyle's finding that in the language sphere some modification of development might be possible. What is now needed is a research of long duration with subjects randomly assigned to control and experimental conditions. Kolstoe (1958) in fact carried out a 5½-month study of the effect of language training on low-grade mongols. No marked gains occurred, but the period was not very long, and mongols of course exhibit fairly considerable speech defects over and above their general language deficits. The fact that significant differences in speech between home-based and institutionalized imbeciles occur suggests at least that the common deprivation effect on the speech of the latter might be prevented or reversed.

STUDIES OF DISCRIMINATION LEARNING AND TRANSFER

Transfer of training has in recent years been variously described as either 'an enduring problem' or as a 'psychological will-o'-the-wisp'. It will be argued here that while it is certainly the former, it is far from being the latter. In particular, it will be stressed that, as in other processes, transfer studies have suffered because on the whole a non-developmental approach has been adopted. Furthermore, it seems likely that, so far as imbeciles are concerned, there has probably been a deeply ingrained although not always explicit assumption that they are so rigid that transfer would be unlikely to occur. The view that a relationship exists between intellectual level and rigidity underlies some interesting, if controversial experiments by Kounin

(1941), based on a theory put forward by Lewin (1935). His studies, which involved both mildly retarded and severely retarded subjects, have been criticized by Zigler (1962) in a most important article to which further reference will be made later in this chapter.

Interest in transfer was revived in the post-war years by, on the one hand, Hebb (1949), who advanced in effect a transfer theory of development, and, on the other, by Harlow's (1949) work on learning sets in monkeys. The work of Piaget, now belatedly acknowledged by experimental psychologists, also implies transfer of learning from one stage of development to the next.

Harlow demonstrated that rhesus monkeys learned successive non-spatial discrimination problems with greater and greater facility, this reflecting the formation of a learning set. He considered that this represented a particular form of transfer of training, the transfer between many problems of a single class instead of the more commonly studied transfer between problems of disparate classes (Harlow, 1959). In the earlier (1949) paper it is noted that 'training on several hundred specific problems has not turned the monkey into an automaton exhibiting forced, stereotyped, reflex responses to specific stimuli. These several hundred habits have, instead, made the monkey an adjustable creature with an increased *capacity* to adapt to the ever-changing demands of a psychology laboratory environment' (op. cit., p. 59). In brief, Harlow sees as the most important problem the study of the organism's response to situations it frequently encounters.

The work of Hebb and Harlow is mentioned here because the findings of both authors gave an immense impetus to research on transfer, and because of its relevance to studies reviewed in this chapter.

Some of the first post-war studies of imbecile learning in England, notably the paper by Tizard and Loos (1954) already referred to, revealed the presence of considerable inter-task transfer. In America, Barnett and Cantor (1957) investigated transfer in an experiment involving the discrimination of geometrical shapes. The subjects were 40 adult male defectives, mean age 34·1 years and I.Q. range 24–58. In a carefully controlled study they showed that learning transfer occurred at all intellectual levels in this range. This result seemed similar to that of Gardner (1945), who carried out discrimination learning tasks using imbecile and idiot children.

Another study emanating from Peabody College concerned

discrimination learning sets in normal and mongoloid children with widely discrepant I.Q.s (means: 38·8 and 115·9 respectively). Ten normals and ten mongols were trained to a criterion of eleven successive correct responses on each of five form discrimination problems. Both groups formed learning sets, improving their discrimination. On two of the five problems, the normal children were significantly superior to the mongols, and on the three others the non-significant difference was in the expected direction. An additional finding was that the mongol requires more problems to form learning sets than does the normal child of the same mental age (Girardeau, 1959).

From the late 1950's onwards, a large body of data, mainly by House and Zeaman, has come from the Department of Psychology at the University of Connecticut. Most of the papers by these authors are concerned with discrimination learning in severely retarded children. A few of their many contributions will be briefly described; House and Zeaman (1958a) point out that normal children between the ages of 2 and 4 years have an ability on discrimination problems roughly equivalent to that of infra-human primates. Their study aimed to provide data from imbecile children with mental ages between 2 and 4. The apparatus was a version of Harlow's Wisconsin General Test Apparatus, consisting essentially of a sliding stimulus tray with two circular food wells. The subject was separated from the experimenter by a one-way screen, and candy was placed in one or other of the food wells which were then both covered by the stimuli. The subject was thereafter allowed to pick each of these up, one at a time, and take the candy reinforcement for a correct choice. The stimuli consisted of five different simple geometrical forms, each repeated in five different colours, so that there were in all 25 different stimuli. Each subject was assigned two stimuli, picked at random, but each differing both in colour and form. Correct and incorrect stimuli were designated randomly.

Twenty-five trials per day were carried out for each subject with varying positions of correct choice and the reward always being associated with a particular stimulus. The trials were maintained until the criterion of 20 out of 25 correct choices were reached during a session. The median number of total errors by the imbeciles was 119, and for monkeys in Harlow's study, only 4. It was therefore concluded that imbeciles with mental ages between 2 and 4 were significantly inferior to monkeys, and, by implication, to normal children. The authors find their results surprising in view of those of other studies contrasting the abilities of monkeys and the mentally deficient on various tasks. They feel, however, that their tasks may have been more difficult.

In a second paper (1958b), House and Zeaman made a direct comparison between the discrimination learning of normal and mentally deficient children. Using 30 nursery school children with mental ages of 4 and 5, and 32 defective children of roughly the same mental age, the procedure outlined in the first paper was again followed. With mental age controlled, it was clear that I.Q. and discrimination learning speed were significantly related, as had been inferred in the earlier research, and as found by Girardeau.

In reviewing these and many other researches of their own and of their colleagues, House and Zeaman have produced an important monograph (1960c) on Learning and Transfer. Among their general conclusions are the following: it is considered that the main deficit in discrimination learning 'is caused by failure to direct and maintain *attention* to relevant stimulus dimensions'. They point to the repeated occurrence of ogival discrimination learning curves, and their final negatively accelerated approach to asymptote, which are almost identical, regardless of wide differences in the length of the early, flat portions. The duration of the latter appears to be controlled by stimulus factors and transfer operations. The stimulus factors include novelty, number or proportion of relevant cues, and their nature. In this latter connexion, form has greater attention value than colour, three-dimensional objects than two-dimensional, and larger than smaller. So far as transfer is concerned, easy-to-hard sequences show dramatic positive transfer where the dimension of cue relevance remains unchanged. Reversal shifts, after overlearning, show positive transfer, and intra-dimensional shift is equally potent. After listing a number of other conclusions, the authors state their view that learning set in any significant amount continues to be absent in the discrimination learning of lower-grade imbeciles. This latter conclusion is not altogether borne out in the work of other investigators.

Among the most thorough experimental analyses of learning sets in imbeciles is that by Ellis, Girardeau, and Pryer (1962), who compared the performance of the very severely retarded with that of normal school children on the one hand and data on infra-human primates on the other.

The subjects were 58 institutionalized adolescent patients with

I.Q.s below 25, and 13 normal children with a mean age of 3 and mean I.Q. of 108. A two-choice discrimination problem with 'common use' objects was employed, the stimuli being drawn from a pool of 300. Food rewards were used for the defectives, and for the normal subjects, tokens, for designating the positive stimulus, these being later exchanged for a toy chosen by the subject before the session. Following an adaptation period, the subjects were practised on a single problem for 25 trials per day until a criterion of 80 per cent. success within a single day was reached; those who failed to reach the criterion within 18 days were dropped from the experiment. Thereafter, 30 defectives (a standard procedure group) were trained on 200 6-trial problems, 10 problems per day for 20 days. The normal children were treated similarly, though they received only 10 days' training and 100 problems. The remaining 28 defectives were divided equally into two groups. One group was always rewarded on trial 1 of each problem and the other group was not so rewarded. For the last 50 of the 200 problems the standard procedure was again used.

The results demonstrated marked differences in learning set formation between the normal and defective groups as well as within these groups. The normal subjects reached a performance level of 80 to 90 per cent. correct within the first few days. Of the defective group, a third (the 10 in the standard group) showed orderly improvement over problems, reaching approximately 98 per cent. correct performance by the end of training; a third reached about 75 per cent. correct response, while the remaining 10 did not profit by training, although they had learned the initial single problem. Neither intelligence test scores, indices of language skills, nor experimental observation yielded information to account for these differences.

It was found that performance in the negative-first-trial group was facilitated over that of the positive-first-trial group on trial 2. An interesting account is also given of error-factor analyses, showing points of similarity in the learning of normal and defective humans and the rhesus monkey, although there were marked differences as well (Ellis, Girardeau, and Pryer, 1962).

Clarke and Blakemore (1961) and Clarke and Cookson (1962) have reported a number of experiments designed to elucidate the role of perceptual-motor transfer in imbeciles. Starting with a hypothesis derived from Hebb (1949) that ability to transfer learning might be optimal early in the life of an organism, Clarke and Blakemore (1961) took three small, matched groups of medium to high-grade imbeciles, aged on the average 9, 17, and 23 years and average I.Q. of about 40. The general procedure was to select pairs of matched, equally difficult visual discrimination tasks, which though similar as to the processes involved were different in content. Ten learning trials (two per day) were given on each, and alternate subjects commenced on alternate forms of each task pair. The experiments involved matching geometric shapes and sorting very small symbols on typewriter key-tops. Task A, a manipulative-motor problem, will not be discussed here. Task B was similar to the form-matching subtest in year IV of the 1937 Stanford–Binet test, Form L. Each part, B1 and B2, consisted of a white cardboard sheet 18 inches by 10½ inches, on which was drawn in outline a set of eight mixed geometrical forms, each covering an area approximately 2½ inches square (e.g. a circle, closed semicircle, equilateral and right-angled triangles, various polygons, etc.). No design appeared in both forms of the task. The shapes were also reproduced on separate cards 2 inches square, with two for each design on the sheet, that is, sixteen cards for each alternate form. These cards were handed to the subject one at a time, and each had to be placed on top of the corresponding design on the sheet. The cards were presented in a set order with no similar designs being consecutive. The results indicated that very much more transfer was shown by the younger than the adolescent and adult imbeciles.

Three other experiments confirmed that greater transfer was shown by the 9-year-olds than by the older imbeciles. It was also clear that two weeks' short daily practice was sufficient for the children almost to achieve adult level. The authors believed that the perceptual processes involved were of considerable importance in training and other activities.

These findings have been confirmed and extended by Clarke and Cookson (1962). Here very much more difficult material was attempted. Thus, after a six-month period of non-practice, a plastic typewriter key-sorting task of greater difficulty than that reported by Clarke and Blakemore (op. cit.) was administered. Fig. 5 shows the stimuli. In (*a*) the earlier, easier pair of tasks are shown. Each key was mounted on a small tin, and there were five keys for each, making a total of twenty-five which had to be sorted from a mixed-up pile on the table. In (*b*) the later, more difficult pair of tasks is shown, with again the same experimental procedure. The 9-year-old subjects who had carried out the two tasks in (*a*) during March 1960 were given the (*b*) tasks during October of the same year. Instead of slower performance, their ability was significantly better on the later more difficult task (see Fig. 6). This indicated a surprising retention of earlier learning over a six-month period of non-practice, and the facilitatory effects of earlier learning upon later. Other experiments showed highly significant retention over one-year and seven-year periods.

A further experiment employed the Minnesota form-boards as a learning task, in the same way that had been suggested by Tizard

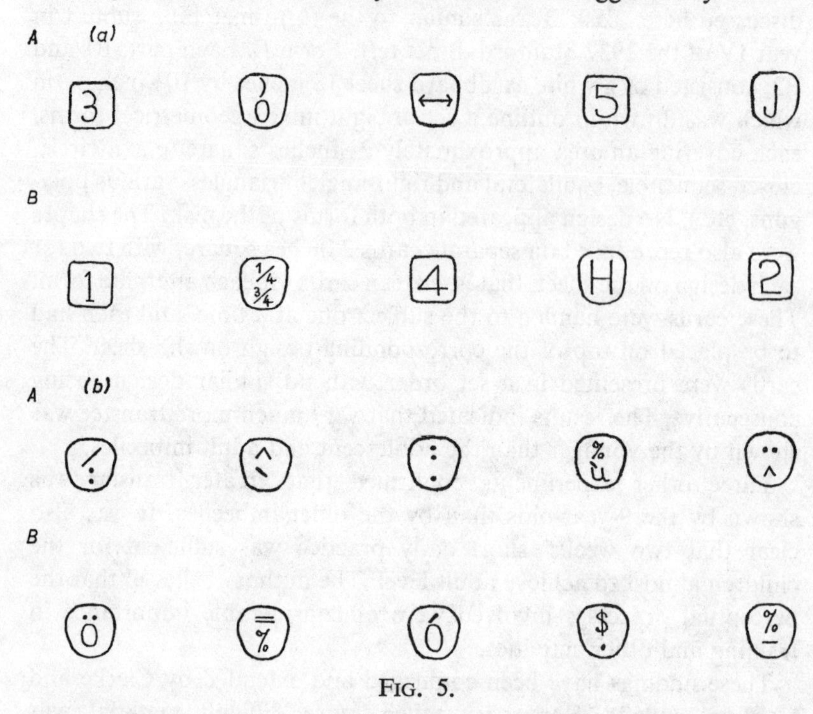

FIG. 5.

and Loos (op. cit.). A small group of children was matched with imbecile adults, and once again the learning gap between them was almost closed. The initial discrepancy on trial 1, Board I, of 640 seconds, was reduced to 45 seconds on trial 8 of Board IV. It seemed apparent here that the amount of transfer is related to the difficulty of the task, and hence probably also to its degree of unfamiliarity.

The authors concluded by relating their work to that of Harlow (1949). It seemed likely that 'learning set' could cover the results which had been gained, but it was possible to break down this concept into three related processes. One experiment, already quoted,

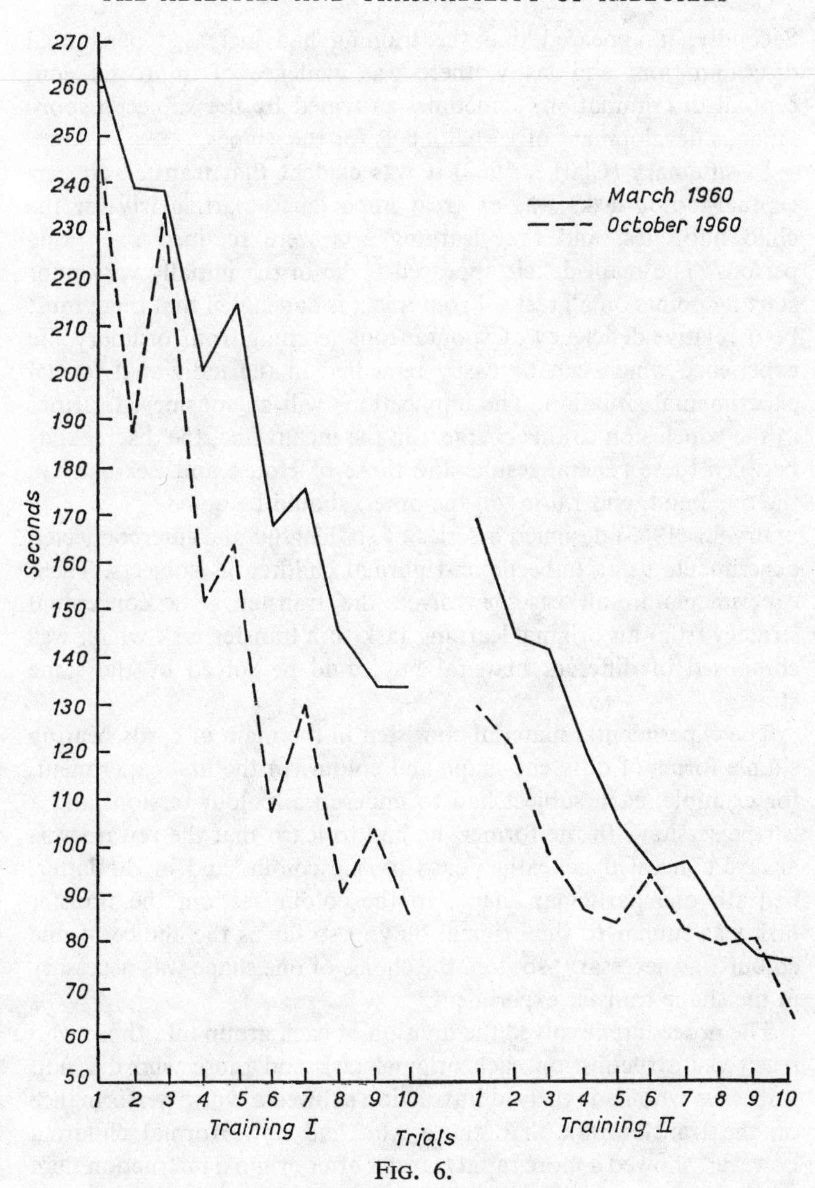

FIG. 6.

involved the repetition of the same typewriter key-sorting task after a year of non-practice. This task was given on the second occcasion *without* instructions. The subjects performed it without hesitation; they had a knowledge or *expectancy* of the demands of the situation.

Secondly, it appeared that the training had increased perceptual discrimination, and lastly, there was evidence of improved conceptual discrimination, sometimes provided by the subject's spontaneous development of verbal labels for the shapes.

In summary (Clarke, 1962) it was evident that transfer on perceptual-motor tasks was of great importance, particularly for the child imbeciles, and that learning sets were retained over long periods. The main deficit appeared to lie in the initially very poor starting points on all tasks. From this it is concluded that there must be a relative deficiency of spontaneous learning from ordinary life experience which can be easily remedied in the individual formal experimental situation. The implications will be considered further in the conclusion to this chapter; in the meanwhile, the discrepancy between these general results and those of House and Zeaman, on the one hand, and Luria, on the other, should be noted.

Bryant (1963) designed a series of six lengthy and interconnected experiments using imbecile and normal children as subjects. These experiments in all cases involved the transfer of a conceptual strategy from an original learning task to a transfer task which was composed of different material but could be solved by the same strategy.

The experimental material consisted in the main of cards bearing simple forms of different shape and colour. In the first experiment, for example, each subject had to undergo a 'colour session' and a 'shape session'. In the former, he had to learn that the reward was always concealed beneath a card of one colour, and in the latter, beneath one particular shape. In the colour session, the transfer task was similar to the original only in so far as the choice of one colour was necessary; so, too, the choice of one shape was necessary in the shape transfer experiment.

The procedure involved the division of each group into those who received instruction on each original task and those who did not. Imbeciles who had received instruction showed a worse performance on the transfer task than those who had not. Normal children, however, showed a more rapid transfer after original instruction than without it. Another major difference lay in the imbecile's greater transfer response with negative than positive learning, while the normal child transferred positive learning more efficiently than negative (see results by Ellis *et al.*, pp. 375–6).

The author advanced the hypothesis that imbeciles are only able to transfer on the basis of general rather than specific learning. Thus when positive learning is specific they transfer on the basis of negative learning which is general. Instruction can impede transfer simply because it strengthens specific positive learning and weakens general negative learning.

Bryant's studies in effect highlight the importance of the type of experimental situation upon the subject. It may well be that different results with the transfer processes relate only to differences in experimental conditions. It is significant, for example, that the work of Clarke and Blakemore (1961) and Clarke and Cookson (1962) used virtually no instructions and only short demonstration by the experimenter. Furthermore, subjects were always rewarded and praised at the end of each session, regardless of performance. It seemed that these conditions maximized transfer.

In considering learning transfer in the severely subnormal, reference should be made to a study by Bensberg (1958), although his subjects do not strictly conform to the criteria of imbecility used in the present chapter. The range of I.Q.s was 40 to 56, and the subjects (aged between 15 and 29 years) had been diagnosed as having mental deficiency due to a familial or undifferentiated (idiopathic) aetiology. Bensberg showed that the severely retarded, in common with normal people, may be affected, on a transfer task, by previously learned perceptual bias.

The 60 subjects were divided into five treatment groups: Group I were taught to respond to the colour aspect of a task to a criterion of one correct complete series; Group II had identical treatment, plus 27 additional trials (over-learning). Groups III and IV corresponded to the former two, except that they were taught to respond to the form aspect of the task. A Control Group were given neither a colour nor a form 'set'. The transfer task involved the use of a form concept, and it was found that, in accordance with prediction, those who had acquired a 'form set' were substantially facilitated in their performance and that those who had acquired a 'colour set' did less well than the other three groups, including the controls.

Current work by the writers attempts to elucidate further the parameters of transfer in discrimination learning. The differences demonstrated earlier in the transfer of adults and children might conceivably be related to the differing starting levels of the two experimental populations.

A method was therefore evolved for either (*a*) increasing the complexity of the adult tasks until starting points in terms of score were identical with those for the children, or (*b*) decreasing task complexity for the children until their starting point reached that of the adults. Both methods yielded similar results: under these conditions, transfer was roughly equal for both groups on typewriter key-sorting tasks and the Minnesota form-boards. The conclusion was reached that task difficulty is an important variable in transfer experiments (Clarke and Cooper, 1964).

A further series of experiments investigated transfer across tasks involving simple concepts. Four groups were matched for age, I.Q. and initial performance on a task where subjects were required to categorize photographs of different objects. These groups were then trained on the sorting of geometric shapes, each condition requiring a different degree of abstraction; one group received no training. The results showed significant transfer for those groups who had been subjected to the more taxing conditions of training, while the control group showed no improvement on retest. Furthermore, within the two groups which showed considerable transfer, the gain was significantly greater for those subjects who learned most in the interpolated tasks. These experiments therefore again indicate that transfer in imbeciles can be considerable, and for the first time suggest that gains on one activity can be reflected in performance on a very different task.

DISCUSSION AND CONCLUSIONS

The field of imbecile behaviour is clearly rich in problems demanding further experimental analysis. The results available so far display both consistencies and a number of apparent inconsistencies. Since precise data to resolve these latter are lacking, the present writers are tempted to offer some speculations to account for some of the different results obtained. These concern the experimental procedures used, motivational factors and the natural history of the subjects.

A. Experimental procedure

1. *Instructions*. The work of Bryant (1963) focuses attention upon this problem. Frequently it is difficult to ascertain from reports the *precise* words used to imbecile subjects, which with this population may be crucial in view of their known weakness in the verbal sphere.

2. *Nature of stimulus material*. It seems possible that familiarity

would facilitate learning, and that, for example, geometric figures may have a stimulus value different from that of common objects.

3. *Length of learning period.* The number of trials needed to reach the criterion, and the number of further learning trials given, are likely to be of great importance.

4. *Type of material reward* and reward conditions do not appear to be important factors. This becomes apparent in any survey of the literature and direct evidence reinforces this view (e.g. Ellis, 1962; Wolfensberger, 1960). However, the human relationship involved in experimentation does appear to be relevant (Ellis and Distefano, 1959). One is impressed by the relative ease with which severely handicapped subjects learn simple tasks, no matter what conditions of material reward or non-reward are employed; it would appear that a 'Hawthorne' effect is operating. It seems likely that the majority of experimenters are positive in their relationship to the subjects, and that for this group of people, accustomed over years to frequent experience of total failure, such an attitude may in itself be of high motivational consequence. It is tempting to speculate that on the rare occasions when negative results are obtained, the personality of the experimenter might be the relevant variable.

5. *The difficulty of the task for the subject.* There is substantial evidence that transfer is positively related to the difficulty of the training condition provided that its threshold is not so high that no learning can occur. Any experiment on transfer must therefore use some method of calibrating optimal task complexity for a given population.

B. Experimental subjects

1. *Social history of the subject.* The majority of experimental studies of learning in imbeciles have been conducted in institutions on both sides of the Atlantic, where the subjects receive a minimum of personal care and attention. This type of deprivation probably acts as a powerful incentive condition. An excellent discussion of the subject is given by Zigler (1962), who came to this conclusion during the course of a polemic on 'rigidity' with Kounin. The subjects used in his experiments were mildly rather than severely retarded persons, but it seems likely that his findings have relevance in the imbecile field.

2. *Effects of previous learning experiments on present performance.* One suspects this to occur much more frequently than is reported –

when subjects from the same institution are used for successive experiments (see Clarke and Cookson, 1962).

3. *Degree of impairment of the subject*. The range of abilities within the imbecile group is large, and there can be substantial differences in response to training between those with I.Q.s in the 20's and early 40's. This view is supported by the findings of a number of studies of employability. It seems that prospects for those of I.Q. 35 and above are considerably better than for those below.

Perhaps the most striking thing about the studies reviewed in the latter part of this chapter is the simplicity and artificiality of the stimulus material commonly used. Many of the experiments are elegantly designed and employ fairly complex statistical techniques on responses to tasks which bear little resemblance to anything a child would normally meet in his environment. A sort of inverted anthropomorphism seems to prevail, whereby techniques designed for the animal laboratory are applied to human subjects, almost without modification. It is to be hoped that the knowledge gained by these researches will form the basis for a development of more imaginative work in the future.

Chapter XIV

VOCATIONAL AND SOCIAL REHABILITATION OF THE SUBNORMAL[1]

by H. C. Gunzburg[2]

INTRODUCTION

A large number of mainly able-bodied persons have been regarded as feeble-minded in this and other countries, many of whom have subsequently spent long periods in institutions without concerted efforts having been made to socialize them and to return them to the community. Two interacting factors have been largely responsible for the existence of a custodial tradition: (1) the person himself and the nature of his disabilities, and (2) the level of tolerance for the subnormal or psychopathic displayed by the community. Both have an important bearing on the general problem of rehabilitating such people, and as far as possible should be differentiated, since conclusions about the social competence or incompetence of individuals are only valid in relation to the community from which they are drawn.

The custodial outlook has been responsible for yet another problem, namely the deterioration of work abilities and habits through lack of use in the institution, and the manifestation of destructive and delinquent behaviour, often explicable in terms of a lack of constructive channels into which energies may be directed,

[1] In this chapter the terms 'subnormal' and 'feeble-minded' are used synonymously.

[2] About a third of this chapter has been contributed by the Editors, and is based on their own work. This material is incorporated within pp. 385–400.

and general frustration in terms of lack of incentive and goal. This difficulty was clearly understood by the Wood Committee (1929) which wrote: 'whether the individual be normal or mentally defective nothing socializes so effectively as work', and pointed out that 'if we were to place greater emphasis upon the activities of the mental defective that can be directed into useful channels we should need to concern ourselves less about their care, supervision, and control'.

In this chapter it is proposed to consider the general qualities of the feeble-minded which make rehabilitation *necessary*, the factors in the community which make it *possible*, and the methods of training which make it *practicable.*

GENERAL QUALITIES (DEFICITS) OF THE FEEBLE-MINDED

It has repeatedly been stressed in this book that the term 'feeble-minded' has been for many years interpreted in a very wide sense; in some ways it would seem that the term 'subnormal social inadequate' would more meaningfully describe them. Since their intellectual abilities range from borderline imbecility to the population average, and occasionally above, they present a sample, albeit non-representative and non-proportional, of about half the population. It might also be worth remarking that the majority of those with I.Q.s between 60 and 80 are never certified and make a reasonable social adjustment; thus the certified person within even this narrow range is atypical. This being so, the general qualities of such persons need examination, and these are set out below. It must be remembered, however, that like all averages these do not contain the whole truth and may fail to describe an individual case (Clarke, 1957).

(1) *Subnormal intelligence*

The majority of the certified feeble-minded are intellectually subnormal, and a number of researches have suggested that an I.Q. of about 70 represents the mean, at any rate for the adolescent or young adult patient.

It has already been indicated (pp. 114–27) that in many cases intellectual changes are likely to occur, particularly in those from the worst social backgrounds (about 40 per cent. of most samples), so that to varying extents subnormal intelligence tends to be a self-curing condition.

(2) *Educational backwardness regardless of I.Q.*
Most feeble-minded patients are found to have educational attainments much lower than their intellectual potential would theoretically make possible. The following factors seem relevant: (*a*) poor living conditions, with lack of intellectual stimulation, lack of incentive, and lack of parental interest; (*b*) overcrowded classes, poor teaching, and truancy; (*c*) late intellectual maturation as an effect of adverse circumstances. Many factors such as these have been excellently described by Burt (1937) during the inter-war years.

(3) *Lack of general knowledge regardless of I.Q.*
Much the same causes operate here as in educational backwardness. In addition, restricted experiences of community life and the process of institutionalization all play a part, and the mere fact of illiteracy frequently limits informational experience.

(4) *Background of adverse experiences*
It is well known that the feeble-minded tend to be drawn from the lowest socio-economic groups, and often their case histories reveal a background of almost unbelievable social degradation, which cannot fail to have had profound psychological effects. In an unpublished study Clarke and Clarke found that in a representative sample of adolescent and young adult feeble-minded patients, 40 per cent. were drawn from really adverse conditions characterized by neglect or cruelty, 50 per cent. came from unsatisfactory and poor conditions, or had been brought up entirely in institutions, and 10 per cent. (largely known organics) from good homes.

(5) *Emotional instability*
Instability is very common, although, surprisingly, is seldom really severe in degree. Inferiority feelings, often justified, are prevalent, for the patient's whole history tends to have been one of failure. There is little doubt that emotional instability is greater among the female than the male certified population. Two hypotheses, as yet untested, might account for this. First, the sort of girl regarded as being a social problem may be more unstable than the equivalent boy; it is well known that unstable youths tend to commit criminal

offences more often than girls, whose delinquency tends to manifest itself in sexual misdemeanours, which society looks upon with a greater degree of toleration; thus, in order for a girl to render herself 'subject to be dealt with' she has to manifest unusually unstable behaviour. Second, there tends to be a more repressive and autocratic control over females in hospitals than of males; this in itself leads to frustration and aggressive behaviour.

(6) *Poor conative development*
Again much the same adverse social causes militate against proper conative development. Frustration tolerance tends to be poor, and consequent 'short-circuit' reactions typical (MacMahon, 1952).

(7) *Poor work habits*
Both the poor social background of feeble-minded patients and the often slow tempo of institutional life tend to lead to poor work habits. On the whole, patients are not used to hard work, have never developed concentration and application, and often possess totally unrealistic attitudes towards what the community expects of them. Allied with this, is an *extreme conservatism* based on fear of what change may bring, with often absurd results; for example, refusal to do a job slightly different from their usual one.

(8) *Emotional hunger*
The deprivation so typical of the feeble-minded leads to an intense need for personal contact with others, although, paradoxically, there is often great difficulty in making such relationships (cf. Bowlby, 1951). Often, too, the patient desires to maintain an association with thoroughly bad parents from whom he has been rescued and whose cruel behaviour he remembers well.

(9) *Ambivalence to authority*
Most of the patient's contacts with authority have had unfortunate associations, and not unreasonably this leads to suspicion or even hostility to anyone in authority. The normal tendency to project blame increases the strength of these attitudes.

THE COMMUNITY

Despite the fact that medical and other authorities are those immediately concerned with decisions relating to hospitalization, ultimately, in a broad sense, the responsibility for segregating certain individuals from society rests with the community. The type of person disposed of, and the reasons for this disposal, varies from country to country and within a country from generation to generation, bearing a relationship to, on the one hand, the economic situation, and on the other, the degree of general enlightenment.

At the present time none of the so-called 'under-developed' countries has legal provision for the mentally deficient. The severely subnormal tend not to survive the rigours of birth and the first few years of life in communities where infant mortality is high. The very dull are looked after by their families, and manage to effect a reasonable adjustment in simple village communities; furthermore it follows that in such communities few will be found to be 'inadequate'.

A similar situation no doubt pertained in England two hundred years ago. 'Feeble-mindedness' or 'psychopathy' had not been invented nor presumably did they manifest themselves on anything like the scale that they do now. This is not only because of better diagnosis following a deeper understanding of psychological principles but also because these conditions, unlike well-defined diseases such as leprosy, tuberculosis, and syphilis, are to a large extent social concepts, which do not have an existence independent of the society which produced them. In fact, it may be said with some truth that the Industrial Revolution created the problem of feeble-mindedness.

The structure of society will also to some extent determine the type of care given to individuals deemed social inadequates. Where large-scale unemployment exists, those who are incapable of competing on equal terms with their fellows (*vide* Royal College of Physicians' definition of feeble-mindedness) will to a large extent receive custodial care. A few will be capable by virtue of special training of taking their place in a competitive community, but the majority will have to be maintained, in receipt of public assistance in one form or another, since there is no place in the community for their level of productivity.

The type of employment available and suitable will also vary with the type of society. In Britain fifty years ago a considerable proportion of the population had homes staffed by relatively large numbers of domestic workers, and there was room for feeble-minded women to perform one or two menial tasks. Today homes are to a larger extent mechanized, and the work done in former years by, say, four women, tends to be performed by one person with the help of a variety of mechanical aids. This situation demands a level of intelligence and versatility which few feeble-minded women possess.

Agriculture, which formerly absorbed many dull and feeble-minded men in a menial capacity, is similarly becoming more and more mechanized, and it is increasingly uneconomic to employ individuals who cannot adapt themselves to new circumstances and take a considerable degree of responsibility. Thus today it is largely in the stratified industry that the feeble-minded person is most likely to find the relatively repetitive tasks to which he is most suited at wages on which he can maintain himself.

Training programmes, undertaken in institutions, must therefore reflect the needs of the community, and select the type of work at which the patients in their care are most likely to make an adequate social adjustment.

VOCATIONAL TRAINING IN AN INSTITUTION

The background

The hospital of the traditional type provides a wide variety of occupations and thus much formal and incidental training. The patients' labour contributes in one way or another to the maintenance of a fairly self-contained organism, and helps substantially towards the economical management of the institution. Besides the service and maintenance departments (laundry, sewing rooms, carpenters, bricklayers, engineers, etc.) there often exist workshops producing goods which are not of direct use to the hospital, though they have been found to offer useful occupation within the practical abilities of many of the lower-grade type of patient (rug-making, basket-work, embroidery, weaving, and other crafts). Work of this kind has been described in some detail in all relevant literature on mental deficiency and will not be discussed here, except to point out that many such departments play an important part in helping the custodial patient lead a happy, contented, and comparatively busy life. On the other hand, it cannot be assumed that the high-grade feeble-minded patient will obtain in this way the necessary social and vocational skills to enable him to make a satisfactory adaptation to the community.

Earl (1942) in an address to the R.M.P.A. stated the problem as follows:

> The occupation of patients is important. I would like to see clearer thinking on this point. We are out to train our patients. If possible we are out to socialize them. If that is not possible we are out to occupy them usefully both from their point of view and from ours. But we do *not* want to exploit them, though we want to use their labour in the interests of economy. I am getting very suspicious of workshops, for example. A fine range of shops is a noble sight. An output of first-rate work is an excellent thing. An account book which shows a profit is something to be proud of. But patients capable of first-rate work shouldn't be in the Institution at all unless they are cripples or unstable. And we should reckon our profits – even from the strictly financial viewpoint – in terms of patients returned to society rather than in terms of baskets woven or envelopes made. The output of my own shops has fallen in recent years. And we have had to employ one or two extra farm hands and install electric milking. But I have sent nearly 200 patients on licence and have a further 50 on daily work outside.
>
> I think we should differentiate clearly between employment for the patient's benefit and employment for the benefit of the institution. Every employed patient should have an employment card, to be checked at regular intervals, and stating quite clearly *why* he is doing whatever job he is doing. If he is working, for example, in the bootshop we should have evidence in writing to tell us why. Is he being trained as a bootmaker with a view to earning his living at it outside? That may be so in a very small number of cases only. Is it because he shows some manual aptitude for that type of work? Or because he likes the job? Or because he likes the man who teaches it? And so on. Or is it because there was a vacancy in the bootshop when he started – and nobody has bothered about him ever since. Is he there for his own benefit or for ours? Let us say quite clearly why he is there.
>
> The fact is that it is not possible to earn a living at most of the handicrafts provided in Colony life. What a patient really learns in the shops – or what he should learn in them – is not how to do a job but how to hold one down. What the low grades learn is how to occupy themselves. The various patients employed at maintenance jobs round the place are perhaps learning to handle tools of various sorts but far more importantly they should be learning to do an honest day's work and take some pride in it.
>
> I am sure that all employment of patients should be under the care of a single person – *not* a shops master and preferably not a doctor but rather a lay officer, possibly an industrial psychologist, working in co-operation with the medical staff. It should be the province of this officer to see that the best is got out of every patient for that patient's own sake first and foremost. [See also Beard, 1953; Hill, 1953.]

Tizard and O'Connor (1952), in their discussion of hospital workshops and methods of rehabilitation, make the following criticisms of traditional training methods:

(1) Most training is designed to promote successful occupation, rather than successful employment.

(2) There is little relationship between the type of work performed in institutional workshops and the employment opportunities provided by the community.

(3) Equipment in workshops is almost without exception obsolete as far as industry is concerned, and there is a dearth of machines. The tempo of production is commonly slow, which again affects adversely community placement.

(4) Little contact is made with commercial firms which might be induced to take trained patients into their own factories.

(5) The work is too often carried out in an atmosphere devoid of all incentives.

(6) Too little attention has been paid to the selection and training of supervisors.

(7) The supervision of patients in daily service, or on licence, has often been inadequate, and there is still a lack of trained social workers.

Industrial training and rehabilitation

It is most important that individual training be given to those patients young enough to profit by it; this should be carried out in separate units, and the programme designed to remedy the personality defects outlined earlier in this chapter. General education and psychotherapy which are discussed separately (Chapters XII and XV) will, where appropriate, form part of the rehabilitation scheme. The necessity for a team of trained personnel, working in close co-operation, is immediately apparent.

The practical work executed within the framework of a rehabilitation scheme will obviously depend on local conditions and the labour market. Industrial areas offer great advantages and it has often been found possible to enlist the co-operation of manufacturers who supply materials and tools for carrying out industrial processes in the hospital. Among these are found: assembly of switchboxes, filing and trimming, cleaning of rubber mouldings, drilling of holes into metal discs, soldering of wireless terminals, folding of cardboard boxes, making of paper bags, cutting of rubber hoses, painting and cleaning of plastic discs, etc. (Clarke and Clarke, 1954a; Gunzburg, 1957, 1960). The great advantage of such skilled and semi-skilled work is its realistic nature and that it can provide the basis for industrial habit training. The repetitiveness of the job enables the worker to develop gradually increasing skill and speed and with that a certain pride in his accomplishments. Most of these above-mentioned tasks are within the capabilities of the average feeble-minded patient; they can be scaled, and appropriate daily or weekly targets for output can be set; they offer opportunities for impressing the trainee with the need for maintaining satisfactory quality and quantity, with the necessity for punctuality, and with the paramount demand of persisting with the job, despite its dullness. (See Plates 4, 5, pp. 362–3.)

The success of schemes of this type obviously depends on suitable motivation. Clearly defined incentives should be employed, both short-term and long-term. These include: payment by results leading to an increasing personal savings account; adequate pocket money; the right to buy clothes and other personal possessions (under guidance where necessary); the right to regular parole in the community; and above all, the certain knowledge that when work and behaviour have reached a defined level a job 'outside' will be obtained, with prospects of indefinite leave and ultimate discharge. In order for such incentives to be effective, they must be clearly and repeatedly explained to the trainees, who must never be left in doubt as to their present position and future prospects (Tizard and O'Connor, 1952; Clarke and Clarke, 1954a; Gunzburg, 1957; Smith, 1957).

Training should involve a gradual change from simpler to more complex work which at first should be broken down into its constituents. The more varied the tasks learned the better. In this connexion the attitude of the supervisor is crucial; high-grade defectives tend to be very conservative, disliking and fearing change, and it is all too easy to let them settle into one task and leave them to it. Only by planned changes of work can this tendency be overcome. The safest rule would be that whenever a patient has learned a task to perfection he should be given a new one to master. In this way he will become used to change which is essential to life outside.

Much of the patient's resistance to institutional training and treatment really originates in the indefiniteness of the period of his detention and the vagueness of promises regarding his future. Giving the patient an opportunity to see himself as he appears to his supervisors and an indication of his proximity to the next stage leading

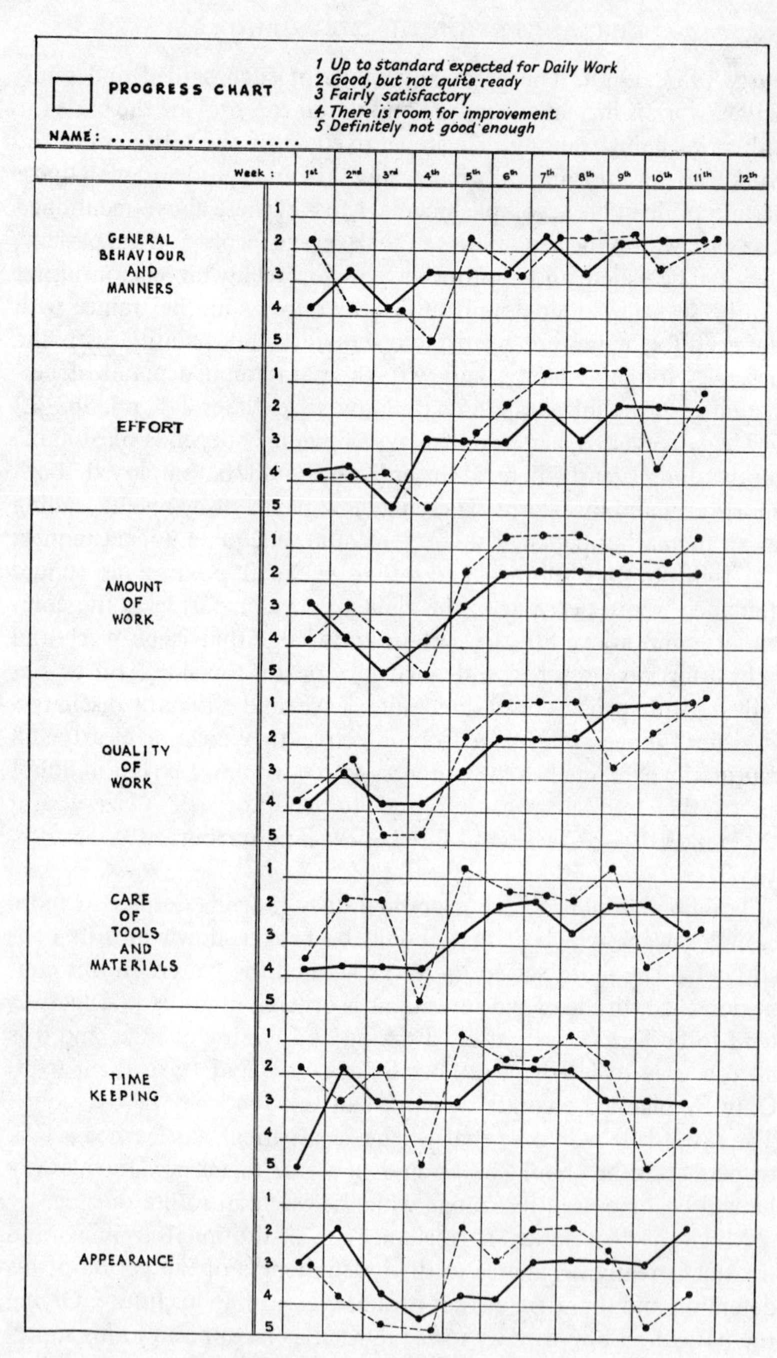

Fig. 7. Workshop Progress Rating Chart

to his discharge, can be an extremely helpful method if judiciously handled.

Fig. 7 shows a Rating Chart as used at Monyhull Hospital in England. The chart is always on full view to the patient and is discussed in weekly group meetings and in personal interviews. It indicates weekly the supervisor's opinion of a patient's standing, his progress, or slackening. Instead of giving an overall judgment which has little concrete meaning to the patient, the supervisor rates him on seven clearly defined work and behaviour aspects: general behaviour; work behaviour; amount of work; quality of work; care of tools and materials; time keeping; appearance. This gives the individual patient the opportunity of seeing for himself which specific areas require most urgently his attention.

The five-point Rating Scale has definite practical meaning. The lowest rating (5) means not simply 'very poor', but so poor as to be 'definitely not good enough for Daily Work'. The highest rating (1) indicates not merely first-class performance, but also that the defective is 'up to the standard expected for Daily Work'. The defective has an incentive to strive for and maintain these top marks because they secure transfer to 'Daily Work' (see p. 407) and the connected ratings form a graph which indicates visually his position in relation to this target.

A refinement of this procedure can be used therapeutically in discussion groups by giving each patient an opportunity to rate his own behaviour independently of the Supervisor. Comparing their own judgment with that of the 'foreman' helps some patients to gain an understanding of standards and requirements and to view their own performance through the eyes of others.

The illustration shows the chart of a rather unstable youth, Richard W., aged 21, Wechsler Full Scale I.Q. 61, Full Mental Age 9·0, who made fairly good progress during 11 weeks as shown by the ratings of his supervisor (heavy line). His own estimate of his behaviour during that time (broken line) shows typical swings of mood and though on the whole he realized quite well when there was an improvement, he tended quite markedly to overestimate the degree of improvement and to judge himself very severely for faults, real or imaginary, which were scarcely reflected in the supervisor's rating.

Judgments in extremes and neglect of the finer shades of 'not so good' and 'not so bad' appear to be very typical for the mental defective and the use of such a device as the progress chart and self-estimate for the purpose of therapy and rehabilitation requires careful and tactful handling of the patient. Rating Charts for workshop performance and work prognosis have been often described, but have not often been used as a therapeutic tool. This particular use requires constant explanations from the staff as well as the practical possibility of keeping promises of employment – a fortunate combination of circumstances not always obtainable. The effect of knowledge of results shown visually on the quality and accuracy of social discrimination was demonstrated by Clark (1960). Using the progress chart as described above in a slightly modified form, Clark showed also a high correlation (0·90 after correction for attenuation) with the Vineland Social Maturity Scale.

A training workshop in a hospital cannot be an exact replica of a factory and often special methods, like the progress charts system, have to be introduced to induce an understanding for the conditions of ordinary working life. Nevertheless, despite the artificiality of such a system that has more in common with 'school' than 'shop', the realistic features of the work itself, the payment by results, the insistence on production, etc., will help to direct attention 'outwards' rather than towards the easier institution life which surrounds this busy island on all sides (Gunzburg, 1950b, 1951; Clarke and Clarke, 1954a; O'Connor, 1954).

Flexibility is required from the supervisory staff. *Laissez-faire* supervision is not often found in industrial life and is just as unsupportive for our patient as the non-directive passive therapist attitude discussed in the next chapter. Strict supervision – not harsh supervision – where criticism and blame, but no praise for work well done, are given – is bearable by many patients except the anxious and neurotic ones. The compromise between those two extremes, the friendly supervision, where praise and encouragement are given, appears to succeed like the strict supervision, even though some tough-minded patients might take advantage of the situation. This has been demonstrated in a research under controlled conditions (Tizard, 1953a) where it also became clear that individual patients showed considerable differences in their response to different types of supervision.

Under favourable conditions and skilful direction a training unit within the hospital may achieve considerable financial success, granted an ample supply of industrial sub-contract work. In Darenth Park Hospital, where O'Connor and Tizard carried out their first investigations, 24 boys in the training unit earned £1,250 in the first eight months, and £2,750 in just over a year (O'Connor and Tizard, 1956). Clarke and Clarke (1954a) mention that at The Manor Hospital the income of two units for men and women, mainly undertaking the preparation of television components and cardboard-box making, totalled £2,300 since the initiation of the scheme in 1952, of which nearly £1,000 had been earned during the eight months preceding their report. Some men in the final stages of training before being placed in the community were earning an average of £7 per week each, with a range of from £5 to £9. They had thus achieved normal production output.

The role of the social worker

The ultimate aim of industrial training and general rehabilitation as described is the successful settlement of the patient in the community. The skilled social worker is obviously an important member of the rehabilitation team. The procuring of suitable jobs in which the patients may be placed, their immediate supervision while in the community on trial, and the maintenance of liaison with the managers of industrial concerns are all tasks which naturally fall to the social worker. A procedure frequently adopted in hospitals for the subnormal is that the patient who is ready for community trial proceeds to a job while still residing in the hospital, and begins to contribute towards his upkeep. If this period proves successful the patient is placed in a hostel or lodgings where after a further period of probation he will gain his discharge.

During these two probationary periods, of crucial importance in the patient's career, a considerable degree of help and aid will often be required as the men and women encounter situations and problems to which they may not be accustomed.

Results of industrial rehabilitation schemes

For a genuine assessment of the rate of success emerging from training schemes, a long-term follow-up such as that of Charles (1953) or Wildenskov (1957) is needed, and no industrial training project for the feeble-minded has been running sufficiently long for such a final evaluation to have been made. (See also Chapter XVII.)

Success rates themselves are affected by a number of factors:

(1) The type of person rehabilitated.
(2) The quality of training.

(3) The type of job.
(4) The quality of supervision while first in the community, both by the hospital and by the employers.
(5) The economic circumstances at the time.

O'Connor and Tizard (1956) analysed the success and failure of patients placed, on the one hand, in a large factory and, on the other, in non-industrial forms of employment. The follow-up was short, being a maximum of two years, but it was shown that only 18 per cent. failed in the factory while 44 per cent. failed in other employment, a figure almost exactly corroborated in an unpublished study at The Manor Hospital. With longer periods of follow-up, failure rates obviously will tend to increase and Clarke and Clarke (1954a, 1957) estimate that over about three years between one-quarter and one-third fail in their first job in industry. What emerges quite clearly from longer periods of study, however, is that the vast majority, even under traditional methods of training and placement, succeed perhaps in their second, third, or even fourth job. Thus Stanley and Gunzburg (1957) show that of 75 discharges, 13 patients gained it after three or more attempts on licence. The few permanent failures are probably limited mainly to the genuinely 'psychopathic' members of the hospitalized subnormal which MacMahon, Clarke, and Clarke (1958) estimate as comprising 5·4 per cent., a figure very close to Gunzburg's (1952) estimate that 7 per cent. were in need of permanent hospital care. The physically handicapped no doubt form a proportion of such cases.

Stanley and Gunzburg (op. cit.) believe that character defects are the major category under which failures can be subsumed but indicate that most of these are remediable. In evaluating success and failure of the feeble-minded, it is profitable not only to compare the effects of different types of training and placement but also to study failure rates of normal young men and women in similar jobs. Thus O'Connor and Tizard (op. cit.) showed that the failure rates of defective boys employed on a building site were less than those of normal day-labourers. Moreover, it is sometimes not appreciated that many normal young men and women change jobs quite frequently for various reasons, including those which would be termed 'failure' in mental deficiency practice. In this connexion, it is worth noting that a proportion of failures result from breaches of mental deficiency regulations (e.g. attachment with members of the opposite sex, consumption of alcohol, etc.) and that sometimes more puritanical standards of conduct are demanded of the mentally deficient than society asks of normal people, and this demand is imposed on persons presumably less able to exercise normal emotional control.

Gunzburg (1957), commenting on factors affecting success on leave in general, states that (1) the tested intellectual level can be quite low before setting a definite limit to employability outside the hospital (some of the young men in his study having Wechsler I.Q.s below 40) and (2) the repetition of delinquency – even of a sexual nature – is so infrequent that pre-admission delinquency does not suggest a poor social prognosis. The latter point is supported by the work of Tong and MacKay (1959) who found that an early history of heterosexual misbehaviour and violence was associated with a good prognosis. Low intelligence by itself is not necessarily an obstacle to living and working in the community. Saenger (1957) found that 27 per cent. of his sample of severely subnormal people living in the community were employed for remuneration. Craft (1962a) showed that 75 per cent. of an imbecile group were employed, compared with 77 per cent. of a group with I.Q.s above 50. The figures of the Birmingham Education Authority (1956) showed that 20 per cent. of their imbecile children obtained gainful employment.

Types of industrial employment

Subnormal patients have entered a variety of jobs in industry, ranging from unskilled labouring to semi-skilled work. Women have earned £4 per week binding insoles, £6 per week preparing dental tubes and £6 10*s*. per week making navigation equipment or packing cosmetics. Similarly, men have been employed as general factory handymen at £5 10*s*. per week, £8 per week spraying vacuum cleaners, £11 on television assembly, and a similar amount on 'progress-chasing' in a television firm. Thus a whole range of work of this nature can be successfully undertaken by such persons.

Domestic training and employment

The placement of women as domestic helpers in private residences and institutions, and of men as handymen in the kitchens and gardens of hotels, restaurants, and boarding-houses, has been undertaken by many hospitals for the mentally deficient over a long period of time, often with successful results.

The advantages of such a procedure are:

(1) That during periods of full industrial employment feeble-minded patients are frequently acceptable to private employers.

(2) That such jobs often offer residential accommodation, providing the patient with an opportunity of becoming entirely self-supporting relatively rapidly.

(3) That for some patients the intimate, supportive atmosphere of a good home or domestic departments of hotels provides the most suitable environment for their adjustment.

The disadvantages appear to be:

(1) The risks of exploitation are much greater than in industry, where usually standard rates of pay, hours of work, and conditions of service obtain. This danger applies, of course, more to private establishments than to hospitals.

(2) The work involved may demand a considerable degree of versatility, initiative, and a variety of skills, and will tend to be of a non-repetitive nature.

(3) Not infrequently patients brought up in institutions or large subcultural families feel insecure, lonely, and out of their depth in the new cultural milieu of a middle-class home. The problem of interpersonal relationships may present great difficulties, particularly where the patient is unstable.

(4) The opportunities for economic and trade advancement tend to be poor.

For those patients who have a clear preference or aptitude for domestic work, the problem of vocational inadequacy may be dealt with by having at the institution a domestic science centre as installed in progressive schools, staffed by a trained domestic science teacher.

Few institutions have, however, been looking even further ahead to the time when the girls will be discharged, get married and will have to look after a family. Dealing openly with these aspects introduces the vexed sex problems which have often been responsible for admission and later difficulties in the girl's institutional career. However, a policy of preparing for the later stage of freedom impresses not only the girl with the fact that the authorities themselves reckon with her discharge, but helps to dispel much anxiety over the future demands of life.

The absence of a matter-of-fact training for future household responsibilities for our subnormal girls may easily be the beginning of a 'sub-standard' family claiming much of the time, energy, and financial resources of the welfare authorities. A curriculum for defective institutionalized girls should, therefore, contain simple practical demonstration and 'tutorials' in: cooking, mending, and housework, lessons in laying out the housekeeping money, personal hygiene, 'grooming', etc. Much of that knowledge is, of course, best impressed on them by the example of sympathetic and competent staff and does not require formal teaching. Yet, despite its apparently incidental and informal nature, a full domestic programme should be planned carefully to pay attention to the many domestic exigencies with which women are faced in life outside the hospital. Though the theoretical discussion of certain practical questions, like bringing up the baby, may lead to emotional disturbance, it appears to be preferable to a complete avoidance of the subject. Work of this kind has been described (Kelly, 1948; Thorne and Dolan, 1953; Parsons, 1960; Gunzburg, 1960), but has still not been carried out systematically in most institutions.

The Van den Bergh Institution in Holland has a domestic training unit where adolescent girls are taught to deal with various domestic tasks. They learn cooking and laundry on different types of machinery – as may be encountered in smaller households – gas, electricity, paraffin. Reading, writing, and arithmetic are taught in the context of making out shopping lists, checking bills, and the learning of food prices.

The less adaptable type of female patient is given a simplified type of training, involving less machinery and making them suitable for employment in families not enjoying the advantages of labour-saving devices.

It must, however, be pointed out that domestic training is not necessarily vocational training for domestic employment, which is often considered the most suitable career for young subnormal girls. Many of the unstable girls admitted to institutions have rebelled against family pressure and placing them into domestic employment may revive conflict situations. Training for factory work may be better and more promising rehabilitation and a female industrial training unit would be required in the hospital on similar lines as for young subnormal men (Burr, 1931; Abel and Kinder, 1942).

The successful placement of men and women in homes in an agricultural community has been excellently described by Wildenskov (1957). He discusses the provisions for community care of the mentally deficient in Denmark, with particular reference to their placement with families. Long-term studies of such patients (all with I.Q.s below 75) showed that of those placed 76 per cent. became fully self-supporting and 1 per cent. partially self-supporting. Wildenskov also cites impressive evidence that many cases for whom the prognosis had at one time looked exceedingly bad learned with help to adjust to society. He also shows how after-care in the form of centres where ex-patients may seek advice is valuable in assisting their rehabilitation.

GENERAL SOCIAL TRAINING

Despite the fact that failure in community adjustment – often associated with the patients' ignorance of the social give and take, with their lack of social knowledge, and with their inability to use their spare time in a socially approved manner – is a common problem, systematic research in this field is very meagre. Education and training have concentrated on improving the defective's abilities to do work and to retain it, but there is no doubt that many defectives also come to grief when having to deal with situations outside the routine of work.

Residence in an institution involves depriving the inmates of freedom of action, of initiative, of decision, and of ordering the time-table, because administrative needs as well as the proven social inadequacy of the patient necessitate supervisory arrangements. Nevertheless a programme where everything is planned and ordered for the patient is not conducive to furthering his sense of responsibility, his initiative, his reliability, and his ability to plan and weigh the consequences of his actions.

(a) 'A course in economics at the concrete level'

This phrase, used by Earl (1942), indicates exactly one of the most pressing requirements for the successful economic adaptation of our patients. The unrealistic financial arrangement of pocket money issued by the institution to their able-bodied working patients is bound to lead to a distorted concept of earnings and spendings. Clothes, food, lodgings, cigarettes, sweets, and pleasures are arranged wholesale for the institution population, who have thus never an opportunity to appreciate the relative value of goods obtainable for a given amount of money. When these patients are being tried on indefinite leave and are left to fend for themselves, their frugal institutional habits may continue and lead to the amassing of enviable bank balances. Others, however, dazzled by the apparent fortune in their weekly pay packets, fritter it away in a naïve, indiscriminate orgy of spending and are liable to cause themselves and the supervising authorities serious difficulties.

Much of this could probably be avoided if the institutional training were to impress in realistic terms the meaning of the cost of living. Paying for 'board and lodging', buying clothes, accessories, toilet articles, or sweets, out of a 'wage-packet' issued by the hospital until not much more than pocket money is left, may give the patient a feeling for relative values.

It is obviously uneconomical and unnecessary to attempt such a wholesale reorganization for an entire hospital, but it should be realized that the present system is of little help in learning how to set about with a wage packet. Arrangements can, however, be made for small selected groups in special wards and hostels and some of the 'board and lodgings' aspects can be explained within the framework of an educational system (see Chapter XII) in the form of a paper transaction. The payment in the hospital of industrial rates, which depend on work output (Clarke and Clarke, 1954a), provides also a starting point for a planned instruction in spending.

(b) 'Parole'

In the chapter on Education (XII) reference has been made to the desirability of anticipating and overcoming potentially irritating situations by rehearsing everyday occurrences. It needs, however, more than that to develop in the patient some sense of responsibility, of planning, and of foresight. 'Parole' – a short time of unsupervised absence from the hospital after working hours – is one of the means by which a certain degree of maturation in these aspects can be encouraged. Many hospitals permit selected patients to leave the grounds several times during the week to visit picture houses, go shopping, attend football matches, etc. Most hospitals tend to regard this arrangement as a 'privilege' acquired by excellent conduct, after having graduated from the 'closed ward' through the stage of 'ground parole' (within the institution grounds in prescribed areas) to 'accompanied parole' and lastly to 'full parole'. This parole is the hospital's recognition of the patient's adjustment to the institution demands which foster conformity rather than encourage a sense of personal responsibility.

Some institutions tend to be more generous with parole, using it therapeutically and constructively. They believe that it must be adequately shown why parole should *not* be permitted rather than why parole should be granted. In other words an ordinary and reasonable amount of freedom is not withdrawn from the patient – provided it does not interfere with hospital regulations and the law – unless there is an overwhelming reason against the absence of supervision during parole hours (e.g. indecent exposure cases). This is opposed to the other, older school of thought, which restores that freedom after prolonged withdrawal and as a premium for good institutional behaviour.

A good deal can be said in favour of both policies and the choice between them depends on the final aim of the institution – whether an adjusted or an adjustable personality should be the final result (see p. 429).

Permitting a patient a certain amount of freedom without supervision involves the acceptance of considered risks. If a patient is well known over years and has graduated to the 'privilege' the risks are reduced; they are hundredfold increased if the patient is allowed freedom of parole comparatively shortly after admission. Yet safeguards against a repetition of a-social and anti-social conduct are probably just as much provided by intensive investigations and observations, as by the mere fact that the psychotherapeutic atmosphere of the hospital avoids inducing overreactions. But for occasional technical infringements of rules, like timekeeping, or meeting a girl round the corner, most patients live up to the trust placed in them. Generous and early parole is a practical demonstration of the loyalty to and the faith in the patient, and avoids frustration. The opportunities of testing his behaviour in these frequent unsupervised parole situations provide valuable evidence for planning and deciding on his further life.

(c) Leisure time

The adequate preparation for leisure, once the patient leaves the immediate care of the hospital, is of the utmost importance since it has been shown that breakdowns during 'indefinite leave' (see p. 409) are very often due to the defective's inability to handle his free time (Rudolf, 1950; Horne and Allen, 1942). Many of the city-dwelling youths spend most of their free time in the 'pictures' and are unable to develop more active interests. It may be possible to widen the range of interests if patients are encouraged to develop hobbies while still in hospital. Fitzpatrick (1956) reports that patients on 'parole' have outside interests which they pursue in the company of their normal contemporaries. Many belong to a speedway club, others join local football clubs. 'The more solitary may prefer to explore the countryside on bicycles or join fishing clubs and take part in their competitions. Recently, a band of healthy young men volunteered their services to the local flower show committee; others, more conscious of the power of money, take on spare-time jobs in the weekend.'

Far too little time has been spent guiding the subnormal patient into organizations and clubs which would give him support, interest, and occupation during those hours when he is left to his own devices. He should be taught and trained in hobbies, skills, and games in the hospital to overcome his distrust in his own abilities when facing competition in sport and games with normal people, but also to establish a further bridge to normal, busy, ordered life (McBride *et al.*, 1953).

(d) Relations with opposite sex

One of the most neglected topics of discussion in mental deficiency is the controversial and emotionally charged subject of the relationships between the sexes when under institutional care.

A proportion of female patients are admitted to the institution because their mental subnormality had been associated with promiscuity and illegitimate offspring. The mental defective, however, whether male or female, does not appear to be more libidinous than the normal contemporary despite the great number of women admitted to hospital for so-called immorality.[1] But for a few 'oversexed' girls (Burt, 1944, estimates there were no more than 7 per cent. of this type in the sample) most of the immorality of the young girls can be traced to the mental defective's impulsiveness, lack of judgment, great suggestibility, and lack of control. Their inability to resist temptation on one side and their desire for sexual gratification, affection, and a home, make them a particularly difficult problem. They are even more resentful than the men of the sexual frustration imposed upon them (Milner, 1949) and training seems to make little inroad in this sphere. Much of the trouble, however,

[1] Kaplun (1935) finds that institutional admissions over a ten-year period indicate that 91 per cent. of the delinquency problems of girls are sex problems in the United States.

is due to adolescent instability and if assistance is given during that period, time itself may effect stabilization. This must not be interpreted as suggesting that one should wait until the childbearing age has been passed and the 'safe time' has arrived. The reaction of many feeble-minded women who see their years slip by with the maternal, home-making, and sex instincts unsatisfied and without a possibility of sublimation, is severe. Even the risk of venereal disease, or pregnancies, seems scarcely large enough to justify their continued segregation. There is no evidence to suggest that patients on parole or licence produce considerably more illegitimate children than the general population, and in fact reports indicate a very low rate; e.g. 14 illegitimate children borne to 1,439 mentally deficient girls during 14 years under supervision (quoted by Wallin, 1956); 25 pregnancies during 20 years for 1,174 women sent on full licence in Birmingham (Middleton, 1956). Withdrawals from 'leave' are often due to association with the opposite sex which is against the conditions of this period on trial. It must, however, not be forgotten that much of this so-called sexual misdemeanour, while not exactly ethical or moral, is condoned by society in the case of the ordinary man and woman, and is a biologically inescapable necessity.

In the Emma Hjorths Hjem in Norway 'several of our patients of all ages have during many years kept "firm company" with their sweethearts. The couples have kept together.' The authors of this report also state that 'the patients themselves arrange their leisure time, and have mixed freely "outdoors" for several years. Ample opportunities for free intercourse between the sexes are present and, in fact, to the same extent as if they were living outside the institution. . . .' Nevertheless they came to the conclusion that this permissive and tolerant institutional arrangement has not led to a worsening of the situation but resulted in well adjusted, happy and more content patients (Birkelund and Jacobsen, 1960).

Hospitals on the whole tend to enforce a very strict segregation policy and breach of such regulations is considered a serious offence. This seems to be of little avail and the patients find means and ways to contact each other even when pretending a lack of interest. The opportunities offered by 'parole', 'Daily Work', and 'indefinite leave' for breaking these institution regulations may become more tempting and irresistible in the same degree as they are strictly enforced and it might avoid a lot of heartache and worry if the consequences of a more liberal policy could be studied.

Social occasions like weekly dances, or sports days, permit a certain supervised and limited relaxation of these rules, but few hospitals have attempted to come nearer to the ordinary social conventions as encountered outside the institution. Harris and Kinney (1947), in describing a comprehensive treatment programme in an institution, emphasize co-education as providing the residents with opportunities for casual social relationships which they consider particularly important during adolescence. There is no formal tabulation of success and failure, but the authors conclude that one of the factors which seems to have played a direct part in reducing the incidence of maladjustment in the institution was due to 'providing a co-educational programme which approximates as nearly as possible with that of the community'. Smith (1957) describes an employment project in an institution where for the last ten years patients were permitted 'working in couples – a boy with his best girl'. No major problems arose and 'tone and discipline have . . . always been excellent, and it was achieved with little effort and fuss'.

(e) 'Daily work'

This term covers a practice, nowadays followed by a number of mental deficiency hospitals, of sending patients to work outside the institution whilst resident in the hospital. It is a definite step towards final social rehabilitation and tests, in this very loosely supervised work situation, the patients' abilities in employment and community relations. The jobs are usually of the kind which the patients may take up later permanently. They receive mostly full trade rates, money being credited to them after a deduction for maintenance. Men work as builders' labourers, in factories, in gardens and parks, in hotels, practically anywhere where semi-skilled and unskilled labour is required. Most women are absorbed in domestic and hospital situations and a few go into industry for assembly or press-work (Rohan, 1954).

Trial on 'Daily Work' must not be considered a reward for outstandingly good behaviour in the institution. Though it is obvious that a certain degree of stabilization has to be achieved before a patient can be given a status which entails a large amount of freedom, in many cases stabilization of the patient is a consequence of his placement on 'Daily Work'.

Fitzpatrick (1956), describing the system of vocational guidance in a large English hospital, states that placement of patients on

'Daily Work' is in the hands of a professional staff committee, meeting weekly, which has at its disposal special vocational reports by Nursing and Training staff. Patients are sent to work on clinical considerations, sometimes irrespective of the reports, and actually 'scrutiny of individual report forms shows that a patient, who is successful outside the hospital, is sometimes rated low within the hospital'. Though planning ability of most patients was low, it was seen that 'the more successful patients were rated significantly higher for ambition, self-reliance, and quality and output of work'. One may add that it is the ambitious patient with some drive who fits least into the institution routine.

The placing of a patient in a stimulating, normal environment outside the hospital is likely to improve considerably his efficiency in various aspects. Marchand (1956) reports changes in intelligence scores of patients employed outside compared with those inside the hospital (see p. 108).

Judging from published reports, the extent of 'Daily Work' arrangements of hospitals differs considerably, depending no doubt on the local labour market and the composition of the institution population as well as on the therapeutic policy of the hospital. The time taken by the patient to achieve the coveted stage of 'Daily Work' obviously varies quite considerably in the individual case from hospital to hospital and depends on employability and the employment situation. In some cases the interim period between admission and trial on 'Daily Work' may be as short as a few weeks – in other cases it may extend to some years. One published report indicates that 22 per cent. of the young men are sent to work within half a year after admission and that 42 per cent. of them are tried out in this way by the end of the first year (Gunzburg, 1957).

(f) Hostels

A further step towards rehabilitation is provided by the hostel arrangement where a large degree of freedom can be given without sacrificing supportive supervision before proceeding to the comparative independence of 'indefinite leave'. In some cases, however, social abilities are not equal to requirements and discharge would be unjustified. These people may be quite capable of commanding a reasonable wage packet; institutionalization would mean unnecessary emotional hardship whilst their presence in the hostel can exercise a steadying influence on the younger and more impetuous elements.

The provision of many hostels for various grades and types of defectives, giving more than a mere 'board and lodging' service, has often been advocated (Morris, 1948; Earl, 1942; Gunzburg, 1950b; O'Connor and Tizard, 1956), but never been realized. If properly managed, from the therapeutic point of view, they might contribute considerably to a more efficient service for the unstable, but trainable, defective and might, in many cases, even be used to by-pass the disturbing experience of admission to an institution of pronounced custodial character (Esher, 1964). The community care provisions envisaged in the Mental Health Act, 1959, have happily recognized this great need, and it is planned to have 464 hostels available by 1972.

(g) Indefinite leave

The final testing period, for judging the defective's social adequacy, requires a complete separation from the hospital, either in his own home or in approved lodgings. The supervision afforded by the hospital authorities is generally very loose and the arrangement is, in fact, a type of 'probation period'. Good work conduct and reasonable behaviour are insisted on and attention is paid to possible sources of breakdown, such as too much interest in the opposite sex, reckless spending, undesirable associations, or frequent changes of jobs. Patients are encouraged to settle and to lead a normal regulated life and to keep to a groove which affords the required support.

Analyses of the many reports nowadays available on the special problems encountered by the mentally deficient patient in his rehabilitation efforts, agree to a large extent (Tarjan and Benson, 1953; Shafter, 1954, 1957; Badham, 1955; Stanley and Gunzburg, 1957). First and foremost are the 'personal and inter-personal problems' comprising inadequate relationships with employers, licensees, or opposite sex, as well as disturbing family conflicts (Di Michael and Terwilliger, 1953). Employment difficulties are also of great relevance, though very often less due to inability to do a given job than to unhelpful handling of the patient by his fellow workers, foremen, and employers, who are obviously not familiar with his special adjustment problems.

Whilst the institutional training can do a good deal towards an acceptable handling of the personal and inter-personal problems, the adequate, careful and selective placement outside the institution is of utmost importance. It requires close co-operation between the agencies concerned, mindful of the fact that socialization of the defective depends just as much on the adjustment of the community to the defective as on his adjustment to the community.

The average employer is obviously not familiar with the problems involved and tends to type the subnormal as an 'abnormal' human being. He is often oblivious of the fact that he has among his workers probably quite a few with as little, or even less, intelligence as the patient in his care and tends to react at times rather more extremely to the behaviour of the certified subnormal than he would in similar circumstances to others of comparable standing. He is apprehensive and on the look-out, perhaps exaggeratedly 'good and understanding', and makes the patient feel insecure and defensive. It is from this point of view that it appears particularly desirable to maintain close liaison between the hospital and employer to enable him to see the patient in the correct perspective.

The employment of social workers, who are familiar with the patient, as supervisors in the initial time of indefinite leave prevents much unnecessary failure, but a certain proportion of breakdowns is probably unavoidable, despite the most careful selection of suitable patients and employment, owing to our own inadequate sizing up of all variables and factors. One might even speculate whether, at our present state of knowledge, an absence of failure among patients on indefinite leave could not be interpreted as being due to an over-cautious policy in placing out only those about whom complete confidence is felt, rather than due to some infallible system of training, selection, and placement.

The length of this probationary period of indefinite leave has been progressively reduced over the years of mental deficiency practice. The Mental Health Act, 1959, effects an automatic discharge from hospital care after six months on indefinite leave and envisages that community services will give further support if required. The great many 'Informal Admissions' are, of course, not at all affected by this arrangement.

There is no doubt that discharge from the supervision and protection given by the hospital raises some very controversial issues. The main argument in favour of the present short time on 'indefinite leave' is purely an administrative one: it is not the task of the hospital to provide extended supervision once a patient has ceased to receive treatment and training. If further supervision is required it should be given by the local community care services.

This type of arrangement gives little opportunity to judge whether the social inadequacy, which originally led the admission to hospital, is no longer existent. The discharge depends largely on negative criteria – the patient has not actually displayed social inadequacy during the short time on indefinite leave – and is thus rather different from the original positive statement at admission which contained concrete evidence of social incompetence. Many patients, some of them elderly and of low intelligence, function without trouble in the sheltered environment of their helpful family, of an understanding and tolerant employer and under the guidance of a closely supervising authority. They are entirely dependent on advice and actual help from others to buy a few odds and ends, to bank their wages, to arrange for a holiday. They may be able to carry on like this for years, provided circumstances do not change. Neither a good bank balance nor a satisfactory employment record is prima facie evidence of social adequacy, yet there is no real reason why a discharge from the Mental Health Act should not take place, provided further care and supervision are exercised by another authority when and where it is wanted.

There is little doubt that society cannot discard its obligation towards the subnormal after discharging him from institutional care. The amount of assistance he may require is – in financial terms – probably less expensive if rendered adequately and timely in the open community, than when its absence leads to re-institutionalization. The hospital for the trainable defective will then truly represent a transitional stage in the patient's career and initiate curative processes, which are brought to a successful end by the social agencies in the community.

(h) Community provisions

Whether a mentally retarded person passes through the readjustment programme of a hospital, or has to find his place in society unaided, community provisions will have to give a certain amount of support (Di Michael, 1952).

Di Michael and Terwilliger (1953), describing vocational rehabilitation arrangements in the U.S.A., point out that in a representative sample of retarded people showing reasonable job stability it required from two to fifty interview sessions to effect a satisfactory rehabilitation in the community. Training for unskilled and semi-skilled jobs proved often necessary, and it required frequently from two to nine job try-outs to decide the suitability of a specific occupation.

Tizard and O'Connor in their very full review of the literature on the employability of mental defectives (1950) point to the substantial numbers of successful adjustments made by patients returned from hospital to the community. Though 'perhaps more liable to emotional instability than those of higher intelligence, there is no reason to suppose that the defective is less persistent, or more suggestible, than other members of the community of comparable socio-economic status'. In times of economic prosperity and full employment many feeble-minded manage successfully with only little support. Times of unemployment and economic depression screen those with personality flaws from others with equally low mentality but with stable personality make-up.

(i) Training Centres and Sheltered Workshops

This chapter and the other ones dealing with the practical aspects of treatment in mental deficiency have been emphasizing the institution-hospital problems. This was unavoidable because most treatment of the feeble-minded defective has up to now taken place within the institution-hospital. The Mental Health Act, 1959, has recognized that similar forms of treatment could be offered by suitable community provisions. This would avoid in many cases the increase of emotional tension due to admission to hospital, and the undeniable fact that the artificial and unstimulating atmosphere of essentially custodial arrangements interferes with rather than encourages rehabilitation.

Local Authorities in England and Wales provide 'Junior' and 'Senior' (Adult) Training Centres and 'Sheltered Workshops' to give full education and training outside the hospital. There are now well over 600 Training Centres and plans have been made to increase this number to over 900 by 1972. The Junior Training Centres provide day-training for the child 'unsuitable for education at school' and the Senior Training Centres have facilities for workshop training for subnormals over the age of 16. Children and young people live at home, which is generally an advantage from the humanitarian point of view. Living at home does, however, very often fail to encourage self-reliance and confidence and a moderate degree of independence because many will tend to over-protect the mentally handicapped child. Training Centres with attached hostels, working a five-day week, may be the solution to this particular problem of encouraging 'social maturity'.

The Junior Training Centre should provide a type of education which aims at 'social' rather than 'academic' efficiency. Many of the 'social skills' required in adult life should be taught as early as possible and less emphasis should be put on teaching 'school-subjects' in which the subnormal may not obtain a modest but *useful* degree of efficiency on account of his mental handicap. 'Social skills', however, are very much the result of careful and skilled training and in some respects the social maturation processes can be accelerated by using adequate diagnostic methods (see p. 322) and applying directed social training (Cain and Levine, 1961; Gunzburg, 1964b).

The Senior Training Centre aims to train the subnormal to work, and, if possible, to live in normal conditions. A workshop setting is introduced but since 'the process of education, training and work is continuous' (Scott Report, 1962), the programme of the Senior Training Centre should not be radically different from that pursued in the Junior Training Centre. Social training must be emphasized to make the vocational training as useful and widely applicable as possible.

Training of this type is entirely different from that given in the 'Sheltered Workshop' which is, in fact, a factory where special provisions have been made to provide suitable work within a more or less permanent protective workshop environment. In other words, the Senior Training Centre *prepares* for work and life in the open community, but the Sheltered Workshop *provides* work and life in a separate community.

It is not always clearly recognized that these two different aspects of vocational training affect the scope and efficiency of the social training. In the first case of the Training Centre proper, work opportunities are arranged to further the aims of preparing for life and work amidst ordinary, normal people. Attaining comparative efficiency at work is only one of the targets of social rehabilitation and the training leading to it takes its place beside other aspects of education and training.

In the Sheltered Workshop, opportunities are provided for those who are not able to work in normal conditions and for whom a special place has to be reserved in a protective environment placed, for preference, in the community rather than a hospital. There is hardly any general social training involved because the final aim of 'social rehabilitation' cannot be realized largely on account of an extremely severe mental handicap or advanced age. Work is essentially of an occupational character but there is nowadays a demand that it should be carried out more efficiently and be more financially rewarding than in the past. The training of imbeciles for specific jobs (see Chapter XIII) is a good example for sheltered workshop practice.

Work carried out is nowadays largely of an industrial nature and the mat- and brush-making occupations are generally regarded as obsolete. Workshops undertake sub-contract work for firms and many industrial operations are carried out with relative speed and efficiency by the mentally defective. The obligations of industrial sub-contract work (delivery times, regular output, speed of execution, etc.) can interfere quite substantially with the demands of other training activities. It appears, therefore, that only a minimum of industrial sub-contract work can be accepted as long as social training is emphasized. Sheltered workshops, however, catering for those subnormals who have only to be fully and happily occupied, are able to accept suitable work in large quantities and they can arrange their production methods (assembly lines, jigs, etc.) without interfering with educational work.

There is no doubt a danger that therapeutic aims are lost sight of in an over-emphasis on approximating the work output and work efficiency of ordinary factories. Profit and turnover may become more important as a concrete indication of success than the number of people returned to the community (Carstairs *et al.*, 1955; Hall *et al.*, 1957; Gunzburg, 1963b).

CONCLUSIONS

Generally speaking every feeble-minded patient admitted to an institution is socially and often also emotionally maladjusted. The hospital's task is to initiate rehabilitation of the patient so that an early return to the community has a good chance of success.

Much hope has been placed on the effects of the deterrent of institutionalization, on maturation processes and on careful selection of placement in the community – all of which play an important part in the stabilization and rehabilitation of the patient. This, in many ways passive approach, uneconomical in time and often causative of new problems, has been augmented and often supplanted nowadays by new concepts which demand a more active, individualized and planned utilization of the hospital and community organizations. Also required is a full integration of research results to overcome the consequences of traditional prejudices and of distrust in the defective's abilities as well as to indicate more suitable methods of training and socialization. The consideration of the problem of mental deficiency largely in terms of supervision and care, was bound to lead to answers emphasizing the defective's disabilities; the modern approach, which does not consider the hospital to be the only and the best solution to the problem, emphasizes the overcoming of these disabilities – which, on closer investigation, have turned out less formidable than originally thought.

The vocational and social training is for many patients the only therapeutic help required – they are not in need of special psychotherapy nor do they care for educational help. It attempts to instil those skills which have remained underdeveloped for lack of encouragement, stimulation, lack of application, absence of opportunity, and many other reasons; it is never primarily an attempt only to occupy the patient during his stay in hospital, but always a systematic effort to make him acquire modes of behaviour acceptable to society outside the institution walls.

The Training Centres organized in the community are, in some ways, better placed than the institution to carry out vocational and social training. The Senior Training Centre must, however, appreciate that teaching and training of 'social skills' are the main activities even though carried out in the more adult atmosphere of the workshop. Unless this task is accepted and the Senior Training Centre manages to provide an 'educative environment' (Scott Report, 1962) the differences between Training Centre and Sheltered Workshop will become indistinct; similarly, the difference between community provisions and the hospital's occupational therapy and maintenance workshops will be merely one of day versus full-time attendance for the purpose of being occupied.

The vocational and social training provides the broadest, most comprehensive, and most realistic area of rehabilitation efforts. We have at present, however – as with so many other areas of mental deficiency – no reliable evidence which would 'prove' the efficacy of particular approaches – as has been shown by the conflicting opinions regarding length of time on leave. This state of affairs is scarcely good enough – traditional beliefs, emotional thinking, and narrow experience ranges affect too much the validity of our conclusions. Much of the evidence gathered from past reports and researches is outdated and invalid – not only have methods changed and with them the attitudes of the patients, but so have the economics of society and the attitudes and views which have made the defective more tolerated than ever before.

It cannot, therefore, be too strongly emphasized that even in the field of vocational and social training which has the longest history in mental deficiency work, we must not rely too much on the findings of the past, but must reconsider the problem against the background of a changing world.

Chapter XV

PSYCHOTHERAPY WITH THE FEEBLE-MINDED

by H. C. Gunzburg

INTRODUCTION

Many patients admitted to hospitals for the mentally deficient have been unable to use competently their meagre but often fairly adequate resources and have become maladapted in their attempts to find a *modus vivendi*. The segregation from an unfavourable environment effected by the hospital, and the regulated life and work there, should represent a large-scale attempt to help the defective eventually to deal with the problems of living and working outside the institution. Some patients – and it is impossible as yet to say how many[1] – present emotional problems of such a nature that they require a form of specialized guidance and treatment.

Nowadays the existence of neurotic problems in mental deficiency cannot be denied, though they may be overlooked or suppressed. The case of a young soldier reported by Feldman (1946) is interesting because the young man tested very low intellectually (I.Q. 41 and 39) but 'revealed a surprising depth of feeling regarding his failures and inadequacies. He recounted his simple achievements in work and at home before entering service and asked several times "Why can't I do things like everybody else?" and "Why am I different?" '

Jolles (1947) found such severe emotional maladjustment in a

[1] It is difficult to estimate the prevalence of neurosis in the mentally deficient because there is no agreement on the forms of behaviour which can be identified with neurotic reaction patterns in such persons. Moreover, much of the neurotic defence may be 'institution-reared' and occurrences may differ widely in the various institutions depending on the degree of restrictiveness that has to be exercised. See also Penrose's Colchester Survey (1938), O'Connor (1951), Pollock (1945), Weaver (1946).

group of 34 mentally deficient children that he concluded that

> mental deficiency of the familial and undifferentiated types is, in many instances, a symptom of personality disorder, and it is unlikely that in such cases it represents a failure of the intellect to develop normally. It is quite probable that many mental defectives may be treated successfully by psychotherapeutic techniques.

Similar views have been voiced by other research workers (Ackerman and Menninger, 1936; Hackbusch and Klopfer, 1946; Sloan, 1947a).

Psychotherapy involves the establishing of a positive relationship between therapist and patient. The classical method – psychoanalysis as exemplified by the work of Freud, Jung and others, and their followers – investigates the patient's mental processes by verbal means, and brings largely unconscious material to consciousness.

Psychotherapy may be undertaken with either individuals or groups; it may be directive or non-directive; it may seek to explore and modify the fundamental personality structure, or it may be concerned with relatively superficial problems, frequently acknowledged by the patient, though probably not fully understood by him. This latter approach, often called counselling, attempts to modify behaviour patterns which have resulted in social maladjustment. It appears to be a method which is admirably suited to the needs of people who require only guidance and assistance in sorting out problems which, despite their distressing nature, are fairly near to the surface and are easily accessible to the therapist. Counselling is most frequently directed towards the solution of specific, limited problems of adaptation as they occur from day to day and aims at finding practical *ad hoc* solutions without attempting to change the basic personality organization. Faced with the emergence of deep-seated conflicts under the assistance of the therapist, few defectives would have either the ability, or insight, to deal with them.

Psychotherapy with children, attempting to reopen disturbed communications between the child and the environment, is often less concerned with working out and solving problems than with providing the warmth and affection of which the child has been starved. This applies to young and older children, who often come from severely disturbed home backgrounds and have become confused in their emotional relationships. They are withdrawn and isolated and deeply worried about their own disloyalties towards the parents, and their parents' disloyalty towards them. Therapy with these children takes place on an entirely emotional plane, the therapist providing a father and mother substitute with a warm, close bodily contact offering shelter, acceptance, and love. Not infrequently hugging and cuddling – so essential for the development of a mentally healthy child – has to be provided by the therapist in a late stage and in unfavourable conditions and he has to be fully aware of the responsibilities he shoulders in creating a transference situation. Social adjustment will follow once the security of the relationship is comprehended emotionally.

Both approaches, deep psychotherapy and counselling, represent considered attempts by a trained therapist to modify and improve *by word and deed* the conditions which will enable a person to live and work with others and to adjust to their reasonable demands. These forms of treatment, particularly counselling for adults, are given increasingly more weight in modern mental deficiency practice with the mounting realization that the factors of character and temperament are frequently more decisive in the rehabilitation of the feeble-minded than the intellectual aspects.

Generally speaking, workers in the mental deficiency field have been sceptical about the use of psychotherapy because they have thought mainly of deep analysis and have largely disregarded the possibilities of systematic, therapeutic counselling. Deep psychotherapy appeared to be excluded because the defective's limited verbal/abstract abilities prevented him from understanding the often highly symbolic processes of psychoanalysis (Wiest, 1955). Moreover, it has been (perhaps debatably) argued that 'a person of low intelligence is less likely to have a mental conflict than a person of high intelligence' (Morgan, 1950).

The difficulties assumed to face the therapist when dealing with subnormal patients have been summarized by Sarason (1949). Such persons, he states, have been considered unable to delay or control emotional expression; to seek or to accept socially appropriate substitute activities in the face of frustrations and restrictions; to view objectively the behaviour of others; to adjust or to want to adjust to the needs of others; to realize the sources and consequences of their behaviour; to verbalize the interpersonal nature of their problems; to seek help or to understand the purpose of the individual offering it. It must, however, be pointed out that many of these opinions derive from prior concepts of mental deficiency.

Low intelligence test results alone are not indicative of a patient's inability to respond to therapeutic approaches. The test scores may have been lowered by emotional problems and do, in any case, not express the patient's ability for establishing some kind of a relationship with the therapist (Williams and Belinson, 1953). Slavson (1950) included dull patients in his group therapy and, though they participated only occasionally in group discussions, they proved to be capable of keeping up with the general trend of the talks and seemed to derive considerable benefit from them. It was found that in order to formulate and verbalize the problems and to have some understanding of interpretation 'the intelligence level need not be very high' (Slavson, 1950). Glassman (1943) and Cooley (1945), comparing the treatment results of dull children with those of bright children, came to the conclusion that therapy with those of lower mentality was at least as favourable, if not better, as with bright children. Shapiro (1962) points out that

> the hypothesis on which treatment is based is that the therapeutic effect is due not to the intellectual appreciation of the theoretical constructs, but to the working through the previous phases of negatively affected development within the therapeutic relationship. This is possible at any level of intelligence within the feeble-minded range. Psychoanalysis of children as young as 4 or 5 years is regularly and successfully carried out, and the feeble-minded has a mental age well above this.

Mundy (1957a), working with imbecile children, comments that a sound transference situation can easily be established and that therapy leads to a marked development of verbal ability. It can well be argued that withholding psychotherapy on grounds of lack of intelligence may deprive a person of just that treatment which might be successful in restoring effective mental functioning.

Counselling must not be thought to be equivalent to making 'authoritative statements' and 'to administering the proper teachings' (Morgan, 1950). For therapy to be effective there must be a realization of the human problems which require a tactful and sympathetic understanding and of the need to establish secure relationships before new learning processes can be expected. Many of the patients, particularly the very young ones, exhibit considerable emotional hunger and often the need for a positive attachment will have to be satisfied before social adjustment can take place.

Findings such as those of Healy and Bronner (1936), who recorded failure of psychotherapy in 66 per cent. of children with I.Q. 70–79, but only in 10 per cent. of children with I.Q. above 110, suggest only that the usual type of psychotherapeutic treatment is unsuitable for the mental defective patient, but not that the patient is unsuitable for psychotherapeutic treatment.[1]

PSYCHOTHERAPY

(a) Aims of psychotherapy with feeble-minded adult mental defectives

In a discussion of group therapy Slavson suggested that its real value for dull patients is the 'discharge of emotions through anger, rage, disgust, and quarrelling' because their inability to express themselves verbally requires acting out of their feelings (Slavson, 1950). Therapists in institutions, whilst keeping in mind the cathartic effect of group experience, tend to express their aims more positively. Some want, for example, to 'create a ward atmosphere in which patients could make as adequate a social adjustment within the hospital as allowed by the intelligence . . . also desired was the reduction in the minds of patients of the importance of an extramural placement' (Stubblebine and Roadruck, 1956). This use of psychotherapy as a sedative is in some contrast to therapy aimed at better adjustment to an environment of a non-institutional character. In this latter case patients receive therapy to make them more capable of dealing with problems outside the institution, to correct and improve social and personality defects and to re-establish better interpersonal relationships (Ringelheim and Polatsek, 1955; Astrachan, 1955). Milner (1962), who asserts that guilt feelings have given rise to delinquency, finds that treatment alleviated these guilt feelings and raised 'morale and personal value to a level at which there was no need to express guilt through antisocial conduct'.

Abel (1953) suggests a programme of gradual steps because

> the goal of treatment should be modest and simpler than the goal one usually, but not necessarily, anticipates in working with more intelligent individuals. . . . If we set out at first with the purpose of

[1] A closer study of these unpromising cases in the lower I.Q. range reveals such a complexity of other factors involved in the poor response to psychotherapy that it seems hardly permissible to single out the low intelligence by itself. The 33 per cent. favourable adjustments in Healy and Bronner's study received all the sympathetic support of a good and understanding environment in addition to psychotherapy – but that factor was missing in the other cases.

> changing total attitudes, and many aspects of behaviour, we are likely to be defeated, but this does not mean that as one goal is achieved another one cannot be set and further work done.

Wilcox and Guthrie (1957) describe four stages in therapy to develop increased frustration tolerance and to make the defectives more socially competent: (1) to reduce the suspiciousness felt towards outsiders, (2) to release aggressions, (3) to encourage feelings of self-confidence and self-work, (4) to develop feelings of responsibility for their actions.

The general aim expressed by practically all therapists consists of alleviating 'emotional and behavioural abnormalities that are inexplicable on the basis of mental deficiency alone' (Fisher and Wolfson, 1953). Yet it appears desirable that a statement of aims should be specific and provide guidance for therapeutic work.

Such a programme was published in 1948 by Frederick C. Thorne, then Medical Director of a mental deficiency hospital. He pointed out that

> psychotherapy with defectives involved: (*a*) accepting the mental defective as being a worthy individual in spite of his defects, (*b*) permitting expression and clarification of emotional reactions, (*c*) patiently teaching him methods for resisting frustration and achieving emotional control, (*d*) outlining standards for acceptable conduct within the ability of each child, (*e*) building up self-confidence and respect by providing experiences of success, and (*f*) training the child to seek help intelligently through counselling when faced with insurmountable problems (Thorne, 1948).

The same author also pointed out (1950) that

> the constitutionally inadequate are characteristically dependent upon others because of inability to compete well, and become involved in circular reactions of frustration, secondary unhealthy personality reactions, social reflection, and dependency. Lacking the personality resources to solve major problems alone, it may require active directive methods of counselling to supplement what the mental defective can do for himself.

(b) Subjects for psychotherapy

Even though the selection of patients is primarily dependent on the aims, method, and magnitude of the planned investigation or therapeutic situation, local conditions have obviously to be taken into account.

The most common principle of selection of patients for treatment appears to be in terms of behaviour. Patients are chosen who are 'creating problems in their classrooms' (Cotzin, 1948), who 'show overt anxiety as their principal symptom' (Ringelheim and Polatsek, 1955), or are either 'aggressive, unco-operative, hyperactive, and attention demanding' or in whom the tendencies of submissiveness, withdrawal, and phantasy indulgence are prominent (Fisher and Wolfson, 1953). A slightly different idea seems to underlie Stubblebine and Roadruck's (1956) approach who used psychotherapy as a preventative measure because 'adolescent males with their high energy levels and pubertal troubles seemed to need an improved treatment programme'. Thorne, looking not only at the behavioural aspect, but also at the patient's accessibility to treatment, selected from his 'most unstable and maladjusted mental defectives' those who had sufficient personality resources to assume some responsibility for self-regulation and 'who were integrated enough to enter into a therapeutic relationship long enough for reasonably adequate counselling to be performed' (Thorne, 1948).

With a few exceptions (Mehlman, 1953; O'Connor and Yonge, 1955) most groups lack homogeneity in important variables like age and intelligence levels. In both these aspects the range is usually very wide though the groups are comparatively small (Astrachan, 1955; Vail, 1955; Stubblebine, 1956, 1957). At times patients are included whose diagnosis suggested clinical abnormality. Few therapists attempted to deal with mixed groups, and sex is the only variable held constant by most investigators, except those using sociodrama methods (Sarbin, 1946; Lavalli and Levine, 1954; Pilkey *et al.*, 1961). While the pioneering character of these first tentative steps in psychotherapy made it permissible to cast the net often indiscriminately wide, it is well to keep in mind the heterogeneous composition of the groups, the different selection principles and the varying aims of therapeutic endeavours when comparing the results reported in the literature.

It is inadvisable to make general statements regarding defectives suitable for therapy of one or the other kind. Low intelligence scores, extreme resistance, shallow personality may well be the result of maladjustment, and it will require careful appraisal in the individual case before treatment is withheld on these grounds. Generally speaking, however, therapeutic assistance of varying degree and form should be made available to all defectives, who have enough 'insight' to be concerned about their failure to adjust. Limits will be imposed by the existence of organic factors, of sensory defects, of particular low intelligence on one side and time and competence of the therapist on the other side.

A fact only too often overlooked and leading to rash and unjustified conclusions is the need for flexibility in therapeutic techniques. In the same way as responses of patients may vary with different therapists and with different projective tests, inappropriate therapeutic media may also fail to obtain always full rapport. The techniques so far discussed require verbalizing and listening. Schaefer-Simmern (1944, 1948) demonstrated the therapeutic value of artistic activity in the mentally deficient. A silent, morose 16-year-old boy of borderline intelligence became accessible to therapy only after four months of frequent 'drawing sessions'. The same paper refers also to another report showing 'how only through finger painting a deficient child was able at first to communicate his problems' (Abel, 1953). A concerted approach through therapy in occupation, music, speech, and remedial reading for the treatment of a retarded and hyperactive child has been described by Knight *et al.* (1957). Other examples have been reported by Lowenfeld (1941).

Epileptic defectives, who are particularly vulnerable to physical hazards, present a special problem in the institution and are in many ways excluded from the activities and privileges and from the usual stages in the rehabilitation process. Their comparative isolation and the seeming 'unfairness' of their situation produces a characteristic anti-social disgruntled attitude. Stubblebine (1957), giving psychotherapy to six epileptics of the non-working institution population, describes them as '. . . disliked by their fellows . . . chronically sullen, irritable, temperamental, and having . . . an extremely narrow range of social activities'. Though this author thinks that 'insight in the dynamic sense does not seem possible in the brain-damaged patient' the results of therapy indicated that some of the patients 'seemed to profit from the greater than average time spent with them in a group-setting while searching for some measure of mutual understanding'.

Mundy (1957a) reports changes in intelligence scores and social adjustment in a group of imbecile children, aged 5–12 years. Among them were deaf mutes, post-meningitis cases, and children with aphasia, many of whom showed social improvement. She observed also that cases with cerebral palsy, or epilepsy, do not profit considerably from therapy.

(c) Methods of psychotherapy with the feeble-minded

Deep individual psychotherapy has been used on occasions though not very frequently (Pierce Clark, 1931; Chidester, 1934; Chidester and Menninger, 1936; Stogdill, 1938; Friedman, 1961). Chidester and Menninger (1936) stated 'how extraordinary it is to get such information and fantasies from retarded children'. Ackerman and Menninger (1936) write that:

> For the higher grades of retardation with an I.Q. of 75–90 with co-existing anxiety states, schizoid reactions, or delinquent behaviour, a therapeutic method based on psychoanalytic technique is employed. Particularly is this used when a thorough study indicates a strong suspicion that early psychodynamic distortions have contributed in degree to the inhibition of intellectual development.

Mundy (1957a) used non-directive play therapy and attempted 'analytical interpretation of a simple, but deep-going, kind'. She found 'that this was understood more often than might have been expected at the apparent mental level in some cases'. Play therapy was used in the case of a brain-damaged six-year-old boy with an I.Q. 'rather below 70' because of persistent and continuous soiling by day. Soiling ceased completely with regular treatment for six weeks (Tredgold and Soddy, 1963).

Milner (1952–53) described his method of individual analysis of mental defectives with mental ages between 7 and 8. After establishing a positive transference at a simple level, he elicited a life-history of the patient with particular attention to family relationships and friendships. He stated that a history of cruelty in childhood is often difficult to obtain, as the knowledge of being unloved and unwanted strikes at the root of the patient's self-esteem and much resistance and shame is attached to disclosures of ill treatment. The following, most difficult stage of treatment – the catharsis – is the attempt by the patient to rid himself of the effects of past misdeeds and unhappiness. This is followed by an attempt to establish new, valid values in the patient.

> This was done by down-valuing certain incidents and up-valuing others, and in particular by relieving the patient of pathological guilt feelings. But in addition to establishing a healthy standard of values in the patient, it was necessary to offer him suitable goals for which he could strive – e.g. parole, licence, and the ultimate goal of rehabilitation in the community as a self-supporting citizen.

In another paper, the same author (Milner, 1962) asserted that the origin of delinquency was always the same whatever the intellectual grade. Since he found sex guilt in practically all cases of juvenile delinquency, and sometimes death-guilt in childhood, he suggests that the methods of treatment are essentially the same for the defective and non-defective patient.

The majority of published reports deal with therapeutic methods applied to groups: play therapy (Maisner, 1950; Mehlman, 1953; Mundy, 1957a; Leland *et al.*, 1959; Stacey and de Martino, 1957; Leland and Smith, 1962), discussion groups, and less often with individual counselling. Group therapy has found much favour with the therapists because it is economical of time and energy and concentrates on the weak personal relationships of the defective. Discussion of problems in a group setting makes the individual patient aware that his case is one of many, and helps to break down tendencies of isolation and withdrawal. Working through problems in a group setting makes it possible to reorientate the patient towards his immediate environment, to give opportunities for becoming aware of the other people's viewpoints and of *feeling* instead of only *knowing* the implications of social approval and disapproval.

Group sessions provide an opportunity to relieve situational anxiety caused by misunderstood, or only half-understood, happenings. Questions freely answered by the therapist provide an opportunity for disseminating information, counteracting disturbing rumours, and for utilizing institutional incidents for concrete demonstrations of community demands and regulations. They make it possible to clarify misunderstandings on the spot, to dispel doubts, to reassure the insecure and to suggest solutions to the hesitant (Ringelheim and Polatsek, 1955; Stubblebine and Roadruck, 1956; Wilcox and Guthrie, 1957; Kaldeck, 1958; Morris *et al.*, 1959; Shapiro, 1962).

Though true insight is perhaps rather exceptional among these patients, it seems quite possible that in this way an understanding may dawn on them of their limitations and position in society. In group therapy 'the concrete samples of behaviour or personality difficulties given by themselves and seen by them in others may be the source of insight. Such an artificially structured situation may approach, for defectives, the discussion in groups for people with normal intellect' (Cotzin, 1948). The problems and conflicts of the mentally deficient are of a very concrete, realistic nature; they relate to the present, to the immediate past, the immediate future, and the assistance of the therapist must, therefore, be given on the same realistic plane on which the problems are experienced (Burton, 1954). Counselling, whether used in a group setting or individually, tackles the conflicts when they arise and usually in a very direct fashion. The immediate problems encountered most frequently are the patient's position as a certified defective, his future, his personal relationships. Here the counsellor will reassure and encourage, persuade and explain in an effort to overcome feelings of personal inferiority, of rejection, of anxiety, and of insecurity (Sarason, 1949; Feldman, 1946; Gunzburg, 1956a, 1957).

Counselling must begin from the moment of admission. It must not be left to other patients to 'mis'-explain and misdirect; a discussion of the events leading to a patient's admission, his prospects, the institution rules and privileges, will help considerably in overcoming uncertainty and hostility. The therapist's ready offer to render assistance, to mediate between the 'institution' and the patient, to shorten the institution stay as much as possible, coming at a particularly bleak moment, will help to initiate the warm and supportive relationship required by therapy. The patient, by accepting the help given to him personally by the 'other side', will unobtrusively be introduced into this novel version of a community he has not experienced before.

In the literature one finds much mention of directive and non-directive approaches, but the actual descriptions of the various investigations suggest that differences are more of degree than of kind. Many investigations used a non-directive, though not passive, approach, and this meant in practice that the group members had much freedom to express themselves even though the therapist had to provide initiative and guidance. As Vail (1955) has shown in an extremely valuable account of failure in psychotherapeutic work, 'insufficient divergence from standard, classical non-directive techniques' can result in much disturbance and no improvement. As he pointed out therapeutic activity 'without more concrete supplementation' is 'too remote and too refined to provide gratification' for the emotional needs. The counselling therapist in a hospital for mentally deficients is a representative of the community, the interpreter and the guide to its laws and regulations. The patient expects and requires his help in this capacity and the therapist will have to become more active and directive than his theoretical leanings would perhaps permit.

The therapist's personal 'warmth', his sympathetic and helpful presence, and the time he is able to devote to the patient, provide the climate for emotional problems to become verbal and to be identified. The permissive atmosphere in the small therapy group provides a safety-valve by allowing the patient to 'let off steam' and consequently reduces frictions in the often more rigid and suppressive institution setting. The therapy session, or any other setting in the institution, must not try to imitate the 'warmth' of the love and affection of a healthy family atmosphere. It can and must, however, succeed in impressing on the patient the therapist's faith in his abilities, his unwavering loyalty which cannot be disturbed by misdemeanour, or disciplinary action. It is this loyalty, rather than an overdone and false-sounding kindness and permissiveness, which restores a feeling of security in the patient by providing him with new bearings.

The therapist's mediation should lead to an acceptance by the patient of his group relationship and to a realization that the community at large expects him to fit in with its requirements. He must be made to realize that he is neither clever enough nor strong enough to set himself up *against* society and that he will get hurt unless he goes *with* society. Many frictions between him and society are due to misunderstandings and to his desire to hide his ignorance. He has to learn that asking people for advice will not reflect adversely on him, but will on the contrary help in avoiding further trouble and complications. Though he must be made aware of his limitations, he must be shown at the same time the security found in keeping to a narrowly circumscribed field where perseverance and application to work provide a full measure of compensation.

The community requires him, like everyone else, to accept a reasonable amount of frustration and to exercise control over his emotional life. He will often not be able to understand the ethical and moral implications of good and bad, but simply repeat what he has learned and heard. This will, however, provide a guiding line for him, just as he may learn to curb his impulsiveness by asking the simple habitual question: 'Does it pay? – Is it worth it?' before acting.

Many desirable social habits are, of course, learned the hard way over long years of constant trial and error which may bring the realization that obeying the rules means security and happiness, going against them trouble and misery. Many persons break down during this extensive learning period and are finally unable to benefit from their own experiences. The psychotherapeutic effort will be directed, therefore, towards shortening this time of learning.

Psychotherapy has initially to deal with basic issues before suggesting a new outlook on life and helping the patient to develop new techniques for handling his problems. This approach, if successful, appears to be superior to the older methods which seem to aim at something like a conditioned reflex in the patient's behaviour pattern. There he is 'adjusted' to certain situations in the hope that he will not encounter novel situations to which the appropriate responses have not been learnt. Now, we aim at making the defective 'adjustable' rather than 'adjusted' only (Yepsen, 1952) and, though perhaps this goal is not within reach of many defectives who are too 'rigid', careful individual work may achieve some degree of adjustability in many patients.

Psychotherapy does not aspire to 'cure' mental defect nor to make the defective function to his 'full mental capacity' – which is largely an unknown quantity despite our test assessments.[1] Psychotherapy introduces and makes acceptable new behaviour patterns, but the consolidation of the new outlook on life will depend on the day-to-day experiences in the open community.

A programme like the one outlined above may seem pedestrian, missing in many cases the root of the trouble. This method, as practised by most therapists in the field, does not deal radically with personality malformation, but seems to skirt along the edge of the problem. It is doubtful whether the majority of our patients require deep personality analysis and likely that they could function fairly effectively with supportive counselling. This alone is practicable in

[1] It may happen in course of treatment that one test score representing one specific achievement becomes level with another test score representing mental age. This incidental gain may be suggestive of a better functioning but not of attaining the limits of the full overall capacity. Since all aspects of personality are intimately interrelated, changes in one field must affect other fields as well.

TABLE 26

Synopsis

Approach	Number, age, sex, intell. level	Length of therapy	Method of evaluation	Results	Reference
I. PLAY THERAPY					
Non-directive	N = 32 CA 7–12 M, F I.Q. 52–78	16 weeks, 29 sess. @ 50 min. twice per week	2 control groups; intell. tests; adjustment rating; personality tests. No follow-up	Significant increase in adjustment ratings; no change in intelligence quotients	Mehlman (1953)
Non-directive analytical interpretations 'scientific mothering'	N = 23 CA 5–12 M, F Imbeciles Av. I.Q. 45	9–12 months	Control group; comparison with pre-treatment development; I.Q. testing; descript. of social adjustment. Follow-up	Significant increase of I.Q.; increased social adjustment	Mundy (1957a)
Combined with psychological counselling	N = 18 CA 9–16 M, F I.Q. 61–87	Not indicated	Observational comparison of behaviour changes with Raven's Matrices. No follow-up	Correlation of test pattern with improvement resp. non-improvement	Johnson (1953a)
II. DISCUSSION GROUPS:					
Directive	N = 97 CA 15–43 F I.Q. 53–90	25 sess. @ 1 hour 3 times a week (12 therapy groups)	Control group ratings based on 'critical incidents' and 'adjustment scale'. No follow-up	Statistically significant differences between exper. and control group	Wilcox and Guthrie (1957)
	N = 16 Ca (av.) 19 M I.Q. (av.) 62	13 sess. @ 1 hour once a week	2 control groups; checklist on behavioural violations, housing reports before and after treatment. Follow-up	Statistically significant differences between exper. and control groups showing superior institutional adjustment	Snyder and Sechrest (1959)

Non-directive permissive but not passive therapist	N = 7 CA 16–20 M I.Q. 52–77	6 mths., 32 sess. @ 1 hour twice a week	2 control groups; checklist of attitude, objective measures of workshop behaviour; psychometric tests. No follow-up	Significant changes in attitudes – improvement in work – significant increase in I.Q. rating	Yonge and O'Connor (1954) O'Connor and Yonge (1955)
Combined with interview, therapist passive	N = 31 CA 15–43 F I.Q. 49–104	2½ years, 1 hour twice a week (aver. 8 pat. per sess.)	Observational. Follow-up	Conspicuous reduction of feelings of shame, isolation, and fear	Astrachan (1955)
Activity interview, passive therapist. Discussion and interpret. (Slavson)	N = 12 CA 10–13 F MA 5–8	Not indicated	Observational, psychometric testing. No follow-up	66% of group members improved. No psychometric change; change to 'out-group' interests	Fisher and Wolfson (1953)
Strictly non-directive	N = 21 CA 12–37 I.Q. 35–72	7½ mths., 54 sess. @ 1 hour twice a week (aver. 7 pat. per sess.)	Observational. Follow-up	Those patients who had attended least often showed greatest improvement	Vail (1955)
Directive but permissive	N = 6 /Epilep/ CA 19–55 M I.Q. 55–105	6 mths., 36 sess. @ 1 hour twice a week	Observational. No follow-up	Four patients became better socialized; two were unchanged	Stubblebine (1957)

TABLE 26—*Synopsis—continued*

Approach	Number, age, sex, intell. level	Length of therapy	Method of evaluation	Results	Reference
III. ENVIRONMENTAL THERAPY:					
Combined with intensive counselling	N = 68 CA 9–49 M, F From imbecile to borderline normal	2 years continuous	Conduct records, count of breaches of discipline; school and work records, clinical judgments. No follow-up	Improved 66%. Unchanged 23%. Deteriorated 10%	Thorne (1948)
Combined with counselling	N = 50 CA 17–44 M MA 5–13	Not indicated	Ratings by staff. No follow-up	Improved 28%. Moder. impr. 66%. No impr. 6% (in behaviour and social adaptation)	Chase (1953)
IV. VARIOUS APPROACHES					
Artificial situation indirectly controlled by therapist – 'Court room scene'	N = 9 CA 11–15 M I.Q. 50–79	3 weeks, 10 sess. @ 1 hour 15 mins.	Observational by therapist and teachers. Follow-up	Improvement in social adjustment	Cotzin (1948)
Interview groups, play-therapy, activity groups, and individual interview	N = 42 CA 13–20 M I.Q. (av.) 60	1 year	Observational. No follow-up	Increased maturation and self-reliance, improved behaviour and social abilities	Stubblebine and Roadruck (1956)
Counselling and psychoanalytic approach; non-directive principles	N = 7 CA 17–38 M I.Q. 65–86	7 mths., 30 sess. @ 1 hour	Observational. Follow-up	Little observable change in personality dynamics or mental level. Alleviates situational anxiety	Ringelheim and Polatsek (1955)

Non-specified psychiatric treatment of various types	N = 25 CA 6–16 M, F I.Q. 80–90	Not indicated	Comparison with control group of higher than aver. intell. using reports. No follow-up	Improved 10 cases; ameliorated 7 cases; no improvement or deterioration 8 cases	Glassman (1943)
Play therapy, interviews, etc.	N = 25 CA 3–15 M, F I.Q. 61–84	Not indicated	Comparison with control group of aver. intell. using reports. No follow-up	Improved 10 cases; ameliorated 10 cases; no improvement 5 cases	Cooley (1945)
Discussions, art sessions	N = 33 CA 15–55 M, F Feeble-minded	Approx. 2 years for female patients, 44 sess. @ 1 hour	Observational by therapist	42% very good and good response 49% slight and poor response 9% negative response	Heller (1955)

view of their general mental qualities, our present inadequate knowledge, and the number of available therapists. In effect we do running repairs to a none too efficient mechanism, but it is surprising how well it can function if it is not overtaxed.

(d) Evaluation of psychotherapeutic approaches

Evaluating success or failure of formal psychotherapy has proved delicate, difficult, and perhaps impossible in the case of neurotic patients of normal intellect where a wealth of evidence is available. When it comes to the handful of studies relating to mental deficiency the position is even more unsatisfactory. Most experiments have been undertaken in a pioneering clinical spirit with more thought for the patient than for objective criteria for evaluating results.

Not only the group compositions, the intelligence levels, ages, and the clinical categories differ considerably from one experiment to the other; methods are different, and often inadequately described; such important factors as local conditions, hospital regulations, and 'general atmosphere', vary also to a large extent. Criteria for improvement, or non-improvement, even when supported at times by hospital records, are not only subjective but may also differ with different investigators. The length and frequency of psychotherapy sessions vary a good deal and there is nearly a complete lack of follow-up studies to indicate whether the results of therapy are of a permanent nature. Published investigations tend to report 'successes' rather than 'failures' and no one seemed to have had either the same experience, or the same courage, as Vail who declared 'that those patients who attended the group the least number of times have shown the greatest progress' (1955).

Nevertheless, while the general emphasis of publications on success advises caution in evaluation, the wide consensus of opinion regarding the value of psychotherapy for defectives cannot be disregarded. The synopsis (Table 26) of the scope and results of some typical investigations of psychotherapy with mental defectives suggests that there is much evidence to encourage more systematic work.

Besides the reports on systematic investigations of group methods there are a few case studies which confirm the findings of most group therapists. Four years' psychoanalytic treatment of a mentally deficient boy resulted in the disappearance of his extreme selfishness, his inability to establish relationships, and his isolation. There was a marked improvement in his attitude and relations with other children – 'he began to see himself in relation to his environment and made definite efforts to be like others and to accept reality' (Chidester and Menninger, 1936).

Sarason reports that at the end of ten months of counselling Lottie's 'periods of sullenness and depression had noticeably decreased, she was more spontaneous, she did not avoid new people and situations with as much apprehension, her efficiency at work had improved and she did not feel as personally isolated as previously'. Stephen 'by facing rather than avoiding certain problems . . . was able to resolve conflicts which had previously reinforced unhealthy attitudes towards self and others. He was not plagued as much by feelings of guilt and worthlessness, he achieved a more realistic conception of his physical adequacy' (Sarason, 1949).

Two months of counselling treatment of a mentally deficient soldier resulted in evident improvement. His tension had disappeared and he spoke no longer of his feelings of inferiority, stating 'that he considered himself "one of the fellows" again' (Feldman, 1946).

From a scientific point of view the results of these investigations cannot, of course, convince. In view of the lack of control groups it is not known, for example, whether these changes would not have been brought about in the same way by traditional methods, or by time itself. More impressive is the changed attitude of the staff because 'perhaps the most difficult thing is to convince employees that they largely make their own problems through failure to use psychological methods of studying and handling the children under their care'. Their observations indicated that the patients were happier, that the 'total abolition of corporal punishment and repressive methods . . . (and) minimal use of punishment has been associated with improved behaviour', that the patients had 'become extremely critical of offenders' and 'to a large extent . . . discipline themselves', that there was a 'lessened incidence of reactive emotional disturbance', and that there was 'greater loyalty and co-operativeness' (Thorne, 1948). Similarly, Stubblebine and Roadruck (1956) quoted the opinions of people having known the patients before treatment and who 'commented on their increased maturation, self-reliance and improved behaviour and social abilities'.

Only a few experiments published so far make use of control groups and objective criteria for the assessment of patients under treatment (Mehlman, 1953; Yonge and O'Connor, 1954; O'Connor and Yonge, 1955; Mundy, 1957a; Wilcox and Guthrie, 1957). Mehlman's carefully designed investigation reports statistically significant increases in adjustment measured by ratings but no significant changes in intelligence scores. His main observation was 'that the mentally retarded child, despite his intellectual limitations, can grow in therapy because therapeutic progress does not depend on intellectual ability'. O'Connor reported significant changes in the attitude of the group under therapy accompanied by changes in behaviour and performance in a workshop situation. In particular there was an increase in 'zest' coupled with an increase in 'fanciful ambitions', but even more in 'feasible aspirations'. There was a definite change in attitude to 'authority figures' from negative to positive and the 'progressive release of hostility to be expected in a permissive group atmosphere showed in negative attitudes to group members as well as in increase of the "criticism of others" '. The end of the six months of psychotherapy saw also a nearly complete disappearance of initially fairly frequent masochistic, sadistic, and other morbid ideas.

Some information relating to I.Q. changes is contained in a few studies (Axline, 1948, 1949) and one of the most striking features is the variability of the I.Q.s reported. Sarason's cases, Lottie and Stephen, show I.Q.s ranging from 45 to 74 and 63 to 76 (Sarason, 1949), an imbecile soldier testing 41 and 39 before treatment showed on retest an I.Q. 59 which appeared 'to be considerably lower than the Rorschach indication which suggested dull normal intelligence' (Feldman, 1946). A boy under Freudian treatment showed a change in I.Q. from 62 to 90 (Chidester and Menninger, 1936).

A large pilot study by Tarjan and Benson (1953) mentions that several patients undergoing psychotherapy 'showed a distinct rise in measurable intelligence. In some cases this increase amounted to as much as 20 I.Q. points.'

Mundy (1957), comparing the Stanford–Binet I.Q.s of 15 young children before and after psychotherapy with the I.Q. of 10 untreated children, found a highly significant increase of 7 I.Q. points in the first group. In a second comparison she used eight children as their 'own controls' and found that there was a highly significant increment of 22 I.Q. points during the therapy period, but only a 2 I.Q. points change in the pre-therapy period of comparable length. The I.Q. changes of these very young children were paralleled by very pronounced improvement in social adjustment.

Obviously much will depend on the selection of tests used and of patients treated, and not every intelligence test may be sensitive to the particular changes brought about by treatment. Thus while Ringelheim (1955) reports little observable changes in personality dynamics or mental level (without indicating what tests were employed) a recent investigation (O'Connor and Yonge, 1955) arrived at quite different results. Using three groups, two of which served as controls, all matched on sex, age, and I.Q., they observed that pre- and post-treatment scores of the experimental group showed a significant change at the 5 per cent. level on the Wechsler Verbal Scale but not on Raven's Progressive Matrices. The control groups did not change. The gain in I.Q. had a mean of 9 points and was equivalent to one standard deviation with this group. The improvement was mostly due to an increase in the comprehension subtest of the Wechsler Scale, significant at the 2 per cent. level.

The final judgment as to whether psychotherapy directly contributes to an increase in intellectual efficiency measurable by intelligence tests, will have to be postponed until more carefully designed studies are available. Most of the work so far available is no more than suggestive and those I.Q. changes reported could just as well be attributed to maturation, changes in environment, spontaneous stabilization, inadequate testing and to familiarity with the test situation at a second occasion (Kriegman and Hilgard, 1944), as well as to selective factors favouring the more promising patients being chosen for therapy.

Conclusion

In summary one might well be cautious and merely state that the published evidence suggests that apparently changes take place in attitude, behaviour, and outlook of mentally deficient patients who receive some special attention. The changes seem to be most marked in patients showing behaviour disorders, even if of a degree permitting the label 'psychopathy'. The psychotherapeutic approach seems to have no, or little, effect in schizophrenics, or even simple schizoid cases (Astrachan, 1955; Stubblebine and Roadruck, 1956). Viewing the vagueness of the methodology of the actual therapeutic methods one might well wonder whether the form of approach is of considerable importance since all activities and all relationships are potentially psychotherapeutic if handled with this intention. Much of the success of psychotherapy with the mentally deficient may be due to the presence of 'someone to think both with him and for him' (Hartwell, 1940).

Perusing the literature one gains the impression that a good deal of the work reported has been carried out by complete novices who embarked on the venture of psychotherapy with little or no knowledge of methods or patients. While this is unavoidable in a first generation of therapists in mental deficiency, it may perhaps also account for the difficulties met, and for the sceptical reception of these attempts.

One or two further considerations are indicated before engaging in an indiscriminate experimentation in therapy. Many of the therapeutic investigations appeared to be of fairly short duration. In some cases a practical result was placement of patients in more congenial employment, but in most cases the end of the therapy sessions coincided with the end of any special endeavours to help. The ensuing disappointment, when 'warm' therapeutic sessions which have aroused hope end abruptly and the everyday institution life comes into full force again without any apparent changes, throws some doubt on the value of such isolated experimentation for the patient. It seems that far from being helpful, the lack of concrete results, and the disappearance of the personal interest, may well strengthen the anti- and a-social attitudes of the patients who have once again been 'let down'.

There seems to be little justification for initiating therapy of that type merely in order to learn, or to prove that it has value, unless it can be reinforced and followed up by concrete achievements. The therapist must, therefore, have some definite administrative power and some weight in the decisions concerning the future life of his patients (Thorne, 1948; Gunzburg, 1956a, 1957).

Group and individual therapy sessions break the ground and encourage the adoption of a new outlook by persuasion and explanation, but therapy can only initiate and not carry the whole burden of readjustment. The proof of the veracity of the therapist's assertions is given through the patient's reception by his immediate environment, when with great doubts he makes his first hesitant attempts at reorientation. The final therapy is administered by the environment, the institution in the first place and the community after that.

ENVIRONMENTAL THERAPY

(a) The role of the institution

The environment provided by the good mental deficiency hospital can operate therapeutically by offering a concrete object lesson in living and working in a community. In practice the average institution harbours a large number of custodial patients of low mentality and, for that reason, has in many ways to adjust to their needs rather than to the requirements of the minority of trainable feeble-minded patients. This, in effect, means that the whole atmosphere, the speed, the working efficiency is geared to the abilities of the less capable ones among the patients, and the feeble-minded, in consequence, though potentially more trainable, falls in only too easily with diminished demands. The outcome may be that the institution will adapt him only to institutional life; he is a 'good' or a 'bad' patient according to his integration with institution demands and he learns to expect and accept 'privileges' as rewards rather than as 'rights' which depend on his demonstrated ability to shoulder responsibility. Many of the American writers refer to their deficient patients as 'children' regardless of their age or mental status, and this characterizes well an attitude of benevolent paternalism which may easily deprive the 'child' of his chance to develop a sense of responsibility which is required for his final discharge (Gunzburg, 1950b, 1957; Stanley and Gunzburg, 1957).

The task of the institution environment must not merely be conceived in negative terms as providing shelter where a patient can be calmed or chastened by the deterrent 'punishment' of institutionalization. Its task, in more positive terms, must be the provision of a community life which is understood, felt, and accepted, as a preparatory stage for living and working in the larger community. It must support the therapist's attempt to give the patient a new orientation by its everyday handling of routine situations, by the staff–patient relationship, and by the way it offers opportunities to the patient for demonstrating his improved social competence. Establishing a supportive and helpful atmosphere is not too easy a task particularly in the case of the delinquent who considers the indefinite nature of his stay in hospital to be harsher than a specified prison sentence and out of proportion to the offence leading to admission. For the patient, the hospital may easily represent society at its revengeful worst where his further life is believed to depend on the whim of an unknown authority. It would be an uphill task of some magnitude and with a doubtful chance of success if individual and group therapy were to try to overcome in isolation the resistance, distrust, fear, apprehension, and insecurity of the patient in face of an institution environment which is impersonal, repressive, and incomprehensible (Morris *et al.*, 1959; Shapiro, 1962).

Integrating the therapeutic efforts, on whatever plane they take place, will, however, overcome in most cases the unavoidable irritations and frustrations, since reassurance and support come forth from different quarters. The repeated trials and failures of the defective to achieve social approbation can only too easily assume in his eyes sinister aspects of an endless 'snake-and-ladder' game, and unless everyone and everything in the institution counteracts this at the time, it will lead to needless suffering, dejection, and prolonged institutionalization.

(b) Staff education

There is much agreement among the reports on therapeutic programmes that success 'in an institutional setting is in a large measure dependent on the interest and co-operation of all employees who play a role in the everyday life of the patients' (Ringelheim, 1955). Though the programme is planned by the counsellor, 'therapy itself must be delegated on a 24-hour basis to other administrative units, including the cottage, the classroom, and the recreation staffs' (Cotzin, 1948). The staff must be 'both intellectually and emotionally involved in treatment programme' (Stubblebine and Roadruck, 1956), which may at times even require an initial settlement of the staff's own interpersonal relationships. Thus the above-mentioned two authors did not hesitate to state that they felt

> that the maturation of patients was directly proportional to the earnestness and effectiveness with which the adults about them obtained some measure of personal insight. In so far as each staff member was able to face his own feelings with regard to life requirements and satisfactions, he seemed able to appreciate the problems of the patients.

A supportive milieu, which offers the unstable patient sufficient opportunity to acquire self-discipline, demands a staff with a feeling of security, absence of apprehension, and a not easily undermined self-confidence. Unless it is possible to lay aside their problems (mostly revolving round inter-staff relations and adherence to regulations) the nurse–patient relationship may easily develop into a situation where the staff is more concerned in overcoming and suppressing symptomatic reactions of the patients, than in assisting their emotional development with the many accompanying disappointing failures (Stogdill, 1938; Thorne, 1950; Chase, 1953; Dennis, 1956; Farrell and Forsley, 1956).

(c) Absconding

The effects of environmental therapy on an institutional problem such as absconding are worth a short consideration. A T.A.T. analysis of 'run-away girls' concluded that these patients are

> more keenly sensitive to their environment and react emotionally to restrictions and aggressive attitudes. Their ceiling of tolerance is low and their only mode of reaction to what they deem an intolerable situation is escape. They have vague fears and anxieties projected upon people in authority and the environment and inability, or fear, to express aggression freely toward these forces turns aggression upon themselves (Gothberg, 1947).

Thorne decided, on the basis of psychiatric interviews, that 45 per cent. of the cases of absconding were directly due to emotional disturbance by frustration, home-sickness, or specific grievances later demonstrated to be fair. In an attempt to reduce the problem of absconding he eliminated repressive methods and unnecessary irritants rigorously and re-educated his staff. Institution freedom was increased by 'trusting' patients to look after themselves without close supervision and he concluded 'that the absence of continuous surveillance and maximum personal freedom has lessened the impulse to elope and encouraged individual children to assume responsibility for their conduct' (Thorne, 1947).

A similar programme of staff education and 'a senior staff member to provide the trainee with personal guidance and to serve as an outlet for the immediate ventilation of complaints and personal troubles', as well as relaxation of restrictions, resulted in a remarkable lowering of the rate of absconding. The total number of runaways dropped from 14·3 per cent. of the total population to 1·6 per cent. after introduction of these changes. This meant that the proportion of 32·8 per cent. of runaways of the population capable of absconding had been reduced to 2·4 per cent. (Fraser, 1951).

Absconding must in many cases be regarded primarily as a symptom revealing the necessity for special attention. The over-discipline of a restrictive institution setting will result mostly in *running away* from it (Allen, 1949). In the more permissive type of institution absconding may assume greater proportions, though this is not necessarily always the case as shown by Fraser's investigation, but it is *running to* a desired goal rather than *running away* from a hated place. It may not be a strong fear and frustration reaction, but only a mild form of protest, a desire to be with one's own family and often only an urge for childish adventure. When dealing with this type there is no need to overcome hostility, anger, and fear – the good relationship between therapist and patient has not been broken, but only temporarily and insignificantly interrupted.

(d) Discipline and punishment[1]

Disciplinary actions, conceived not merely as a necessary mortar to maintenance of order, but as a therapeutic agent, can help a great deal to encourage the patient in the acquisition of feeling for social order and for the organization of relationships. He must acquire the realization that his interference with order leads to trouble and that, therefore, 'he must be more considerate for his own welfare, that he must look out for himself, as the organization must function and if he gets in the way he will have to take the consequences' (Miller, 1943).

The need for punishment must be explained by the counsellor and accepted by the patient in order to avoid resentment and the reinforcement of the defective's childishly stubborn immature attitude. It should only be introduced when other, positive methods have failed (rewards, incentives) and must only indicate disapproval of a specific action, but on no account rejection of the person who has committed the offence. 'Rehabilitational punishment' (Thorne, 1950)

[1] A psychologically conceived punishment is an important and often indispensable aid in the adjustment effort – the word carries nowadays unfortunately an aura of savage brutality (corporal punishment, 'bread and water'), and of inhuman rule-of-thumb application, and has been replaced in hospital practice by more precise descriptive terms like restrictions, or withdrawal of privileges. In dealings with the patient, however, 'punishment' is a comprehensive and comprehensible term indicating to the simple-minded society's reaction to misdemeanour. There is no need for 'punishment' to be automatically associated with feelings of fear, anger, or hate, if it is handled correctly.

is a therapeutic measure and must not be identified with punishment of an administrative nature; it is rather the spirit in which it is given and accepted than the severity which differentiates the two approaches. The environmental pressure of a rigid institution atmosphere may actually create the 'behaviour problem' which it then tries to overcome by recourse to even stricter punishment and sedative treatment. Milner (1949) points out that institutional training, or segregation, is itself liable to cause violent reactions in patients who had not shown violence before admission and that particularly the high-grade female is less tolerant of colony segregation than the male.

The use of punishment and discipline in an institution should help the development of moral judgments. Yet the disciplinary actions, more often than not, pay attention to the fact of infringement of rules rather than to the underlying motives. This encourages the continuation of an immature attitude of *moral realism*, as it has been described by Piaget, where only the manifest form of an act is considered irrespective of subjective modifying factors. The adult point of view, which accepts the need for differential treatment, must appear unfair and unjust to the institutionalized patient, who has not been given an opportunity to acquire the social stand-point towards punishment and misbehaviour. Abel (1941), in a careful examination of this question, showed how institutionalization tended to increase the frequency of judgments in terms of *moral realism*, particularly when prolonged. Whilst in the open community increasing mental age permits even a subnormal to grasp the subjective factors and intentions, institutionalization appears to hamper maturation of moral concepts. There the need for maintaining order and discipline over hundreds of patients exposes them 'to a mode of treatment that includes *moral realism* and one that cannot but fail to influence them'.

In this context it is interesting to study the various reports from the Wayne County Training School and the Balderton (England) Psychopathic Unit where discipline is put into the hands of the patients themselves (Kirk, 1935; Kephart, 1938a, b; McCandless, 1942; Rossettie and Strauss, 1945; Kirk and Johnson, 1951; Craft, 1960, 1962b). This system may serve well to impress on the individual patient the necessity for submitting to 'group pressure'. It can help the patient in considering his actions and their consequences and can assist in reducing the disproportionately big share of thinking and acting which the hospital staff undertakes on the patient's behalf (Shafter and Chandler, 1960).

Another approach permitting a behavioural self-rating has been described in Chapter XIV. There every patient has an opportunity to compare weekly his opinions regarding his behaviour and work with that of his supervisor and to discuss the disagreement. This procedure appears to be a valuable aid in making the patient aware of his often inflated and unrealistic judgment of himself.

Environmental therapy was successfully employed in the case of 298 delinquent juveniles under the age of 16, average I.Q. 65. These children were 'little rebels, simple street-bred urchins, smashing and tearing everything, swearing, suspicious of all authority, looking constantly for "the catch in it", looking on every adult as an enemy whom they tried to annoy in every way'. The stabilization programme was carried out by 'male nurses . . . trained to put into practice the theory which recognizes the value of expression in contradistinction to repressive measures'. As much freedom as possible was given, yet the right balance between freedom and discipline was maintained. The boys 'look on their teachers as comrades, call them by their first names as they do all the other male nurses' and scholastic attainments compare favourably with those of other special schools. Seventy per cent. of the admissions were stabilized to a degree permitting a final discharge from the institution (Foale, 1952).

A social assessment of 112 defective delinquents indicated feelings of conscious inferiority resulting in negative attitudes to society. This was observed in 71·4 per cent. of admissions, but after a period of resocialization, lasting three months or more, only 34·8 per cent. still displayed the same attitude. Among the admissions were 29·5 per cent. who showed co-operation; the proportion increased to 62·4 per cent. (Morris, 1948).

In mental deficiency practice little use has so far been made of the new technique of sociometry and exploration of group structure (Sutherland *et al.*, 1954). Murray (1953) investigated the stability of personal relations among retarded children and pointed out its bearing on therapeutic endeavours. Sociometric techniques were used in evaluating the success of specialized therapeutic activities on group homogeneity (Kephart, 1938a).

(e) Conclusions

Every experience, activity, and personal relationship should be regarded as having therapeutic potentialities for the patient and it is through their unified and concentrated impact that significant changes in outlook come about. Formal psychotherapy, if carried out in isolation and very often against the deadweight of custodial institution philosophy, has very little chance of achieving lasting results. The probabilities are that its ventilating effect disturbs the general hospital framework to such an extent that over-reaction destroys whatever good may have been initiated in the individual sessions.

It appears that the original naïve optimism, which asserted the value of psychotherapy carried out by itself on a very small scale in some corner of the institution, has nowadays given way to the realization that psychotherapy must grow and develop from a therapeutic programme which comprises every aspect of hospital life. Many of the problems, which appear to call urgently for individual or group therapy, are simply the result of unhelpful institutional dealings, have developed there and have a spontaneous remission when the patient is transferred to a new therapeutic hospital environment. Their treatment by formal psychotherapy would be often unnecessary and may be destined to failure in the face of a multitude of adverse environmental factors.

Psychotherapy in mental deficiency is a feasible and indeed necessary form of treatment for many severely maladjusted patients and even the few meagre exploratory excursions reported so far have indicated a fair degree of effectiveness. It is true that as far as scientific evaluation of these efforts is concerned, very little has been produced which is so significant and convincing as to demonstrate in facts and figures the value of psychotherapy. Even recent careful researches resulting in positive findings have so far proved no more than that changes of certain variables have taken place. How far these are achievements of some duration and how far they will contribute to a successful adjustment – whatever we may mean by this – we do not know. On the other hand, negative research findings may be due to the crudeness of our measuring devices and to our failure to ask the relevant questions and cannot be said to prove the uselessness of a psychotherapeutic approach.

Decisions regarding the most suitable and effective type of formal psychotherapy in mental deficiency are less important than the realization of the need for a humane and understanding approach to the personality problems of the defective. In the last analysis the common factor among the various methods appears to be that individualized attention, reassurance, and acceptance by the therapist have in themselves a soothing effect on the patient and make him accessible to help and guidance.

Much of what has been achieved has so far often been effected without support from the hospital environment – the few therapy sessions coexisting, as it were, side by side with the traditional and old-fashioned custodial arrangements. The prospects for the success of a therapy programme, extending uniformly over twenty-four hours, should be well worth close investigation.

Whatever name, or whatever form, we choose for these individualized therapeutic efforts, there is little doubt that recognition of the emotional needs of the defective, and the planned attempt to meet them by therapist and environment, introduce new factors into the treatment of the social incompetence of the mental defective, the exact weight of which we cannot appraise as yet, though we may be confident they are positive and constructive.

Chapter XVI

SPEECH DISORDERS AND THERAPY IN MENTAL SUBNORMALITY

by Margaret Fawcus

INTRODUCTION

Criteria will obviously differ in deciding whether speech is defective, and any such decision must take the intellectual, social, and dialectal background into account. What may be regarded as a defect of articulation in one social group, for example, may be accepted as a normal speech characteristic in another.

Speech may be regarded as defective when it interferes with communication, causes the speaker anxiety or embarrassment by virtue of its difference from the accepted norm, or involves conscious physical effort to produce. Similarly, language may be considered inadequate where it fails to express a speaker's thoughts and feelings, and is generally an unsatisfactory means of satisfying his physical and emotional needs.

Speech in the sense it has been used in the title of this chapter is an all-embracing term, including language (both written and spoken), articulation, and phonation. Any, or all, of these aspects of speech may be affected, particularly where there is extensive brain damage.

We shall be considering the relationship between intellectual and verbal ability; the aetiological background of speech, voice and articulation disorders, with special reference to mental deficiency; the value and justification of speech therapy, and the special problems encountered in treatment.

THE DEVELOPMENT OF LANGUAGE

From the moment he first draws breath, the baby is vocal and loudly expresses his discomfort. Some time will elapse before he realizes that crying has what we might call its 'social uses', and that he can, to some extent, control his environment by crying. But there will be other times, when the baby is warm and fed, that he will make small cries of comfort, which Lewis (1957) has called 'comfort sounds'. Lewis has described in some detail, on a purely physiological basis, the sounds which emerge during production of 'discomfort cries' and 'comfort sounds'. He mentions, for example, the well-fed contented baby lying with his mouth slackly open, and the back of the tongue lolling against the soft palate, with the result that back consonants ('ga-ga') are produced. He says the bilabial consonants arise from sucking movements which tend to occur before or after a meal. The child is learning to talk, as Van Riper (1956) says, as he sucks and swallows, belches and smiles, for co-ordinations used in these activities are used in speech. In fact, in these early stages, the sounds of speech arise from the more or less reflexive, involuntary movements of tongue, lips, palate, and jaw.

The transition to the stage known as babbling follows on quite naturally towards the end of the third month, although sometimes sooner, when he begins to produce repetitive strings of sounds when contented and comfortable. Lewis says: 'When a child is babbling he gives us the impression that he is making sounds for their own sake, that he derives satisfaction from the utterance itself, that he is playing with sounds, playing with his vocal organs in the same way as he plays with movements of his fingers and his toes.'

In the early stages of babbling – what has been called the prelinguistic phase of babbling – the stimulus for the repetition of such sounds is obviously the pleasure the baby gains from 'the complex stimulus', as Lewis puts it, 'of motor and auditory sensations'. The importance of babbling in the development of language lies, as Lewis says, 'in that it is a means by which a child, through repeated practice, acquires skill in making sounds. As other forms of play give a child the rudimentary skills upon which his later complex skills are based, so babbling gives him the beginnings of the highly complex skills that go to the production of the sounds of speech.'

The child is developing an awareness of his own body and of

separateness from his mother – and at the same time a growing awareness of parental approval and consciousness of his ability to gain attention and win approval. It is at this stage that the parent, who has hitherto satisfied the child's material needs, with food and warmth and close physical contact, gives the stimulus of social approval and the give and take of imitation which brings us to the stage of linguistic babbling. She reinforces his babbling by showing obvious signs of pleasure at his vocal attempts, develops his imitative faculties and further reinforces the process by imitating the babbling of the child. The 'Mamma' and 'Dadda' of this stage are not attached to any object – his babbling has no meaning, although meaningful words will begin to occur around the age of 10–14 months in the normal child. His small initial vocabulary will not be very discriminating: 'Dadda' will be applied to all males and 'doddie' to all animals. Obviously, it can be seen how vital is the mother's role at this stage in talking to the child – in naming the objects and activities of his daily routine. Gradually the child's vocabulary increases – a very concrete but increasingly discriminating vocabulary. This is still hardly language in the sense of communication, and the child will be 18 months old before he begins to communicate in the sense of expressing his basic wants or ideas. The words can begin to symbolize the object even in its absence. Two words begin to be put together from the age of 18 months and at the age of 2 years he starts to verbalize his immediate experiences.

The sentence develops, initially in a telescopic form. He uses concrete nouns and verbs associated with his immediate physical environment. Three-word sentences and the use of a few prepositions begin to appear at the age of two years. When his limited vocabulary and language are insufficient for his needs, he will lapse into jargon speech, and carry on long 'conversations' whilst he plays. Comprehension considerably outstrips expression during the first two or three years. Later, he will begin to use narrative and planning speech, and to verbally formulate his ideas. He talks to himself as he plays, externalizing his thoughts. Later still, this 'external' speech will become 'internal' speech.

The teacher and the therapist working with the retarded child need to be familiar with these stages of development, since any attempt at language work or training must obviously proceed from the level at which language assessment shows the child to be. We cannot force the process of maturation, although we can facilitate progress, and can advise the parent on how best to help her child develop speech.

Factors within the child or his environment which may facilitate or retard language development will obviously operate within both the normal and the mentally retarded child. The retarded child, being intellectually less well endowed, is obviously going to be more vulnerable to adverse conditions of learning, and less able to overcome, or compensate for, any adverse influences.

INCIDENCE

In studying surveys of the incidence of speech defects, it must be remembered that the criteria used in assessing speech may vary considerably. A statistical survey carried out in London by Burt in the 1920's (1951) showed that 'severe defects of speech' occurred in just over 1 per cent. of normal children (the control group); in over 5 per cent. of backward children; and in nearly 11 per cent. of those children considered to be mentally deficient. Burt also mentions the results of a survey carried out by Lloyd in Birmingham at the same time, in which severe speech defects were found in 0·5 per cent. of the (normal) control group, in just over 5 per cent. of the backward, and in nearly 15 per cent. of the mentally deficient. In the London survey, and taking mild defects into account, Burt estimated that nearly one-quarter of mentally deficient children surveyed showed some defect of speech. It is interesting to compare these figures with those of Wallin (1949) who states that in St. Louis over 26 per cent. of pupils in special schools had defective speech, compared with 2·8 per cent. in 'the regular elementary and high school grades'. Wallin also showed that there are a higher number of articulatory disorders among the mentally deficient children examined than among the normal group – just over 81 per cent. of all defects in the former, and 57 per cent. in the latter.

A much more recent survey carried out by Schlanger and Gottsleben (1957) among 516 residents at The Training School, Vineland, New Jersey, showed that no less than 79 per cent. had 'varying types and levels of speech defectiveness'. They comment, 'It is interesting to note that practically all the subjects with voice and stuttering defects had, in addition, some degree of articulatory impairment.' The authors attempted to discover the incidence of defective speech amongst the different aetiological groups which come under the broad heading of mental retardation. They found that the greatest incidence occurred in the Mongol group (of whom 95 per cent. had defects of articulation, 72 per cent. had voice disorders, and 45 per cent. stammered). In the Organic group, defective articulation occurred in 84 per cent., 56 per cent. had a voice disorder, and 18 per cent. stammered. They discovered that the lowest incidence of defective speech was in the Familial group, where 66 per cent. had some defect of articulation, 22 per cent. had voice disorders, and 10 per cent. stammered. The lower incidence amongst the Familial group 'is to be expected because of a lesser degree of pathology underlying their retardation'. Schlanger and Gottsleben themselves suggest that the very high incidence of defective speech at The Training School is in part due to the fact that only 12 per cent. of the school population come in the Familial group. In addition, both authors have training and considerable experience in speech pathology and therapy, and their criteria are therefore probably more strict in deciding what constitutes defective speech.

Although there have been several studies of the incidence of speech defects amongst the mentally retarded, not all of these have shown the relative incidence in the three main grades. Kennedy (1930) attempted such a survey, and found that 42 per cent. of 249 feeble-minded patients had speech disorders ranging from slight to severe; 71 per cent. of 27 imbeciles had speech defects; and none of the 32 idiots examined showed meaningful speech. The age range of the group studied was 5 to 38 years.

In a study of 2,522 institutionalized patients, Sirkin and Lyons (1941) found that 31 per cent. of patients with I.Q.s over 69 had speech defects; 47 per cent. of the feeble-minded group showed defective speech; and 74 per cent. of the imbecile group. Sachs (1951) in a study of 210 feeble-minded and imbecile patients (aged 10–20 years) reported that 57 per cent. had defective speech. An analysis of the patients with speech defects showed that 18 per cent. of the 'borderline' group had speech defects, 44 per cent. of the feeble-minded group, and 79 per cent. of the imbecile group.

As Matthews (1957) points out, 'Variations in the incidence figures are probably due to differences in criteria of what constitutes a speech defect, and to differences in the composition of the retarded group studied.' None the less, they all agree in one direction: that there is undoubtedly a markedly higher incidence of defective speech amongst the mentally retarded, and furthermore, that the percentage of speech defects increases as the I.Q. decreases.

SPEECH AND LANGUAGE DISORDERS AND INTELLIGENCE

This high incidence of speech defects would seem to suggest that mental deficiency is the *cause* of many of these disorders of speech and language. As Kastein (1956) has pointed out, however, 'The child's label of gross (mental) impairment does not necessarily indicate the cause for his language and speech deficiency.' She continues,

> The intelligence quotient of a child is not directly related to language development. Thus a child with good intelligence may have absent or defective speech whereas a child with an I.Q. as low as 40 may have surprisingly good speech. The low I.Q. itself is not necessarily the cause of the lack of speech development.

Matthews (1957) has said, 'In view of the high incidence of speech and hearing problems among mentally retarded children, it is not surprising that communication disorders are often thought to result from mental deficiency.' He goes on to say, 'The well-trained speech and hearing therapist should recognize that there may be many explanations of delayed or defective speech which have no relation to intellectual retardation.'

Becky (1942), in a study of 50 children with delayed speech, found that there were a number of constitutional, environmental, and psychological factors, other than mental retardation, to explain the retardation of speech. Matthews (1957) lists brain injury, glandular dysfunction, emotional disturbance, and hearing loss as aetiological factors of speech disorders in mental deficiency.

Berry and Eisenson (1956) are in agreement with these findings and point of view. They say,

> Despite the very high incidence of speech defects among the feeble-minded, low intelligence is probably not a direct cause of defective speech production, though it is undoubtedly directly associated with poor linguistic ability. There are many organic conditions, such as cretinism, mongolism and brain damage, which are responsible at once for both the lowered intelligence and the

defective speech of the individual. The amount of intelligence needed for the correct production and control of speech sounds is not great.

These writers emphasize the point that there may be a common aetiological factor (or even factors) underlying both the mental deficiency and the speech or language problem. Furthermore, it will be shown that the speech defect itself may be largely or in part responsible for the retarded intellectual development.

IS SPEECH THERAPY JUSTIFIED?

What evidence is there to show that the time spent on speech correction procedures with the mentally deficient patient is justified by the results achieved? In the past, and even today, many speech therapists have taken a pessimistic view of the possibilities of improving or developing the speech of the mentally retarded. They argue that the therapist's time and skill should be devoted to the needs of the 'normal' child and adult, and there is a natural tendency to eliminate patients on the grounds of mental deficiency where the therapist has a heavy case load, and is forced to make a selection on the basis of priorities. Cases do occur, however, where the chance of treatment is denied on no other grounds than mental retardation, in the belief that this will preclude the patient from responding to treatment.

Recent work, however, showing that the I.Q. is not the constant factor we had imagined (Clarke and Clarke, 1953b, and others – see Chapters IV and V), and the increasing awareness of the adverse effects of poor environment on intellectual development, have encouraged some therapists to take a more optimistic and constructive view of the problem. Also, at the same time, more therapists are being employed to work with the mentally deficient, both in residential schools and institutions, and in special day schools and occupation centres.

Certainly, without speech as an adequate means of self-expression and communication, the child's intellectual and emotional development will suffer, and the resulting anxiety and frustration may produce behaviour problems. Regarding the effect of defective speech on education, Burt (1951) has this to say, 'The handicaps imposed by defective articulation are most easily seen in oral and linguistic subjects. More particularly it is liable to hinder the child's early efforts at phonic analysis, and so prevent him from learning to read as quickly as the rest.' Defective speech may, in fact, be a considerable factor in producing backwardness and, further still, in preventing the child from benefiting from special educational or training programmes available.

Nisbet (1953) has made an interesting contribution on the relationship between environment, verbal ability, and intellectual development. He says,

> Previous studies have shown from the testing of children from institutions, of only children, and of twins, that lack of contact with adults results in retardation of verbal development; and there is substantial evidence to suggest that ability with words is of importance not only in verbal tests but in all abstract thinking.

He quotes Terman and Merrill (1937), who say, 'Language, essentially, is the shorthand of the higher thought processes, and the level at which this shorthand functions is one of the most important determinants of the level of the processes themselves.'

While it is generally recognized that there is an intimate connexion between thought and language, what is not always appreciated is the effect of language deprivation on the thought processes of a child, for example, the deaf mute. It is obvious that thought must use symbols of some sort, or what Pavlov (1941) termed 'the signals of signals'. Clearly the deaf mute builds up some sort of process of symbolization, but words are the most obvious, the most flexible, discriminative, and the widest in range of all possible symbols. Nisbet (op. cit.) quotes Ballard's (1934) conclusion: 'Admitting frankly that thought can function without language, we must also point out that it cannot function well without it, and that though it can do without it, it very rarely does.' Thus speech deprivation may not only restrict communication and experience, but depending upon its degree, may even limit the development of the thought processes, and hence intelligence.

The famous study of twins of normal intelligence by Luria and Yudovich (1959) should now be mentioned. A pair of twins were studied who, at the age of 5 years, communicated only with one another, possessing a very limited vocabulary. Their comprehension was also limited, and they showed no interest in listening to stories. 'While our twins understood perfectly speech that was directly related to an object or action which preoccupied them, they were not in a position to understand speech when it was not directly connected with a concrete situation and took a developed narrative form.' Their play was primitive and monotonous. There was no constructional play, and play of a meaningful creative character was rare. They were unable to draw or model in clay. Speech which consisted mainly of exclamations was, as Luria described it, 'locked in activity', and was not used in any way to organize or direct activity. After an initial period of observation, the two children were removed from the twin situation, and were each placed in a separate kindergarten group. This separation rapidly resulted in an improvement in play activity and the development of constructional activity, with the ability to formulate a project. Instead of scribbles, the children's drawings became, to use Luria's words, 'Goal driven, differentiated and objective'. 'Even more significant,' he said, 'was the fact that the whole structure of the mental life of the twins was simultaneously and sharply changed. Once they acquired an objective language system, the children were able to formulate the aims of their activity verbally, and after only three months we observed the beginnings of meaningful play.'

Furthermore, language training in one twin resulted in increased perception of speech and certain intellectual operations, such as the ability to classify. Hermelin and O'Connor have commented, 'The role of language may be decisive for the degree of efficiency with which imbeciles may be able to master problems as distinct from acquiring skills' (1963).

Schneider and Vallon (1955) have published the results of their work with mentally retarded children at the Westchester School for Retarded Children, and have concluded that,

> There is definitely a place for speech therapy in the educational or training programmes for the moderately and severely retarded child, and that not only can speech therapy be successfully integrated into almost any training programme for such children but that inherent in such a programme are potential values that challenge the imagination.

Supporting their contention that speech therapy has a place in the rehabilitation of the defective child, they say,

> Those children who proceeded to develop the ability to communicate verbally have gained considerably more than can be

measured by the number of words they have learned. The mere ability to express one's wants or needs in a socially acceptable manner, let alone the facility of fulfilling one's wants or needs through verbal communication, is indeed an invaluable asset to the child, on an intellectual, an emotional, and a social level. . . . With greater facility in verbal expression seemed to come a reduction in anxiety-producing situations, which in turn led to a reduction in a-social behaviour, and has, in many instances, made for a happier and better adjusted individual.

Rittmanic (1958) reported a noticeable improvement as a result of a three-month oral language programme, in which a group of institutionalized but educable mentally retarded children were seen five times a week for a period of 15–20 minutes. Kolstoe (1958) found that language training with low-grade mongoloid children resulted not only in an increase in language abilities, but also in a statistically significant increase in I.Q. Of 169 institutionalized patients selected for a 3½-year therapy programme (mean length of treatment 5 months), Sirkin and Lyons (1941) reported that 52 per cent. of the total benefited. Divided into categories, improvement was shown in 79 per cent. of the borderline, 59 per cent. of the feeble-minded, and 26 per cent. of the imbecile group.

These results show that whilst progress may be made in any of the three main categories of mental defect, most success may reasonably be expected with higher grade defectives.

Encouraging reports on the results of speech and language therapy with mentally retarded children have also been published by Schlanger (1953a, b) and Strazzulla (1953).

A successful response to speech therapy may be predicted, provided that:

1. the patient has sufficient ability to co-operate with the therapist in carrying out simple instructions;

2. the patient's attention can be gained and then maintained for a reasonable period of time;

3. rapport between patient and therapist has been established, so that the patient has confidence in the therapist and will co-operate with her;

4. anxiety has been eliminated from the learning situation, enabling the patient to function at his highest intellectual level;

5. all distracting stimuli have been removed, such as noise and unwanted equipment;

6. the patient is adequately motivated;

7. the material used is meaningful, and so presented that the patient's interest is stimulated;

8. stages in treatment are so graded that the patient may always succeed at one stage before the next is attempted;

9. speech correction can be carried out at frequent intervals (at least two or three times a week), or else followed up by regular and wisely supervised practice periods;

10. the co-operation of parents, teachers, and all those responsible for the patient's welfare has been gained;

11. the physical handicaps are such that they may to some extent be overcome.

Where the prognosis is in any doubt when the patient is first assessed, a trial period of speech therapy may provide the answer to the question, 'Can this child benefit from treatment?' As Kastein (1956) says, 'The child's response to integrative language and speech therapy should be taken into consideration before his mental potential can be assessed with any degree of accuracy. His response to such therapy is, in fact, an index of his potential.' The same may be said to be true of the adult patient. As Berry and Eisenson (1956) comment, 'Low intelligence undoubtedly is responsible for many cases of delay in speech, but speech delay also is the cause for much apparent low intelligence.' Furthermore,

> There is some evidence to the effect that when children are taught to speak there is a concomitant increase in their I.Q.s. Whether this increase results directly from the ability of the child to use language in a conventional manner, or whether the child who speaks generally makes a more adequate adjustment to his environment, and to the taking of intelligence tests, is not certain.

Let Matthews (1957) have the final word: 'In making a decision it would be well to remember that in a high-grade defective adequate speech may make the difference between self-sufficiency and dependency – between a lifetime in an institution at tax-payers' expense and vocational adjustment in society.'

AETIOLOGY

It is quite impossible, within the limitations of a single chapter, to give a complete aetiological background of all speech, voice, and language disorders. Some conditions, for example the concomitants of mongolism, are specifically related to mental deficiency; other conditions, such as cleft lip and palate, show an even distribution amongst both the normally intelligent and mentally deficient. Any omissions in this section will be due to lack of space, and not to disregard for the aetiological factor itself.

Disorders of articulation

A. Articulation disorders of organic origin

(1) *Dental anomalies.* In practice, it will often be found that good speech may occur in the presence of severe dental irregularity, whilst multiple errors of articulation are associated in some cases with relatively slight dental anomalies. Irregular dentition may be regarded as a causative factor in articulatory disorders, but only when the possibility of some other physical abnormality or functional disturbance has been eliminated. Where such another factor is found to exist, then the abnormal dentition may be of little significance or at most a contributory cause. There are various ways in which irregular teeth, or the abnormal relationship of mandible and maxilla, may affect articulation, only some of which can be mentioned here: the production of *s* is most likely to be affected, for example, by an anterior open bite, by absent or badly spaced teeth, or by a prognathic mandible; a recessive mandible may make lip closure impossible for the labial consonants *m*, *b*, and *p*.

Tredgold and Soddy (1956) state that 'anomalies of teeth are very common' in the mentally deficient, and they go on to say, 'A good set of teeth is rare in mental defectives. Often late to appear, malformed and unhealthy when present, and prone to early decay and disappearance.' Whilst this statement suggests a higher incidence than may be found in actual fact, poor dentition is frequently found amongst the mentally deficient patients referred for therapy. Rather than being a 'stigma of degeneracy', however, these anomalies are more probably due to such factors as poor nutrition, neglect of dental care, and lack of orthodontic treatment, and may also be associated with disease, such as congenital syphilis.

(2) *Cleft palate.* Figures quoted by Tredgold and Soddy (1956) show that the incidence of cleft palate and lip in mental deficiency is no higher than the incidence among the normal population, and they thus assume that these conditions cannot be regarded as 'stigmata of degeneracy'. (Figures quoted by Morley, 1945, show that cleft palate occurs once in approximately every 1,000 births.) On the other hand, Tredgold and Soddy (1956) show that there is a higher incidence of high, narrow, arched palates amongst mentally deficient patients.

Whilst the chief problem of an unrepaired (or unsuccessfully repaired) cleft of the hard and/or soft palates is excessive nasal resonance, the presence of an incompetent palato-pharyngeal sphincter may also give rise to defective articulation, characterized by nasal escape on consonant sounds, and in some cases sound distortions, omissions, and substitutions. Many of the latter represent the child's attempt to compensate, however inadequately, for the physiologically inefficient mechanism with which he was born. For example, being unable to build up sufficient oral air pressure for plosive consonants such as *p* and *t*, he will produce the sound at a level where air pressure can be built up and then released – that is, below the level of the closed glottis, producing the glottal stop sound which is such a characteristic feature of the speech of some cleft palate patients.

Other children articulate consonants in the correct position, but due to nasal escape of air and inadequate oral pressure, plosive, fricative, and affricate sounds are weak and even inaudible. Nasal escape may be gross, so that speech is virtually unintelligible. Where nasal escape is less severe, speech will be intelligible, but with marked nasal resonance and characteristic nasal grimace on speaking.

Dental irregularities may also be present, associated with a unilateral or bilateral cleft of alveolus and lip. These will all contribute to the child's difficulties in producing normal patterns of articulation.

(3) *Dysarthria.* This is a disorder of articulation due to a breakdown in the control and co-ordination of the muscular movements of tongue, lips, jaw, and palate required for speech. There may be a gross disturbance of articulation in cases of ataxic, athetoid, or spastic forms of cerebral palsy. On the other hand, there may be a dysarthria associated with quite minimal motor disability, or even in the absence of other neurological signs. Morley (1957) has given a

most comprehensive account of developmental dysarthria, and other disorders of articulation.

Any lesion affecting the innervation of the tongue and other muscles of articulation (jaw, lips, and palate) will result in dysarthric speech. There are many neuropathologies in which speech may be affected: bilateral upper motor neurone lesions (e.g. pseudo-bulbar palsy); lesions of the basal nuclei or ganglia (e.g. Parkinsonian syndrome, chorea, and athetosis); cerebellar lesions (e.g. ataxic dysarthria, disseminated sclerosis); bulbar lesions (e.g. chronic bulbar palsy, bulbar form of poliomyelitis); myopathies (e.g. Myasthenia gravis).

Obviously, there will be a group of mentally retarded patients whose defective articulation and mental retardation have a common aetiological background. Very careful examination and investigation should be made to determine the cause of articulatory defects in the mentally retarded (or indeed normal) child. To label speech as 'typically mentally defective' is to risk overlooking a possibly neurologically based disorder. In the absence of obvious neurological signs, the parent may report difficulties in sucking, chewing, and swallowing, and examination may reveal poorly co-ordinated and limited movement of the articulators.

In cases of mongolism, the tongue may be abnormally large in relation to the oral cavity, giving rise to clumsy and indistinct articulation. Macroglossia is not, however, an inevitable concomitant of this condition, and many mongols have surprisingly good speech. Tongue-tie, popularly regarded as the cause of many speech defects, is a relatively uncommon condition, and seldom found in the cases referred for speech correction.

(4) *Dyspraxia*. Dyspraxic dysarthria (Morley, 1957) is a defect of articulation in which the patient has difficulty in initiating and organizing the complex movements required for speech, in the absence of any muscular paralysis. The degree of difficulty experienced may vary greatly, and may show itself in a tendency for articulation to deteriorate to a marked extent in connected speech, whilst isolated sounds and words may be produced correctly.

(5) *Hearing loss*. Hearing loss must be considered in terms of its effect on language development, the articulatory pattern, and on the pitch, volume, and quality of voice.

The effects of impaired hearing on speech will depend on the type of hearing loss, the severity of that loss, and the age of onset. A congenital high-frequency deafness, for example, will mean that certain sounds (e.g. *s*, *sh*, and *t*) will not be perceived, and will therefore not be incorporated into the speech pattern. The child born with a very profound hearing loss will, in the absence of special training, fail to develop speech at all.

Research undertaken by Foale and Paterson (1954) at Lennox Castle Institution showed that 13 per cent. of 100 feeble-minded boys given audiometric tests showed hearing loss sufficient to 'handicap them in ordinary life activities'. They compare these findings with the figure of 6 per cent. in Scottish (normal) schools, and from 5·17 per cent. to 8·35 per cent. as the incidence of all grades of deafness in schools in England and Wales. The same authors quote the investigation of Birch and Matthews (with rather lower grade boys) at Polk State School in the United States. They found an even higher incidence of deafness (32·7 per cent.). Foale and Paterson conclude that, 'Impaired hearing may be a contributory factor in low scoring in intelligence tests and a person carrying out psychometric tests should be alert for signs of such impairment, particularly when the subject being tested has an articulatory speech defect.' Of the child with high-frequency deafness, they remark that he is

> most handicapped by his inability to appreciate fully the finer shades of meaning in spoken language. He has to rely more on context and is handicapped in anything which relies on spoken explanation and he, therefore, can become educationally retarded, show inadequate responses to social situations, and have only a limited vocabulary. Handicapped as he is, he may well become emotionally unstable because he is less able to cope with his environment. The clinical picture is thus similar to that found in feeble-mindedness.

Kodman (1958) in a recent survey of data on hearing loss amongst the mentally retarded says, 'The results agree in one direction; namely, that the incidence of hearing loss amongst mentally retarded children is significantly greater than the incidence of loss among our public school children.' He goes on to predict that 'improved testing techniques and uniformity in reporting the results will find the incidence of 30 db. or greater losses among the mentally retarded to be three to four times that found in our public school children'.

Perception deafness sometimes occurs as a concomitant of such conditions as cerebral palsy and mongolism, and as a sequela of disease such as meningitis. Conduction deafness amongst mentally deficient patients may result from parental neglect of chronic middle-ear infections.

B. Articulation disorders of functional origin

'Functional' is here used in the widest possible sense, to include those disorders of emotional origin, as well as those due to learning of deviant articulation patterns. Curtis (1948) comments,

> Most articulatory deviations seem to be traceable to no other cause than a simple failure to learn the correct patterns of normal speech. For various reasons incorrect habits have been formed and have become strongly established. The ordinary environmental pressures of home, community, and school do not seem to be sufficient to counteract them and replace them with habits which make for accepted normal speech.

Many of these cases are probably due to a combination of several factors, only a few of which can be mentioned here: Parents and older siblings who are defective and/or rapid speakers, may provide poor speech models for the child to imitate; short auditory memory span and/or poor auditory discrimination may handicap the child in discriminating between sounds of similar acoustic character, and in analysing the component parts of the sound pattern which constitutes a word; the speech defect may reflect emotional immaturity in an over-dependent and protected child.

Disorders of voice

Voice disorders may be characterized by abnormalities of pitch, volume, or quality, and may be either organic or psychogenic in origin.

A. Organic disorders

Pathological conditions of the larynx, or of the nerve supply to the larynx (the recurrent laryngeal nerves), will affect phonation. Only those conditions where speech therapy is indicated will be considered here.

The speech therapist is concerned with those cases where the organic changes (e.g. chronic laryngitis, nodules on the vocal cords) are felt to be the direct result of continuous vocal misuse and abuse. Speech therapy is also indicated where the dysphonia is part of an extensive lesion involving both phonation and articulation (e.g. cerebral palsy, Parkinsonian syndrome), and, finally, where there is a lesion producing a unilateral recurrent laryngeal paralysis affecting the movement of one vocal cord.

Hoarseness of voice is often found in the mongoloid patient – it may also be unusually deep in pitch. This is presumably due to some morphological abnormality in the structure of the larynx, but the presence of nerve deafness (another concomitant of mongolism in some cases) will contribute to the abnormal voice. Deafness will also account for intensity disorders and lack of normal inflection patterns.

B. Functional disorders

In this sense, functional is confined to those disorders of voice directly resulting from misuse and abuse, but without the organic changes. The patient, frequently a professional voice user, may complain of vocal fatigue, discomfort in the region of the larynx, and loss of voice after prolonged use. Deafness, with its effects on pitch, volume and quality of voice production, can be considered as a cause of functional voice disorder.

C. Psychogenic

A bilateral adductor paralysis of the vocal cords is almost always a sign of a dysphonia of psychogenic or hysterical origin. The patient may show great generalized and localized tension, and as a result of this, complains of strain and fatigue on talking.

Disorders of resonance

A. Insufficient Nasal Resonance. This may occur where some form of nasal obstruction (e.g. adenoids, chronic catarrh) results in an inadequate airway. This may lead to mouth breathing and characteristic 'cold in the nose' speech. Not only will the production of the nasal consonants (*m*, *n*, and *ng*) be difficult, but vowel quality will also be affected.

B. Excessive Nasal Resonance. This condition has already been discussed at some length under Cleft Palate, but there are several other causes of the same speech condition: sub-mucous cleft; a short soft palate associated with a congenitally large pharynx; paresis of the soft palate associated with a developmental dysarthria (this often occurs in cerebral palsy); paralysis of the palate following an infective lesion such as bulbar poliomyelitis.

Excessive nasal resonance may be a temporary, or in a few cases a more permanent sequel to adenoidectomy. Occasionally, the presence of a large adenoid pad makes normal speech possible where the child would otherwise be unable to make adequate closure between the soft palate and the posterior wall of the pharynx. Removal of the adenoids in these cases results in a sudden deterioration in speech, with gross nasal escape. Where the adenoid pad has *prevented* full movement of the palate, and the sphincter mechanism is otherwise adequate, the nasal escape results from a purely functional condition, and speech should improve rapidly and spontaneously. Caution should be exercised, however, in carrying out routine removal of adenoids in association with tonsillectomy, particularly in cases of successfully repaired cleft palate, or where there is any evidence of a sub-mucous cleft.

Delay or failure in speech development

A. Mental retardation

In cases of gross intellectual deficiency (i.e. idiots), the patient is unlikely ever to develop meaningful speech. He may acquire a vocabulary of a few familiar words, and even understand simple commands, but he will not use speech as a means of communication in any real sense. In some low-grade defectives 'there may be an excessive flow of words, but the thought content is elementary, frequently irrelevant, and the vocabulary is limited' (Morley, 1957). Of 32 idiots examined, Kennedy (1930) found that 20 were mute, 10 'jabbered' with an occasional intelligent word, one showed echolalia, and one had irrelevant speech.

Various investigators have shown that the age at which children first begin to use words and sentences is directly related to intelligence, and general mental retardation is probably the most common single factor in speech retardation. However, only in cases of gross intellectual deficiency would it be true to say that mental retardation is responsible for failure to develop speech at all.

Imbeciles vary considerably in their language ability, and much will depend on the stimulation provided by their environmental background. They show a very marked delay in the acquisition of speech: Wallin (1949) found that they used their first words at 2 years 3 months, and their first sentences at 3 years 7 months on the average. They will be unable to comprehend complex commands, and will experience difficulty in formulating sentences for narrative purposes – in describing a picture for example. Attempts may be telegrammatic in form, but they can communicate, and may 'converse' on a simple, concrete level. Vocabulary is limited to words within their more immediate physical environment.

Feeble-minded children may use normal sentence construction, but may always prove to be linguistically inadequate in giving complex explanations. Onset of first words and sentences may be retarded, but much of their later verbal limitations may be the result of a restricted language background. This is particularly true where the Familial group is concerned.

B. Hearing loss

If hearing loss is sufficiently profound, and is either congenital or acquired before the development of speech, then speech and language will fail to develop once the babbling stage has passed. The child may learn to lip-read and understand simple and familiar speech without special training, but will be able to communicate himself solely through gesture and sub-linguistic utterances. Should speech fail to develop, then the possibility of hearing loss should be investigated as early as possible. Unfortunately, deafness is often not suspected, so that the most critical period for listening to and learning speech may be lost (Fry and Whetnall, 1964). Once again, the importance of early investigation and careful differential diagnosis cannot be over-stressed – not only because of the importance of early auditory training, but also because of the danger of incorrectly labelling the child as mentally defective. This is particularly true of the child with high-frequency deafness (Foale and Patterson, 1954).

C. Aphasia

Aphasia is a disorder of language or symbolization in which the patient fails to comprehend the spoken or written word (receptive or sensory aphasia), or is unable to express himself through language (expressive or motor aphasia). Few cases show an isolated receptive or expressive disturbance, and most patients show some impairment of other language faculties, such as reading (alexia) or writing (agraphia). Aphasia is a comparatively common condition in the middle-aged and elderly, associated with cerebral vascular lesions, but it is symptomatic of any infective or traumatic lesion involving appropriate areas of the cerebral cortex. Associated with these disturbances of language is a condition known as apraxia. Russell Brain (1952) defines apraxia as 'an inability to carry out a purposive movement, the nature of which the patient understands, in the absence of severe motor paralysis, sensory loss, and ataxia'.

Walshe (1952) considers that 'motor aphasia and dysgraphia are but special examples of motor apraxia'. He also says, 'we sometimes encounter a condition in which the subject no longer recognizes the nature or use of a familiar object which he sees perfectly. To this defect the name agnosia is given. Sensory aphasia (word deafness and word blindness) is but a special form of agnosia.'

In mental deficiency, and in considering delay or failure in speech development, we are naturally much more interested in developmental aphasia. Mykelbust (1957) mentions anoxia, Rh incompatibility, rubella, cerebral haemorrhage due to birth injury, and encephalopathic diseases such as meningitis and encephalitis, as the most common aetiological factors in aphasia in children. Aphasia may or may not be associated with mental retardation. Receptive aphasia is believed to be an uncommon condition in children, but varying degrees of expressive aphasia may be more common than we realize. This is particularly true of the condition known as word blindness or dyslexia. The possibility of aphasia should always be considered where a child shows an atypical or patchy performance on intelligence tests, performing well on performance tests, but showing a markedly lower score on verbal tests. West (1957) has said, 'The striking thing about the aphasic is the disparity between his language associations and the rest of his mental processes; his power to associate experiences is relatively normal, except for those which have only arbitrary and symbolic meanings.' He continues, 'He thinks in terms of real objects. Words are abstractions; they constitute a type of association with which he cannot deal.'

D. Lack of stimulation and motivation

Cases are sometimes referred for treatment where speech has failed to develop in the absence of any apparent mental retardation, organic cause, or emotional disturbance. Such cases may occur when the young child is left alone a great deal, and generally deprived of human contact. On the other hand, the need for speech may never be created if parents are over-solicitous and anticipate the child's every need. As Van Riper (1952) says, 'The law of least effort is a rather fundamental determinant of human effort, and when children can get their wishes fulfilled without employing speech, they never acquire this all-important tool.'

Deprivation of affection and maternal care (such as may result in the case of children from institutions and large families) may be a very potent factor in the delayed acquisition of speech. The deprived child has little stimulation or motivation to acquire speech, and may therefore be very backward in learning to talk. Nisbet (1953) has already been quoted in this chapter on the relation of family size to verbal ability, and he also mentions the verbal retardation of institutionalized children.

Ainsworth (1962) has said: 'The specific aspects more seriously affected by continuing deprivation have been found repeatedly to be in language and social development.' The whole question of deprivation and its effect on language, and in turn the possible effects on intellectual growth, suggests the importance of a comprehensive and systematic programme of language training.

E. Emotional disturbance

Emotional conflict or trauma may be responsible for a child's mutism. There are many possible causes of such conflict which cannot be enumerated here, but which careful investigation of the child's background may reveal. A negative attitude towards speech, with a complete refusal to make any speech attempt, may result when a mentally retarded child is over-stimulated by demanding or ambitious parents.

Failure to develop speech, or failure to use speech meaningfully (or to make any attempt at communication), may be symptomatic of psychosis in children. They may exhibit echolalia, in which the whole or last part of speech addressed to them is echoed without apparent understanding or meaning.

There are many practical problems in making a differential diagnosis between autism and mental deficiency. The subnormal child who has been rejected, or who, through institutionalization, has been emotionally deprived in the early years, may also present a picture of emotional disturbance. If sufficiently severe, this may lead to the problem of non-communication. The psychotic child tends to regress to infantile or lower levels of behaviour, which may make accurate assessment of aetiology even more difficult.

Any delay in speech development, or failure to develop adequate language as the child grows older, may be due to a complex aetiology in which two or more physical, intellectual, or emotional factors may be involved. Any of the conditions outlined above may be associated with varying degrees of mental retardation. The label 'mentally defective' may well obscure the child's need for special help with specific language difficulties or emotional problems.

Cerebral palsy

The aetiological background of this condition has already been fully discussed in Chapter X, and so will not be mentioned here. It has been estimated that from 60 to 70 per cent. of the cerebral palsied have some type of speech involvement. Where there are difficulties in sucking, chewing, and swallowing, and there is inco-ordination of the movements of respiration, we may well expect phonation to be uncontrolled and speech to be dysarthric. Whilst dysarthria is generally the most obvious and severe speech problem, the speech therapist may find associated language difficulties, and sensory defects affecting speech.

There is a fairly high incidence of deafness associated with cerebral palsy, particularly of the perceptive type, which will obviously have an adverse affect on the acquisition of both language and normal articulation. In some cases, there may be evidence to suggest a developmental aphasia. Language will also tend to be retarded where severe physical handicaps have resulted in a limited environment and consequently limited experience.

Any attempt at speech may precipitate athetoid movements, or the patient may go into spasm, even when passive movements are attempted. Inco-ordination of respiration and phonation will affect the voice. West, Kennedy, and Carr (1947), describing phonation, say, 'The voice lacks flexibility, resonance and control; instead of a well-modulated, even flow of voice, erratic intensity and sudden pitch changes occur irregularly.'

Stammering

The aetiological background of stammering has been, and still is, the subject of much conjecture, experimental research, and controversy. Many authorities regard stammering as symptomatic of an emotional disturbance, and believe that a transference of symptoms will result if the disorder is treated symptomatically and the basic conflict not resolved. Other authorities believe that stammering is caused by an underlying neurological diathesis, and is associated with a lack of unilateral cerebral dominance. It has been suggested in connexion with the same theory that the stammerer's basic hesitancy arises from poorly timed nervous impulses reaching the paired speech musculature from the integrating centres of the central nervous system.

Attempts have been made to associate stammering with a breakdown in the feed-back chain of the speech servo-system. Most of this work has, in the past, shown support for the claim for an organic aetiology. When the problem is viewed from a broader observation of stammering behaviour, however, there are many features which tend to suggest a functional rather than neuropathic breakdown in organization.

Wendell Johnson (1944, 1948, 1957) holds the view that stammering arises from the natural hesitations and repetitions found in the young child's speech. Should these be misinterpreted and become the object of undue attention or social penalty, through the emotional effect they have upon others, then the child may, in turn, learn to react as if there is some real defect in his speech.

Primary stammering, occurring in the young child as yet unaware of any speech difference, is characterized by comparatively easy repetitions and prolongations of the initial sounds or syllables of random words. The child or adult who has learnt to react emotionally towards speech in general, and situations, words, or sounds in particular, develops blocking behaviour involving a blind effort designed to produce speech. This frequently entails an unconscious closure of the vocal cords robbing him of air supply and voice. He ceases his interference either to replenish his lungs or with the satisfaction that he has tried for as long as is necessary. He is immediately rewarded by the production of the word, convincing him that 'trying' works. In his struggle for speech, the stammerer may show concomitant movements of the speech musculature, head, trunk, and limbs, resolutely believing these to be an essential part of 'getting the word out'. Far from facilitating speech, however, they only add to the abnormality of his behaviour.

The negative attitudes which are a common feature of the secondary stammerer are perhaps more serious than his interference. He will tend to avoid specific words and sounds and withdraw from speaking whenever he feels there is a risk of stammering. His speech contains characteristic interjections or 'back-tracking' (repetition of a word or phrase which has already been uttered in order to procure a running start on the feared word), and other devices designed to hide or minimize his stammer. Fear of speech and stammering increases, and is reinforced by subsequent avoidance. The effect of this fear, which is, in itself, a normal reaction, is the basis of the stammerer's apparently obsessional and ritualistic behaviour. He may show a tendency either to a protective introversion, or a compensatory aggressiveness, still lying, however, in the majority of cases, within the bounds of normal behaviour.

Two of the most significant facts known about stammering are the higher incidence of this disorder in males, and that in most cases the onset of stammering occurs in childhood between the ages of 2 and 5 years, and in almost all cases before the onset of puberty. This means that the symptoms of stammering generally appear before the process of maturation is complete, and when speech might be expected to be particularly prone to such disintegrating factors as emotional or physical shock, severe illness, and anxiety. The ratio of male to female stammerers has been quoted as varying from 3 : 1 to 8 : 1.

Schlanger and Gottsleben (1957) in their survey of speech defects amongst the mentally retarded at the Vineland Training School found that 17 per cent. of the 516 residents examined had a stammer. In the individual aetiological groups considered, the highest incidence was amongst the Mongoloid subjects (45 per cent.). Only 10 per cent. stammered in the Familial group, and 18 per cent. in the organic group.

THERAPY

Special problems

Mental deficiency presents its own special problems in speech therapy which will inevitably affect the prognosis to some extent. Lack of motivation is one of the most important problems to be encountered, and this is particularly true where the patient is institutionalized, or the member of a large family of low social and intellectual status. Conversely, the question of over-stimulation arises where the mentally retarded child has intellectually superior and demanding parents, rendering the child thoroughly negative and unresponsive to all attempts at speech correction.

Far from the mental and physical lethargy popularly associated with mental deficiency, the therapist is often faced with the treatment of an over-active and highly distractible child. In such cases, it may prove extremely difficult to gain and then keep the patient's attention, and it is essential that distracting stimuli should be reduced to the minimum and that optimum conditions for learning should be obtained before therapy is attempted.

Emotional factors, including a tendency to defeatism in many high-grade patients, may make the initial stages of speech correction difficult, but these will tend to become progressively less of a problem as good rapport between therapist and patient is established. Resentment and anxiety may result in a refusal to speak and to co-operate in treatment, or in an exhibition of aggressive behaviour. Whether such problems of behaviour arise will depend to a great extent on the patient's awareness of, and attitudes towards, his mental retardation and/or speech defect. The adjustment of negative attitudes, with consequent reduction of feelings of inferiority, anxiety, and embarrassment, are very much the therapist's concern, and should, wherever the problem occurs, constitute an essential and major part of therapy.

Finally, the patient's mental and/or physical limitations must be considered. Successful therapy can only be carried out where these limitations are properly understood. Otherwise, the resultant failures in reaching unrealistic goals will produce a state of anxiety and frustration which will adversely affect the patient's performance still further. Such a statement may seem to be too obvious to be worthy of mention, but in practice it is too easily forgotten. The recognition of a patient's limitations will save a great deal of 'wear and tear' on patient and therapist alike, by avoiding adverse emotional repercussions during treatment.

Disorders of articulation

Where physical anomalies exist, and are thought to be a contributing factor, patients should be referred for corrective treatment (e.g. orthodontia) wherever possible. Routine hearing tests are always advisable to eliminate the possibility of hearing loss. Where hearing loss is found to be substantial, and felt to be responsible for either the speech defect or educational retardation, the child should be issued with a hearing aid, and furthermore, be taught how to use it. A thorough programme of auditory training should be carried out, in order that the fullest possible use is made of the child's residual hearing.

Exercises for muscular control and co-ordination are only required where there is an obvious impairment of tongue, lip, or jaw movement. Where there is evidence of an articulatory dyspraxia, then visual stimulation through the medium of mirror work will be an essential adjunct to auditory stimulation. Where the patient is able to read, then reading practice may help to establish the correct patterns of movement required for speech (Morley, 1957).

A phonetic assessment of the patient's speech should be made before correction is attempted. The aim of such a speech analysis is to discover which of the speech sounds are omitted, distorted, or have incorrect substitutions – and whether these defects occur both in isolated words or only in connected speech. With the mentally retarded patient it is advisable to commence correction of a sound which can be both seen and heard, and is therefore comparatively easy to imitate. These patients are easily discouraged, and everything must be done to reward their efforts with success. A patient who experiences constant failure, because speech correction work is too difficult, and beyond the scope of his abilities, will soon become discouraged from making any effort at all. Each step must be so carefully graded that the physical and mental effort required in its attainment are kept to a minimum – failure to do so will result in the rapid onset of fatigue, confusion, and anxiety.

The next important stage in treatment is to make the patient aware of his articulation errors. Providing he is sufficiently intelligent to respond to simple instructions, a fairly intensive programme of auditory training should be undertaken. The aim of such training is first to help the patient recognize and discriminate between gross sounds (e.g. money clinking, matches being rattled in a box); secondly, to discriminate between phonically dissimilar speech sounds; thirdly, to hear the difference between acoustically related sounds; and finally, to recognize the difference between errors and the correct pronunciation. Such a training should be fundamental to all speech correction work in disorders of this kind. Providing the patient's attention can be gained, and his interest held, simple hearing training techniques can be very effective. Speech correction, following such auditory training, will tend to proceed far more smoothly and rapidly, and sounds may come spontaneously during this period, even before any direct attempt has been made to elicit them.

Either following on or overlapping with hearing training techniques, the defective or omitted speech sounds must be elicited in isolation. With younger pupils, most of these sounds are obtained through play activities, and it has been found extremely useful to associate speech sounds with some concrete activity or object (thus, *sh* becomes associated with running water for the bath, and *p* is the sound made when blowing out a candle). Such associations help to make the sounds more vivid in the child's mind, and also make the whole business of speech correction more pleasurable and interesting for him. The use of a mirror may prove invaluable in maintaining the mentally deficient child's interest, and so may the provision of his own 'speech book', in which pictures can be drawn and credit stars stuck.

The next step, in which the correct sound is integrated into words obviously cannot proceed until the sound can be produced easily and at will in isolation. It must be stressed that in carrying out speech correction work with the mentally deficient, each step must be firmly consolidated before the next step is attempted, otherwise there is a tendency for any achievements to break down under the pressure of new demands made upon it. This is not to say that patient and therapist should persevere with a new sound until it is absolutely correct, whatever the amount of time and difficulty involved – rather should the therapist move to a different and easier sound, and when this has been achieved or improved, return to the original sound. Correction should proceed as Greene (1955) suggests, 'by horizontal strata rather than by vertical sections. This means that the ground covered must be traversed again and again, each time aiming at a higher level of attainment, but this gives the patient a sense of achievement and raises the whole standard of speech in a very short time.' The aim is achievement, however modest that achievement may be, and it is the therapist's duty so to plan treatment, and modify her methods and approach, that the speech defective has the satisfaction of making some progress each time he comes for treatment.

Perseveration presents a particular problem in the treatment of articulatory defects. It will be found that once a new sound has been elicited and fairly well established, the patient will tend to perseverate in using it when another consonant is being corrected. For this reason, the correction of two phonically similar sounds should never be attempted simultaneously or consecutively.

The use of a tape or disc recorder is an invaluable asset in the treatment of articulation disorders, since the play-back of the recording enables the patient to hear and analyse his defects more objectively. It also provides a useful source of motivation. Van Riper (1952) gives many valuable suggestions for hearing training procedures and other remedial techniques for articulation disorders.

Everything possible should be done to make the learning process as vivid as possible, and to develop the fullest possible use of auditory, visual, and kinaesthetic senses in speech correction.

Disorders of voice

Within the limitations of this chapter, it is not possible to deal more than briefly with the techniques used in the treatment of dysphonia. Voice disorders normally represent a relatively small proportion of those cases referred for speech therapy.

In cases of misuse and abuse, it is essential to give the patient an understanding of the part played by excessive tension in the region of the larynx and thorax, and by poor postural and breathing habits. He must be helped to achieve a good ear for the auditory discrimination of good and poor voice production, and the ability to recognize and correct the sensations of unnecessary tension in the larynx during abnormal phonation. Remedial voice work is given, based on sound acoustic and physiological principles, showing the patient how to achieve the most efficient use of voice with the very minimum of strain and fatigue.

In cases of unilateral paralysis, the aim is to encourage movement of the affected cord if possible, and where this is not possible, to facilitate compensation by the unaffected cord. Where dysphonia is part of a total neurological condition, in which dysarthria may be the main problem, treatment is part of a total plan to improve respiration, phonation, and articulation.

Non-directive counselling (Rogers, 1942) has proved to be an effective approach in the treatment of voice disorders of primarily psychogenic origin. Psychological readjustment is often found to be just as necessary, however, in dysphonias of organic and functional aetiology.

Disorders of resonance

In cases of insufficient nasal resonance due to enlarged adenoids, surgical treatment will be necessary. In some cases, speech therapy may still be necessary after the obstruction has been removed, due to the persistence of poor speech habits, and the continued tendency to mouth breathing.

In the treatment of cases of excessive nasal resonance auditory training is essential if the patient is to discriminate between his faulty voice production and that which is required of him. As Morley (1945) says, 'Not only is the ear of the child becoming accustomed to the sound he hears himself producing, but these abnormal auditory images are being inevitably correlated in his mind with the normal sounds he hears around him, and which he is trying to imitate.'

In cases of cleft palate, the speech therapist's work normally begins where the surgeon's ends. When an unrepaired cleft is encountered, the possibilities of surgical repair should be explored. Should operative treatment not be recommended, the patient may be referred for prosthetic treatment. Following an anatomically and functionally successful repair before the onset of speech, normal speech may develop, and therapy prove unnecessary. The speech therapist is therefore concerned with those cases where surgery has failed to provide a competent palato-pharyngeal sphincter, or where a successful repair was carried out after poor speech habits had been established, and which therefore persist post-operatively. Such cases, in addition to audible nasal escape of air during speech, frequently present errors of articulation. The patient, because of nasal escape which he cannot prevent, is unable to obtain sufficient air pressure to produce plosive and fricative consonants correctly. The problem of speech correction in cleft palate cases may be further complicated by the presence of gross dental irregularities and a short and/or immobile upper lip.

The speech prognosis in cases of an incompetent palato-pharyngeal sphincter has, in the past, been considered poor, but Greene (1955) indicates that good results, and even normal speech, may be obtained in such cases, and she outlines an excellent programme of speech rehabilitation. In considering the factors influencing prognosis in these cases, she rates co-operation in treatment higher than intelligence. This observation is of particular significance in connexion with the possibilities of achieving results with high-grade defectives.

In cases of excessive nasal resonance, due to an incompetent palato-pharyngeal sphincter, speech therapy aims to: stimulate movement of the soft palate as far as possible; encourage oral breath direction, with the minimum of physical effort, and the consequent elimination of the characteristic nasal grimace; correct excessive resonance on vowel sounds, principally through ear-training, and by encouraging more 'open' production of vowel sounds; and finally, correct articulation of consonants, both by reducing nasal escape of air, and by correcting placement of speech sounds (e.g. where glottal stops and pharyngeal fricatives have been substituted for normal consonant sounds).

Delay or failure in speech development

Treatment will obviously depend on the aetiological factors involved in each case. The importance of making a careful differential diagnosis has already been stressed, not only because it is all too easy to blame mental retardation for delayed or inadequate language development, but also because a failure to recognize the real cause may deprive the child of the appropriate treatment or training he needs.

The speech therapist working in the E.S.N. School, the Occupation Centre, or Institution will probably spend as much time on language stimulation and development as on speech correction of articulatory defects. Indeed, it is in encouraging the development and use of language that there is most possibility of achievement. Irwin (1959) has stated that, 'For the mentally defective child the improvement of language is a much more realistic goal than the correction of specific sound defects', and she recommends a programme in which 'improvement in language should take precedence over the correction of specific sounds'.

The possibility of deafness should of course always be investigated. The responsibility for the development of language and the teaching of speech in the deaf child is normally in the hands of the teacher of the deaf, and there are special schools for the child who is both deaf and mentally deficient. Children may be excluded from these schools, however, having failed to make progress or because of behaviour problems, and sent to residential institutions for the mentally deficient, where they then become a problem for the speech therapist. Speech correction presupposes that a child or adult must have some language to correct, therefore the therapist working with the born deaf will be primarily concerned with the acquisition of language, and only secondarily with the teaching of speech.

The speech therapist will need to make the greatest possible use of visual aids, and lip-reading will be taught concurrently with language work. As with aphasics, work begins with the association of words with concrete objects and easily demonstrated activities. A great deal of repetition will be necessary in the initial stages, and the associations must be as vivid as possible. New and more abstract words must be explained within the framework of the language the child already knows. As language increases, so the child becomes more accessible, and behaviour problems tend to decrease. Intellectual development is stimulated as language concepts are acquired and the child becomes more capable of abstract thought.

Any residual hearing present should be developed as far as possible, not only by the issue of a hearing aid but also by a thorough and systematic programme of auditory training. Where hearing loss is profound, the teaching of articulate speech will depend on the use of visual and tactile methods of approach. The intelligibility of the speech obtained will be affected by several variable factors, including the degree of hearing loss, the intelligence of the child, and the age at which speech training commences.

In the treatment of developmental aphasia, whether predominantly expressive or with some associated receptive difficulties, progress will inevitably be very slow, and therapy will necessarily extend over a period of several years. It is impossible here to do more than outline treatment. In view of the complexity of the problem, the rehabilitation programme will need to be very carefully planned to cover all aspects of language function. Basically, the therapist aims to build strong and vivid associations between concrete objects or activities, and the verbal symbols or words which we use for them. Rather than bewilder the child with a wealth of auditory stimuli, the therapist aims to establish a small vocabulary of familiar words. The whole speech situation is built up round the new word: for example, 'Give me the ball. Throw the ball. Catch the ball.' Abstractions are avoided, and the initial stages of therapy are based upon the most concrete material. Nouns and verbs are taught first, and only as language begins to develop are more abstract language concepts taught.

In the case of the physically neglected and emotionally deprived child, every effort should be made so to adjust the environment that his physical and emotional needs are satisfied. The therapist can do much to help parents provide home conditions which will facilitate the optimum development of language within the framework of the child's mental ability and his level of physical maturation. Parents need an acceptance and understanding of the child's limitations, and an awareness of his need for additional stimulation and encouragement. He must be treated as a 'belonging' member of the family unit, in which he may feel loved and secure. He needs an environmental background in which he is exposed to (but not bombarded by) rich and varied sensory experience. He needs, far more than the normal child, to be played with and talked to, and must experience success at his own level of attainment. His speech attempts, however poor and late these may be, must be received with pleasure and approval if further attempts are to be made. The therapist must help the critical and demanding parents to accept their child's limitations, and to realize how much their attitude is responsible for the child's lack of speech attempt.

Goda (1960) has given an interesting account of very early sound and language stimulation in non-speaking children, and says, 'Speech stimulation methods for each of these children should be consistent with his or her level of development.'

The therapist may work with these children individually, or in small groups matched for chronological and mental age, and for the type of language difficulty presented. A group has the advantage of simulating a more natural social situation; it creates a greater need for speech; and the therapist may make good use of the competitive element inherent in it.

Where the environment provides little stimulus for speech (e.g. in an institution) the therapist must endeavour to create a need for speech; help build the vocabulary and language to meet this need; and give adequate praise and encouragement when speech is attempted, however inadequate that attempt may be. Within the confines of the institution she must be responsible for increasing the child's experience as far as possible (by taking him shopping, or for a bus ride).

Where the child has been subjected to too much pressure to acquire speech, she must be undemanding in her approach. Once he recognizes that no demands are being made on him, and that his speech attempts, however poor, are accepted without adverse comment (or even with enthusiasm), then he will begin to explore the possibilities of using speech as a means of communication.

Cerebral palsy

The first aim in treatment is to establish correct feeding habits as far as possible, since little can be done to improve speech until this has been done. It is also important to correct head and neck posture, and movements of respiration in the early stages of treatment.

Bobath and Bobath (1952) have described the reflex inhibiting postures in which the cerebral palsied child may experience normal muscle tone, and in which movement, active or passive, may be carried out with a minimum of interference by abnormal spasm or involuntary movement. Accounts of the application of this approach in the field of speech therapy have been given by Marland (1953) and Parker (1957). Phelps (1958) has described the Bobath technique as well as other methods of physical therapy in the treatment of cerebral palsy.

General relaxation is also widely used, and the therapist normally works from facilitated or assisted movements of vocalized babbling, so that the child may experience some of the sensations of normal effortless speech.

Cerebral palsy is an extremely specialized field, and speech therapy is always part of a total programme of physical treatment. Many therapists have evolved their own approach to the problems encountered, through clinical practice and their associations with other workers (e.g. Physiotherapists and Occupational Therapists).

Stammering

The treatment of the young primary stammerer, as yet unaware of any speech abnormality, is entirely indirect. We are anxious that, as far as possible, he should remain unaware of his easy prolongations and repetitions as a definite and socially penalized handicap. Any states or situations which tend to precipitate or increase stammering (such as fatigue, excitement, and anxiety) should be avoided, so that the amount of stammering is reduced to a minimum. Emotional conflicts which are felt to be responsible for either the onset or the maintenance of the stammer must be removed or resolved as far as possible. It is essential to gain the co-operation of parents, relatives, teachers, and others in the child's environment in order to see that the stammer is not commented upon in front of the child, and that he is not made the object of such misguided advice as, 'Take a deep breath before you speak.' Every effort must be made to avoid thoughtless social penalties (such as mimicry) by other children. The chances of the child 'outgrowing' his stammer will be greatly increased if he can thus be prevented from developing attitudes of anxiety and embarrassment in relation to his speech. Such attitudes result in an attempt to prevent, hide, or disguise his stammer, and so lead to the development of those secondary symptoms which characterize the speech of the older child, the adolescent, and the adult stammerer.

A direct approach is employed with the adult stammerer and the child who is already aware of his stammering. Tongue exercises, articulation drills, and breathing control play no part in present-day therapy. The technique of relaxation still enjoys a certain measure of popularity and success. It involves teaching the stammerer to control tension in the body. The resultant increase in fluency is pointed out to him. He learns this in a permissive atmosphere, and often finds the principle difficult to apply in the everyday situations which he fears.

A more radical approach, influenced by certain American authorities, has been evolved in recent years. It is basically a symptomatic therapy, directed at the specific interference carried out by the stammerer, and seeks to secure the development of insight into the feelings and beliefs which underlie his behaviour. It is carried out preferably with groups of stammerers, as this presents far more opportunities of communicative interaction than individual work. With the support of the group, the stammerer is enabled to enter situations and communicate instead of avoiding speech. He is encouraged to accept his stammering instead of attempting to deny it; to discuss it, rather than pretend it does not exist.

An objective attitude is engendered by study of the characteristics of stammering behaviour, both from a physiological and psychological point of view. When the stammerer has lost his worst fears of speech, he can begin to learn to modify his blocking. During his struggle he must become aware of what is happening. He must ask, 'Is it really possible to produce normal speech in this way?'

He begins to reject his interference, and finds that it is unnecessary. As he gradually learns to react calmly to his blocks, and to control his speech behaviour, the stammerer gains immeasurably in confidence, and his whole attitude towards his speech, and his audience, becomes more objective and less emotional. With this improvement in attitude, the blocks gradually decrease in frequency and severity. Whenever blocking does occur, he knows how to handle those blocks, and to reject his old, struggling reaction in favour of a normal approach to the feared word. He has learned that certain sounds and words are only difficult because he fears them and approaches them abnormally.

SUMMARY

It is recognized that speech and language are essential to the individual's intellectual and emotional development. Therefore, any impairment of speech and language functions, which prevents communication and the satisfaction of his emotional and physical needs, will tend to produce maladjustment and behaviour deviations. Furthermore, the absence of language concepts will hinder abstract thought, and prevent the individual from functioning at his highest potential mental level.

Current research in the field of mental deficiency has encouraged a more optimistic view of the possibilities of speech rehabilitation, and indicate that speech therapy should be available as part of the total training programme for the mentally retarded patient. Certainly, no patient should be denied treatment simply because he bears the label 'mentally deficient', since he may subsequently prove to have a much higher mental potential, and since the speech disorder itself may be largely, or in part, responsible for his mental retardation.

A great deal of carefully planned research is still needed to investigate the fullest possibilities and best use of speech therapy in mental deficiency. Comparatively little has been written on the subject, although there are signs of an increasing interest in, and awareness of, the special problems of the speech defective who is also mentally deficient.

Chapter XVII

LONGITUDINAL AND FOLLOW-UP STUDIES

by J. Tizard

INTRODUCTION

Interest in longitudinal and follow-up studies of the mentally deficient derives from several sources. Parents, medical statisticians, and physicians are interested in the expectation of life of persons suffering from different diseases or handicaps. Teachers want to know how much of the skills taught at school is retained, and what use is made of them. The effect on social competence of education and training is of obvious importance to those responsible for planning training programmes, and decisions about when to recommend institutional care, and under what circumstances should leave from institutions be granted, must clearly be influenced by what has happened in the past to other mental defectives. Concern has also been shown over the dysgenic implications of mental defect, and, more recently, over the social competence of the mentally subnormal as parents. In much of the literature these problems have not been treated separately, so that the total picture is a confusing one.

EXPECTATION OF LIFE OF IDIOTS AND IMBECILES

It has been shown by Penrose (1938) and others, that idiots and imbeciles are born to parents who approximate to the general population in social status and mental ability. Idiots themselves, and the great majority of imbeciles, are not fecund, and for social reasons those imbeciles who are fecund are rarely fertile.[1] Low-grade defectives thus give rise to no dysgenic problems. The problems of family planning which the parents of a mentally deficient child face are outside the scope of this book (see Penrose, 1949, and Hilliard and Kirman, 1965, for a discussion of them).

Little is known about the expectation of life of low-grade defectives in the general population, and we are therefore obliged to rely largely on longevity studies made of institutional populations. These are unsatisfactory for a number of reasons: hospitalized defectives include an unduly high number of gross and seriously ill cases; the standard of institutional care compares in general unfavourably with that given to defectives living at home, and infectious diseases are more common; cases are admitted to institutions at different ages; finally, in the published studies standardized death rates related to the vital statistics of the general population have usually not been worked out.

Figure 8 compares the cumulative death rate per thousand deaths, by age, up to age 60, of idiots and imbeciles who died in institutions in England and Wales in 1956 with the corresponding proportion of the general population who died in the same year. More than one-quarter of all idiot deaths occurred in patients under the age of 5 years, and nearly half the deaths were of children less than 10. Among the imbeciles one-quarter of the deaths occurred before the age of 20 and one-half before the age of 40. In the general population, on the other hand three-quarters of all deaths occur *after* the age of 60; and half of them occur in people who are aged 73 or more. The data given in Fig. 9, which are taken from the Registrar General's Statistical Review of England and Wales for the year 1956, and from the Registrar General's Supplement on Mental Health 1954–6, illustrate the close relationship between physical disease and defect on the one hand and severe mental (behavioural) subnormality on the other. The figures for the subnormals, which are for institutional cases only, underestimate the numbers dying in infancy, since many babies with congenital malformations with associated central nervous system damage which would result in severe mental defect die before going into hospital and are included among the deaths in the general population. Pence *et al.* (1961), Kramer *et al.* (1957), and Dayton (1931) have discussed this problem; and ongoing research at Pacific

[1] The term 'fecundity' is applied to the ability of a person to produce children; the number of children born to a person indicates their fertility.

State Hospital, Ponoma, California, under Harvey Dingman, should contribute greatly to our knowledge of 'population movements' of mental defectives.

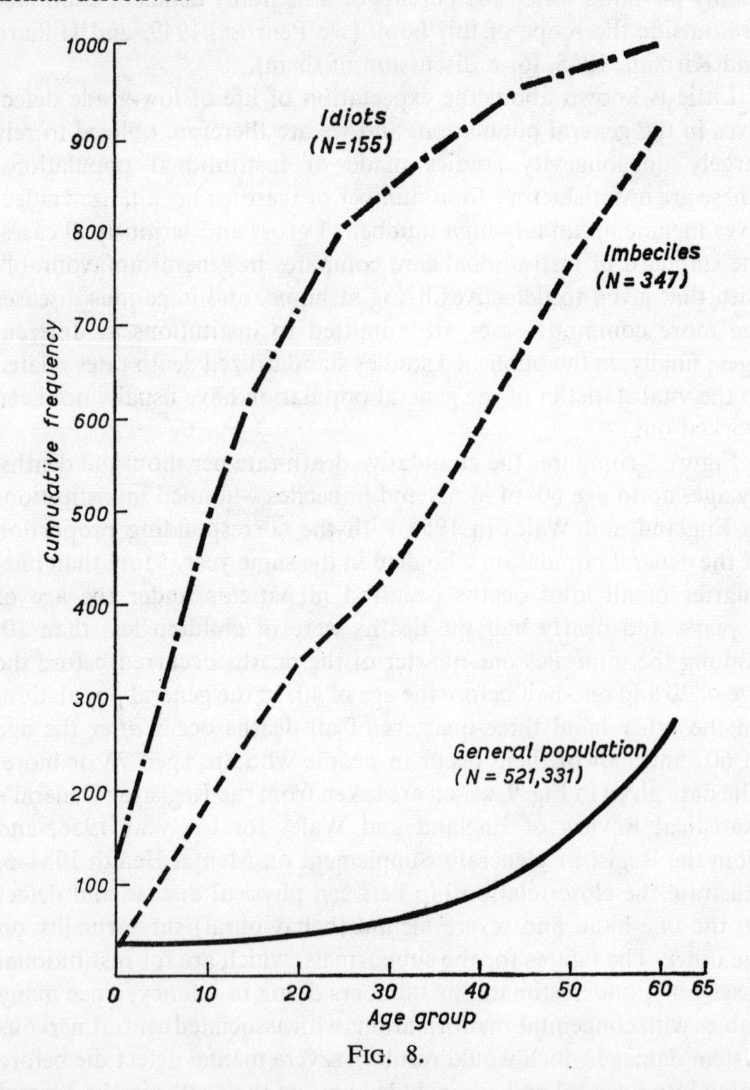

FIG. 8.

Special interest attaches to mongolism because of its high incidence (one in every 600 to 700 live births), and the ease with which the condition can be diagnosed. A study carried out by Carter (1958), which is described in more detail in Chapter II, has indicated that in the London area at the present time 30 per cent. of live-born mongols are dead by the age of one month, 53 per cent. by one year, and 60 per cent. by 10 years. The expectation of survival to the age of 10 years doubled between 1929 and 1949, and doubled again between 1949 and 1958.

These data suggest that the life-span of *all* low-grade defectives born alive is probably increasing. If the numbers born alive remained stable over the years (or perhaps even increased, since the still-birth rate has declined somewhat in the last 30 years) the number surviving would have increased very markedly. There is, however, little evidence that such an increase has in fact taken place except as far as mongolism and possibly a few rare, genetically determined conditions are concerned. Thus in a recent study Goodman and Tizard (1962) attempted to assess the prevalence of mental defect in Middlesex and to compare it with findings obtained by E. O. Lewis (1929) for England and Wales. These writers concluded that the evidence supported the belief that, mongolism excepted, there had been a decline of something like one-third in the prevalence of severe mental defect in children. The data are, however, suggestive rather than conclusive and further studies are needed (Tizard, 1964). If they confirm this finding they would suggest that the public health measures which have brought about a striking fall in infant mortality have also served to reduce morbidity, as Pasamanick has argued in a series of papers (e.g. Knobloch and Pasamanick, 1962). Because the criteria of severe mental defect are, however, uncertain, and one can never be sure that case-finding is complete, it would still be open to anyone to argue that any changes found were entirely due to differences in criteria, or to administrative arrangements, though such arguments would not, in the present writer's opinion, be wholly convincing. Moreover whatever the truth of the matter as far as the biological problem is concerned, there is no evidence that the size of the *administrative* problem has increased, or is increasing. If anything it is decreasing as social services improve – at least as far as children are concerned.

THE SOCIAL COMPETENCE OF LOW-GRADE DEFECTIVES

To be able to assess the long-term effects of education, or training, and to plan suitable occupation and welfare services for adult imbeciles, information is needed about the numbers of imbeciles who survive to adult life, and about the kind of lives they lead. Surprisingly little information, however, exists at present about older defectives who remain at home. A paper by Evans and Carter (1954) describes the problem of management of mongols referred to a children's hospital, but their cases were mainly children at the time the investigation was carried out. A study by Delp and Lorenz (1953) of children who had attended a 'Beta class' or occupation centre, is one of the very few which describes the after careers of adult imbeciles. The investigation was concerned with 84 children, all with I.Q.s under 50, who had at one time attended an occupation centre in St Paul, Minnesota. Of the 84, 41 were living at home, and 25 in institutions at the time of the inquiry. Nine of the other 18 had died, and the remainder had moved out of the state. The information reported refers to those in the first two categories, the majority of whom appear to be classifiable as high-grade imbeciles.

At the time of the investigation the median age of the defectives was 22 years, and the median time they had spent in the Beta class was nearly 5 years. The median I.Q. was 36. Three subjects had I.Q.s probably below 25 and three had I.Q.s above 50. Twelve of the home sample had shown changes in I.Q. of 5 or more points; three rose in I.Q. (25 points, 19 points and 5 points), while the remaining 9 lost in I.Q. from 8 to 18 points. Of the 25 institution cases 4 rose in I.Q. between 5 and 18 points, and 9 lost between 6 and 17 points.

Referring to social adjustment, the authors say that most of the subjects were well accepted in their neighbourhoods. One avoided people, 3 were not accepted by their families, and 10 were 'tolerated'. The other 27 fitted in well. Seventeen subjects were able to move about their neighbourhood freely, with no supervision, and 7 went about the city, using public transport. Only 9 cases were seldom out of doors. In speech, 20 were rated good or very good, 12 as understandable, and 7 as having little or no speech. The remaining 6 were not interviewed. Of the 25 institution cases 16 were sufficiently better adjusted than the average to have caused some notice by the institution authorities. The speech of the institution cases was much poorer than that of the home cases, 12 having little or no speech.

Twenty of the subjects were able to do some writing and printing and 3 to write simple letters to friends. Although it is normally considered impossible to teach such children to read for enjoyment, one subject with a I.Q. of 42 read children's stories up to first-grade level of difficulty, while another of I.Q. 40 read 'serial type books' with fair comprehension. Three others read pre-primers, four more were interested in comics and household magazines, and three others read enough to be able to follow weather reports, photograph captions, and theatre, radio, and T.V. programmes in the paper. For those in institutions few magazines or books were available, and they had fewer opportunities for cards, jigsaw puzzles, and other household games enjoyed by the home sample.

One-quarter of the group suffered from respiratory illness, and one-fifth had had accidents serious enough to require medical attention. Thirty-one of the 41 home cases needed no help in dressing, and the majority chose their own clothing to wear each morning, and helped to purchase their own things. Thirty-five of these children had good table manners. Of the institution cases 15 were able to dress themselves.

A final section deals with occupational status. Of the males, 10 were gainfully employed, 2 on full-time jobs, 3 with regular part-time jobs, and 5 doing odd jobs. One earned $145 a month as a hospital janitor, and had been employed for nine years on the job. A further 25 of the home cases did worth-while jobs round the home, and in only two instances did the parents say that the tasks were given just to keep the defective busy. In 23 of these cases the jobs were done with little or no supervision. Of the 25 institution cases, 11 were able to perform useful tasks such as doing the dishes, scrubbing, making beds, and so on, and 6 were paid for their useful work.

Very much more striking findings, because they are based on much larger numbers of unselected cases, are reported by the City of Birmingham (1956) in the Annual Report of the Special Services After-Care Sub-Committee of the Education Committee. They present a table showing among other data the employment of those who as children had been excluded from school as ineducable prior to 1956. Table 27 summarizes these data.

No fewer than 20 per cent. of these formerly 'ineducable' children (who presumably include a small number of psychotic or severely maladjusted children in addition to imbeciles and idiots) were in gainful employment at the end of 1956. Unfortunately few further details are given about them, or about the employment they are following and the problems they and their families face. The data are remarkable, however, in showing how many severely handicapped adults are employable when there is a plentiful supply of work and an efficient

TABLE 27

Summary of cases excluded from school prior to 1956

	M.	F.	M. & F.	%
At home and gainfully employed	158	74	232	20·3
At home and not gainfully employed	425	438	863	75·4
In homes, hospitals, etc., during 1956	28	21	49	4·3
TOTALS, 1956	611	533	1,144	100·0

after-care service. (Even before the war the City of Birmingham was able to place 10 per cent. of the 'ineducables' in gainful employment.)

Another large and well-documented study is that by Saenger (1957, 1960) who interviewed the parents of a carefully selected sample of 520 severely retarded adults who had attended classes for 'trainable retarded' in New York. He gives the best documented picture we have of the factors influencing the health and adjustment of a large sample of mentally retarded adults. In general his conclusions support those of Delp and Lorenz, but are more detailed. His study is described on p. 502. Of 60 imbeciles and idiots over 16 years of age who formed part of a large inquiry undertaken by Dr J. C. Grad and the writer (Tizard and Grad, 1961), 5 had full-time jobs with a regular wage; 3 had casual employment; 21 were useful at home, and 31, including 8 idiots, did nothing or only minor household tasks. These studies suggest that while we still have no clear conception of the potentialities of adult imbeciles, at least 10 per cent. and probably more may be capable of earning a living in the community. Others can work in sheltered employment, given suitable conditions. It is also apparent that imbeciles continue to develop in personality and in social competence until adulthood. Further studies are needed to show the course of this development and the factors that influence it (see also Chapter XIII).

Apart from intelligence, little is known about personality qualities and their development. Does motor proficiency, for example, mature along with mental age? What is the relation between emotional development and general cognitive development, and how do these change with age? Is there a critical age during which imbecile children are particularly susceptible to emotional trauma if removed from home, and if so, does their development in this respect differ from that of normal children? What are the experiences of childhood that are remembered best by mental defectives, and what determines their selective forgetting? Questions such as these can be asked but not answered at present.

HIGH-GRADE DEFECTIVES

Two fields of social inquiry about high-grade defectives have been explored: first, family studies of mental defect and its transmission from one generation to another; secondly, longitudinal studies of individuals thought at some period in their lives, usually childhood, to be feeble-minded.

Family studies of mental defect

The investigation of pedigrees is of sociological and genetic rather than of direct psychological interest, and the administrative consequences of the early American work were touched upon in Chapter I. Such inquiries have, however, a direct relevance to the psychology of mental deficiency, because they rest upon a theory of how the personal qualities of individuals are determined; and it happened that the person most responsible for carrying out the American studies was in fact a psychologist – Dr Henry H. Goddard. Goddard's studies were based on three assumptions: (1) that mental defect could be diagnosed from reports about an individual's conduct; (2) that the condition was determined wholly by heredity; (3) that it was incurable. His method of investigation can be illustrated by a description of what he actually did.

His first study, which was reported in a paper read to the American Breeders' Association in 1910, was into the family histories of a number of mental defectives at the Vineland Institution. Charts were produced showing the presence of mental defect in the families generation after generation. No comment or conclusion was made by Goddard, but the material itself strongly suggested to the audience the transmission of defect in a typical Mendelian way (Davies, 1930).

A year later this material was used by Davenport as the basis for formulating a clearly expressed statement about the transmission of mental defect. He says,

. . . there are laws on inheritance of general mental ability that

> can be sharply expressed. Low mentality is due to the *absence* of some factor, and if this factor that determines normal development is lacking in both parents, it will be lacking in all of their offspring. *Two mentally defective parents will produce only mentally defective offspring.* This is the first law of inheritance of mental ability. It has now been demonstrated by the study of scores of families at the Vineland Training School for defectives by Dr H. H. Goddard. . . . The second law of heredity of mentality is that, aside from 'Mongolians', probably no imbecile is born except of parents who, if not mentally defective themselves, both carry mental defect in their germ plasm.

In 1912 Goddard published a study of the Kallikak family, purporting to show the transmission of mental defect in one family through five generations. (An earlier work on the Juke family published by Dugdale in 1910, which is also very well known, had been concerned with criminality and destitution rather than with mental defect, but about this time a further history of the family was written up, and the findings reinterpreted in terms of mental subnormality by Estabrook, 1915.)

Goddard published a second volume (1914), in which he presented 327 family histories of feeble-minded persons. This study can be regarded as the first major scientific attempt to discuss the hereditary aspects of mental deficiency in a systematic way. The data were collected by three field workers, and information was obtained about no fewer than 13,711 persons. Attempts were made to check the reliability of the data by having some families visited independently by more than one investigator; mental tests were used for the first time in a social inquiry, and alternative hypotheses to account for the facts were examined. In these respects the investigations were an advance not only over previous studies, but also over many which have followed them. Goddard traced his families back for several generations, deciding in each case whether an individual had been feeble-minded or not –

> Three generations back is easy, and six is not impossible [he says]. It is not difficult for one versed in the subject to tell whether or not a man was feeble-minded even though he lived 100 years ago, providing he made enough impression upon his time for traditions of him to have come down . . . any person living or dead who was so abnormal that his neighbours or friends or descendants

always spoke of him as 'not quite right' is certain to have been decidedly defective (pp. 28–9).

The following case report is typical of the material on which Goddard based his conclusions:

Case 2. Florence and Byron T. (Brother and Sister). Florence T. 23 years old. Mentality 8. Has been here 10 years. Was born in New Jersey, parentage uncertain, but probably American.

Byron T. 19 years old. Mentality 11. Has been here 13 years.

When admitted Florence was spoken of as always smiling and silly; mouth open; went upstairs sideways. Her memory and attention were fair. She was sulky, could do errands and house work, was excitable, gluttonous, affectionate, fond of children and play, indolent, and vulgar; did not know any school work and has not learned much since.

At the present time, she does fancy work, house and laundry work. She is a good worker, always cheerful and happy. In the Binet tests she can count thirteen pennies, describe the pictures, sees the lack in the unfinished pictures, can copy the square but not the diamond; recognizes colours and names them; can compare the butterfly and fly, etc., cannot count backwards; repeats the days of the week and the months of the year. She cannot count the stamps nor repeat five figures. She is good natured and a willing worker. If not in the care of the Institution she would probably be the wife of some low-grade worker and the mother of many children, probably defective like herself.

The brother, Byron T., is 19 years old and tests 11; has been here 13 years; when admitted, was excitable and nervous, cried and laughed without cause, was gluttonous, destroyed clothing and furniture, was dangerous with fire, not truthful, nor trustworthy; active, obstinate, sly, and passionate. When put into school here, he made very good progress for a defective and learned to read fairly well, to write some, was less lazy, took more interest in things. He reached his limit, however, in school work, even in basketry; did something in music, but was more especially a farm boy, since he was strong and able to do a good deal of work under direction. As will be noted, he is three years higher grade than his sister. He can remember six figures but not seven. He can repeat 60 words in three minutes, can make rhymes, but cannot put together the dissected sentences. He is one of our highest grade boys and is entirely lacking in stigmata of degeneration; indeed, is a handsome lad.

A glance at the chart (not reproduced here) shows what a very bad family this is. The parents were feeble-minded, syphilitic, and sexually immoral. The father, who was also alcoholic, died in an almshouse. This is one of the worst histories, socially and morally, that we have. It is said that the miscarriages and infant deaths in the family were syphilitic cases and were due directly to the contamination. An older brother is sexually immoral and criminalistic. Three others are dead. The father's two sisters and brother are feeble-minded. The mother had a brother and a half-sister who were feeble-minded. The father's mother was feeble-minded and was twice married. By her first husband she had four children, all normal, with the possible exception of one, but her defect was transmitted to her grandchildren, two out of five being feeble-minded. The father of our boy and girl was one of the four children resulting from the second marriage of this woman with a man who was alcoholic and immoral. Our children's mother's parents were both feeble-minded.

The paternal grandfather was the child of a woman who was twice married, he being the son of the second marriage, of which nothing else is known. By her first husband, who was considered normal, there were five children two of whom were feeble-minded. One of these married a supposedly normal woman and two children out of five were feeble-minded. It is evident that the defect here runs back at least into the fifth generation.

This is a remarkable family. They have been largely objects of charity, although they inherited some property which they quickly squandered. Neither of the children would be recognized as defective if out in the world, and both would undoubtedly go the way of their ancestors in crime and immorality as well as in the matter of marrying and reproducing defective children.

Following Goddard's example, other investigators added to the list of families such as the Jukes and the Kallikaks (see Louttit, 1947, for reference to these studies). His work thus had a widespread influence on psychologists both in the United States and in this country. It formed a basis for the first article on mental defect to appear in the *Encyclopaedia Britannica* (1919). As late as 1933 Pintner cited the conclusions uncritically in his chapter on feeble-mindedness, in Murchison's *Handbook on Child Psychology*, summing up as follows: 'The chief cause of feeble-mindedness is heredity. Numerous family histories support this contention. A very small proportion of cases is due to disease or accident. There is at present no cure. The care and control of the feeble-minded consists of education, segregation, and sterilization' (p. 838).

Contemporary writing about mental defect is highly critical of the early studies described above. As has been mentioned in Chapter VI, we now know that the causes of mental defect are very much more numerous than was realized at the time Goddard was writing. It is a fundamental postulate of modern genetical theory that traits are determined independently of each other, and the notion of a whole conglomeration of qualities being transmitted through the presence or absence of a single 'factor' finds no support from present-day studies. It is as though one were to conclude from family studies of 'sickness' that good or bad health was attributable to the presence or absence of a single 'health' factor transmitted from parents to children according to simple Mendelian principles.

Not only can the mechanism of transmission of many forms of mental defect be questioned, but often even the facts of transmission are by no means clear. To base a diagnosis of mental subnormality on verbal reports about people's great-grandparents is manifestly absurd, as any social worker knows today. Even written records of the eighteenth or nineteenth centuries, assuming that they are complete, are likely to tell us only that certain individuals were penniless at some time in their lives, or that others were in prison or in hospital, or were believed to drink to excess. Why they behaved like that is usually not known, and whether the information is correct is often by no means certain.

No one today regards the majority of mentally subnormal persons as potential criminals, or thinks that most criminals are mentally deficient. In concluding that they were, Goddard made a simple methodological error. He had found, on testing the inmates of Vineland Institution with the newly devised Binet–Simon test which he had introduced into the United States, that practically no adult patients had a mental age of more than 12 years. Without testing a control group of normal individuals in the community, he drew the erroneous inference that a mental age of 12 marked the borderline between normal and subnormal intelligence. When other workers found that the majority of prisoners had mental ages below 12, it was naturally assumed that they too were 'feeble-minded'. It was not until experience in the mental testing of American soldiers during the First World War showed that the mean Binet mental age of white recruits was only 13 years, and that of negro soldiers just over 10 years, that the confusion between 'mental age' as defined psychometrically, and mental maturity, began to become apparent. The importance of cultural factors in depressing the mental age of American negroes was recognized still more recently (Klineberg, 1935). Finally, the way in which cultural factors influence conduct is only now beginning to be studied, though the effect of such an influence is abundantly clear.

Before leaving family studies something should be said about work carried out in England. The interest in this country has been in 'problem families' rather than in mental defect as such, and the main genealogical inquiries, which were never completed, were those of Lidbetter (1933), begun in 1910. During the last 20 years several cross-section studies have been made. The best summing up of present-day views about problem families is to be found in Blacker's (1952) discussion of some recent studies:

> Of the five commonly recognized features of problem families, namely mental subnormality, temperamental instability, ineducability, a squalid home, and the presence of numerous children, the first two, though less immediately conspicuous than the last three, can best be regarded as having causal status. But a vicious circle readily establishes itself when conditions of squalor, at first a consequential feature, can become a cause of further demoralization.
>
> Environmental conditions can undoubtedly produce mental subnormality and temperamental instability. Bad social or family traditions, intra-family conflicts and tensions, and maternal deprivation, can in various ways retard, corrupt, distort, and blight the developing personality of a child. Maternal deprivation, defined in a comprehensive sense to include the effects of psychopathy in the parents, can give rise to self-perpetuating sequences; these can reproduce themselves throughout successive generations in a manner which might simulate a genetically determined process. But though such vicious social sequences commonly occur, as also do the converse sequences whereby favourable nurtural conditions are self-perpetuating, neither is invariable or necessary. Temperamental no less than physical qualities of human beings are in part inborn. The interaction of nature and nurture is here so close as to make it exceedingly difficult to distinguish the separate effects of each. Further research is needed, but fallacies must be avoided especially those arising from too wide an assessment of psychopathy among the parents.

It is very important to distinguish between familial mental defect and problem families who 'for their own well-being and the well-being of others, require a substantially greater degree of supervision and help over longer periods than is usually provided by existing services'. Psychopathic instability, and in many cases, psychosis, rather than mental defect, seems to be a prominent feature of many social problem families. Moreover, as Blacker points out:

> Problem families will tend to be selected by reason of their high fertility. Childless families will be excluded; and one-child or two-child families will be little represented because the rearing of a family of one or two children taxes the inadequate mother less than does the rearing of numerous children. Thus their high fertility becomes (indirectly) a cause of these families presenting 'problems'. There can be no cruelty, neglect, lousiness, truancy from school, homelessness, and mental defect of children if there are no children. The fertility of problem families is therefore not

readily comparable with the fertility of any special group or class. . . .

In particular little can be deduced about the social adjustment of 'typical' mental defectives from longitudinal family studies such as those of Goddard, or from cross-section surveys of problem families (see also Wilson, 1962).

Longitudinal studies of individual defectives

The studies already discussed have been concerned with families rather than with individuals. Even assuming the data to be correct, they give a biased picture of the social competence of the mentally deficient, because the samples contain only families in which the propositi are both fertile and produce offspring who are themselves social problems. Individual studies are free from this bias; but in most of the follow-up studies the results are biased to an unknown extent because some cases cannot be traced over a period of years.

Individual studies have been of two main sorts: first, studies of the effects of different types of education or environmental conditions on the mental functioning of mentally subnormal persons; second, studies of the after-histories of children ascertained as feeble-minded or mentally subnormal. These are both related to the question raised by Goddard's work as to the 'incurability' of mental defect in an individual case.

The effect of different educational regimens on the mental functioning of the educationally subnormal is discussed by Gunzburg in Chapter XII. In summary it may be said here that though for every study reporting large gains in I.Q., or educational achievement, a similar study can be quoted in which the findings are largely negative, the evidence taken as a whole shows clearly that good teaching and a stimulating environment can effect very substantial changes in educability and social adjustment, and smaller changes in I.Q.

The many studies of the after-careers of mentally subnormal children have been undertaken mainly to find out how many benefit from the particular form of training being investigated. The literature has been briefly reviewed by several writers (Porteus, 1942; Schmidt, 1946; Louttit, 1947; Sarason, 1949; Tizard and O'Connor, 1950). European studies during the first two decades of the century have been summarized by Descœudres and more recent ones by Ramer (1946). A painstaking and exhaustive review of the prognosis of *institutional* defectives has been compiled by Windle (1962) who in an appendix summarizes over 100 papers, describing 170 different studies. The 12 studies summarized below illustrate the kind of inquiries that have been made, and the methods used. Differences in methodological sophistication, the representativeness of the samples, the opportunities made available to the patients and the economic situation at the time the investigations were carried out, make detailed comparison between one study and another unprofitable.

TABLE 28

Synopsis

Abel and Kinder (1942)

Subjects: 84 mentally subnormal girls placed in industry over a three-year period, beginning work at age of 17. I.Q. range 50–90 on Otis Scale.

Method: Trained for from one to two years in adjustment classes in New York City, learning simpler processes of women's garment making. Placed doing similar work; followed up by placement officer of their school; social worker visited their homes periodically. If not able to be placed on machine work, sent as factory workers doing packing or other unskilled work. Employers not told they were subnormal.

Results: During first year half the girls succeeded in one concern. 35 per cent. unable to hold a job for more than two weeks. In third year, 55 per cent. worked steadily in one concern, half total number doing work for which trade training was useful; others doing light packing and factory work. 20 per cent. failed. Remainder partially successful, working steadily for less than trade union rates. Factors contributing to success were I.Q., other aspects of personality, employers' attitudes, work drive or ambition, home stability and luck.

General remarks: The book gives a useful, mainly qualitative account of the major problems of subnormal adolescent girls during the 1930's, and of the exacerbation of their problems through the economic depression. The authors comment that better placement could have been secured if more time had been given to training.

Badham (1955)

Subjects: 108 male patients who had been on daily employment or resident licence from a M.D. hospital for at least 12 months. Age range 19–50; I.Q. range 50–90; length of institutional care $1\frac{1}{2}$–10 years.

Method: Hospital records, opinions of senior nursing staff; good social worker reports. Analysis of 160 items of information.

Results: 61 considered as successful and self-supporting; 36 as successful and partially self-supporting; 11 failures. Pointers to success were: skilled placing, depending on selection of patient, suitability of employment and employer, i.e. work environment; suitable place of residence; skilled supervision. Reasons for failure: 'reverting to type' in those with a history of sexual or conduct disorder, particularly the former; unsuitability of employer; home or off-duty environment; employment; personal shortcomings.

General remarks: Critical review of some recent literature; discussion of main findings; suggestions as to organization of services.

Bronner (1933)

Subjects: Cases referred to Judge Baker Foundation.

Results: Three studies reported. In the first 189 'defectives' with I.Q.s between 75 and 103 followed up over at least 4 years. 53 per cent. successful (i.e. regular work and no trouble caused); 21 per cent. failures (irregular work, or court records, or placed in institution); 26 per cent. doubtful (unstable work record, or caused concern through petty misdemeanour). Second study, 50 defectives, mean I.Q. 68, all with I.Q.s under 75, matched for age and crime with 50 non-defectives, mean I.Q. 96, range 90–110. Defectives 20 per cent. success; non-defectives 16 per cent. success, defined as above. For a group of first offenders, 39 per cent. success for defectives; 54 per cent. success for non-defectives. Third study, 500 adolescents on probation, of whom 19 per cent. were defectives. Five-year follow-up. Of 400 boys, non-defectives 44 per cent. success; defectives 40 per cent. success; of 100 girls, non-defectives 84 per cent. success; defectives 68 per cent. success.

General remarks: 'Summarizing the three independently conducted researches, it seems thoroughly justifiable to conclude that the defective, even the defective who in childhood or adolescence presents a problem serious enough to warrant referral to a guidance centre for study, may be so managed that he stands a fair chance of becoming no great burden to the community . . . equated for type and degree of offence there is little difference in outcome as related to intelligence.'

Crawford (1956)

Subjects: 97 patients admitted to a mental deficiency institution during the previous five years from an urban population of 233,000.

Method: A medical and social study.

Results and general remarks: '. . . 44 may be expected to train to the level of competitive employment; 29 will always require some measure of support and, perhaps, mild medical supervision; 24 require prolonged nursing and medical care not easily, or properly, available at home or as out-patients . . . only 25 per cent. of the admissions are grossly physically and mentally handicapped. The other 75 per cent., although deemed mentally defective, could conceivably be dealt with by other means elsewhere. . . . 35 of the 44 "high-grade" patients might have been dealt with outside hospital by the provision of, first, male and female training units with ancillary hostel accommodation for those adults convicted of often mild antisocial behaviour and, secondly, more adequate residential special school accommodation. Too many children with intelligence quotients in the sixties are being excluded from the educational system today.

'Amongst the 29 patients admitted who were definitely subnormal in intelligence and often subnormal in physique only 10, by reason of chronic physical disability, e.g. epilepsy, really justified care in a large, well-equipped hospital. By the placement, in strategic areas, of "Country house" establishments minimally staffed and equipped, a very large number of patients like this, whose home care has deteriorated or ceased, could be cared for. With only slight support and supervision they can minister to their own daily wants and, possibly, staff a sheltered workshop.

'Alternative care has now been proposed for 54 of the 97 admissions. Of the 24 cases in the grossly defective group at least 6 might continue under home care if certain community facilities were provided or improved. These are: (1) better out-patient investigation, advice, and treatment; (2) increased social work from both hospital and Local Health Authority level; (3) increased financial aid for parents; (4) increased occupation centre accommodation; (5) increased short-stay accommodation for times of household emergency and holidays.

'In conclusion, if better diagnostic and alternative facilities came into being and mental deficiency practitioners could play their full part in conjunction with all other branches of medicine and the Social Services it might be possible to keep approximately 50 per cent. of the present type of admission in the community. In so doing not only would better use be made of the available beds but many young children now deemed ineducable and mentally defective might receive the comprehensive investigation and highly specialized treatment which is, at present, largely denied to them.'

Fairbank (1933)

Subjects: 122 adults from a group of 166 who had been ascertained as mentally defective 17 years before. Adjustment compared with that of 90 adults who had been regarded as normal children. 173 children of the 'defective' group, of whom 79 were at school and 64 given Stanford–Binet test.

Results: 78 per cent. totally self-supporting as against 88 per cent. for 'normal' group; remainder partially self-supporting 5 per cent., receiving family assistance 10 per cent., living with parents 4 per cent., state care or widow's pension 3 per cent. 30 per cent. owned or were buying a home, as against 24 per cent. for the 'normal' group, and 16 per cent. as against 36 per cent. were saving money.

More marriages and slightly more sex delinquency among subnormals; more dependence on charitable organizations; living conditions were not so good as those of the 'normals'; more juvenile court records but the police records were about the same; less migration to better parts of the city. Of their children only 3 were defective with a mean I.Q. of 66; 24 were dull, mean I.Q. 89; 7 were average, mean I.Q. 109; 4 were of superior intelligence, mean I.Q. 118.

General remarks: This study was carried out during the economic depression of the 1930's and ran counter to the predictions of Campbell who had considered that self-support was impossible for 22 of the original group, and a 'dubious probability for the remaining 144'.

Ferguson and Kerr (1955, 1958)

Two studies describe the after-histories of girls and boys who left special schools for educable mentally handicapped (E.S.N.) children in Glasgow.

Subjects: 207 women, 22 years of age, who were consecutive school leavers from special schools for the educationally subnormal in Glasgow six years previously; 225 men aged about 25 who had left similar schools 9 years previously.

Method. Study of records, and by interview.

Results: 'The final impression left by the performance (of both boys and girls) is one of amazement that they have been so successful in holding jobs, even in their middle twenties, when the mad scramble for juvenile employment has largely passed. With meagre educational equipment, usually without the advantage of a pushing parent and often with all the handicaps of an indifferent home, the great majority have contrived to keep in steady work. Certainly many of the jobs they held were jobs that have to be done, even in this stream-lined age. But if the picture from the employment point of view is reasonably satisfactory, the general social condition of many of these young people leaves much to be desired; for many have had little chance in life, little chance to make the most of what talents they have. The police records of these youths can only be viewed with grave concern; it is obvious that many of our young criminals are recruited from the ranks of high-grade mental defectives. Nor is this surprising; for too many are inhibited dull and simple and find it easy, almost natural, to develop anti-social behaviour through suggestibility and lack of "insight". There is no lack of suggestion.'

Remarks: This careful study shows the appalling material and cultural poverty which still is to be found in a welfare state in the middle years of the century, and the distressing social consequences for handicapped young people and their families. The attention paid on the one hand to physical handicaps and on the other to material deprivation make it an unusually informative study.

Hilliard (1956)

Subjects: 250 feeble-minded women admitted to the Fountain Hospital 1946–55, and placed in an 80-bed hostel.

Method: Medical and social follow-up study.

Results: 152, that is, 60 per cent. of all admissions, have been discharged from the M.D. Act; a further 40 employed in the community on licence; 12 in residential jobs, and 28 in daily employment. Six have been placed under Guardianship. 'Of 250 consecutive feeble-minded patients dealt with in this hospital under the M.D. Act, more than 75 per cent. are living or working in the community.' Of the 152 discharged patients, 21 (14 per cent.) subsequently married.

General remarks: 'One of the factors which has contributed to the high proportion of these patients being discharged is that I have often disagreed with those who certified them on the necessity to invoke the Mental Deficiency Act. If one thinks of them as mentally defective one is naturally pessimistic as to their ability to manage in the community. If one believes that medical, social, or emotional factors are the main cause of their difficulties one is more likely to give them a chance in a different environment. . . .

'Life in an institution is not always the best preparation for life in the world outside. Long periods of segregation among mental defectives, many of whom would be of considerably lower mental capacity than these patients, may produce either a dulling of the intellect and emotions or lead to rebellion, with disturbed behaviour and emotional instability. The most troublesome patients in an M.D. hospital are often those who are within the average range of intelligence and who justifiably feel that they are not in the most helpful surroundings.

'These persons do best with the maximum opportunity for exercising, within their individual capacities, their powers of choice, judgment, and self-restraint. Such patients should be encouraged rather than coerced and it is surprising how co-operative they will be if they feel they are being given a fair chance to take an active part in their own rehabilitation. Every patient at the South Side Home was on parole immediately on arrival even if she had been in a locked ward at the previous hospital. Patients were allowed to work outside as soon as a job was available, and if a patient found herself a job instead of waiting to be placed in one she was always licensed to it, although it would be checked for suitability by the social worker. Small hostels would be of great assistance in the rehabilitation of such patients who have obtained daily work but have no homes.'

Hoyle (1951)

Subjects: Mentally defective persons under supervision in the City of Leeds. Comparison made between situation in 1929 and 1949. (Both high-grade and low-grade cases are included.)

Method: Analysis of official returns.

Results: In 1929, of 772 defectives under supervision 12 per cent. lived under good home conditions; 79 per cent. under fair conditions; and 9 per cent. under poor ones. In 1949 the corresponding figures were 66 per cent., 31 per cent., and 3 per cent. In 1929 12 per cent. over 16 years of age were self-supporting; 39 per cent. partially self-supporting; 12 per cent. useful at home; 29 per cent. unemployable; and 8 per cent. out of work. Corresponding figures for 1949 were: 44 per cent., 20 per cent., 9 per cent., 26 per cent., and 1 per cent. An Industrial Centre employs 53 youths and 30 girls, included in the 'partially self-supporting group'. Full employment and better social services are responsible for the change.

Kennedy (1948)

Subjects: 256 'morons' living in the community (I.Q.s 45–75), and diagnosed as mentally subnormal when at school. Mean age at the time of the inquiry 24·5 years. Control group of 129 adults of normal I.Q. matched for age, sex, and socio-economic status.

Method: Careful and comprehensive social investigation. Adequate statistical treatment of results.

Results: Comparing the two groups morons came from poor backgrounds. More parental instability. No significant difference in number married or in number of children born to them. Morons with more step- and adopted children and with higher divorce rate. Some tendency for more morons to have an unsatisfactory work record. Little difference in economic adjustment. More morons in trouble with the police. Morons showed less tendency than controls to participate in recreational activities, including cinema, sport, and dancing. They read less and participated less in group activities.

General remarks: 'In final summary, our study reveals that morons are socially adequate in that they are economically independent and self-supporting; and that they are not serious threateners of the safety of society, but are rather frequent breakers of conventional codes of behaviour. . . . The morons we studied are, by and large, successful in their social adjustment within limitations, . . . apparently imposed by their inferior mental capacities. Doll's remark . . . that "they find some humble niche in society which they can fill without becoming such a social menace that society becomes gravely concerned about them", seems to fit the actual situation very well.'

This account is remarkable for its detail and thoroughness, and the above summary does less than justice to the mass of detailed information given in it.

Mickelson (1947)

Subjects: 90 families from State of Minnesota in which one or both parents are certified (committed) mental defective. (74 per cent. with wife certified; 9 per cent. husband; 17 per cent. both parents.) Mean I.Q. 58·6, range approximately 35–80. Age range not stated. 62 per cent. with one or both parents sterilized following birth of children.

Method: Information from Welfare Boards on living conditions, income, health, family relations, personality traits, care and adjustment of children, supervision given, persistent problems.

Results: Average number of births 5·4 per family, with 3·3 children living at home. 33 per cent. thought to be of 'average or above' mentality; 29 per cent. mentally backward; and insufficient information for rating in 28 per cent. 34 per cent. of families with serious physical health problem in one or both parents; 41 per cent. with serious mental health problem. 42 per cent. rated as having given satisfactory care to children, 32 per cent. 'questionable', and 26 per cent. unsatisfactory. Little relation between quality of care and mother's I.Q. High correlation between harmonious family relationships and adequate child care. Percentage of families with adequate, marginal, and inadequate income was 37, 55, and 8 for families classed as giving 'satisfactory' care to children, and nil, 75, and 25 for 'questionable' and 'unsatisfactory' groups.

General remarks: Author comments: 'The number of major health problems, and the still larger proportion of such minor problems . . . suggest that we may be underestimating the ability of the feeble-minded to feel strain, to worry and to be unhappy over the problems in their personal life.' Data permitting a more complex analysis needed to indicate how the various problems discussed are interrelated. A later study (1949) attempts to evaluate the value of social case work with these families.

Ramer (*1946*)

Subjects: 626 special school pupils and 589 control cases in Stockholm, born 1905–17. Purpose: to examine how many had failed in life, had to apply for public assistance, became invalids or were delinquents. Ss between 26 and 38 years of age at the time of inquiry. I.Q.s as children mainly 70–84.

Method: Examination of official records concerning outdoor relief, invalid pension, drunkenness, court records, etc. (It should be remembered that Swedish social records are extremely well kept.)

Results: More of the subnormal from broken families or from unstable homes. Lower social status on the whole. Higher mortality; lower marriage rate; higher divorce rate; more in unskilled jobs. One in three of special class pupils and one in five of controls had been in receipt of poor relief or invalid pensions. More of subnormal group in institutions. No differences in criminal record or in types of crime. Twice as many of the *controls* in trouble for vagrancy. Little difference in alcoholism.

General remarks: ' "Temperament" plays a greater part in criminality than intelligence.' Study very carefully carried out and appropriate statistical comparisons made. Data are not, however analysed separately for the period of the economic depression and the later period of full employment. A valuable review of European literature given.

Saenger (*1957*, *1960*)

Subjects: A carefully constructed representative sample of 520 severely retarded adults who had attended classes for the 'trainable retarded' in New York City between 1929 and 1955. Age range 17–40 years. I.Q.s mainly between 40 and 50 points. 20 per cent. were mongols.

Method: Interviews by trained psychiatric social workers, using interview schedules and check lists. Careful attention paid to training of interviewer, piloting study and checking validity of conclusions.

Results: Most of retarded alert and lively, taking an interest in life around them. One-third markedly self-confident, only 13 per cent. lacking in affect, and 7 per cent. lifeless and inattentive. Neurotic trends suspected in 20 per cent. and psychotic tendencies in 6 per cent.

Secondary physical handicaps in three-quarters; 20 per cent. had motor abilities; 40 per cent. speech defects; but 83 per cent. able to dress and feed themselves and take care of bodily functions. Two-thirds able to express themselves in complete sentences and one-third able to pick out a car fare and distinguish coins. But only one in nine able to read even simple passages.

Saenger gives a wealth of data on the factors affecting institutionalization, and on family adjustment. One-quarter were in institutions and 14 per cent. had spent some time in an institution. No relation was found between institutionalization and parental income, education, or family size. Nor did secondary handicaps influence placement to any marked degree. Behaviour problems and disturbed family relations were the most important factors.

The adjustment of the defectives in their own families was surprisingly good. 75 per cent. of parents reported no major difficulties and only 5 per cent. had serious problems. These in general were those commonly found in formal 5–6-year-old children, namely restlessness and tantrums, stubbornness, fears, and overdependence.

About half took responsibility for their own things, and rooms, 20 per cent. assumed major housekeeping responsibilities and an additional third did household chores. 80 per cent. were left alone safely, and probably others could have been.

The great majority spent most of their leisure time in the home but went out occasionally. Only about one-half had friends and only half of these had friends of the opposite sex. Only 4 per cent. appeared to have had sex relations and only 12 children had been born. Delinquency was extremely uncommon.

The employment data were remarkable. 27 per cent. were working for pay, and an additional 9 per cent. had worked in the past. Four times as many men as women worked and Saenger believes that the numbers could have been increased, perhaps even doubled.

General remarks: These two monumental studies by Saenger provide data of extraordinary interest and importance regarding the low-grade defectives and their families. They are, moreover, models of research design, and should be studied by anyone contemplating research in this field.

One other study, of outstanding interest, has been selected for more detailed description. This was an investigation begun by Baller in 1935 and continued by Charles (1953). The Baller–Charles study deals with the 'ability and accomplishment of persons earlier judged mentally deficient'. Baller investigated the social and occupational status of 206 individuals who had been in 'opportunity rooms' of the Lincoln, Nebraska, public schools. They included nearly all children who had been in these classes from the inception of the programme up to the date of the research. The criteria for judging their mental deficiency were:

(*a*) opportunity room classification, and

(*b*) intelligence quotients not above 70 as measured by individual tests, and

(*c*) definite evidence that they were considered by teachers and the school psychologists as mentally deficient, and were for that reason placed in opportunity room classes where they spent more than one year.

Fifteen years later Charles succeeded in finding 75 per cent. of the survivors of the original group, whom he investigated. The two studies give a unique picture of changes in social and personal adaptation during a period of economic change. Charles reports the following findings.

A hundred and fifty-one, or about three-quarters of both the men and the women of the original group, were 'located' (this number includes those who were dead at the time of the follow-up). Seventeen had died from illness, and a further 7 owing to accident or violence. Nine of the subjects were in institutions. About 10 per cent. of those still alive had been successfully discharged or were on parole from institutions. About 80 per cent. of the sample were married, and 21 per cent. of the married subjects had been divorced. The figures for marriage and the divorce rate were somewhat less than the average figures of the United States in 1951, when the field work was carried out, while the death rate was somewhat greater. About 80 per cent. of the married subjects had children, and the number of children per family was 2·03 on the average. As has been found in other surveys (for example, Ramer's), the number of children per family was somewhat less than the national average of 2·62.

School records were available for 73 children, the great majority of whom were making satisfactory progress at school. Two children were in a mental deficiency institution, and a third was crippled. Intelligence test scores of 46 children for whom I.Q.s were available, ranged from 50 I.Q. to 138 I.Q. with a mean of 95 and a standard deviation of 16.

There was a wide range in the types of homes in which subjects lived – 'from filthy shacks to costly new houses with landscaped grounds. The majority were reasonably clean and not considered detrimental to health.' Charles found that all but seven of the non-institutional subjects had at least part-time jobs, and most of them were regularly employed. In all, 83 per cent. of the total group, as in 1935, were self-supporting, and of the gainfully employed half had been at the same job or type of work for from 3 to 20 years. The range of occupations was from 'managerial positions to unskilled labour', labouring being the most common occupation for the males, and housekeeping for the women. Twenty-four of the subjects were retested on the Wechsler Bellevue Intelligence Scale. The mean Wechsler scores were – verbal I.Q. 72, performance scale 88, and full scale 81. These were considerably higher than the I.Q.s obtained originally, using the 1915 Stanford–Binet test (mean 58). Charles believes that the social data obtained in 1935 and 1950 indicate that a sizeable proportion of the subjects were 'dull' rather than mentally deficient.

Forty per cent. of the subjects still living in Lincoln, and nearly 60 per cent. of the men, had been involved in violation of the law since 1935. One-quarter of the violations were traffic offences, and the rest civil, with drunkenness accounting for half of the civil cases. None of the offences had been serious.

Data about dependence on relief were collected and separated into three five-year periods, 1936–40, 1941–5, 1946–50.

> The subjects showed a decreasing need for relief each successive period. This decrease suggests that the subjects were able to take advantage of improving economic conditions. In the first period over 40 per cent. were self-sufficient, in the second over half, and in the third over 65 per cent. A substantial part of the family income was provided by relief for a fourth of the subjects in the first period, and for less than 10 per cent. in the second and third periods. Over the entire period more than a third were entirely self-sufficient, less than half had some assistance from public relief funds, and the remainder, about 20 per cent., were institutionalized or living with parents. These data show an improvement over 1935, when a fourth were self-sufficient and over half required assistance. It is apparent that fewer subjects needed assistance and that the proportional amount of relief they received decreased each five-year period.

In summary Charles concluded that his study reinforces the view of Baller (1935), which gave an optimistic view of the social adjustment of this group of subjects. He points out that with maturity the subjects have been able to profit from improved economic conditions, and have become more self-sufficient. The large proportion are 'effective and desirable members of society. They have not produced numerous feeble-minded offspring, as some persons fear is the case with populations of low intelligence. Instead, their children have fared better intellectually and academically than did the subjects themselves.' Charles does not feel that the evidence supports any claim of actual improvement in native intelligence, but adds that the 'great variation in the present abilities and achievements of the subjects should dispel any notion that persons who give evidence of low ability in childhood develop and perform according to rigid stereotype'.

CONCLUSIONS

It is apparent from what has been said that even during the depression years substantial numbers of mentally subnormal children were able, upon leaving school, to find jobs for themselves and live as self-supporting, socially competent members of society. In Baller's study, for example, 42 per cent. of the mentally subnormal group were on relief during the economic depression, but 16 per cent. of a control group of normal adults were also on relief. In the post-war years during which full employment has come to be accepted as something more than a mere temporary phenomenon, the proportion of mentally subnormal persons who are socially competent has, of course, increased markedly. As a result, many who would have been considered high-grade defectives in the past are today regarded – and rightly so – as ordinary citizens; and the majority of high-grade defectives who go into institutions are coming to be thought of as potentially normal persons who need training and guidance to enable them to adapt themselves in the community. Lip service has been paid to this idea for many years, but mental deficiency practice is only now basing itself on this conception. Thus, the average time spent by those mental defectives in institutions in this country, who are discharged, is still about eight and a half years, and the situation is probably no better in the United States and elsewhere. The number of institutions which devote themselves seriously to problems of resocialization, and which have adequate numbers of psychologists, teaching and training staff, and social workers, is small, despite the high cost of keeping patients under institutional care, and the long waiting lists for admission.

Windle's (1962) review illustrates very clearly the barrenness of much of the research that has been done on 'prognosis'. It is fairly clear that whether a defective ever goes into an institution in the first place will depend upon a host of factors: the amount of provision available, the admission policy adopted, the alternative provision for care or education in the community, community attitudes to mental retardates, the state of the labour market, the circumstances both material and social of the defective's own family; the advice they are given; the amount of help they are given; handicaps, both physical and mental. How long a patient stays in hospital is also dependent upon a large number of factors, only a few of which relate to the personal qualities of the patient. The discharge or rehabilitation policy may be liberal or conservative; the community services may be generous or inadequate – in the way of opportunities for employment in the open market or in sheltered workshops in the case of adults, or in special classes or schools, or 'day hospitals', in the case of children or very severely handicapped adults; moreover the availability of services will depend on their proximity or on the transport which is provided; the provision of hostels or alternative forms of residential care outside hospital will influence discharge policies; and the amount of social work which is provided will profoundly influence the willingness of families to have a mentally retarded person home on trial, and will also help them to cope with his problems. Such 'casework' will also assist in the finding of jobs for the defective and in enabling the families to deal with problems which are not related to his presence but which decrease their general efficiency and happiness and thus indirectly make it more difficult for them to cope with him at home.

Likewise how long a patient stays outside an institution is dependent upon constellations of factors which differ for different individuals, living in different environments. To regard return to the community as 'success' and placement in hospital or institution as 'failure' leads to the reactionary and absurd conclusion that the fewer beds there are available for the mentally disordered the better a country's health service. Judged by this criterion Spain and Egypt are more 'advanced' than England, and Mexico and Brazil than the United States.

The Baller–Charles study and similar investigations carried out of the after careers of institutional defectives make further purely descriptive studies of little general interest. (One of the reasons for reporting previous work in such detail has been to demonstrate this.)

It can indeed be said that half a century of investigation has done little more than correct the false ideas that have been put forward during the same period. The twentieth century discovered the high-grade defective; many people are still trying to make him normal again – by argument.

This is not the most useful thing one can do today. What are most needed today are properly controlled experimental studies and surveys designed to answer particular questions about the social costs of various types of administrative arrangements for dealing with mentally subnormal individuals. On the psychological side, we need to discover the most efficient methods of teaching or training those who are grossly subnormal in intelligence, or handicapped in other ways. The efficiency of different forms of treatment, including the psychological effects of medical treatments, must be studied, and new methods developed. How to teach social skills to dull, badly educated people has hardly been studied at all as yet, nor has the treatment of emotional maladjustment or psychopathic instability.

On the social side the problem today is not whether some defectives can be resocialized, but how many could be better dealt with in the community without ever going into an institution, and what services would be needed to make this possible; what kinds of regimen will best fit institutional defectives for life in society; how training programmes can be organized; what kind of supervision is needed, and how much; and what kinds of job are most suitable for enabling mental defectives to live in the community or do useful work.

To carry out psychological studies effectively we need to know more about the basic psychological processes of the mentally subnormal, and the laws which govern their interaction and development. On the social side what needs to be stressed is that investigators must consider not only the defective, but his family and society. In planning services we must weigh up all the social costs – personal, family, and community costs – and consider not only the advantages of different forms of care, but the injustices, the hardships, and the cruelties that are so often entailed in any system. Finally, psychologists must look again at the problems and opportunities presented by low-grade defectives.

Unfortunately the amount of research being carried out on these social and psychological problems of mental defect is still small. In 1959, Lipman, Blackman, and Stevens reported on several aspects of research on mental subnormality being undertaken in residential institutions in the United States. Ninety-five institutions having a population of 300 or more resident patients were sent a questionnaire asking for information about their research activities. Only 47 (49·5 per cent.) replied: they presumably included the ones most interested in research. Of these, 35 reported that some research was being undertaken, but only nine had a research programme which involved personnel spending at least half their time on research. Research classified as 'medical' accounted for 46 per cent. of all research being undertaken (with biochemistry comprising 36 per cent. of this, medical surveys 31 per cent., and research on tranquillizers 15 per cent.). 'Psychology' accounted for 37 per cent. of the total (personality adjustment 28 per cent. of this, human learning 18 per cent., perception 15 per cent., tests and measurements 12 per cent.). Only 17 per cent. of all research fell into the categories of education (10 per cent.), sociology (5 per cent.), and administration (2 per cent.).

On the basis of an informal inquiry carried out in this country by Tizard, it was concluded that in the whole of England there were, in 1961, only about a dozen to fifteen people engaged on research on social and psychological aspects of mental subnormality. Lipman, Blackman, and Stevens in their paper reported that the amount spent on research by institutions in the United States was only one-fifth of 1 per cent. of their budgets. The proportion spent on social and psychological research would be no greater here. It must be concluded that although it is no longer necessary to have to plead for humane and enlightened treatment of the mentally subnormal, there is still an astonishing lack of recognition that research in the social and behavioural sciences can contribute either to their welfare or to scientific knowledge.

Chapter XVIII

ADOPTION AND FOSTERING OF CHILDREN OF THE MENTALLY DEFICIENT

by Ann M. Clarke and A. D. B. Clarke

INTRODUCTION

Children of the mentally deficient are often illegitimate, and their parents may be either incapable of, unwilling to, or are prevented from, rearing their own offspring. (For a discussion of characteristics ascribed to mentally deficient mothers, see pp. 521–2.) These, therefore, for a variety of reasons are separated from their parents and are therefore *potentially* available for adoption or fostering, and doctors or psychologists are often asked to advise would-be adopters on their prospects. At the same time, although there are large numbers of children under public or private care, there is in fact a shortage of children considered suitable for adoption, and those who wish to take such children may have to wait years before achieving this (see Bowlby, 1951, Chapter II). In the past, adoption agencies have shown an extremely cautious attitude towards recommending children of the mentally deficient for adoption, although at the present time, partly due to the general demand and partly due to changes in our knowledge, such attitudes are beginning to alter. Thus, a United Nations study (1953) indicates that:

> It was thought formerly that a child offered for adoption must be 'perfect' from every point of view. It has come to be realized that a great many adopters are quite willing to care for and love a child who has some defect, provided they are told about it. Many agencies report instances of children who were below par physi-

> cally, slightly retarded mentally, or difficult to handle, who after a little while blossomed under the care of loving adoptive parents and became quite normal (op. cit., p. 55).

In the present chapter we shall consider under what circumstances the adoption of children of the mentally deficient is justified, and discuss the risks involved. So far as middle-class persons are concerned, adoption often takes place via private channels, and therefore much of our evidence concerns children from the lower socio-economic groups.

The main problem in any individual case is the problem of prediction of future development, for commonly and rightly, adoption takes place at a very early age. The most elementary requirement of prospective adopters is that the child will not turn out to be mentally deficient, or, alternatively, they may perhaps desire an assurance that the child will be bright. But we have already seen that prediction of development is hazardous (Chapter IV) even in children of normal parents and that we can only deal in terms of probabilities.

The adoption agency has three main sources of information from which to make its prediction: the parental background and history, the examination of the infant, and the assessment of the prospective adopter. Each of these will be examined in turn with special reference to the problem of children of the mentally deficient.[1] Before so doing, however, the main factor which has bedevilled scientific work on this subject must again (see Chapter V) be mentioned; this is the selective placement commonly practised by adoption authorities. These, to varying extents, tend to place infants in foster or adoptive homes as near as possible in every way to the sort of homes they would have had if the need for adoption had never arisen. On account of this policy, therefore, if a child placed in a superior foster home develops into a person of superior ability, while one in an average home develops average ability, this might be due either to hereditary factors, noted by the adoption agency, or to the environmental factors of the new home, or indeed to a combination of both. Until we learn what happens to children randomly placed in different types of home it is exceedingly difficult to identify the various influences which are operative.

[1] The general problem of adoption is considered in detail in a United Nations study (1953) and, so far as mental health aspects are concerned, in a World Health Organization report (1953).

HISTORY OF TRUE PARENTS

It has often been considered that children available for adoption have in some sense a 'tainted' history, particularly when, as in the majority of cases, they are illegitimate. Greenland (1957), however, has challenged this view. He demonstrated that illegitimate children have a much higher mortality rate (in 1953, the infant mortality rate was 30 per 1,000 live births, compared with 51 per 1,000 for illegitimate children) and indicated that many of the survivors face a host of new hazards – social, emotional, medical, moral, and legal. But he quoted evidence suggesting that pre-marital chastity is now the exception rather than the rule, and it is therefore no longer possible to regard the unmarried mother as necessarily less stable or less moral than her married sister when the only difference may be her very much higher fertility. His data

> do not appear to support the view that unmarried mothers as a whole, apart from having conceived out of marriage, differ in important respects from other women of the same age and social class. If there is a difference it is in their relatively higher reproductive capacity which has a physical as well as a psychological basis. . . .

Nevertheless, an examination of the record of the true parents is the first and obvious step in considering whether a child is adoptable. Discussion in this chapter is of course confined to parents known to be mentally deficient; the following points are relevant:[1]

(1) The majority of defectives are born to parents who cannot themselves be regarded as mentally deficient, and so too the majority of the children of the mentally deficient are not themselves mentally deficient, even when brought up by their own parents or in institutions, although on the average they test lower than the general population. This is one aspect of the phenomenon of biological regression; the children of parents at either extreme of the intelligence distribution on the average function at less extreme levels. While

[1] Throughout this chapter intelligence alone is considered in relation to fostering and adoption. We have not reviewed the evidence relating to the genetic basis of some forms of epilepsy and of schizophrenia, which might complicate the problem in those comparatively rare cases where these conditions co-exist with mental deficiency. Nor have we discussed the controversial issues regarding the relative roles of heredity and environment in relation to temperamental differences.

these generalizations are important, they are clearly of only limited help in an individual case. Perhaps the most important figures available are those given by the Departmental Committee on Sterilization (1934):

> These relate to 3,733 defective parents drawn from various parts of the country (3,247 females and 486 males). These defectives produced a total of 8,841 children; of this number 2,001 or 22·5 per cent. had died, leaving 6,840 for investigation. Children under the age of 7 years were not included owing to the difficulty of ascertaining their mental status. Of those of the remainder who were over 13 years old, 32·4 per cent. were *defective*, 13 per cent. were *mentally retarded*, and 0·5 per cent. were of *superior mentality*; in other words, 45·4 per cent. of these children were suffering from either certifiable mental defect or dullness.

So far as the group between 7 and 13 years was concerned, 40·4 per cent. were either defective or retarded.

Burt (1937) examined the children of 500 defectives, previously investigated by him, and found that 14 per cent. were defective within the meaning of the Education Act, and another 32 per cent. dull and backward. 87 per cent. had an I.Q. of less than 100. He adds that among the children of the unmarried defectives the proportion was higher.

Penrose (1938) in his study of the antecedents and children of 1,280 patients in a Colchester institution found that 7·6 per cent. of the parents available for assessment were mentally defective. Ninety-five of the total of 2,560 could not be traced, but if these were added, the percentage would probably rise to 11·9. The proportion of defective parents was largest (12·1 per cent.) among the patients of simpleton (feeble-minded) grade, and the proportion was least (2·7 per cent.) for idiots.

Of the 570 female patients studied, only 67 had offspring (there were also two males who were known to have had children). The children of the female patients numbered 124, of whom only 56 lived long enough to be included in this survey, and most of these were examined with standardized tests. 23 of them were mentally normal, 16 were dull, 11 were simpletons, 3 were imbeciles, and 3 idiots, but the grade of the child appeared to be almost independent of the grade of the mother.

(2) During the last twenty years or so the interpretation of the

British Mental Deficiency Act widened, and consequently relatively large numbers of persons presenting social problems, who were of normal or only mildly subnormal intelligence, were certified as feeble-minded. Recent English evidence suggests that even under the Mental Health Act, 1959, the situation has not changed markedly. Thus paradoxically the label 'mentally deficient' applied to a mother of an illegitimate child does not necessarily connote a very low mental status. The first requirement is therefore an accurate assessment of the mother's I.Q., and where anything is known of the father the best that can be hoped for is an inference of his ability from occupational level, and any other relevant details.

(3) The cause of the mother's or father's deficiency must if possible be established for it is highly relevant. If it can be shown that the condition was acquired through disease or injury then in general we can state that genetically that person is normal, so that his or her children have a normal chance in this respect. A good control in this sort of case is to find out as much as possible about the defective's siblings (i.e. the child's uncles and aunts) or about the parents (i.e. the child's grandparents). In a similar environment the child would be likely to resemble them rather than the affected mother. It should be noted, however, that although sometimes organic defect is easy to diagnose (e.g. history of normal development until severe meningitis in early childhood), at other times it may be extremely difficult.

If the mother or father suffered from a rare genetically determined disorder (e.g. Huntington's chorea) or from some forms of epilepsy, then there would be an increased likelihood of the child being similarly affected, although occasionally the infant examination could rule this out. If, on the other hand, the defective parents had no history of organic involvement, nor of rare genetically determined conditions, then their I.Q. would be of some importance – the higher the better. Thus any certified person with an I.Q. of over about 80 must be regarded as genetically within the normal range of intelligence. This does not mean that children of parents below this figure can be automatically excluded from consideration, for as has been noted (Chapter V), the I.Q. must be related to the social background of the person. Thus if the mother comes from very adverse circumstances herself, her own I.Q. is likely anyway to increase until the age of 30, and even so, may well be depressed from her 'true potential' due to early experiences.

A further complicating feature is that it may well be that the ordinary principles of assortative mating (i.e. the mating of persons who tend in important ways to resemble each other) may not operate so strongly where illegitimate births by mentally deficient mothers are concerned. Sometimes the father, though of dubious morality, may be genetically well endowed intellectually, and this may counterbalance the mother's own mental subnormality.

Sometimes children have been excluded from adoption because of the parents' 'immoral way of life'; it is obvious that immorality is a learned form of behaviour which may have no relevance to genetical factors. The following case serves to illustrate the point.

William, now aged 17, has a Wechsler verbal I.Q. of 89, performance I.Q. 96, and full scale I.Q. of 92. On the Progressive Matrices his equivalent I.Q. is 102. He has been in various homes and institutions all his life, being illegitimate, and as one might expect, he is a rather shy, withdrawn youngster with poor educational attainments. As a baby he had been placed in a home by a County Council but was later withdrawn when the owner was prosecuted for neglecting children in her care. At the age of 2 years William was reported to be 'quite suitable for adoption' but was later removed from the list because of the mother's immoral way of life; she was thought to be a prostitute. This lad shows some of the features one would expect in a deprived child, yet is intellectually normal, and happens to be a devoutly religious person. There is no doubt that he was suitable for adoption and that he would have benefited from it inestimably, but he was denied this on the basis of what is in fact a hoary superstition. This took place as recently as 1942, and there must be many who have so suffered.

Finally, it should be stated that there is direct evidence (Skeels and Harms, 1948; Skodak and Skeels, 1949) that adopted children with inferior social histories and dull or mentally subnormal mothers usually develop to a higher level than might be expected from a knowledge of their true parents. In above average adoptive homes they had an average chance of normality, subnormality, or superiority. These studies need repetition and extension if there are to be advances in the understanding of the relevant factors (See Chapter V).

HISTORY AND EXAMINATION OF THE CHILD

The history of the child needs careful scrutiny; prolonged labour, forceps delivery, asphyxia, or prematurity may all be of relevance if they depart markedly from the normal, as may be malnutrition, attempted abortion, and so forth. Most cases of severe mental or physical deficiency can be recognized at birth or within a few weeks, particularly where clinical stigmata are present. Thus the history and physical examination by the doctor are important first steps in excluding abnormality or serious subnormality. Illingworth (1955), in an excellent discussion of the whole problem of recognizing serious mental retardation at a somewhat later age in the infant and pre-school child, believes that such a diagnosis must be made in four essential stages:

(1) *Developmental history*, which must be exceedingly comprehensive, 'since the cardinal feature of mental retardation in an infant is that he is retarded in all fields of development, except occasionally in sphincter control'. Thus the dates of passing the milestones of muscular development, sensory development, and the growth of understanding, concentration, learning to take solid food, and the acquisition of passive and active vocabularies are all important.

(2) *Family and environmental history*. Illingworth points out that lateness in certain fields of development, especially walking, talking, and sphincter control, often 'runs in the family' and therefore a history of this must be sought. Detailed information is required on how the child is handled by the mother, including any superstitions she may hold which may have influenced her child-rearing practices. He points out that institutional infants are usually retarded and 'it is essential to take this into consideration in assessing such children for adoption'. Such children usually make good their loss if placed in an adequate foster home, and, it might be added, if such placement is early in life.

(3) *Physical examination*, as mentioned, involves exclusion of gross forms of mental deficiency. The optic fundi should be examined for choroido-retinitis, optic atrophy, or other abnormalities. Hearing should be tested where relevant. Assessment of the infant's developmental level should be done in the child's normal play-time under optimum conditions. Unfavourable signs are general apathy, lack of prolonged concentration, and the slowness with which acts are performed.

(4) *Interpretation of findings* must avoid positive or negative 'halo

effects'; no diagnosis of mental retardation can be made on a few signs, mental or physical, unless these are crucial (e.g. phenylpyruvic acid in the urine).

Very often it is hoped that examination during the first few weeks or months of life will not only exclude gross defect but that it will be successful in predicting future development. Such a viewpoint has been most clearly expressed by Gesell (1940) who stated that:

> in no instance did the course of growth prove whimsical or erratic. The behaviour biographies gave clear evidence of a high degree of latent predictability, even in infancy. . . . Such examinations indicate whether an infant or child is of 'normal' mentality, and therefore a good adoption candidate, or if he is so subnormal that he is not a fit candidate. They further can to some extent discriminate within the normal group children, among average, above-average, and below-average endowment – thus giving a good clue as to what kind of home each child would best fit (op. cit., p. 149).

There is no doubt that Gesell is correct in believing that many of the grosser forms of mental defect can be excluded by his standardized form of clinical examination, and there is little doubt, too, that one aspect of the validity of his technique, namely the assessment of *present* developmental status, can be accurately undertaken. There is considerable doubt, however, about the second aspect of validity, the power of the examination to predict the course of future development within a normal group. In a most able monograph Wittenborn and his colleagues (1956) specifically evaluate the predictive validity of the Yale Developmental Examination of Infant Behaviour. Earlier investigators had in fact suggested that the predictive validity of infant assessments was nil (e.g. Bayley, 1940; Honzik, 1938; Honzik *et al.*, 1948). Wittenborn stated that: '. . . we have sought exhaustively to disprove the hypothesis of no predictive validity of the infant examination . . .' Two samples were studied, one of 114 children mostly in their fifth or sixth year at the time of follow-up, and the other 81 children mostly in their eighth or ninth year. Some of the children had been placed in homes before the infant examination, and others after it. The only reliable relationship between Gesell's General Maturity Quotient and Binet I.Q. was with the group placed *after* the infant examination and for whom at that time there had been a confident classification. The correlation was therefore likely to be an effect of selective placement.

Wittenborn stated in conclusion:

> our exploration of the relationships between the numerous facets of the infant examination and the numerous criteria for development which we have employed has yielded a lengthy and monotonous series of correlations which were not only unreliable but which were too small to be of any practical interest had they been based on huge samples.

He goes on to say that the correlations between aspects of the infant examination and his criteria which were statistically significant and large enough to suggest some practical value were so infrequent that they might result from chance or from selective placement (see also Wittenborn, 1957).

Macfarlane (1953) has reviewed for the World Health Organization the uses and predictive limitations of intelligence tests for the appraisal of intelligence and intelligence potential in infants and young children, in order to answer the question whether such tests 'show enough predictive validity to be dependable criteria on which to base adoption policy?' She indicated that infant tests have little or no predictive validity of adult status, and believed that those adopting parents who could only give responsiveness to a child of very high ability should be discouraged from adopting infants and should wait until older children are available when more accurate predictions can be made (e.g. at the age of 8 or 9). If in the meanwhile, however, such children are retained in institutions, they are likely to suffer maladjustment as Bowlby (1951) has shown. Thus the prospective adopter might be sure of reasonably high intelligence in a child at the cost of poor mental health, to say nothing of the greater difficulty of integrating a child of this age into the family and of personal identification with it. In summary, apart from excluding gross defect and severe retardation, the various forms of clinical examination have no practical long-term predictive validity before about the age of 4 years, and even at this stage it is comparatively small. It should be added that there is considerable resistance among workers in this field to accepting this fact.

ASSESSMENT OF PROSPECTIVE ADOPTERS

Some sort of assessment of prospective adoptive or foster parents is always made by adoption agencies. The main quality they look for is that these should be suitable to have care of a young child, and usually considerable effort is expended in ascertaining their respectability and standing.

> Agencies believe that such time should be devoted to the home study as will permit a thorough knowledge to be gained of the motives of the adopting parents for wanting to adopt a child; of their ability to deal with the educational problems presented by a growing child; of their attitude to each other and to the proposed adoption; and of the attitude to the adoption of the other members of the family. . . . The essential aim of the home study is to determine whether the applicants possess the qualities that make for good parenthood, and secondly, to find out whether they are likely to be able to deal more successfully with a particular type of child (United Nations study, 1953).

Apart from these important questions however, attention is far more concentrated upon the child.

There is evidence suggesting that even more attention should be paid to the qualities of the home and the general attitudes of the couple to the bringing up of children, because many important aspects of personality are thought to be linked with the cultural and emotional background in which the child is reared. This whole problem has been discussed in detail by Bowlby (op. cit., pp. 104–8). He points out that

> to dub a baby unfit for adoption is usually to condemn him to a deprived childhood and an unhappy life. Few are qualified to reach this decision and the grounds on which it is commonly reached today in Western countries are more often well-meaning than well-informed. For instance, many adoption agencies place an absolute bar on the children of incestuous relationships, however good the stock. Naïve theories of genetics may also lead to a child being blackballed for such reasons as having a sibling mentally defective or a parent suffering from mental illness. . . . In the days when it was the accepted psychiatric view that all mental illness was hereditary this may have been a reasonable policy. Now that this is no longer so it is unreasonable, except in those cases where the incidence of mental defect or illness in the family is clearly much above the average. . . .

Wittenborn's (1956) monograph once again reaches a new level in respect of care and experimental control. Using the same two samples of children (see p. 108) he pointed out that a standard body of specific information concerning child-rearing practices had emerged from semi-structured interviews with adoptive mothers. This information was organized into clusters on psychological and statistical grounds (e.g. eagerness on the part of the mother, lack of sympathy, severity of toilet training, etc.). The interviews had also cast light upon the values in the home and its general atmosphere, in fact on the general conditions of child-rearing.

Wittenborn obtained information about the child's personal and social development from the child's own statements about his behaviour, from the adoptive mother's description, and from examiner's ratings. He pointed out that heredity may be suspected as a 'confounding third variable' in the correlations between developmental criteria and environmental measurements when the particular aspect was usually considered to have an hereditary component (e.g. intelligence). Such correlations would be a likely effect of selective placement. Where, however, developmental aspects not considered to have an hereditary basis were shown to relate to conditions of child-rearing, there would be some reason to believe that these were not due to selective placement but emerged as a response to these particular practices. It was, however, emphasized that the environmental measures were relatively crude and that confirmatory studies would be needed before their practical importance was completely established.

Wittenborn and his collaborators, for example, showed that in the younger sample there was a correlation of 0·33 between phobic reactions and unsympathetic child-rearing practices (operationally defined). For the older sample, anxious reactions correlated to the extent of 0·35 with unsympathetic child-rearing.

The relationships described were not particularly strong, and if, as the authors suspected, many were an expression of the formative role of the environmental differences, they should not be taken as indications of the possible maximal importance of such differences; their importance may be much greater than indicated. It seems likely, the authors concluded, that inharmonious, incompatible, and rejective adoptive parents may tend to produce children who are aggressive and fearful. We might suspect that much of the effort commonly devoted to an exact evaluation of the children could more profitably be devoted to a study of the applicants who desire to be adoptive parents (see also Wittenborn, 1957).

Furthermore, some of the Iowa studies, already referred to in this chapter (see also Chapter V), have a direct bearing on this problem. In general, the illegitimate children of mentally deficient mothers, when adopted early by families of above average socio-economic status, showed a normal distribution of intelligence quotients, when followed up later; as this statement implies a proportion of them were below average in I.Q. with a small number of very subnormal persons. A corresponding number were of very superior intelligence, with I.Q.s up to 150, and the rest were in the normal range (mean I.Q. for groups of this type was usually a little above 100). The reasons for this may have been a combination of biological regression, organic damage in a parent, non-assortative mating, and a superior environment from an early age. The main implication is, however, that most of these children developed normally and in a way quite different from what would have been predicted, on the assumption that each generation is a faithful copy of the previous one, by an analysis of the intellectual and social status of the true mothers.

SUBNORMAL WOMEN AS PARENTS

In this connexion Sarason (1953) states a number of hypotheses about child rearing practices in mentally deficient families which he hopes will focus interest in this subject, although he fully expects that they will be modified by subsequent research. These can be summarized as follows:

(1) 'The defective mother does not plan to have a child, probably its presence is an unnecessary annoyance, does not possess adequate knowledge of or receive guidance in child care, and is probably more concerned with her own than the child's needs. In other words, the defective mother is not adequately aware of or set to respond to the child.'

(2) She will probably deny her child adequate fondling, caressing, and play.

(3) She will probably lack reassuring responsiveness to the child when distressed, may be inconsistent and even punitive in her handling of it.

(4) By virtue of her intellectual limitations, she is unlikely to understand the importance of correct feeding, or be able to make wise decisions in this connexion.

(5) Since the number of children may well be large, the infant may receive little maternal attention and may frequently be entrusted to siblings.

(6) The defective mother is unlikely to stimulate the child's initial attempts at verbalization or locomotion, and in fact may restrict these if they interfere with her own activities.

(7) The children of defective parents are unlikely to enjoy the stimulation of toys and educational material and may not be encouraged in the acquisition of correct discriminatory responses.

Burt (1951) has described vividly some of the material and psychological deprivations suffered by children reared in pre-war London slums, and focuses particular attention upon the 'efficiency of the mother' as being of major importance for the young child (op. cit., p. 333). Obviously, in addition, a higher incidence of disease, overcrowding, accidents, and the acquisition of subcultural moral standards combine to give the child reared in such surroundings the worst possible chance of developing to the full his innate potential, and may well determine a pattern of inadequate or irresponsible behaviour which may ultimately culminate in official intervention. Recent work by Brandon (1957), however, has raised the issue of the desirability of mothers who have been classed as defective bringing up their own children. She examined the children of 73 certified mentally defective mothers from the Fountain Hospital, most of whom at the time of the study were working or living in the community. Those who were married were found on ratings to be 'at least average, for their broad social group, when rated as wives, housewives and mothers'. Of the 150 children, 41 had died, this figure including (personal communication) 8 miscarriages and 5 still-births. The average I.Q. of those who survived was found to be 91, but since 51 of the 109 children were below the age of six, these results are more in the nature of an estimate without long-term implications in individual cases.

So far these results are in accord with those of previous investigations. Unfortunately, however, they do little to advance our knowledge, for much crucial evidence seems either to be lacking or not to have been presented. Thus, one general theme in Brandon's papers concerns genetic factors, and the considerable difference between mothers and children. In this connexion the following difficulties arise:

(1) A near-zero correlation between parental and child I.Q.s is quoted. Since, however, most of her sample were very young, and since it is well known that the size of correlation is dependent on the age of the children (see Chapter V and also Jones, in Carmichael,

1954), we asked Mrs Brandon for the correlation for the group excluding those under five years of age. She found (personal communication) that the correlation between children's and averaged parental I.Q. became 0·25, and when three severely defective children (probably 'organic') were excluded, this again rose to 0·41, which is what would normally be expected. Her discussion of genetic factors was thus based on insufficient analysis.

(2) The probability that organic factors were of aetiological significance in at least some of the mothers is not mentioned. Such persons are likely to be genetically normal. The fact that maternal-child I.Q. correlation is much smaller than paternal-child correlation adds support to this possibility.

(3) Non-assortative mating and its genetical effects are not mentioned, but from further material, which Mrs Brandon kindly supplied, it seems likely that mating was non-assortative within the group.

(4) The number of children dealt with as mentally deficient or educationally subnormal was found to be 18, although not all these had very low I.Q.s. Brandon calculates various percentages as proportions of her total group of 109 children, yet, since nearly half her sample is within the age range 0–5 years, it is clearly illegitimate to discuss educational subnormality, or indeed to assess mental deficiency accurately at such ages. In fact, if those who have at any time been dealt with as mentally deficient or E.S.N. are calculated as a proportion of the 58 cases aged six and above, the percentage rises to 31.

(5) The exceptionally large proportion of the group which had died before two years of age (16 per cent.), together with high miscarriage and stillbirth rates, needs explanation, as the author comments. Until such explanation is attempted, with full supporting evidence which is often very difficult to obtain, we can go little further than the Departmental Committee on Sterilization (1934) which drew attention to the striking death rate in children of such persons, and considered this to be due to the adverse circumstances in which many live, their inability to take proper care of their children, and to the possibility of some correlation between mental defect and poor physique. Brandon has informed us, however, that with six possible exceptions, the dead children were never in the care of their mothers.

(6) Several different intelligence tests seem to have been administered during the research but taking the group of mothers who had been given the most appropriate test for their age, the Wechsler, a

mean I.Q. of 83 was demonstrated. This placed them on the borderline of dull-normality, and an average of ten points higher on this test than is representative of the certified feeble-minded in institutions. They may not therefore be completely typical cases. The estimated I.Q.s of the fathers for some reason were not given, but Mrs Brandon (personal communication) states the average as 94. The children's mean I.Q. of 91 is thus entirely in accordance with expectation on the basis of a genetic theory.

More important than the I.Q.s, however, is the problem of the success or otherwise of the mothers in rearing their children. While theoretically one would assume from the facts quoted that some of these women would be adequate as mothers, one would also assume, in the absence of crucial evidence to the contrary, that a large proportion of those certified as mentally deficient who are (*a*) really subnormal intellectually, and (*b*) have all too often themselves been reared in most adverse circumstances, would not make adequate mothers. In fact, there is little doubt that severely subnormal and unstable women often have a deplorable effect on their children (cf. Burt, 1937; H. Lewis, 1954, and others).

Mrs Brandon's belief that the mothers were average for their neighbourhood is not qualified by assessment of the neighbourhoods themselves; obviously it would mean very little for those living in slum conditions. Research from many viewpoints has stressed that deprived and institutionalized persons tend to hand on to their offspring their own environmentally-induced instabilities; moreover, Sarason's list of qualities one would expect in such persons (Chapter VI) is also relevant. It would therefore be very surprising if many such mothers were able to adopt reasonable child-rearing practices and indeed examination of some illuminating but perhaps not typical case histories summarized in Brandon's Appendix 1 indicates the problems involved. The fact that inadequate or adverse mothering is not confined to the mentally deficient is, moreover, no great comfort to their children.

In summary, this is a very important investigation which must unfortunately be regarded as unsatisfactory because of a lack of detailed analysis of the data and gaps in the information available to its author. It seems that the whole problem of whether it is in the child's interests to be brought up by a truly subnormal mother is still very much an open question upon which planned, as opposed to retrospective, research is needed. Discussion with Mrs Brandon has, however, indicated that, due to a number of difficulties, it was impossible to collect some of the data which we considered essential.

CONCLUSIONS

Adoption, like ordinary parenthood, involves risks, and in a society in which a premium is placed upon intelligence it may be a grave misfortune for intelligent parents to have children below average or even of average ability. There is little doubt that for such persons the risks involved with children of the mentally deficient are much greater than the risks with their own children, although the difference is smaller than at one time was thought.

From all viewpoints – integration in the family, early security, emotional identifications, and so forth – early adoption or fostering is of great importance both to the child and to the adoptive parents. At such ages, however, prediction of future development from examination of the child (apart from excluding gross mental or physical handicap) is impossible. Similarly, prediction of the child's future from a study of the true parents may also give a misleading picture, complicated in the case of mentally deficient parents by the possibility of organic defect in a genetically normal person, by biological regression, by non-assortative mating or by subcultural deficiency which may result, partly at least, from early adverse experiences which, though profoundly damaging to the person, will have no genetic effect. There is direct evidence of some value which shows the discrepancy between the status of mentally deficient parents and their children's development in above average adoptive homes.

It is a truism that many important aspects of personality are formed in the early years, and that mother–child relationships and cultural opportunity and stimulation are of the utmost importance. It may well be that closer study of variations in child-rearing practices will indicate more certainly those in the child's best interests and those which are not, and which are likely to lead to frustration, aggression, anxiety, and poor mental health. Preliminary work in this field is encouraging, and thus much more attention must be paid to the prospective adopters, their motivation and attitudes, than has commonly happened in the past.

When parents wish to adopt children of the mentally deficient they should be told the full facts about the child in so far as these are known, and they should seek advice from an expert competent to weigh the relevant factors; thus every case must be treated on its merits and wide generalizations are unwise, but it does seem worth re-stating one such rule, that the majority of the children of the mentally deficient, even though brought up by their own parents or in institutions, are not themselves mentally deficient, although under such conditions (as opposed to foster homes) they are generally dull, unless they are the offspring of subnormals with a clear 'organic' history.

Where some assurance of superior ability is desired by prospective adopters they should be discouraged from adopting children when these are very young. It should be explained that adoption of older children also has hazards in terms of emotional maladjustment, even though one can be more certain of prediction of intellectual abilities. Fostering a child followed by later adoption may be a possible compromise because the foster parents are not then fully committed, but this means having a child 'on approval' with all that this implies. Such an experiment with another human being can be damaging to all concerned. There is no doubt, however, that fostering is a minimal desirable requirement of every child who cannot be maintained by his own parents, and every child, unless grossly defective, should be given such a chance. At the present time this is increasingly being recognized, and there is in fact a change from the earlier belief that children of the mentally deficient should automatically be excluded from adoption; this is a welcome tendency and one in accord with our greater knowledge.

REFERENCES

A. A. M. D. PROJECT (1964) 'Technical Planning in Mental Retardation.' Monograph published as Supplement to *Amer. J. ment. Defic.* **68.**

ABEL, T. M. (1941) 'Moral judgments among subnormals.' *J. abnorm. soc. Psychol.* **36,** 378–92.

ABEL, T. M. (1945) 'The relationship between academic success and personality organization among subnormal girls.' *Amer. J. ment. Defic.* **50,** 251–6.

ABEL, T. M. (1953) 'Resistances and difficulties in psychotherapy of mental retardates.' *J. clin. Psychol.* **9,** 107–9.

ABEL, T. M. and KINDER, E. F. (1942) *The Subnormal Adolescent Girl.* New York: Columbia Univ. Press.

ABERCROMBIE, M. L. J. (1960) 'Perception and eye movements. Some speculations on disorders in cerebral palsy.' *Cerebral Palsy Bull.* **2,** 142–7.

ABERCROMBIE, M. L. J. (1964) *Perceptual and Visuo-motor Disorders in Cerebral Palsy. A Survey of the Literature.* Little Club Clinics in Developmental Medicine No. 11. London: Spastics Society, Medical Education and Information Unit, and Heinemann (Medical Books) Ltd.

ABERNETHY, E. M. (1936) 'Relationships between mental and physical growth.' *Monogr. Soc. Res. Child Develpm.* **1,** No. 7.

ACKERMAN, N. W. and MENNINGER, C. E. (1936) 'Treatment techniques for mental retardation in a school for personality disorders in children.' *Amer. J. Orthopsychiat.* **6,** 294–313.

AINSWORTH, M. D. (1962) *Deprivation of Maternal Care: A reassessment of its Effects.* Geneva: World Hlth. Org.

ÅKERRÉN, Y. (1955) 'Early diagnosis and early therapy in congenital cretinism.' *Arch. Dis. Child.* **30,** 254–6.

ALBERT, K., HOCH, P. and WAELSCH, H. (1946) 'Preliminary report on the effect of glutamic acid administration in mentally retarded subjects.' *J. nerv. ment. Dis.* **104,** 263–74.

ALDERDICE, E. T. and BUTLER, A. J. (1952) 'An analysis of the performance of mental defectives on the Revised Stanford–Binet and the Wechsler–Bellevue Intelligence Scale.' *Amer. J. ment. Defic.* **56,** 609–14.

ALDRICH, C. G. and DOLL, E. A. (1931) 'Problem solving among idiots.' *J. comp. Psychol.* **12,** 137–69.

ALEXANDER, W. P. (1935) 'Intelligence, concrete and abstract.' *Brit. J. Psychol. Monogr. Suppl.* No. 19.

ALLAN, J. D., CUSWORTH, D. C., DENT, C. E. and WILSON, V. K. (1958) 'A disease, probably hereditary, characterized by severe mental deficiency and a constant gross abnormality of aminoacid metabolism.' *Lancet* **i,** 182–7.

ALLARDYCE, R. H. (1939) Corporation of Glasgow, Education Department. 'Statistical report on the qualifying examination held in May, 1939.'

ALLEN, M. K. (1942) 'A comparison between test scores on the Original and the Revised Stanford–Binet Intelligence Scales administered to a group of retarded and mentally deficient subjects.' *Amer. J. ment. Defic.* **46,** 501–7.

REFERENCES

ALLEN, R. M. (1947) 'The test performance of the brain injured.' *J. clin. Psychol.* **3,** 225–30.

ALLEN, R. M. (1949) 'Why some girls "run away".' *Amer. J. ment. Defic.* **53,** 438–40.

ALTUS, W. D. and THOMPSON, G. (1949) 'The Rorschach as a measure of intelligence.' *J. consult. Psychol.* **13,** 341–7.

ANASTASI, A. and FOLEY, J. P. (1949) *Differential Psychology* (reprinted 1956). New York: Macmillan.

ANDERSON, A. L. (1951) 'The effect of laterality localization of focal brain lesions on the Wechsler–Bellevue Subtests.' *J. clin. Psychol.* **7,** 149–53.

ANNETT, J. (1957) 'The information capacity of young mental defectives in an assembly task.' *J. ment. Sci.* **103,** 621–31.

ANTHONY, E. J. (1962) 'Low grade psychosis in childhood.' *Proc. Lond. Conf. scient. Stud. ment. Defic.*, 1960. **2.** 398–410. Dagenham: May & Baker.

ARBITMAN, H. D. (1953) 'Rorschach determinants in mentally defective and normal subjects.' *Train. Sch. Bull.* **50,** 143–51.

ARCHIBALD, H. M. (1958) 'Influence of maternal malaria on newborn infants.' *Brit. med. J.* **2,** 1512–14.

ARMITAGE, S. G. (1946) 'An analysis of certain psychological tests used for the evaluation of brain injury.' *Psychol. Monogr.* **60,** 1–47.

ASHER, P. and SCHONELL, F. E. (1950) 'A survey of 400 cases of cerebral palsy in childhood.' *Arch. Dis. Child.* **25,** 360–79.

ASTRACHAN, M. (1955) 'Group psychotherapy with mentally retarded female adolescents and adults.' *Amer. J. ment. Defic.* **60,** 152–6.

ATTENBOROUGH, J. and FARBER, M. (1934) 'The relationship between intelligence, mechanical ability and manual dexterity in special school children.' *Brit. J. educ. Psychol.* **4,** 140–61.

AXLINE, V. M. (1947) 'Non-directive therapy for poor readers.' *J. consult. Psychol.* **11,** 61–9.

AXLINE, V. M. (1948) 'Some observations on play therapy.' *J. consult. Psychol.* **12,** 209–16.

AXLINE, V. M. (1949) 'Mental deficiency – symptom or disease.' *J. consult. Psychol.* **13,** 313–27.

BAAR, H. S. (1959) 'Kernicterus.' *J. Maine med. Ass.* **50,** 111–17.

BADHAM, J. N. (1955) 'The outside employment of hospitalized mentally defective patients as a step towards resocialization.' *Amer. J. ment. Defic.* **59,** 666–80.

BADT, M. I. (1958) 'Levels of abstraction in vocabulary definitions of mentally retarded school children.' *Amer. J. ment. Defic.* **63,** 241–6.

BALINSKY, B., ISRAEL, H. and WECHSLER, D. (1939) 'The relative effectiveness of the Stanford–Binet and the Bellevue Intelligence Scale in diagnosing mental deficiency.' *Amer. J. Orthopsychiat.* **9,** 798–801.

BALLARD, P. B. (1934) *Thought and Language*. London: Univ. Lond. Press.

BALLER, W. R. (1936) 'A study of the present social status of a group of adults who, when they were in elementary schools, were classified as mentally deficient.' *Genet. Psychol. Monogr.* **18,** 165–244.

BARKER, R., DEMBO, T. and LEWIN, K. (1941) 'Frustration and regression: an experiment with young children.' *Univ. Iowa Stud. Child Welf.* **18,** No. 1.

BARNETT, C. D. and CANTOR, G. N. (1957) 'Discrimination set in defectives.' *Amer. J. ment. Defic.* **62,** 334–7.

BAROFF, G. S. (1957) 'Bender–Gestalt visuo-motor function in mental deficiency.' *Amer. J. ment. Defic.* **61,** 753–60.

REFERENCES

BAROFF, G. S. (1959) 'W.I.S.C. patterning in endogenous mental deficiency.' *Amer. J. ment. Defic.* **64,** 482–5.

BARR, M. L. and BERTRAM, E. G. (1949) 'A morphological distinction between neurones of the male and female, and the behaviour of the nucleolar satellite during accelerated nucleoprotein synthesis.' *Nature* (*Lond.*) **163,** 676–7.

BARR, M. L., SHAVER, E. L., CARR, D. H. and PLUNKETT, E. R. (1960) 'The chromatin-positive Klinefelter syndrome among patients in mental deficiency hospitals.' *J. ment. Defic. Res.* **4,** 89–107.

BARTLET, D. and SHAPIRO, M. B. (1956) 'Investigation and treatment of a reading disability in a dull child with severe psychiatric disturbances.' *Brit. J. educ. Psychol.* **26,** 180–90.

BAYLEY, N. (1940) 'Mental growth in young children.' *Yearb. Nat. Soc. Stud. Educ.* **39,** 11–47, quoted by Jones in Carmichael (1954).

BAYLEY, N. (1949) 'Consistency and variability in growth of intelligence from birth to 18 years.' *J. genet. Psychol.* **75,** 165–96.

BAYLEY, N. (1955) 'On the growth of intelligence.' *Amer. Psychol.* **10,** 805–18.

BAYLEY, N. and ODEN, M. H. (1955) 'The maintenance of intellectual ability in gifted adults.' *J. Gerontol.* **10,** 91–107.

BEACH, F. A. and JAYNES, J. (1954) 'Effects of early experience upon the behaviour of animals.' *Psychol. Bull.* **51,** 239–63.

BEARD, R. J. (1953) 'Industrial therapy with mental defectives.' *Amer. J. ment. Defic.* **57,** 547–53.

BECK, H. S. and LAM, R. L. (1955) 'Use of the W.I.S.C. in predicting organicity.' *J. clin. Psychol.* **11,** 154–8.

BECK, S. J. (1930) 'The Rorschach Test and personality diagnosis.' *Amer. J. Psychiat.* **10,** 19–52.

BECK, S. J. (1932). 'The Rorschach Test as applied to a feebleminded group.' *Arch. Psychol.* **136,** 1–84.

BECKY, R. E. (1942) 'A study of certain factors related to retardation of speech.' *J. Speech Dis.* **7,** 232–49.

BELL, J. (1940) 'A determination of the consanguinity rate in the general hospital population of England and Wales.' *Ann. Eugen.* (*Lond.*) **10,** 370–91.

BENDA, C. E. (1942) 'Congenital syphilis in mental deficiency.' *Amer. J. ment. Defic.* **47,** 40–8.

BENDER, L. (1933) 'Gestalt function in mental defect.' *Proc. Amer. Assoc. ment. Defic.* **38,** 88–106.

BENDER, L. (1938) *A Visual Motor Gestalt Test and its Clinical Use.* New York: Amer. Orthopsychiat. Assoc. Research Monographs 3.

BENDER, L. (1940) 'The Goodenough Test (Drawing a Man) in chronic encephalitis in children.' *J. nerv. ment. Dis.* **91,** 277–86.

BENDER, L. (1953) *Aggression, Hostility and Anxiety in Children.* Springfield, Ill.: Chas. C. Thomas.

BENDER, L. (1954) 'Symposium on Juvenile Schizophrenia.' *In Neurology and Psychiatry in Childhood.* Assoc. for Research in Nervous and Mental Diseases. New York: Williams & Wilkins.

BENDER, L. (1955) 'Twenty years of clinical research on schizophrenic children with special reference to those under six years of age.' *In* Caplan, G. (Ed.) (1955).

BENDER, L. (1960) 'Organicity in schizophrenic children.' *Proc. Lond. Conf. scient. Stud. ment. Defic., 1960.* **2,** 411–17. Dagenham: May & Baker.

BENNETT, A. (1929) 'Reading ability in special classes.' *J. educ. Res.* **20,** 236–8.

BENSBERG, G. J. (1952) 'Performance of brain-injured and familial mental defectives on the Bender-Gestalt Test.' *J. consult. Psychol.* **16,** 61–4.

BENSBERG, G. J. (1953) 'The relation of academic achievement of mental defectives to mental age, sex, institutionalization and etiology.' *Amer. J. ment. Defic.* **58,** 327–30.

BENSBERG, G. J. (1962) 'Concept learning in mental defectives as a function of appropriate and inappropriate "attention sets".' *J. educ. Psychol.* **49,** 137–43.

BENSBERG, G. J. and CANTOR, G. N. (1957) 'Simple and discriminative reaction time in mental defectives of organic and familial etiology.' *Amer. J. ment. Defic.* **62,** 534–7.

BENSBERG, G. J. and SLOAN, W. (1950) 'A study of Wechsler's concept of "Normal Deterioration" in older mental defectives.' *J. clin. Psychol.* **6,** 359–62.

BENTON, A. L. (1956) 'The concept of pseudofeeble-mindedness.' *Arch. Neurolog. Psychiat.* **75,** 379–88.

BENTON, A. L., HUTCHEON, J. F. and SEYMOUR, E. (1951) 'Arithmetic ability, finger localization capacity and right-left discrimination in normal and defective children.' *Amer. J. Orthopsychiat.* **21,** 756–66.

BERG, J. M. (1690) 'Postnatal head injury as a cause of mental defect.' *Arch. Pediat.* **77,** 207–11.

BERG, J. M. (1962a) 'Meningitis as a cause of severe mental defect.' *Proc. Lond. Conf. scient. Stud. ment. Defic, 1960* **1,** 160–4. Dagenham: May & Baker.

BERG, J. M. (1962b) 'Whooping cough encephalopathy.' *Indian Practitioner* **15,** 559–61.

BERG, J. M. (1963a) 'Causal factors in severe mental retardation.' *Proc. 2nd int. Congr. ment. Retard., Vienna, 1961* **1,** 170–3.

BERG, J. M. (1963b) Unpublished observations.

BERG, J. M., CROME, L. and FRANCE, N. E. (1960) 'Congenital cardiac malformations in mongolism.' *Brit. Heart J.* **22,** 331–46.

BERG, J. M. and KIRMAN, B. H. (1959) 'Syphilis as a cause of mental deficiency.' *Brit. med. J.* **2,** 400–4.

BERG, J. M. and KIRMAN, B. H. (1960) 'The mentally defective twin.' *Brit. med. J.* **1,** 1911–17.

BERG, J. M., KIRMAN, B. H., STERN, J. and MITTWOCH, V. (1961) 'Treatment of mongolism with pituitary extract.' *J. ment. Sci.* **107,** 475–80.

BERGMAN, M. and FISHER, L. A. (1953) 'The value of the thematic apperception test in mental deficiency.' *Psychiat. Quart. Suppl.* **27,** 22–42.

BERGMAN, M., WALLER, H. and MARCHAND, J. (1951) 'Schizophrenic reactions during childhood in mental defectives.' *Psychiat. Quart.* **25,** 254–333.

BERKSON, G. (1961) 'Responsiveness of the mentally deficient.' *Amer. J. ment. Defic.* **66,** 277–86.

BERNREUTER, R. G. and CARR, E. J. (1938) 'The interpretation of I.Q.s on the L–M–Stanford–Binet.' *J. educ. Psychol.* 312–14.

BERNSTEIN, B. (1960) 'Language and social class'. *Brit. J. Sociol.* **11,** 271–6.

BERNSTEIN, B. (1962a) 'Linguistic codes, hesitation phenomena, and intelligence.' *Language and Speech* **5,** 31–46.

BERNSTEIN, B. (1962b) 'Social class, linguistic codes, and grammatical errors.' *Language and Speech* **5,** 221–40.

BERRIEN, F. K. (1935) 'A study of the drawings of abnormal children.' *J. educ. Psychol.* **26,** 143–50.

BERRY, M. F. and EISENSON, J. (1956) *Speech Disorders.* New York: Appleton-Century-Crofts.

BERRY, R. J. A. (1933) *Stoke Park Monographs on Mental Deficiency and Other Problems of the Human Brain and Mind.* London: Macmillan.

BICE, H. V. and CRUICKSHANK, W. M. (1955) 'The evaluation of intelligence.' Chap. III *in* Cruickshank and Raus (Ed.) (1955).

BIJOU, S. W. (1942a) 'The psychometric pattern approach as an aid to clinical analysis – a review.' *Amer. J. ment. Defic.* **46,** 354–62.

BIJOU, S. W. (1942b) 'A genetic study of the diagnostic significance of psychometric patterns.' *Amer. J. ment. Defic.* **47,** 171–7.

BIJOU, S. W. (1944) 'Behaviour efficiency as a determining factor in the social adjustment of mentally retarded young men.' *J. genet. Psychol.* **65,** 133–45.

BIJOU, S. W. and MCCANDLESS, B. (1944) 'An approach to a more comprehensive analysis of mentally retarded pre-delinquent boys.' *J. genet. Psychol.* **65,** 147–60.

BINET, A. and SIMON, T. (1914) *Mentally Defective Children* (trans. W. B. Drummond). New York: Longmans, Green.

BINET, A., SIMON, T. and VANEY, F. A. (1907) 'Pedagogie scientifique.' *L'Année Psychologique*, **12,** 233–74.

BIRCH, J. W. (1949) 'The Goodenough Drawing Test and older mentally retarded children.' *Amer. J. ment. Defic.* **54,** 218–24.

BIRCH, J. W. and MATTHEWS, J. (1951) 'The hearing of mental defectives: its measurement and characteristics.' *Amer. J. ment. Defic.* **55,** 384–93.

BIRKELUND, L. and JACOBSEN, J. R. (1960) 'Normal relationships between institutionalized subnormals.' *J. ment. Subnormal.* **6,** 13–18.

BLACKER, C. P. (1952) *Problem Families: Five Enquiries*. London: Eugenics Soc.

BLACKETTER-SIMMONDS, L. D. A. (1953) 'An investigation into the supposed differences existing between mongols and other mentally defective subjects with regard to certain psychological traits.' *J. ment. Sci.* **99,** 702–19.

BLACKMAN, S. S. (1937) 'The lesions of lead encephalitis in children.' *Bull. Johns Hopk. Hosp.* **61,** 1–62.

BLAKE, R. R. and MCCARTY, B. S. (1948) 'A comparative evaluation of the Bellevue–Wechsler Mental Deterioration Index distributions of Allen's brain injured patients and normal subjects.' *J. clin. Psychol.* **4,** 415–18.

BLANK, C. E. (1960) 'Apert's syndrome (a type of acrocephalosyndactyly) – observations on a British series of thirty-nine cases.' *Ann. hum. Genet.* **24,** 151–64.

BLAU, A. (1936) 'Mental changes following head trauma in children.' *Arch. Neurol. Psychiat.* (Chicago) **35,** 723–69.

BLISS, M. and BERGER, A. (1954) 'Measurement of mental age as indicated by the male figure drawings of the mentally subnormal using Goodenough and Machover instructions.' *Amer. J. ment. Defic.* **59,** 73–9.

BOARD OF CONTROL (1954) *Memorandum of Evidence before the Royal Commission on the Law relating to Mental Illness and Mental Deficiency.* Day 1. London: H.M.S.O.

BOBATH, K. and BOBATH, B. (1952) 'A treatment of cerebral palsy.' *Brit. J. phys. Med.* **15,** 107–17.

BODIAN, M., WHITE, L. L. R., CARTER, C. O. and LOUW, J. H. (1952) 'Congenital duodenal obstruction and mongolism.' *Brit. med. J.* **1,** 77–8.

BODMAN, F. (1946) 'Social maturity test.' *J. ment. Sci.* **92,** 532–41.

BOEHM, A. E. and SARASON, S. B. (1947) 'Does Wechsler's formula distinguish intellectual deterioration from mental deficiency?' *J. abnorm. soc. Psychol.* **42,** 356–8.

BOLDT, W. H. (1948) 'Postnatal cerebral trauma as an etiological factor in mental deficiency.' *Amer. J. ment. Defic.* **53,** 247–67.

BOLES, G. (1959) 'Personality factors in mothers of cerebral palsied children.' *Gen. Psychol. Monogr.* **59,** 159–218.

BÖÖK, J. A., SCHUT, J. W. and REED, S. C. (1953) 'A clinical and genetical study of microcephaly.' *Amer. J. ment. Defic.* **57,** 637–60.

BORDLEY, J. E. (1956) 'An evaluation of the psychogalvanic skin-resistance technique in audiometry.' *Laryngoscope* **66,** 1162–83.

BORRECA, F., BURGER, R., GOLDSTEIN, I. and SIMCHES, R. (1953) 'A functional core vocabulary for slow learners.' *Amer. J. ment. Defic.* **58,** 273–300.

VAN DEN BOSCH, J. (1959) 'Microcephaly in the Netherlands: a clinical and genetical study.' *Ann. hum. Genet.* **23,** 91–116.

BOURNE, H. (1955) 'Protophrenia: a study of perverted rearing and mental dwarfism.' *Lancet* **ii,** 1156–63.

BOURNEVILLE, D. M. (1880) 'Sclérose tubéreuse des circonvolutions cérébrales: idiotie et épilepsie hemiplégique.' *Arch. Neurol.* (Paris) **1,** 81–9.

BOWLBY, J. (1951) *Maternal Care and Mental Health.* Geneva: World Health Organization.

BOWLBY, J., AINSWORTH, M., BOSTON, M. and ROSENBLUTH, D. (1956) 'The effects of mother-child separation: a follow-up study.' *Brit. J. med. Psychol.* **29,** 211–47.

BOWYER, R. (1958) 'The sand tray world as a projective technique with mental defectives.' *J. Midland ment. Defic. Soc.* **4,** 44–55.

BOYD, F. (1949) 'A provisional quantitative scoring with preliminary norms for the Goldstein-Scheerer cube test.' *J. clin. Psychol.* **5,** 148–53.

BRADLEY, C. (1941) *Schizophrenia in Childhood.* New York: Macmillan.

BRADLEY, N. C. (1948) 'The growth of the knowledge of time in children of school age.' *Brit. J. Psychol.* **38,** 67–78.

BRADWAY, U. P. and THOMPSON, C. W. (1962) 'Intelligence at adulthood: a twenty-five year follow-up.' *J. educ. Psychol.* **53,** 1–14.

BRAIN, W. RUSSELL (1952) *Diseases of the Nervous System.* London: Oxford Univ. Press.

BRAND, H., BENOIT, E. P. and ORNSTEIN, G. N. (1953) 'Rigidity and feeble-mindedness: an examination of the Kouin–Lewin theory.' *J. clin. Psychol.* **9,** 375–8.

BRANDON, M. W. G. (1957) 'The intellectual and social status of children of mental defectives.' *J. ment. Sci.* **103,** Part I, 710–24; Part II, 725–38.

BRANDON, M. W. G. and STERN, D. J. (1962) 'An experiment comparing two educational methods with young imbecile children.' *Proc. Lond. Conf. scient. Stud. ment. Defic., 1960,* **2,** 357–60. Dagenham: May & Baker.

BRILL, M. (1936) 'Performance tests as aids in the diagnosis of maladjustment. *J. genet. Psychol.* **49,** 199–213.

BRILL, M. (1937) 'A study of instability using the Goodenough Drawing Scale.' *J. abnorm. soc. Psychol.* **32,** 288–302.

BRITISH MEDICAL ASSOCIATION AND MAGISTRATES' ASSOCIATION (1947) *Interpretation of Definitions in the Mental Deficiency Act, 1927.* London: B.M.A.

BRITISH PSYCHOLOGICAL SOCIETY (1955) *Memorandum of Evidence before the Royal Commission on the Law relating to Mental Illness and Mental Deficiency* Day 17. London: H.M.S.O.

BRITISH PSYCHOLOGICAL SOCIETY (1963) 'Report of the Working Party on subnormality.' *Bull. Brit. Psychol. Soc.* **16,** 37–50.

BROCA, P. (1861) 'Remarque sur le siège de la faculté du langue articulé, suivies d'une observation d'aphémie.' *Bull. soc. anat.* **2.**

BROMLEY, D. B. (1953) 'Primitive forms of response to the Matrices Test.' *J. ment Sci.* **99,** 374–93.

BRONNER, A. F. (1933) 'Follow-up studies of mental defectives.' *Proc. Amer. Assoc. ment. Defic.* **38,** 258–67.

BROWER, J. F. and BROWER, D. (1947) 'The relation between temporal judgment and social competence in the feebleminded.' *Amer. J. ment. Defic.* **51,** 619–23.

BROWN, M. H. and BRYAN, G. E. (1957) 'The Altitude Quotient as a measurement of intellectual potential.' *J. clin. Psychol.* **13,** 137–40.

BROWN, R. I. and DYER, L. (1963) 'Social arithmetic training for the subnormal.' *J. ment. Subnormal* **9,** 8–12.

BRYANT, P. (1963) 'The effects of language on the formation of concepts in imbecile children.' Univ. London unpubl. Ph.D. thesis.

BUCHAN, D. W. (1943) 'Educational methods applicable to adult mental defectives.' *Amer. J. ment. Defic.* **48,** 87–95.

BUCK, J. N. (1946) 'The time appreciation test.' *J. appl. Psychol.* **30,** 388–98.

BUCK, J. N. (1948) 'The H-T-P technique.' *J. clin. Psychol.* Monogr. Suppl. 5.

BÜHLER, C. (1951) 'The world test.' *J. Child Psychiat.* **2,** 69–71.

BÜHLER, C., LUMBRY, G. K. and CAROL, H. S. (1951) 'World test standardization studies.' *J. Child Psychiat.* **2,** 2–69.

BURKE, N. H. M. (1931) 'Stigmata of degeneration in relation to mental deficiency.' *Proc. Roy. Soc. Med.* **24,** 413–28.

BURKS, B. S. (1928) 'The relative influence of nature and nurture upon mental development: a comparative study of foster parent–foster child resemblance and true parent–true child resemblance.' *Yearb. Nat. Soc. Stud. Educ.* **27,** 219–316.

BURNS, P. C. (1961) 'Arithmetic fundamentals for the educable mentally retarded.' *Amer. J. ment. Defic.* **66,** 57–61.

BURR, E. T. (1931) 'The vocational adjustment of mental defectives.' *Psychol. Clin.* **20,** 55–64.

BURT, C. (1921) *Mental and Scholastic Tests.* London: L.C.C. Report No. 2052.

BURT, C. (1922) *Mental and Scholastic Tests.* 2nd edition 1924. London: P. S. King.

BURT, C. (1937) *The Backward Child.* 2nd edition 1946, 3rd edition reprint 1950–1, 4th edition 1958. London: Univ. Lond. Press.

BURT, C. (1935) *The Subnormal Mind.* 1st edition. London: Oxford Univ. Press. 2nd edition 1937.

BURT, C. (1944) *The Young Delinquent.* London: Univ. Lond. Press.

BURT, C. (1947) *Mental and Scholastic Tests.* 2nd edition. London: Staples Press.

BURTON, A. (1954) 'Psychotherapy with the mentally retarded.' *Amer. J. ment. Defic.* **58,** 486–9.

BUTLER, A. (1954) 'Test re-test and split-half reliabilities of the Wechsler-Bellevue scales and subtests with mental defectives.' *Amer. J. ment. Defic.* **59,** 80–4.

BYERS, R. K. and LORD, E. E. (1943) 'Late effects of lead poisoning on mental development.' *Amer. J. Dis. Child.* **66,** 471–94.

BYERS, R. K. and RIZZO, N. D. (1950) 'A follow-up of pertussis in infancy.' *New Engl. J. Med.* **242,** 887–91.

CAFFEY, J. and ROSS, S. (1956) 'Mongolism (mongoloid deficiency) during early infancy. Some newly recognized diagnostic changes in the pelvic bones.' *Pediatrics* **17,** 642–51.

CAIN, L. F. and LEVINE, S. *A Study of the Effects of Community and Institutional School Classes for Trainable Mentally Retarded Children.* San Francisco State College, June 1961. Report for U.S. Office of Education, Department of Health, Education and Welfare, Contract No. SAE 8237.

CANTOR, G. N. (1960) 'A critique of Garfield and Wittson's reaction to the revised Manual on Terminology and Classification.' *Amer. J. ment. Defic.* **64,** 954–6.

CANTOR, G. N. (1961) 'Some issues involved in category VIII of the A.A.M.D. "Terminology and Classification Manual".' *Amer. J. ment. Defic.* **65,** 561–6.

CANTOR, G. N. and HOTTEL, J. V. (1955) 'Discrimination learning in mental defectives as a function of magnitude of food reward and intelligence level.' *Amer. J. ment. Defic.* **60,** 380–4.

CANTOR, G. N. and HOTTEL, J. V. (1957) 'Psycho-motor learning in defectives as a function of verbal retraining.' *Psychol. Record* **7,** 79–85.

CANTOR, G. N. and STACEY, C. L. (1951) 'Manipulative dexterity in mental defectives.' *Amer. J. ment. Defic.* **56,** 401–10.

CAPLAN, G. (Ed.) (1955) *Emotional Problems of Early Childhood.* London: Tavistock Publications.

CAPOBIANCO, R. J. (1954) 'Quantitative and qualitative analyses of endogenous and exogenous boys on arithmetic achievement.' *Monogr. Soc. Res. Child Developm.* **19,** 101–42.

CARMICHAEL, L. (ed.) (1954) *Manual of Child Psychology.* London: Chapman & Hall.

CARR, G. L. (1958) 'Mosaic differences in non-institutionalized retarded children.' *Amer. J. ment. Defic.* **62,** 908–11.

CARRISON, D. and WERNER, H. (1943) 'Principles and methods of teaching arithmetic to mentally retarded children.' *Amer. J. ment. Defic.* **47,** 309–17.

CARSTAIRS, G. M., CLARK, D. H. and O'CONNOR, N. (1955) 'Occupational treatment of chronic psychotics; observations in Holland, Belgium and France.' *Lancet* **ii,** 1025–30.

CARTER, C. O. (1958) 'A life-table for mongols with the causes of death.' *J. ment. Defic. Res.* **2,** 64–74.

CARTER, C. O. (1962) *Human Heredity.* Middlesex: Penguin Books.

CARTER, C. O. and MACCARTHY, D. (1951) 'Incidence of mongolism and its diagnosis in the newborn.' *Brit. J. prev. soc. Med.* **5,** 83–90.

CARTER, C. O. and SIMPKISS, M. (1956) 'The "carrier" state in nephrogenic diabetes insipidus.' *Lancet* **ii,** 1069–73.

CASSEL, R. H. (1949a) 'Notes on pseudo-feeblemindedness.' *Train. Sch. Bull.* **46,** 119–27.

CASSEL, R. H. (1949b) 'Relation of design reproduction to the etiology of mental deficiency.' *J. consult. Psychol.* **13,** 421–8.

CHARLES, D. C. (1953) 'Ability and accomplishment of persons earlier judged mentally deficient.' *Genet. Psychol. Monogr.* **47,** 3–71.

CHARNEY, L. (1963) 'The trainable mentally retarded.' *In* Kirk and Weiner (1963).

CHASE, M. E. (1953) 'The practical application of psychotherapy in an institution for the mentally deficient.' *Amer. J. ment. Defic.* **58,** 337–41.

CHIDESTER, L. (1934) 'Therapeutic results with mentally retarded children.' *Amer. J. Orthopsychiat.* **4,** 464–72.

CHIDESTER, L. and MENNINGER, K. A. (1936) 'The application of psychoanalytic methods to the study of mental retardation.' *Amer. J. Orthopsychiat.* **6,** 616–25.

CITY OF BIRMINGHAM EDUCATION COMMITTEE (1956) *Report of the Special Services After-Care Sub-Committee.*

CLARIDGE, G. S. (1956) 'Factors affecting the motivation and performance of imbeciles.' London Univ. unpubl. Ph.D. thesis.

CLARIDGE, G. S. and O'CONNOR, N. (1957) 'The relationship between incentive, personality type and improvement in performance of imbeciles.' *J. ment. Defic. Res.* **1,** 16–25.

CLARK, D. F. (1960) 'Visual feedback in the social learning of the subnormal.' *J. ment. Subnormal.* **6**, 30–9.

CLARK, J. H. (1949) 'Subtest variation on the Wechsler–Bellevue for two institutionalized behaviour problem groups.' *Amer. Psychol.* **4**, 395 (Abstr.).

CLARK, J. H. and MOORE, J. H. (1950) 'The relationship of Wechsler–Bellevue patterns of psychiatric diagnosis of Army and Air Force prisoners.' *J. consult. Psychol.* **14**, 493–5.

CLARK, L. P. (1931) 'Child analysis: a motion picture dramatization.' *Proc. and Addr. Amer. Assoc. Stud. Feeblemind.* **36**, 111–15.

CLARKE, A. D. B. (1957) 'A symposium: the social adjustment of the mentally deficient. – I. Recent English research.' *Amer. J. ment. Defic.* **62**, 295–9.

CLARKE, A. D. B. (1962) 'Laboratory and workshop studies of imbecile learning processes.' *Proc. Lond. Conf. scient. Stud. ment. Defic., 1960* **1**, 89–96. Dagenham: May & Baker.

CLARKE, A. D. B. (1965) 'Problems in Assessing the Later Effects of Early Experience.' *In* Miller (1966), *in the press.*

CLARKE, A. D. B. and BLAKEMORE, C. B. (1961) 'Age and perceptual-motor transfer in imbeciles.' *Brit. J. Psychol.* **52**, 125–31.

CLARKE, A. D. B. and CLARKE, A. M. (1953) 'How constant is the I.Q.?' *Lancet* **ii**, 877–80.

CLARKE, A. D. B. and CLARKE, A. M. (1954a) 'A rehabilitation programme for certified mental defectives.' *Ment. Hlth. Lond.* **14**, 4–10.

CLARKE, A. D. B. and CLARKE, A. M. (1954b) 'Cognitive changes in the feebleminded.' *Brit. J. Psychol.* **45**, 173–9.

CLARKE, A. D. B. and CLARKE, A. M. (1955) 'Pseudo-feeblemindedness – some implications.' *Amer. J. ment. Defic.* **59**, 507–9.

CLARKE, A. D. B. and CLARKE, A. M. (1959) 'Recovery from the effects of deprivation.' *Acta Psychol.* **16**, 137–44.

CLARKE, A. D. B., CLARKE, A. M. and BROWN, R. I. (1959) 'Regression to the mean: a confused concept.' *Brit. J. Psychol.* **51**, 105–17.

CLARKE, A. D. B., CLARKE, A. M. and REIMAN, S. (1958) 'Cognitive and social changes in the feebleminded – three further studies.' *Brit. J. Psychol.* **49**, 144–57.

CLARKE, A. D. B. and COOKSON, M. (1962) 'Perceptual-motor transfer in imbeciles: a second series of experiments.' *Brit. J. Psychol.* **53**, 321–30.

CLARKE, A. D. B. and COOPER, M. (1964) 'Age and perceptual-motor transfer of training.' *Percept. Mot. Skills* **19**, 849–50.

CLARKE, A. D. B. and HERMELIN, B. F. (1955) 'Adult imbeciles: their abilities and trainability.' *Lancet* **ii**, 337–9.

CLARKE, H. J. (1946) 'The diagnosis of a patient with limited capacity.' *J. Person.* **15**, 105–12.

CLEVERDON, D. and ROSENZWEIG, L. E. (1955) 'A work-play program for the trainable mental deficient.' *Amer. J. ment. Defic.* **60**, 56–70.

COCKBURN, J. M. (1961) *in Cerebral Palsy in Childhood and Adolescence.* (ed. Henderson, J. L.). Edinburgh and London: Livingstone.

COFER, C. N. and BIEGEL, M. M. (1948) 'A study of the Kent and Buck screen tests of mental ability in relation to Otis and Stanford Achievement Test scores.' *J. consult. Psychol.* **12**, 187–9.

COFFEY, V. P. and JESSOP, W. J. E. (1959) 'Maternal influenza and congenital deformities: a prospective study.' *Lancet* **ii**, 935–8.

COFFEY, V. P. and JESSOP, W. J. E. (1963) 'Maternal influenza and congenital deformities: a follow-up study.' *Lancet* **i**, 748–51.

COLLIS, E., COLLIS, W. R. F., DUNHAM, W., HILLIARD, L. T. and LAWSON, D. (1956) *The Infantile Cerebral Palsies*. London: Heineman.

COLLMANN, R. D. and STOLLER, A. (1962a) 'Notes on the epidemiology of mongolism in Victoria, Australia, from 1942 to 1957.' *Proc. Lond. Conf. scient. Stud. ment. Defic., 1960* **2,** 517–26. Dagenham: May & Baker.

COLLMANN, R. D. and STOLLER, A. (1962b) 'A survey of mongoloid births in Victoria, Australia 1942–1957.' *Amer. J. Publ. Hlth.* **52,** 813–29.

COLLMANN, R. D. and STOLLER, A. (1962c) 'A survey on mongolism and congenital anomalies of the central nervous system in Victoria.' *New Zealand med. J.* **61,** 24–32.

COOLEY, J. M. (1945) 'The relative amenability of dull and bright children to child guidance.' *Smith Coll. Stud. soc. Wk.* **16,** 26–43.

COTZIN, M. (1948) 'Group psychotherapy with mentally defective problem boys.' *Amer. J. ment. Defic.* **53,** 268–83.

COTZIN, M. and GALLAGHER, J. J. (1949) 'Validity of short forms of the Wechsler–Bellevue Scale for mental defectives.' *J. consult. Psychol.* **13,** 357–65.

COURVILLE, C. B. (1959) 'Antenatal and paranatal circulatory disorders as a cause of cerebral damage in early life.' *J. Neuropath.* **18,** 115–40.

COUVREUR, J. and DESMONTS, G. (1962) 'Congenital and maternal toxoplasmosis: a review of 300 congenital cases.' *Develop. Med. Child. Neurol.* **4,** 519–30.

CRAFT, M. J. (1960) 'A psychopathic unit.' *Brit. J. Delinq.* **10,** 222.

CRAFT, M. J. (1962a) 'The rehabilitation of the imbecile: a follow-up report.' *J. ment. Subnormal.* **8,** 26–7.

CRAFT, M. J. (1962b) 'Practice and result from a psychopathic unit.' *Proc. Lond. Conf. scient. Stud. ment. Defic., 1960* **1,** 271–5. Dagenham: May & Baker.

CRAWFORD, A. (1955) 'An analysis of children's wrong answers on Raven's Progressive Matrices Test 1938.' *Bull. Brit. psychol. Soc.* **26,** 2.

CRAWFORD, J. M. (1956) 'Use and misuse of the mental deficiency hospital.' *Proc. Roy. Soc. Med.* **49,** 841.

CREAK, M. (1951) 'Psychoses in childhood.' *J. ment. Sci.* **97,** 545–54.

CREAK, M. (1960) 'Juvenile psychosis and mental deficiency.' *Proc. Lond. Conf. scient. Stud. ment. Defic., 1960* **2,** 389–97. Dagenham: May & Baker.

CREAK, M. (1961) 'Schizophrenic syndrome in childhood.' *Cerebral Palsy Bull.* **3,** 501–8.

CREAK, M. *et al.* (1961) 'Schizophrenic syndrome in childhood.' *Lancet* **ii,** 818.

CRESPI, L. P. (1942) 'Quantitative variation of incentive and performance in the white rat.' *Amer. J. Psychol.* **55,** 467–517.

CRITCHLEY, H. and EARL, C. J. C. (1932) 'Tuberose sclerosis and allied conditions.' *Brain* **55,** 341.

CROME, L. (1952) 'Encephalopathy following infantile gastro-enteritis.' *Arch. Dis. Childh.* **27,** 468–72.

CROME, L. (1954) 'Some morbid-anatomical aspects of mental deficiency.' *J. ment. Sci.* **100,** 894–912.

CROME, L. (1957) Chap. 5 *in Mental Deficiency* (by Hilliard, L. T. and Kirman, B. H.). London: Churchill.

CROME, L. (1960) 'The brain and mental retardation.' *Brit. med. J.* **1,** 897–904.

CROME, L. (1961) 'Cytomegalic inclusion-body disease.' *Wld. Neurol.* **2,** 447–58.

CROME, L. and PARE, C. M. R. (1960) 'Phenylketonuria, a review and a report of the pathological findings in four cases.' *J. ment. Sci.* **106,** 862–83.

CROTHERS, B. and PAINE, R. (1959) *The Natural History of Cerebral Palsy.* London: Oxford Univ. Press.

CRUICKSHANK, W. M. (1946) 'Arithmetic vocabulary of mentally retarded boys.' *Except. Children* **13,** 65–9.

CRUICKSHANK, W. M. (1948a) 'Arithmetic work habits of mentally retarded boys.' *Amer. J. ment. Defic.* **52,** 318–30.

CRUICKSHANK, W. M. (1948b) 'Arithmetic ability of mentally retarded children, I. Ability to differentiate extraneous materials from needed arithmetical facts. II. Understanding arithmetic processes.' *J. educ. Res.* **42,** 161–70; 279–88.

CRUICKSHANK, W. M. and BICE, H. V. (1955) 'Personality characteristics.' Chap. IV *in* Cruickshank and Raus (Ed.) (1955).

CRUICKSHANK, W. M., BICE, H. and WALLEN, N. (1957) *Perception and Cerebral Palsy*. Syracuse Univ. Press.

CRUICKSHANK, W. M. and QUALTERE, T. J. (1950) 'The use of intelligence tests with children of retarded mental development. I. Comparison of the 1916 and 1937 Revisions of the Stanford–Binet Intelligence Scales. II. Clinical considerations.' *Amer. J. ment. Defic.* **54,** 361–81.

CRUICKSHANK, W. M. and RAUS, S. (Ed,) (1955) *Cerebral Palsy: Its Individual and Community Problems*. Syracuse Univ. Press.

CURTIS, J. F. (1948) 'Disorders of articulation.' Chap. III *in* Johnson, Brown, Curtis, Edney and Keaster (1948).

CUTTS, R. A. and LANE, M. O. (1947) 'The effect of hospitalization on Wechsler–Bellevue subtest scores by mental defectives.' *Amer. J. ment. Defic.* **51,** 391–3.

CUTTS, R. A. and SLOAN, W. (1945) 'Test patterns of adjusted defectives on the Wechsler–Bellevue Test.' *Amer. J. ment. Defic.* **50,** 98–101.

DAVENPORT, C. B. (1911) *Heredity in Relation to Eugenics*. New York: Henry Holt.

DAVIES, S. P. (1930) *Social Control of the Mentally Deficient*. London: Constable.

DAVIS, K. (1947) 'Final note on a case of extreme isolation.' *Amer. J. Sociol.* **52,** 432–7.

DAWE, A. (1959) 'Progress in curriculum and method with mentally handicapped children.' *Amer. J. ment. Defic.* **64,** 19–23.

DAY, F., HARTOCH, A. and SCHACHTEL, E. (1940) 'A Rorschach study of a defective delinquent.' *J. crim. Psychopath,* **2,** 62–79.

DAYTON, N. A. (1931) 'Mortality in mental deficiency over a 14 year period: analysis of 8,976 cases and 878 deaths in Massachussetts.' *Proc. and Addr. Amer. Assoc. Stud. Feeblemind.* **36,** 127–205.

DEARBORN, W. F. and ROTHNEY, J. W. M. (1941) *Predicting the Child's Development*. Cambridge, Mass.: Sci.-Art Publ.

DELP, H. A. and LORENZ, M. (1953) 'Follow-up of 84 public school special class pupils with I.Q.s below 50.' *Amer. J. ment. Defic.* **58,** 175–82.

DENNIS, W. (1960) 'Causes of retardation among institutional children.' *J. genet. Psychol.* **96,** 47–59.

DENNIS, W. and NAJARIAN, P. (1957) 'Infant development under environmental handicap.' *Psychol. Monogr.* **71,** 1–13.

DENNIS, W. M. (1956) 'A philosophy of discipline derived from a treatment program for mentally retarded adolescents.' *Amer. J. ment. Defic.* **60,** 423–7.

DEPARTMENTAL COMMITTEE ON STERILIZATION (1934) Report of the. London: H.M.S.O.

DE PROSPO, C. J. (1962) 'Realism in education.' *Proc. Lond. Conf. scient. Stud. ment. Defic., 1960* **2,** 429–36. Dagenham: May & Baker.

DE SANCTIS, S. (1931) 'Visual apprehension in the maze behaviour of normal and feebleminded children.' *J. gener. Psychol.* **39,** 463–8.

DESCŒUDRES, A. (1928) *The Education of Mentally Defective Children.* London: Harrap.

DIAMOND, B. L. and SCHMALE, H. T. (1944) 'The Mosaic Test.' *Amer. J. Orthopsychiat.* **14,** 237–50.

DIERS, W. C. and BROWN, C. C. (1951) 'Rorschach "organic signs" and intelligence level.' *J. consult. Psychol.* **15,** 343–5.

DILLER, L. (1952) 'A comparison of the test performance of delinquent and non-delinquent girls.' *J. gener. Psychol.* **81,** 167–83.

DILLER, L. and BEECHLEY, R. M. (1951) 'The constancy of the altitude: a note.' J. clin. Psychol. **7,** 191–3.

DI MICHAEL, S. G. (Ed.) (1951) 'Vocational rehabilitation of the mentally retarded.' *Amer. J. ment. Defic.* **57,** 169–337.

DI MICHAEL, S. G. and TERWILLIGER, W. B. (1953) 'Counselor's activities in the vocational rehabilitation of the mentally retarded.' *J. clin. Psychol.* **9,** 99–106.

DINSMORE, M. (1954) 'Teaching reading to the brain injured child.' *Amer. J. ment. Defic.* **58,** 431–5.

DOCTER, R. F. and WINDER, C. L. (1954) 'Delinquent vs. non-delinquent performance on the Porteus Qualitative Maze Test.' *J. consult. Psychol.* **18,** 71–3.

DODGE, H. W., WOOD, M. W. and KENNEDY, R. L. J. (1959) 'Craniofacial dysostosis: Crouzon's disease.' *Pediatrics* **23,** 98–106.

DOLL, E. A. (1933) 'The psychological significance of cerebral birth lesions.' *Amer. J. Psychol.* **45,** 444–52.

DOLL, E. A. (1940) 'An annotated bibliography on the Vineland Social Maturity Scale.' *J. consult. Psychol.* **4,** 123–32.

DOLL, E. A. (1941) 'The essentials of an inclusive concept of mental deficiency.' *Amer. J. ment. Defic.* **46,** 214–19.

DOLL, E. A. (1946) *The Oseretzky Tests of Motor Proficiency: A Translation from the Portuguese Adaptation.* Minneapolis: Educ. Test Bureau.

DOLL, E. A. (1947) 'Is mental deficiency curable?' *Amer. J. ment. Defic.* **51,** 420–8.

DOLL, E. A. (1953) *The Measurement of Social Competence* (*A Manual for the Vineland Social Maturity Scale*). Washington, United States: Educ. Test Bureau.

DOLL, E. A. and ALDRICH, C. G. (1932) 'Simple conditioning as a method of studying sensory discrimination among idiots.' *J. gen. Psychol.* **7,** 104–43.

DOLL, R., HILL, A. B. and SAKULA, J. (1960) 'Asian influenza in pregnancy and congenital defects.' *Brit. J. prev. soc. Med.* **14,** 167–72.

DONNELL, G. N. and LANN, S. H. (1951) 'Galactosemia. Report of four cases.' *Pediatrics* **7,** 503–15.

DOUGLAS, J. W. B. (1964) *The Home and the School.* London: McGibbon & Kee.

DOWN, J. L. H. (1866) 'Observations on an ethnic classification of idiots.' *Lond. Hosp. Rep.* **3,** 259–62.

DRILLIEN, C. M. (1963) 'Obstetric hazard, mental retardation and behaviour disturbance in primary school.' *Develop. Med. Child Neurol.* **5,** 3–13.

DUGDALE, R. L. (1910) *The Jukes.* New York: Putnam.

DUNCAN, J. (1942) *The Education of the Ordinary Child.* London: Nelson.

DUNN, L. M. (1954) 'A comparison of the reading progresses of mentally retarded and normal boys of the same mental age.' *Monogr, Soc. Res. Child Developm.* **19,** 7–99.

DUNSDON, M. I. (1952) *The Educability of Cerebral Palsied Children*. London: Newnes Educ. Publ. Co. Ltd for National Foundation for Educational Research.

DUNSDON, M. I., CARTER, C. O. and HUNTLEY, R. M. C. (1960) 'Upper end of range of intelligence in mongolism.' *Lancet* **i,** 565–8.

EARL, C. J. C. (1933) 'The human figure drawings of adult defectives.' *J. ment. Sci.* **79,** 305–28.

EARL, C. J. C. (1934) 'The primitive catatonic psychosis of idiocy.' *Brit. J. med. Psychol.* **14,** 230–53.

EARL, C. J. C. (1937) 'The performance test behaviour of adult morons.' *Brit. J. med. Psychol.* **17,** 78–92.

EARL, C. J. C. (1940) 'A psychograph for morons.' *J. abnorm. soc. Psychol.* **35,** 428–48.

EARL, C. J. C. (1942) 'Post war institutions.' Unpubl. paper to the Royal Medico-Psychological Association.

EARL, C. J. C. (1961) *Subnormal Personalities: their clinical investigation and assessment*. London: Baillière, Tindall & Cox.

ECKHARDT, W. (1961) 'Piotrowski's signs: organic or functional?' *J. clin. Psychol.* **17,** 36–8.

EDWARDS, J. H., HARNDEN, D. G., CAMERON, A. H., CROSSE, V. M. and WOLFF, O. H. (1960) 'A new trisomic syndrome.' *Lancet* **i,** 787–90.

EDWARDS, J. H., NORMAN, R. M. and ROBERTS, J. M. (1961) 'Sex-linked hydrocephalus: report of a family with 15 affected members.' *Arch. Dis. Childh.* **36,** 481–5.

ELLINGSON, R. J. (1956) 'Brain waves and problems of psychology.' *Psychol. Bull.* **53,** 1–34.

ELLIS, J. R., MARSHALL, R. and PENROSE, L. S. (1962) 'An aberrant small acrocentric chromosome.' *Ann. hum. Genet.* **26,** 77–83.

ELLIS, N. R. (1962) 'Amount of reward and operant behaviour in mental defectives.' *Amer. J. ment. Defic.* **66,** 595–9.

ELLIS, N. R. and DISTEFANO, M. K. (1959) 'Effects of verbal urging and praise upon rotary pursuit performance in mental defectives.' *Amer. J. ment. Defic.* **64,** 486–90.

ELLIS, N. R., GIRARDEAU, F. L. and PRYER, M. W. (1962) 'Analysis of learning sets in normal and severely defective humans.' *J. comp. physiol. Psychol.* **55,** 860–5.

ELLIS, N. R. and SLOAN, W. (1957) 'The relationship between intelligence and simple reaction time in mental defectives.' *Percept. Mot. Skills* **7,** 65–7.

ELLIS, R. W. B., SHELDON, W. and CAPON, N. B. (1936) 'Gargoylism (chondro-osteo-dystrophy, corneal opacities, hepatosplenomegaly and mental deficiency).' *Quart. J. Med.* **5,** 119–35.

ELPHINSTONE, N. (1953) 'Thiouracil in pregnancy – its effect on the fœtus.' *Lancet* **i,** 1281–3.

ENGLE, T. L. and HAMLETT, I. C. (1954) 'Comparison of mental defectives and normal children in ability to handle clock and calendar situations.' *Amer. J. ment. Defic.* **58,** 655–8.

ESHER, F. J. S. (1964) 'Hostels for the subnormal.' *Proc. Internat. Copenhagen Congr. scient. Stud. ment. Retard.* **2,** 690–2.

ESTABROOK, A. H. (1915) *The Jukes in 1915*. Washington: Carnegie Inst.

EVANS, K. and CARTER, C. O. (1954) 'Care and disposal of mongolian defectives.' *Lancet* **ii,** 960–3.

EWERHARDT, P. J. (1938) 'Reading difficulties in subnormal children.' *Proc. Amer. Assoc. ment. Defic.* **43,** 188–93.

EYSENCK, H. J. (1952) *The Scientific Study of Personality.* London: Routledge & Kegan Paul.

EYSENCK, H. J. (1953) *Uses and Abuses of Psychology.* Harmondsworth: Penguin Books.

EYSENCK, H. J. (1955) 'A dynamic theory of anxiety and hysteria.' *J. ment. Sci.* **101,** 28–51.

FAIRBANK, R. F. (1933) 'The subnormal child – 17 years after.' *Ment. Hyg.* **17,** 177–208.

FARRELL, M. J. and FORSLEY, E. (1956) 'Enhancing patients' adjustment by means of group sessions with attendants.' *Amer. J. ment. Defic.* **60,** 603–7.

FEILING, A. (Ed.) (1951) *Modern Trends in Neurology.* London: Butterworth.

FELDMAN, F. (1946) 'Psychoneuroses in the mentally retarded.' *Amer. J. ment. Defic.* **51,** 247–54.

FERGUSON, T. and KERR, A. W. (1955) 'After-histories of girls educated in special schools for mentally handicapped children.' *Glasgow med. J.* **36,** 50–6.

FERGUSON, T. and KERR, A. W. (1958) 'After-histories of boys educated in special schools for mentally handicapped children.' *Scot. med. J.* **3,** 31–8.

FIELD, J. G. (1960a) 'The performance-verbal I.Q. discrepancy in a group of sociopaths.' *J. clin. Psychol.* **16,** 321–2.

FIELD, J. G. (1960b) 'Two types of tables for use with Wechsler's intelligence scales.' *J. clin. Psychol.* **16,** 3–7.

FINLAYSON, A. (1955) 'Tuberous sclerosis.' *Amer. J. ment. Defic.* **59,** 617–28.

FISHER, G. M. (1960a) 'The altitude quotient as an index of intellectual potential: W.A.I.S. data for familial and undifferentiated mental retardates.' *Amer. J. ment. Defic.* **65,** 252–5.

FISHER, G. M. (1960b) 'Difference in W.A.I.S. verbal and performance I.Q.s in various diagnostic groups of mental retardates.' *Amer. J. ment. Defic.* **65,** 256–60.

FISHER, G. M. (1960c) 'A corrected table for determining the significance of the difference between verbal and performance I.Q.s on the W.A.I.S. and the Wechsler-Bellevue.' *J. clin. Psychol.* **16,** 7–8.

FISHER, G. M. (1961) 'Discrepancy in verbal and performance I.Q. in adolescent sociopaths.' *J. clin. Psychol.* **17,** 60.

FISHER, L. A. and WOLFSON, I. N. (1953) 'Group therapy of mental defectives.' *Amer. J. ment. Defic.* **57,** 463–76.

FITZPATRICK, F. K. (1956) 'Training outside the walls.' *Amer. J. ment. Defic.* **60,** 827–37.

FLORY, C. D. (1936) 'The physical growth of mentally deficient boys.' *Monogr. Soc. Res. Child Developm.* **1,** No. 6.

FLOURENS, H. J. P. (1824) *Recherches expérimentales sur les propriétés et les fonctions du système nerveux dans les animaux vertébrés.* Paris: Crevot.

FLOYER, E. B. (1955) *A Psychological Study of a City's Cerebral Palsied Children.* Manchester: Brit. Counc. Welf. Spastics.

FOALE, M. (1952) 'An approach to stabilisation of male juvenile mental defective delinquents.' *Amer. J. ment. Defic.* **57,** 116–22.

FOALE, M. and PATERSON, J. W. (1954) 'The hearing of mental defectives.' *Amer. J. ment. Defic.* **59,** 254–8.

FÖLLING, A. (1934) 'Über Ausscheidung von Phenylbrenztraubensäure in den Harn abs Stoffwechselanomalie in Verbindung mit Imbezillitäb.' *Hoppe-Seyler's Z. physiol. Chem.* **227,** 169–76.

FONT, M. (1950) 'Some clinical applications of the Rorschach technique in cases of borderline deficiency.' *Amer. J. ment. Defic.* **54,** 507–11.

FORD, C. E., JONES, I. W., MILLER, O. J., MITTWOCH, V., PENROSE, L. S., RIDLER, M. and SHAPIRO, A. (1959) 'The chromosomes in a patient showing both mongolism and the Klinefelter syndrome.' *Lancet* **i,** 709–10.

FOREMAN, M. E. (1962) 'Predicting behavioural problems among institutionalized mental retardates.' *Amer. J. ment. Defic.* **66,** 580–8.

FOSTER, A. L. (1959) 'A note concerning the intelligence of delinquents.' *J. clin. Psychol.* **15,** 78–9.

FOULDS, G. (1945a) 'Frustration types among mental defective juvenile delinquents.' *Brit. J. Psychol.* **36,** 29–32.

FOULDS, G. (1945b) 'The child-family relationship and the frustration types among mental defective juvenile delinquents.' *Brit. J. med. Psychol.* **20,** 255–60.

FOURACRE, M. H. (1958) 'Learning characteristics of brain-injured children.' *Except. Children* **24,** 210–12.

FRASER, A. W. (1951) 'Reduction of runaways among trainees at a Government training school.' *Amer. J. ment. Defic.* **56,** 185–91.

FRAZER, SIR IAN (1947) 'Blindness'. Article in *Encyclopaedia Britannica* **3,** 721–31.

FREEMAN, F. N., HOLZINGER, K. J. and MITCHELL, B. C. (1928) 'The influence of environment on the intelligence, school achievement, and conduct of foster children.' *Yearb. Nat. Soc. Stud. Educ.* **27,** 103–217.

FRIEDMAN, E. (1961) 'Individual therapy with a "defective delinquent".' *J. clin. Psychol.* **17,** 229–32.

FRY, D. B. and WHETNALL, E. (1964) 'The auditory approach in the training of deaf children.' *Lancet* **i,** 583.

FRY, L. M. (1956) 'A predictive measure of work success for high grade mental defectives.' *Amer. J. ment. Defic.* **61,** 402–8.

FURTH, H. G. (1964) 'Research with the deaf: implications for language and cognition.' *Psychol. Bull.* **62,** 145–64.

GALL, F. J. (1835) *On the Functions of the Brain and each of its Parts.* Boston: Marsh, Capen & Lyon.

GALLAGHER, J. J. (1960) *The Tutoring of Brain-Injured Mentally Retarded Children.* Illinois: Charles C. Thomas.

GALTON, F. (1909) 'A comment.' *Eugen. Rev.* **1,** 204.

GANN, E. (1945) *Reading Difficulty and Personality Organization.* New York: King's Crown Press.

GARDNER, L. P. (1945) 'The learning of low-grade aments.' *Amer. J. ment. Defic.* **50,** 59–80.

GARDNER, W. I., CROMWELL, R. L. and FOSHEE, J. G. (1959) 'Studies in activity level: II. Effects of distal visual stimulation in organics, familials, hyperactives and hypoactives.' *Amer. J. ment. Defic.* **63,** 1028–33.

GARFIELD, S. L. and WITTSON, C. (1960a) 'Some reactions to the revised Manual on Terminology and Classification in Mental Retardation.' *Amer. J. ment. Defic.* **64,** 951–3.

GARFIELD, S. L. and WITTSON, C. (1960b) 'Comments on Dr Cantor's remarks.' *Amer. J. ment. Defic.* **64,** 957–9.

GARLAND, H. and MOORHOUSE, D. (1953) 'An extremely rare recessive hereditary syndrome including cerebellar ataxia, oligophrenia, cataract and other features.' *J. Neurol. Psychiat.* **16,** 110–16.

GATES, A. I. (1935) *Improvement of Reading*. New York: Macmillan.

GESELL, A. (1940) 'The stability of mental growth careers.' *Yearb. Nat. Soc. Stud. Educ.* **23,** 149-60.

GESELL, A. and AMATRUDA, C. S. (1947) *Developmental Diagnosis, Normal and Abnormal Child Development*. 2nd edition. New York: Harper Bros. and Paul Hoeber Inc.

GIBB, J. W. G. and MACMAHON, J. F. (1955) 'Arrested mental development induced by lead poisoning.' *Brit. med. J.* **i,** 320–3.

GIBBS, E. L., GIBBS, F. A. and GROSSMAN, H. (1956) 'Electroencephalographic evidence of encephalitis in children with supposedly uncomplicated childhood diseases.' *Trans. Amer. neurol. Ass.*, 81st Annual Meeting.

GIBSON, D. (1964) 'Psychology in mental retardation: past and present.' *Amer. Psychol.* **19,** 339–41.

GIBSON, D., JEPHCOTT, A. E. and WILKINS, R. (1959) 'Academic success among high grade hospitalized mentally retarded children as a function of intelligence and etiological classification.' *Amer. J. ment. Defic.* **63,** 852–9.

GIBSON, R. (1950) 'A tentative clinical classification of the special types in mental deficiency.' *Amer. J. ment. Defic.* **54,** 382–93.

GIRARDEAU, F. L. (1959) 'The formation of discrimination learning sets in mongoloid and normal children.' *J. comp. physiol. Psychol.* **52,** 566–70.

GLASER, L. H. (1958) 'A case of nephrogenic diabetes insipidus.' *Brit. med. J.* **2,** 780–1.

GLASER, M. A. and SHAFER, F. P. (1932) 'Skull and brain traumas; their sequelae.' *J. Amer. med. Ass.* **98,** 271–6.

GLASSMAN, L. A. (1943) 'Is dull normal intelligence a contraindication for psychotherapy?' *Smith Coll. Stud. soc. Wk.* **13,** 275–98.

GLUECK, S. and GLUECK, E. (1950) *Unraveling Juvenile Delinquency*. New York: Commonwealth Fund.

GODA, S. (1960) 'Vocal utterances of young moderately and severely retarded non-speaking children.' *Amer. J. ment. Defic.* **65,** 269–73.

GODDARD, H. H. (1910) 'Heredity of feeble-mindedness.' *Amer. Breeders Mag.* **1,** 165–78.

GODDARD, H. H. (1912) *The Kallikak Family*. New York: Macmillan.

GODDARD, H. H. (1914) *Feeblemindedness: Its Causes and Consequences*. New York: Macmillan.

GOFFMAN, E. (1961) *Asylums: Essays on the Social Situation of Mental Patients and other Inmates*. Garden City (New York): Doubleday.

GOLDBERG, F. H. (1957) 'The performance of schizophrenic, retarded and normal children on the Bender-Gestalt Test.' *Amer. J. ment. Defic.* **61,** 548–55.

GOLDFARB, W. (1943) 'The effects of early institutional care on adolescent personality.' *J. exp. Educ.* **12,** 106–29.

GOLDFARB, W. (1945) 'Psychological deprivation in infancy.' *Amer. J. Psychiat.* **102,** 19–33.

GOLDFARB, W. (1947) 'Variations in adolescent adjustment of institutionally reared children.' *Amer. J. Orthopsychiat.* **17,** 449–57.

GOLDHAMER, H. and MARSHALL, A. W. (1949) *Psychosis and Civilization: Two Studies in the Frequency of Mental Disease*. Glencoe, Ill.: The Free Press.

GOLDSTEIN, H. (1956) *Report Number Two on Study Projects for Trainable Mentally Handicapped Children*. Springfield: Illinois Department of Public Instruction.

GOLDSTEIN, I. and MANN, H. (1949) 'An occupational vocabulary for retarded adolescents.' *Amer. J. ment. Defic.* **54,** 38–72.

GOLDSTEIN, K. (1939) *The Organism.* New York: Amer. Book Co.

GOLDSTEIN, K. (1942) 'Concerning rigidity.' *Character and Pers.* **11,** 209–26.

GOLDSTEIN, K. and SCHEERER, M. (1941) *Abstract and Concrete Behavior. An Experimental Study with Special Tests.* Psychol. Monogr. 53, No. 2.

GOLDSTEIN, L. (1930) 'Radiogenic microcephaly.' *Arch. Neurol. Psychiat.* (Chicago) **24,** 102–15.

GOODENOUGH, F. L. (1926) *Measurement of Intelligence by Drawings.* New York: World Book Co.

GOODENOUGH, F. L. (1931) *Anger in Young Children.* Univ. Minnesota Press.

GOODGLASS, F. A. and QUADFASEL, F. (1954) 'Language laterality in left-handed aphasics.' *Brain* **77,** 521–48.

GOODMAN, N. and TIZARD, J. (1962) 'Prevalence of imbecility and idiocy among children.' *Brit. med. J.* **1,** 216–19.

GORDON, S. (1953) 'Some effects of incentives on the behaviour of imbeciles.' London Univ. unpubl. Ph.D. Thesis.

GORDON, S., O'CONNOR, N. and TIZARD, J. (1954) 'Some effects of incentives on the performance of imbeciles.' *Brit. J. Psychol.* **45,** 277–87.

GORDON, S., O'CONNOR, N. and TIZARD, J. (1955) 'Some effects of incentives on the performance of imbeciles on a repetitive task.' *Amer. J. ment. Defic.* **60,** 371–7.

GOTHBERG, L. C. (1947) 'A comparison of the personality of run-away girls with a control group as expressed in the themas of Murray's Thematic Apperception Test.' *Amer. J. ment. Defic.* **51,** 627–31.

GOTHBERG, L. C. (1949) 'The mentally defective child's understanding of time.' *Amer. J. ment. Defic.* **53,** 441–55.

GRAHAM, F. K. and KENDALL, B. S. (1946) 'Performance of brain-damaged cases on a memory-for-designs test.' *J. abnorm. soc. Psychol.* **41,** 303–14.

GRAJALES, M. L. (1948) 'Porteus' qualitative Maze Test as a measure of delinquency' (quoted by Porteus, 1950). New York: Fordham Univ. Thesis.

GRASSI, J. R. (1953) *The Grassi Block Substitution Test for Measuring Organic Brain Pathology.* Springfield, Ill.: Charles C. Thomas.

GREENE, C. L. (1945) 'A study of personal adjustment in mentally retarded girls.' *Amer. J. ment. Defic.* **49,** 472–6.

GREENE, E. B. (1941) *Measurements of Human Behaviour.* New York: Odyssey Press.

GREENE, M. C. L. (1955) 'The cleft palate patient with incompetent palato-pharyngeal closure.' *Folia Phoniatrica* **7,** 172–82.

GREENLAND, C. (1957) 'Unmarried parenthood: ecological aspects.' *Lancet* **i,** 148–51.

GREGG, N. M. (1941) 'Congenital cataract following German measles in the mother.' *Trans. ophthal. Soc. Aust.* **3,** 35. Quoted by Penrose (1949).

GRIFFITHS, B. C., SPITZ, H. H. and LIPSMAN, R. S. (1959) 'Verbal mediation and concept formation in retarded and normal subjects.' *J. exp. Psychol.* **58,** 247–51.

GUENTHER, R. J. (1956) *Final Report: The Michigan Demonstration Research Project for the Severely Mentally Retarded.* Lansing: Michigan Department of Public Instruction.

GUERTIN, W. H. (1949) 'Mental growth in pseudo-feeblemindedness.' *J. clin. Psychol.* **5,** 414–18.

GUERTIN, W. H. (1950) 'Differential characteristics of the pseudo-feebleminded.' *Amer. J. ment. Defic.* **54,** 394–8.

GULLIFORD, R. (1960) 'Teaching the mother tongue to backward and subnormal pupils.' *Educ. Res.* **II,** 82–100.

GUNN, I. A. (1929) *Problem of Time*. London: Allen & Unwin.

GUNZBURG, H. C. (1948a) 'Experiments in the improvement of reading in a group of educationally subnormal boys.' *J. ment. Sci.* **94**, 809–33.

GUNZBURG, H. C. (1948b) 'The subnormal boy and his reading interests.' *Libr. Quart.* **18**, 264–74.

GUNZBURG, H. C. (1948c) 'An experimental approach to the improvement of reading of educationally subnormal boys.' *Spec. Schools J.* **37**, 77–86.

GUNZBURG, H. C. (1950a) 'The significance of various aspects in drawings by educationally subnormal children.' *J. ment. Sci.* **96**, 951–75.

GUNZBURG, H. C. (1950b) 'The colony and the young high-grade mental defective.' *Ment. Hlth.* **9**, 87–92.

GUNZBURG, H. C. (1951) 'The young subnormal.' *New Era* **32**, 151–6.

GUNZBURG, H. C. (1952) 'Maladjustment as expressed in drawings by subnormal children.' *Amer. J. ment. Defic.* **57**, 9–23.

GUNZBURG, H. C. (1955a) 'Scope and limitations of the Goodenough drawing test method in clinical work with mental defectives.' *J. clin. Psychol.* **11**, 8–15.

GUNZBURG, H. C. (1955b) 'Projection in drawings: a case study.' *Brit. J. med. Psychol.* **28**, 72–81.

GUNZBURG, H. C. (1956a) 'The role of the psychologist in the Mental Deficiency Hospital.' *Int. J. soc. Psychiat.* **1**, 31–6.

GUNZBURG, H. C. (1956b) 'A short version of the Kohs Block Design Test.' *J. Midland ment. Defic. Soc.* **2**, 20–6.

GUNZBURG, H. C. (1957) 'Therapy and social training for the feebleminded youth.' *Brit. J. med. Psychol.* **30**, 42–8.

GUNZBURG, H. C. (1959) 'Earl's moron battery and social adjustment.' *Amer. J. ment. Defic.* **63**, 92–103.

GUNZBURG, H. C. (1960) *Social Rehabilitation of the Subnormal*. London: Baillière, Tindall & Cox.

GUNZBURG, H. C. (1963a) *Junior Training Centres: An outline of the principles and practices of social education and training of the mentally subnormal child.* London: Nat. Assoc. ment. Hlth.

GUNZBURG, H. C. (1963b) *Senior Training Centres: An outline of the principles and practices of social education and training for older mentally subnormal people.* London: Nat. Assoc. ment. Hlth.

GUNZBURG, H. C. (1963c) *Progress Assessment Chart* (*P.A.C.*) (*Form I, Form II*). London: Nat. Assoc. ment. Hlth.

GUNZBURG, H. C. (1964a) *Social Education First Aid* (*SEFA*) *Scheme*. London: Nat. Assoc. ment. Hlth.

GUNZBURG, H. C. (1964b) Social competence of the imbecile child. *Proc. Internat. Copenhagen Congr. scient. Stud. ment. Retard.* **2**, 693–706.

GUNZBURG, H. C. (1964c) 'The reliability of a test of psycholinguistic abilities (ITPA) in a population of young male subnormals.' *J. ment. Subnormal.* **10**, 101–12.

GURVITZ, M. S. (1950) 'The Wechsler–Bellevue Test and the diagnosis of psychopathic personality.' *J. clin. Psychol.* **6**, 397–401.

GUTMAN, B. (1950) 'The application of the Wechsler–Bellevue scale in the diagnosis of organic brain disorders.' *J. clin. Psychol.* **6**, 195–8.

HACKBUSCH, F. and KLOPFER, B. (1946) 'The contribution of projective techniques to the understanding and treatment of children psychometrically diagnosed as feebleminded.' *Amer. J. ment. Defic.* **51**, 15–34.

HAFEMEISTER, N. R. (1951) 'Development of a curriculum for the trainable child.' *Amer. J. ment. Defic.* **55**, 495–501.

HALDANE, J. B. S. (1949) Preface to *The Biology of Mental Defect*, by L. S. Penrose. London: Sidgwick & Jackson.
HALL, D. L., MORIARTY, J. and PATTERSON, A. S. (1957) 'Two camps in the Netherlands.' *J. Midland ment. Defic. Soc.* **5,** 23–32.
HALSTEAD, H. (1957) 'Abilities and behaviour of epileptic children.' *J. ment. Sci.* **103,** 28–47.
HALSTEAD, W. C. (1947) *Brain and Intelligence*. Chicago: Univ. Chicago Press.
HAMLIN, R. (1938) 'Test pattern of high grade mentally defective girls.' *Proc. Amer. Assoc. ment. Defic.* **43,** 161–5.
HAMMER, E. F. (Ed.) (1958) *The Clinical Application of Projective Drawings*. Springfield, Ill.: Charles C. Thomas.
HANSEN, E. (1960) *Cerebral Palsy in Denmark*. Copenhagen: Munksgaard.
HARLOW, H. F. (1949) 'The formation of learning sets.' *Psychol. Rev.* **56,** 51–65.
HARLOW, H. F. (1959) 'Learning set and error factor theory.' *In* Koch (1959).
HARRIS, D. B. (1963) *Children's Drawings as Measures of Intellectual Maturity*. London: Harrap & Co.
HARRIS, H., PENROSE, L. S. and THOMAS, D. H. H. (1959) 'Cystathioninuria.' *Ann. hum. Genet.* **23,** 442–53.
HARRIS, L. A. and KINNEY, C. (1947) 'A program for reducing maladjustments in an institution for the mentally deficient.' *Amer. J. ment. Defic.* **52,** 78–84.
HARTWELL, S. W. (1940) *Fifty-five 'Bad Boys.'* New York: Knopf.
HAUSCHKA, T. S., HASSON, J. E., GOLDSTEIN, M. N., KOEPF, G. F. and SANDBERG, A. A. (1962) 'An XYY man with progeny indicating familial tendency to non-disjunction.' *Amer. J. hum. Genet.* **14,** 22–30.
HAYS, W. (1950) 'A comparison of scatter patterning for mental defectives on the Wechsler Forms I and II.' *Amer. J. ment. Defic.* **55,** 264–8.
HEAD, H. (1926) *Aphasia and Kindred Disorders of Speech*. London: Macmillan.
HEALY, W. and BRONNER, A. F. (1936) *New Light on Delinquency and its Treatment*. New Haven: Yale Univ. Press.
HEALY, W., BRONNER, A. F., LOWE, C. M. and SHIMBERG, N. E. (1932) *A Manual of Individual Tests and Testing*. Boston: Little, Brown.
HEATH, S. R. (1942) 'Railwalking performance as related to mental age and etiological type among the mentally retarded.' *Amer. J. Psychol.* **55,** 240–7.
HEATH, S. R. (1943) 'The military use of the rail-walking test as an index of locomotor co-ordination.' *Psychol. Bull.* **40,** 282–4.
HEATH, S. R. (1944) 'Clinical significance of motor defects with military implications.' *Amer. J. Psychol.* **57,** 487–99.
HEATH, S. R. (1946) 'A mental pattern found in motor deviates.' *J. abnorm. soc. Psychol.* **41,** 223–5.
HEBB, D. O. (1949) *The Organization of Behaviour*. London: Chapman & Hall.
HEBER, R. (1959) *Manual on Terminology and Classification in Mental Retardation*. American Association on Mental Deficiency.
HEBER, R. (1962) 'The concept of mental retardation; definition and classification.' *Proc. Lond. Conf. scient. Stud. ment. Defic., 1960* **1,** 236–42.
HEGGE, T. G. (1942) 'The significance of measurements of adjustment in the institutional and school situation.' *Amer. J. ment. Defic.* **47,** 58–69.
HEIBRUN, A. B. (1956) 'Psychological test performance as a function of lateral localisation of cerebral lesions.' *J. comp. physiol. Psychol.* **49,** 10–14.
HEINIS, H. (1926) 'A personal constant.' *J. educ. Psychol.* **17,** 163–86.
HELLER, A. D. (1955) 'Group therapy with mental defectives.' *Ment. Hlth. Lond.* **14,** 97–9.
HENDERSON, J. L. (1961) *Cerebral Palsy in Childhood and Adolescence: A Medical Psychological and Social Study*. Edinburgh: Livingstone.

HENDERSON, P. (1955) 'The epileptic child.' *Practitioner* **174,** 394–9.

HERMELIN, B. F. (1956) 'Studies of learning and trainability in imbeciles.' Univ. Reading unpubl. B.A. Thesis.

HERMELIN, B. F. and O'CONNOR, N. (1958) 'The rote and concept learning of imbeciles.' *J. ment. Defic. Res.* **2,** 21–7.

HERMELIN, B. F. and O'CONNOR, N. (1960) 'Reading ability of severely subnormal children.' *J. ment. Defic. Res.* **4,** 144–7.

HERMELIN, B. F. and O'CONNOR, N. (1963) *Speech and Thought in Severe Subnormality.* Oxford: Pergamon Press.

HILDEN, A. H. (1949) 'A longitudinal study of intellectual development.' *J. Psychol.* **28,** 187–214.

HILL, I. B. (1953) 'Industrial therapy.' *Amer. J. ment. Defic.* **57,** 544–6.

HILLIARD, L. T. (1956) 'Discussion on community care of the feebleminded.' *Proc. Roy. Soc. Med.* **49,** 837–41.

HILLIARD, L. T. and KIRMAN, B. H. (1957) *Mental Deficiency.* 2nd edition 1965. London: Churchill.

HIMMELWEIT, H. T. and EYSENCK, H. J. (1945) 'An experimental analysis of the mosaic projection test.' *Brit. J. med. Psychol.* **20,** 283–94.

HINRICHS, W. E. (1935) 'The Goodenough drawing test in relation to delinquency and problem behaviour.' *Arch. Psychol.* **175,** 1–82 (and appendix).

HOAKLEY, Z. P. (1940) 'A comparison of the results of the Stanford and Terman–Merrill revisions of the Binet.' *J. appl. Psychol.* **24,** 75–81.

HOAKLEY, Z. P. and FRAZEUR, H. A. (1945) 'Significance of psychological test results of exogenous and endogenous children.' *Amer. J. ment. Defic.* **50,** 263–71.

HOLERAN, I. (1955) 'The employability of cerebral palsied young people,' *Med. Off.* **94,** 337–9.

HOLMAN, P. (1933) 'The relationship between general mental development and mental dexterity.' *Brit. J. Psychol.* **23,** 279–83.

HOLMES, J., TEUBER, H. L. and WEINSTEIN, S. (1958) 'Equipotentiality versus cortical localisation.' *Science* **127,** 241–2.

HOLZINGER, K. J. (1938) 'Reply to special review of "Twins".' *Psychol. Bull.* **35,** 436–44.

HONZIK, M. P. (1938) 'The constancy of mental test performance during the pre-school period.' *J. genet. Psychol.* **52,** 285–302.

HONZIK, M. P., MACFARLANE, J. W. and ALLEN, C. (1948) 'The stability of mental test performance between two and eighteen years.' *J. exp. Educ.* **17,** 309–24.

HOPKINS, T., BICE, H. V. and COLTON, K. (1954) *Evaluation and Education of the Cerebral Palsied Child.* Washington: Internat. Counc. except. Child.

HORNE, B. M. and ALLEN, M. L. (1942) 'A study of the vocational orientation of institutionalized adolescent mentally defective girls.' *Amer. J. ment. Defic.* **46,** 485–95.

HOTTEL, J. V. (1958) *An evaluation of the Tennessee Day Class Program for severely retarded (trainable) children.* Nashville: George Peabody College for Teachers.

HOUSE, B. J. and ZEAMAN, D. (1958a) 'Visual discrimination learning in imbeciles.' *Amer. J. ment. Defic.* **63,** 447–52.

HOUSE, B. J. and ZEAMAN, D. (1958b) 'A comparison of discrimination learning in normal and mentally defective children.' *Child Developm.* **29,** 411–16.

HOUSE, B. J. and ZEAMAN, D. (1958c) 'Reward and non-reward in the discrimination learning of imbeciles.' *J. comp. physiol. Psychol.* **51,** 614–18.

HOUSE, B. J. and ZEAMAN, D. (1960a) 'Transfer of a discrimination from objects to patterns.' *J. exp. Psychol.* **5,** 298–302.

HOUSE, B. J. and ZEAMAN, D. (1960b) 'Visual discrimination learning and intelligence in defectives of low mental age.' *Amer. J. ment. Defic.* **65**, 51–8.

HOUSE, B. J. and ZEAMAN, D. (1960c) 'Learning and transfer in mental defectives.' *Univ. Connecticut Department of Psychology, Progress Rep. No. 2.*

HOVLAND, C. I. (1951) 'Human learning and retention.' *In* Stevens (Ed.) (1951).

HOYLE, J. S. (1951) 'Home conditions and employment of mental defectives.' *Amer. J. ment. Defic.* **55**, 619–21.

HUBBLE, D. V. (1953) *In Diseases of Children.* (Ed. Moncrieff, A. and Evans, P.) 5th edition. London: Arnold.

HUBER, M. B. (1928) *The Influence of Intelligence upon Children's Reading Interests.* New York: Columbia Univ. Teachers' College.

HUDSON, M. (1955a) 'The severely retarded child: educable versus trainable.' *Amer. J. ment. Defic.* **59**, 583–6.

HUDSON, M. (1955b) 'Some theoretical aspects to curriculum building for the severely retarded child.' *Amer. J. ment. Defic.* **60**, 270–7.

HUGHES, R. M. (1948) 'Rorschach signs for the diagnosis of organic pathology.' *J. proj. Tech.* **12**, 165–7.

HUGHES, R. M. (1950) 'A factor analysis of Rorschach diagnostic signs.' *J. gen. Psychol.* **43**, 85–103.

HUMPHREYS, E. J., WATTS, G. W. T. and BOLDT, W. H. (1937) 'An investigation into the case records of one thousand high-grade mentally or developmentally defective children.' *Proc. Amer. Assoc. ment. Defic.* **42**, 9–46.

HUNGERFORD, R. H., DE PROSPO, C. J. and ROSENZWEIG, L. E. (1952). 'Education of the mentally handicapped in childhood and adolescence.' *Amer. J. ment. Defic.* **57**, 214–28.

HUNT, B. M. (1959) 'Performance of mentally deficient brain-injured children and mentally deficient familial children on construction from patterns.' *Amer. J. ment. Defic.* **63**, 679–87.

HUNT, H. F. (1943) 'A practical clinical test for organic brain damage.' *J. appl. Psychol.* **27**, 375–86.

HUNT, J. McV. (Ed.) (1944) *Personality and the Behaviour Disorders.* Vols. I and II. New York: The Ronald Press.

HUNT, J. McV. (1961) *Intelligence and Experience.* New York: The Ronald Press.

HURTIG, M. C., MERLET, L. SANTUCCI, H. and ZAZZO, R. (1962) 'An experimental examination of the concept of mental deficiency.' *Proc. Lond. Conf. scient. Stud. ment. Defic., 1960*, **2**, 650–8.

HUSÉN, T. (1951) 'The influence of schooling upon I.Q.' *Theoria* **17**, 61–88.

ILLINGWORTH, R. S. (1955) 'Mental retardation in the infant and pre-school child.' *Brit. med. J.* **2**, 1–7.

ILLINGWORTH, R. S. (1958) *Recent Advances in Cerebral Palsy.* London: Churchill.

INGRAM, C. P. (1953) *Education of the Slow-learning Child.* New York: The Ronald Press.

INGRAM, T. T. S. (1964) *Paediatric Aspects of Cerebral Palsy.* London: Livingstone.

INGRAM, T. T. S., JAMESON, S., ERRINGTON, J. and MITCHELL, R. G. (1964) 'Living with Cerebral Palsy.' The Spastics Society Clinics in Developmental Medicine No. 14.

INHELDER, B. (1943) *Le Diagnostic du Raisonnement chez les Débiles Mentaux.* Neuchatel: Delachaux et Niestle.

IRWIN, R. B. (1959) 'Oral language for slow learning children.' *Amer. J. ment. Defic.* **64**, 32–9.

ITARD, J. M. G. (1801) *The Wild Boy of Aveyron*. Trans. by G. and M. Humphrey (1932) (2nd edition 1962) New York: Appleton Century Co.

JACKSON, J. H. (1931) *Selected Writings*. (Ed. J. Taylor.) London: Hodder & Stoughton.

JASTAK, J. E. (1949a) 'A rigorous criterion of feeblemindedness.' *J. abnorm. soc. Psychol.* **44,** 367–78.

JASTAK, J. E. (1949b) 'Problems of psychometric scatter analysis.' *Psychol. Bull.* **46,** 177–197.

JASTAK, J. E. (1952) 'Psychological tests, intelligence and feeblemindedness.' *J. clin. Psychol.* **8,** 107–12.

JASTAK, J. E., MACPHEE, H. M. and WHITEMAN, M. (1963) *Mental Retardation: Its Nature and Incidence*. Univ. Delaware Press.

JOHNSON, B. (1919) 'Practice effects in a target test; a comparison of groups of varying intelligence.' *Psychol. Rev.* **26,** 300–16.

JOHNSON, D. M. (1955) *The Psychology of Thought and Judgment*. (Ed. Gardner Murphy.) New York: Harper & Bros.

JOHNSON, E. Z. (1952) 'Sex differences and variability in the performance of retarded children on Raven, Binet and Arthur Tests.' *J. clin. Psychol.* **8,** 298–301.

JOHNSON, E. Z. (1953a) 'The clinical use of Raven's Progressive Matrices to appraise potential for progress in playtherapy; a study of institutionalized mentally and educationally retarded children.' *Amer. J. Orthopsychiat.* **23,** 391–405.

JOHNSON, E. Z. (1953b) 'Individual patterns of emotional functioning in children of comparable I.Q.s; implications for education.' *Amer. J. ment. Defic.* **57,** 681–6.

JOHNSON, E. Z. (1953c) 'Klopfer's Prognostic Scale used with Raven's Progressive Matrices in play therapy prognosis.' *J. proj. Tech.* **17,** 320–6.

JOHNSON, G. O. (1955) 'Mental retardation and cerebral palsy.' Chap. IX *in* Cruickshank and Raus (Ed.) (1955).

JOHNSON, G. O. and CAPOBIANCO, R. J. (1957) *Research Project on Severely Retarded Children*. Albany, New York: Interdepartmental Health Resources Board.

JOHNSON, W. (1944) 'The Indians have no word for it: 1. Stuttering in Children.' *Quart. J. Speech* **30,** 330–7.

JOHNSON, W. (1957) Chap., 'Perceptual and Evaluational Factors in Stuttering.' In *Handbook of Speech Pathology*, Ed. Travis, L. E. New York: Appleton-Century-Crofts.

JOHNSON, W., BROWN, S. F., CURTIS, J. F., EDNEY, C. W. and KEASTER, J. (1948) *Speech Handicapped School Children*. New York: Harper & Bros.

JOHNSTON, A. W., FERGUSON-SMITH, M. A., HANDMAKER, S. D., JONES, H. W. and JONES, G. S. (1961) 'The triple-X syndrome. Clinical, pathological and chromosomal studies in three mentally retarded cases.' *Brit. med. J.* **2,** 1046–52.

JOLLES, I. (1947a) 'The Diagnostic Implications of Rorschach's Test in case studies of mental defectives.' *Genet. Psychol. Monogr.* **36,** 89–197.

JOLLES, I. (1947b) 'A study of mental deficiency by the Rorschach technique.' *Amer. J. ment. Defic.* **52,** 37–42.

JOLLES, I. (1958) 'A teaching sequence for the training of visual and motor perception.' *Amer. J. ment. Defic.* **63,** 252–5.

JONES, H. E. (1954) 'Environmental influences on mental development.' *In* Carmichael (Ed.) (1954).

JONES, H. GWYNNE (1953) 'Experimental studies in the psychology of epilepsy.' *Rev. Psychol. Appl.* **3,** 209–77.

JONES, H. GWYNNE (1956) 'Comments on "The validity and interchangeability of Terman–Merrill and Matrices Test Data".' *Brit. J. educ. Psychol.* **26,** 141–3.

JONES, V. C. (1945) 'Personalized training program for the subnormal.' *Amer. J. ment. Defic.* **49,** 364–8.

KAHN, T. C. (1951) 'An original test of symbol arrangement validated on organic psychotics.' *J. consult. Psychol.* **15,** 439–44.

KAHN, T. C. (1955) 'Cross validation of the organic pathology scale for a test of symbol arrangement.' *J. consult Psychol.* **19,** 130.

KALDECK, R. (1958) 'Group psychotherapy with mentally defective adolescents and adults.' *Int. J. Group Psychotherapy* **8,** 185–93.

KALISKI, L. (1955) 'Educational therapy for brain-injured retarded children.' *Amer. J. ment. Defic.* **60,** 71–6.

KALISKI, L. (1959) 'The brain-injured child – learning by living in a structured setting.' *Amer. J. ment. Defic.* **63,** 688–95.

KANNER, L. (1948a) *Child Psychiatry.* Oxford: Blackwell.

KANNER, L. (1948b) *A Miniature Text-book of Mental Deficiency.* New York: Child Care Publ.

KAPLUN, D. (1935) 'The high-grade moron. A study of institutional admissions over a ten year period.' *Proc. Amer. Assoc. ment. Defic.* **40,** 68–89.

KARPELES, L. M. (1932) 'A further investigation of the Porteus Maze test as a discriminative measure in delinquency.' *J. appl. Psychol.* **16,** 427–37.

KASTEIN, S. (1956) 'Responsibility of the speech pathologist to the retarded child.' *Amer. J. ment. Defic.* **60,** 750–4.

KATONA, G. (1940) *Organizing and Memorizing.* New York: Columbia Univ. Press.

KATZ, E. (Ed.) (1961) *Final Report, Work-Training Centre Project, November 1, 1957–November 30, 1961,* for U.S. Vocational Rehabilitation Administration, Department of Health, Education and Welfare (RD-205). San Francisco; Aid Retarded Children, Inc.

KAUFMANN, H. J. and TAILLARD, W. F. (1961) 'Pelvic abnormalities in mongols.' *Brit. med. J.* **1,** 948–9.

KELLER, J. E. (1955) 'The use of a Bender–Gestalt maturation level scoring system with mentally handicapped children.' *Amer. J. Orthopsychiat.* **25,** 563–73.

KELLEY, D. M. and BARRERA, S. E. (1941) 'The Rorschach method in the study of mental deficiency: A résumé.' *Amer. J. ment. Defic.* **45,** 401–7.

KELLMER PRINGLE, M. L., (1951) 'Social maturity and social competence.' *Educ. Rev.* **III,** 113–28, and 183–95.

KELLMER PRINGLE, M. L. (1960) 'Social learning and its measurement.' *Educ. Res.* **II,** 194–206.

KELLMER PRINGLE, M. L. and TANNER, M. (1958) 'The effects of early deprivation on speech development: a comparative study of four year olds in a nursery school and in residential nurseries.' *Language and Speech* **1,** 269–87.

KELLY, E. M. (1948) 'A family living course for mentally retarded girls at the pre-vocational school for girls, Newark, New Jersey.' *Amer. J. ment. Defic.* **53,** 103–8.

KENNEDY, L. (1930) 'Studies in the speech of the feeble-minded.' Unpublished Ph.D. dissertation, Univ. of Wisconsin.

REFERENCES

KENNEDY, R. J. R. (1948) *The Social Adjustment of Morons in a Connecticut City*. Hartford: Mansfield-Southbury Training Schools (Social Service Department, State Office Building).

KEPHART, N. C. (1938a) 'A method of heightening social adjustment in an institutional group.' *Amer. J. Orthopsychiat.* **8,** 710–17.

KEPHART, N. C. (1938b) 'Group autonomy in a children's institution.' *Ment. Hyg.* **22,** 585–90.

KERR, M. (1939) 'The validity of the Mosaic Test.' *Amer. J. Orthopsychiat.* **9,** 232–6.

KINDER, E. F. and HAMLIN, R. (1937) 'Consistency in test performance pattern of mentally subnormal subjects.' *Proc. Amer. Assoc. ment. Defic.* **42,** 132–7.

KIRK, S. A. (1934) 'The effects of remedial reading on the educational progress and personality adjustment of high-grade mentally deficient problem children.' *J. juv. Res.* **18,** 140–62.

KIRK, S. A. (1935) 'Attitudes toward behavior problems in an institution for high-grade mentally deficient problem children.' *Proc. Amer. Assoc. ment. Defic.* **40,** 368–84.

KIRK, S. A. (1948) 'An evaluation of the study by Bernardine G. Schmidt.' *Psychol. Bull.* **45,** 321–33.

KIRK, S. A. (1957) *Public School Provisions for Mentally Handicapped Children*. Albany, New York: Interdepartmental Health Resources Board.

KIRK, S. A. (1958) *Early Education of the Mentally Retarded*. Urbana, Illinois: Univ. Illinois Press.

KIRK, S. A. (1962) 'The effects of educational procedures on the development of retarded children.' *Proc. Lond. Conf. scient. Stud. ment. Defic., 1960* **2,** 419–28.

KIRK, S. A. (1964) 'Research in Education.' *In* Stevens and Heber (1964).

KIRK, S. A. and BATEMAN, B. (1962) 'Diagnosis and remediation of learning disabilities.' *Except. Children* **29,** 73–8.

KIRK, S. A. and JOHNSON, G. O. (1951) *Educating the Retarded Child*. Boston: Houghton Mifflin.

KIRK, S. A. and JOHNSON, G. O. (1954) *Educating the Retarded Child*. London: Harrap.

KIRK, S. A., KARNES, M. B. and KIRK, W. D. (1958) *You and Your Retarded Child*. New York: MacMillan.

KIRK, S. A., KASS, C. E. and BATEMAN, B. D. (1962) 'The educability of psycholinguistic functions in retarded children.' *Illinois State Dept. ment. Hlth., Progress Report: Inst. for Res. on Except. Child., Univ. Illinois.*

KIRK, S. A. and MCCARTHY, J. J. (1961) 'The Illinois test of psycholinguistic abilities – an approach to differential diagnosis.' *Amer. J. ment. Defic.* **66,** 399–412.

KIRK, S. A. and WEINER, B. B. (1963) (Eds.) *Behavioural Research on Exceptional Children*. Washington, D.C.: Council for Exceptional Children.

KIRMAN, B. H. (1955) 'Rubella as a cause of mental deficiency.' *Lancet* **ii,** 1113–15.

KIRMAN, B. H. (1956) 'Epilepsy and cerebral palsy.' *Arch. Dis. Childh.* **31,** 1–7.

KIRMAN, B. H. (1957) *In Mental Deficiency* (by Hilliard, L. T. and Kirman, B. H.), Chap. 15. London: Churchill.

KIRMAN, B. H. (1960) 'Cerebral palsy and mental handicap research aspects.' *Spastics Quart.* **19,** No. 1.

KIRMAN, B. H., BLACK, J. A., WILKINSON, R. H. and EVANS, P. R. (1956) 'Familial pitrossin-resistant diabetes insipidus with mental defect. *Arch. Dis. Childh.* **31,** 59–66.

REFERENCES

KLEBANOFF, S. G. (1945) 'Psychological changes in organic brain lesions and ablations.' *Psychol. Bull.* **42,** 585–623.

KLINEBERG, O. (1935) *Negro Intelligence and Selective Migration.* New York: Columbia Univ. Press.

KLINEFELTER, H. F., REIFENSTEIN, E. C. and ALBRIGHT, F. (1942) 'Syndrome characterized by gynecomastia, aspermatogenesis without a-leydigism, and increased excretion of follicle-stimulating hormone.' *J. clin. Endocr.* **2,** 615–27.

KLOPFER, B. and KELLEY, D. (1942) *The Rorschach Technique.* New York: World Book Co.

KNIGHT, D., LUDWIG, A. J., STRAZZULLA, M. and POPE, L. (1957) 'The role of varied therapies in the rehabilitation of the retarded child.' *Amer. J. ment. Defic.* **61,** 508–15.

KNOBLOCH, H. and PASAMANICK, B. (1962) 'Medical progress: mental subnormality.' *New Engl. J. Med.* **266,** 1045–51, 1092–7, 1151–61.

KOCH, S. (1959) *Psychology – a Study of a Science.* New York: McGraw-Hill.

KODMAN, F. (1958) 'The incidence of hearing loss in mentally retarded children.' *Amer. J. ment. Defic.* **62,** 675–8.

KOHS, S. C. (1923) *Intelligence Measurement.* New York: Macmillan.

KOLSTOE, O. P. (1958) 'Language training of low grade mongoloid children.' *Amer. J. ment. Defic.* **63,** 17–30.

KOMAI, T., KISHIMOTO, K. and OSAKI, Y. (1955) 'Genetic study of microcephaly based on Japanese material.' *Amer. J. hum. Genet.* **7,** 51–65.

KOUNIN, J. S. (1941) 'Experimental studies of rigidity. I. The measurement of rigidity in normal and feebleminded persons. II. The explanatory power of the concept of rigidity as applied to feeblemindedness.' *Character and Pers.* **9,** 273–82.

KRAMER, M., PERSON, P. H., TARJAN, S., MORGAN, R. and WRIGHT, S. W. (1955) 'A method for determining the probabilities of stay, release and death, for patients admitted to a hospital for the mentally deficient: The experience of Pacific State Hospital 1948–1952. *Amer. J. ment. Defic.* **62,** 481–95.

KRETSCHMER, E. (1936) *Physique and Character.* London: Routledge.

KRIEGMAN, G. and HILGARD, J. R. (1944) 'Intelligence level and psychotherapy with problem children.' *Amer. J. Orthopsychiat.* **14,** 251–65.

KRIVIT, W. and GOOD, R. A. (1957) 'Simultaneous occurrence of mongolism and leukemia.' *A.M.A.J. Dis. Child.* **94,** 289–93.

KUHLMANN, F. (1904) 'Experimental studies in mental deficiency.' *Amer. J. Psychol.* **15,** 391–446.

KUHLMANN, F. (1939) *Tests of Mental Development.* Minneapolis: Educ. Test Bureau.

KULCINSKI, L. E. (1945) 'The relation of intelligence to the learning of fundamental muscular skills.' *Res. Quart. Amer. Assoc. Hlth. phys. Educ. Assoc.* **16,** 266–76.

LANGDON DOWN, J. (1866) 'Observations on an ethnic classification of idiots.' *Clin. Lect. and Repts. of the London Hosp.* **3,** 259–62.

LASSNER, R. (1948) 'Annotated bibliography of the Oseretsky Tests of motor proficiency.' *J. consult. Psychol.* **12,** 37–47.

LAVALLI, A. and LEVINE, M. (1954) 'Social and guidance needs of mentally handicapped adolescents as revealed through sociodramas.' *Amer. J. ment. Defic.* **58,** 544–52.

LAWSON, D. (1955) 'On the prognosis of cretinism.' *Arch. Dis. Childh.* **30,** 75–82.

LAWSON, D. (1958) 'A cerebral palsy service for children.' *Lancet* **i,** 840–2.

LECK, I. M. and MILLAR, E. L. M. (1962) 'Incidence of malformations since the introduction of thalidomide.' *Brit. med. J.* **2,** 16–20.

LEJEUNE, J., GAUTIER, M. and TURPIN, R. (1959) 'Etuces des chromosomes somatiques de neuf enfants mongoliens.' *C.R. Acad. Sci.* (*Paris*) **248,** 1721–2.

LELAND, H. and SMITH, D. (1962) 'Unstructured material in playtherapy for emotionally disturbed, brain damaged mentally retarded children.' *Amer. J. ment. Defic.* **66,** 621–8.

LELAND, H., WALKER, J. and TABOADA, A. N. (1959) 'Group play therapy with a group of post-nursery male retardates.' *Amer. J. ment. Defic.* **63,** 848–51.

LEMKAU, P., TIETZE, C. and COOPER, M. (1942) 'Mental hygiene problems in an urban district.' *Ment. Hyg. N.Y.* **26,** 275–88.

LEONTIEV, A. N. (1954) 'An attempt to investigate thinking experimentally.' In *Questions of Psychology*. Moscow: Acad. Pedag. Sci.

LEONTIEV, A. N. (1957), 'The nature and formation of human psychic properties and processes.' *In* Simon (Ed.) (1957).

LEVY, S. and PERRY, H. A. (1948) 'Pertussis as a cause of mental deficiency.' *Amer. J. ment. Defic.* **52,** 217–26.

LEWIN, K. (1935) *A Dynamic Theory of Personality; Selected Papers*. New York: McGraw-Hill.

LEWIS, A. J. (1951) 'Social aspects of psychiatry. Parts I and II.' *Edinburgh med. J.* **58,** 214–47.

LEWIS, E. O. (1929) *Report of the Mental Deficiency Committee*, Part IV. London: H.M.S.O.

LEWIS, E. O. (1933) 'Types of mental deficiency and their social significance.' *J. ment. Sci.* **79,** 298–304.

LEWIS, H. (1954) *Deprived Children*. London: Oxford Univ. Press.

LEWIS, M. M. (1957) *How Children Learn to Speak*. London: Harrap.

LIDBETTER, E. J. (1933) *Heredity and the Social Problem Group*, Vol. 1. London: Edward Arnold.

LIMB, G. and PARKER, H. T. (1932) *An Experiment in the Teaching of Reading Comprehension*. Melbourne Univ. Press.

LINDSLEY, D. B. (1944) 'Electroencephalography.' *In* McV. Hunt (Ed.) (1944).

LINDSLEY, D. B. (1956) 'Physiological psychology.' *Annu. Rev. Psychol.* **7,** 323–48.

LIPMAN, R. S. (1959) 'Some test correlates of behavioural aggression in institutionalized retardates with particular reference to the Rosenzweig Picture-Frustration Study.' *Amer. J. ment. Defic.* **63,** 1038–45.

LIPMAN, R. S., BLACKMAN, L. S. and STEVENS, H. A. (1959) 'A survey of research in institutions for the mentally retarded.' *Amer. J. ment. Defic.* **63,** 997–1000.

LIUBLINSKAIA, A. A. (1957) 'The role of language in the development of a child's perceptual activity.' *In* Simon (Ed.) (1957).

LOMBARD, J. P., GILBERT, J. G. and DONOFRIO, A. F. (1955) 'The effects of glutamic acid upon the intelligence, social maturity and adjustment of mentally retarded children.' *Amer. J. ment. Defic.* **60,** 122–32.

LONDT, R. (1960) 'Further education for the subnormal I. A tentative outline of general principles.' *J. ment. Subnormal.* **11,** 64–72.

LONDT, R. (1961) 'Further education for the subnormal II. The practical issues.' *J. ment. Subnormal.* **12,** 32–36.

LOOS, F. M. and TIZARD, J. (1955) 'The employment of adult imbeciles in a hospital workshop.' *Amer. J. ment. Defic.* **59,** 395–403.

LORD, E. E. (1930) 'A study of the mental development of children with lesion in the central nervous system.' *Genet. Psychol. Monogr.* **7,** 365–486.

LORENZ, K. (1952) *King Solomon's Ring*. London: Methuen.

LORR, M. (1954) 'Rating scales and check lists for the evaluation of psychopathology.' *Psychol. Bull.* **51,** 119–27.

LOUTIT, C. M. (1947) *Clinical Psychology of Children's Behaviour Problems.* New York: Harper.

LOVELL, K. (1959) 'A follow-up study of some aspects of the work of Piaget and Inhelder on the child's conception of space.' *Brit. J. educ. Psychol.* **29,** 104–17.

LOVELL, K. (1961) *The Growth of Basic Mathematical and Scientific Concepts in Children.* London: Univ. Lond. Press.

LOVELL, K. and SLATER, A. (1960) 'The growth of the concept of time: a comparative study.' *J. Child Psychol. and Psychiat.* **1,** 179–90.

LOWE, C. U., TERREY, M. and MACLACHLAN, E. A. (1952) 'Organic-aciduria, decreased renal ammonia production, hydrophthalmos, and mental retardation.' *Amer. J. Dis. Childh.* **83,** 164–84.

LOWENFELD, M. (1939) 'The world pictures of children.' *Brit. J. med. Psychol.* **18,** 65–101.

LOWENFELD, M. (1954) *The Lowenfeld Mosaic Test.* London: Newman Neame.

LOWENFELD, V. (1941) 'Self adjustment through creative activity.' *Amer. J. ment. Defic.* **45,** 366–73.

LOWREY, L. G. (1944) 'Delinquent and criminal personalities.' In *Personality and the Behaviour Disorders* (Ed. J. McV. Hunt). New York: The Ronald Press.

LUBIN, N. M. (1955) 'The effect of color in the TAT on productions of mentally retarded subjects.' *Amer. J. ment. Defic.* **60,** 366–70.

LUBS, H. A., KOENIG, E. U. and BRANDT, I. K. (1961) 'Trisomy 13–15: a clinical syndrome.' *Lancet* **ii,** 1001–2.

LUMRY, K. (1951) 'Study of world test characteristics as a basis for discriminating between various clinical categories.' *J. Child. Psychiat.* **2,** 24–35.

LURIA, A. R. (1932) *The Nature of Human Conflicts.* Trans. by W. Horsley Gantt. New York: Liveright Inc.

LURIA, A. R. (1957) 'Features of the interaction between the two signal systems in the formation of a motor response in normal and abnormal development.' *In* Simon (Ed.) (1957).

LURIA, A. R. (1959) 'Experimental study of the higher nervous activity of the abnormal child.' *J. ment. defic. Res.* **3,** 1–22.

LURIA, A. R. (1961) *The Role of Speech in the Regulation of Normal and Abnormal Behaviour.* J. Tizard (Ed.). London: Pergamon Press.

LURIA, A. R. and VINOGRADOVA, O. S. (1959) 'An objective investigation of the dynamics of semantic systems.' *Brit. J. Psychol.* **50,** 89–105.

LURIA, A. R. and YUDOVICH, F. I. (1959) *Speech and the Development of Mental Processes in the Child.* London: Staples Press.

LYLE, J. G. (1959) 'The effect of institution environment upon verbal development of imbecile children: I. Verbal intelligence.' *J. ment. defic. Res.* **3,** 122–8.

LYLE, J. G. (1960a) 'The effect of an institution environment upon the verbal development of imbecile children: II. Speech and language.' *J. ment. defic. Res.* **4,** 1–13.

LYLE, J. G. (1960b) 'The effect of an institution environment upon the verbal development of imbecile children: III. The Brooklands residential unit.' *J. ment. defic. Res.* **4,** 14–22.

MACFARLANE, J. W. (1953) 'The uses and predictive limitations of intelligence tests in infants and young children.' *Bull. World Hlth. Org.* **9,** 409–16.

MACHOVER, K. (1949) *Personality Projection in the Drawing of the Human Figure*. Springfield: Thomas.

MACLEAN, N., MITCHELL, J. M., HARNDEN, D. G., WILLIAMS, J., JACOBS, P. A., BUCKTON, K. A., BAIKIE, A. G., COURT BROWN, W. M., McBRIDGE, J. A., STRONG, J. A., CLOSE, H. G. and JONES, D. C. (1962) 'A survey of sex-chromosome abnormalities among 4514 mental defectives.' *Lancet* **i**, 293–6.

MACMAHON, J. F. (1952) 'The adolescent feebleminded in law and practice.' *Brit. med. J.* **2,** 254–6.

MACMAHON, J. F., CLARKE, A. M. and CLARKE, A. D. B. (1958) 'The Royal Commission's proposals related to mental deficiency hospital practice.' *Medic. Press,* **240,** 681–5.

MAHER, B. A. (1960) 'Position errors and primitive thinking in the Progressive Matrices Test.' *Amer. J. ment. Defic.* **64,** 1016–20.

MAIER, K. (1961) Unpublished report on reading problems in the severely subnormal.

MAIER, N. R. F. (1949) *Frustration: the Study of Behaviour without a Goal.* New York: McGraw-Hill.

MAISNER, E. A. (1950) 'Contributions of playtherapy techniques to total rehabilitative design in an institution for high-grade mentally deficient and borderline children.' *Amer. J. ment. Defic.* **55,** 235–50.

MANNE, S. H., KANDEL, A. and ROSENTHAL, D. (1962) 'Differences between performance I.Q. and verbal I.Q. in a severely sociopathic population.' *J. clin. Psychol.* **18,** 73–7.

MARCHAND, J. G. (1956) 'Changes of psychometric test results in mental defective employment care patients.' *Amer. J. ment. Defic.* **60,** 852–9.

MARLAND, P. M. (1953) 'Speech therapy for cerebral palsy based on reflex inhibition.' *Speech* **17,** 65–8.

MARTIN, A. W. and WIECHERS, J. E. (1954) 'Raven's coloured Progressives Matrices and the Wechsler Intelligence Scale for Children.' *J. consult. Psychol.* **18,** 143–4.

MARTINSON, B. and STRAUSS, A. A. (1940) 'Education and treatment of an imbecile boy of the exogenous type.' *Amer. J. ment. Defic.* **45,** 274–80.

MASSERMAN, J. H. and BALKEN, E. R. (1938) 'The clinical application of phantasy studies.' *J. Psychol.* **6,** 81–8.

MATTHEW, G. C. (1964) 'The social competence of the subnormal school leaver.' *J. ment. Subnormal.* **10,** 83–8.

MATTHEWS, J. (1957) Chap., 'Speech problems of the mentally retarded.' *In Handbook of Speech Pathology*. Ed. Travis, L. E. New York: Appleton-Century-Crofts.

MAURER, K. M. (1946). *Intellectual Status at Maturity as a Criterion for Selecting Items in Pre-school Tests*. Minneapolis: Univ. Minneapolis Press.

MAXWELL, J. (1961) *The Level and Trend of National Intelligence*. (Scottish Council for Research in Education, **46.**) London: Univ. London Press.

MAYER-GROSS, W., SLATER, E. and ROTH, M (1954) *Clinical Psychiatry*. London: Cassell (reprinted 1955).

McBRIDE, R., KAPLAN, J. and HALL, M. A. (1953) 'Community planning to meet some of the social needs of the mentally retarded adult.' *Amer. J. ment. Defic.* **58,** 331–6.

McCANDLESS, B. R. (1942). 'Changing relationships between dominance and social acceptability during group democratization.' *Amer. J. Orthopsychiat.* **12,** 529–35.

REFERENCES

McCARTHY, J. J. and KIRK, S. A. (1961) '*Illinois Test of Psycholinguistic Abilities:* Experimental Edition.' Urbana, Ill: Institute for Research on Exceptional Children, Univ. of Illinois.

McCLELLAND, D., ATKINSON, J. W., CLARK, R. A. and LOWELL, E. (1953) *The Achievement Motive*, New York: Appleton-Century-Crofts.

McCORD, and McCORD, J. (1956) *Psychopathy and Delinquency*. New York; Grime & Stratton.

McCULLOCH, T. L. (1947) 'Reformulation of the problem of mental deficiency.' *Amer. J. ment. Defic.* **52,** 139–6.

McCULLOCH, T. L. and GIRDNER, J. B. (1949) 'Use of the Lowenfeld Mosaic Test with mental defectives.' *Amer. J. ment. Defic.* **53,** 486–96.

McCULLOCH, T. L., RESWICK, J. and ROY, I. (1955) 'Studies of word learning in mental defectives. I. Effects of mental level and age.' *Amer. J. ment. Defic.* **60,** 130–9.

McCULLOCH, T. L., RESWICK, J. and WEISMANN, S. (1955) 'Studies of word learning in mental defectives. II. Relation to scores on digit repetition, the Stanford–Binet, M, and the W.I.S.C. verbal scale.' *Amer. J. ment. Defic.* **60,** 140–3.

McELWEE, E. W. (1932) 'The reliability of the Goodenough Intelligence Test used with subnormal children 14 years of age.' *J. appl. Psychol.* **16,** 217–18.

McHUGH, G. (1945a) 'Relationship between the Goodenough Drawing a Man Test and the 1937 Revision of the Stanford–Binet Test.' *J. educ. Psychol.* **36,** 119–24.

McHUGH, G. (1945b) 'Changes in Goodenough I.Q. at the public school kindergarten level.' *J. educ. Psychol.* **36,** 17–30.

McINTIRE, J. T. A. (1938) 'The incidence of feeblemindedness in the cerebral palsied.' *Proc. Amer. Assoc. ment. Defic.* **43,** 44–50.

McINTIRE, J. T. A. (1947) 'A study of the distribution of physical handicap and mental diagnosis in cerebral palsied children.' *Amer. J. ment. Defic.* **51,** 624–6.

McKAY, B. E. (1942) 'A study of I.Q. changes in a group of girls paroled from a state school for mental defectives.' *Amer. J. ment. Defic.* **46,** 496–500.

McKENZIE, R. E. (1951) 'A study of the Wechsler–Bellevue Intelligence Scale and the V.I.B.S. Short Form in an institute for the mentally defective.' *Amer. J. ment. Defic.* **56,** 174–6.

McNEMAR, Q. (1938) 'Newman, Freeman and Holzinger's Twins: a study of heredity and environment.' *Psychol. Bull.* **35,** 237–49.

McNEMAR, Q. (1940). 'A critical examination of the University of Iowa studies of environmental influence upon the I.Q.' *Psychol. Bull.* **37,** 63–92.

McNEMAR, Q. (1942) *The Revision of the Stanford–Binet Scale; an Analysis of the Standardization Data*. Boston: Houghton-Mifflin.

McPHERSON, M. W. (1947) 'A summary of experimental studies of learning in individuals who achieve subnormal ratings on standardized psychometric measures.' *Amer. J. ment. Defic.* **52,** 232–54.

MEHLMAN, B. (1953) 'Group playtherapy with mentally retarded children.' *J. abnorm. soc. Psychol.* **48,** 53–60.

MEIN, R. (1961) 'A study of the oral vocabularies of severely subnormal children.' *J. ment. Defic. Res.* **5,** 52–9.

MEIN, R. and O'CONNOR, N. (1960) 'A study of the oral vocabularies of severely subnormal patients.' *J. ment. Defic. Res.* **4,** 130–43.

MENKES, J. H., HURST, P. L. and CRAIG, J. M. (1954) 'A new syndrome: progressive familial infantile cerebral dysfunction associated with an unusual urinary substance.' *Pediatrics* **14,** 462–7.

MEYER, V. (1957) 'A critique of psychological approaches to brain damage.' *J. ment. Sci.* **103,** 80–109.

MEYER, V. (1959) 'Cognitive changes following temporal lobectomy for relief of temporal lobe epilepsy.' *A.M.A. Arch. Neurol. Psychiat.* **81,** 299–309.

MEYERSON, L. (1957) 'Special disabilities.' *Annu. Rev. Psychol.* **8,** 437–54.

MEYER TAYLOR, E. (1959) *Psychological Appraisal of Children with Cerebral Defects.* Cambridge: Harvard Univ. Press.

MICHAEL, J. C. and BÜHLER, C. (1945) 'Experience with personality testing in the neuropsychiatric department of a general hospital.' *Dis. Nerv. Syst.* **6,** 205–11.

MICKELSON, P. (1947) 'The feebleminded parent; a study of 90 family cases.' *Amer. J. ment. Defic.* **51,** 644–53.

MIDDLETON, T. H. (1956) 'The mental defective on licence: a survey of 20 years in Birmingham.' *J. Midland ment. Defic. Soc.* **2,** 41–9.

MILLER, D. R., FISHER, G. M. and DINGMAN, H. F. (1961) 'A note on differential utility of W.A.I.S. verbal and performance I.Q.s.' *Amer. J. ment. Defic.* **65,** 482–5.

MILLER, E. (1966) (Ed.) *Foundations of Child Psychiatry.* London: Pergamon, *in the press.*

MILLER, F. M. and RAVEN, J. C. (1939) 'The influence of positional factors on the choice of answers to perceptual intelligence tests.' *Brit. J. med. Psychol.* **18,** 35–9.

MILLER, H. G. (1943) 'Toward the development of responsibility.' *Amer. J. ment. Defic.* **47,** 296–300.

MILLIKEN, J. R. and STANDEN, J. L. (1951) 'An investigation into the effects of glutamic acid on human intelligence.' *J. Neurolog., Neurosurg. and Psychiat.* **14,** 47–54.

MILNER, B. (1958) 'Psychological defects produced by temporal lobe excision.' *Res. Publ. Ass. Nerv. Ment. Dis.* **36,** 244–57.

MILNER, K. O. (1949) 'Delinquent types of mentally defective persons.' *J. ment. Sci.* **95,** 842–59.

MILNER, K. O. (1952) 'Psychotherapy with high-grade mental defectives.' *J. Midland ment. Defic. Soc.* **1,** 30–1.

MILNER, K. O. (1962) 'The treatment of delinquent mental defectives by psychotherapy.' *Proc. Lond. Conf. scient. Stud. ment. Defic., 1960* **1,** 258–62.

MINISTRY OF EDUCATION (1956) *Education in 1955.* London: H.M.S.O.

MINISTRY OF HEALTH (1951) Report of the Ministry of Health for 1951. Part I: Appendix XXII, 145.

MINISTRY OF HEALTH (1963) *Health and Welfare: the development of Community Care.* Cmmd. 1973. London: H.M.S.O.

MONTESSORI, M. (1912) *Montessori Method.* Trans. A. F. George. New York: F. A. Stokes.

MOORE, K. L. (1959) 'Sex reversal in newborn babies.' *Lancet* **i,** 217–19.

MORENO, J. L. (Ed.) (1946) *Group Psychotherapy.* New York: Beacon House.

MORGAN, J. J. B. (1950) *The Psychology of the Unadjusted School Child.* New York: Macmillan.

MORLEY, M. E. (1945) *Cleft Palate and Speech.* Edinburgh: E. & S. Livingstone.

MORLEY, M. E. (1957) *The Development and Disorders of Speech in Childhood.* Edinburgh and London: E. & S. Livingstone.

MORRIS, C. C., NELLIS, B. and STROMBERG, C. E. (1959) 'The development of an inter-disciplinary psychotherapeutic program in an institution for the mentally retarded.' *Amer. J. ment. Defic.* **63,** 605–10.

MORRIS, J. V. (1948) 'Delinquent defectives – a group study.' *Amer. J. ment. Defic.* **52,** 345–69.

MORRIS, J. V., MacGILLIVRAY, R. C. and MATHIESON, C. M. (1954) 'The experimental administration of *Celastrus Paniculata* in mental deficiency practice.' *Amer. J. ment. Defic.* **59,** 235–44.

MORROW, R. S. and MARK, J. C. (1955) 'The correlation of intelligence and neurological findings on twenty-two patients autopsied for brain damage.' *J. consult. Psychol.* **19,** 283.

MOWAT, J. (1961) *In Cerebral Palsy in Childhood and Adolescence* (Ed. Henderson, J. L.) Edinburgh and London: Livingstone.

MOWRER, O. H. (1950) *Learning Theory and Personality Dynamics.* New York: The Ronald Press.

MUELLER, M. W. and SMITH, J. O. (1964) 'The stability of language age modifications over time.' *Amer. J. ment. Defic.* **68,** 537–9.

MUENCH, G. A. (1944) 'A follow-up of mental defectives after eighteen years.' *J. abnorm. soc. Psychol.* **39,** 407–18.

MUNDY, L. (1955) 'Environmental influences in intellectual function as measured by intelligence tests.' Univ. Lond. unpubl. M.Sc. Thesis.

MUNDY, L. (1957a) 'Therapy with physically and mentally handicapped children in a mental deficiency hospital.' *J. clin. Psychol.* **13,** 3–9.

MUNDY, L. (1957b) 'Environmental influence on intellectual function as measured by intelligence tests.' *Brit. J. med. Psychol.* **30,** 194–201.

MUNDY, L. and MAXWELL, A. E. (1958) 'The assessment of the feebleminded.' *Brit. J. med. Psychol.* **31,** 201–11.

MUNSTERBERGER KOPPITZ, E. (1958) 'Relationships between the Bender Gestalt Test and the Wechsler Intelligence Test for children.' *J. clin. Psychol.* **14,** 413–16.

MURCHISON, C. (Ed.) (1933) *A Handbook of Child Psychology.* Worcester: Clark Univ. Press.

MURPHY, D. P. (1928) 'Ovarian irradiation; its effect on the health of subsequent children.' *Surg. Gynec. Obstet.* **47,** 201–15.

MURPHY, D. P. (1929) 'The outcome of 625 pregnancies in women subjected to pelvic radium or roentgen irradiation.' *Amer. J. Obstet. Gynec.* **18,** 179–87.

MURPHY, M. M. (1956) 'A Goodenough Scale evaluation of human figure drawings of three non-psychotic groups of adults.' *J. clin. Psychol.* **12,** 397–9.

MURRAY, H. (1953) 'The sociometric stability of personal relations among retarded children.' *Sociometry* **16,** 113–41.

MURSELL, J. L. (1949) *Psychological Testing.* London: Longmans, Green & Co.

MYKLEBUST, H. R. (1957) 'Aphasia in children – diagnosis and training.' *In Handbook of Speech Pathology.* Ed. Travis, L. E. New York: Appleton-Century-Crofts.

NEALE, M. D. and CAMPBELL, W. J. (1963) *Education for the Intellectually Limited Child.* Sydney: Novak.

NEMZEK, C. L. (1933) 'The constancy of the I.Q.' *Psychol. Bull.* **30,** 143–68.

NETCHINE, S. and LAIRY, G. C. (1962) 'Comparison of E.E.G. data and intelligence level in children.' *Proc. Lond. Conf. scient. Stud. ment. Defic., 1960* **2,** 378–83.

NEWELL, H. W. (1937) 'The effect of head injury on the behavior and personality of children: a study of 20 cases.' *Med. Clin. N. Amer.* **21,** 1335–65.

NEWMAN, H. H. (1929) 'Mental and physical traits of identical twins reared apart.' *J. Hered.* **20,** 49–64, 97–104, 153–66.

NEWMAN, H. H., FREEMAN, F. N. and HOLZINGER, K. J. (1937) *Twins: a Study of Heredity and Environment*. Chicago: Univ. Chicago Press.

NEWMAN, J. R. and LOOS, F. M. (1955) 'Differences between verbal and performance I.Q.s of mentally defective children on the W.I.S.C.' *J. consult. Psychol.* **19,** 16.

NICKELL, VERNON (1951) 'Educating the mentally handicapped in the secondary schools.' *Illinois Secondary School Curriculum Program, Bulletin No. 12*. Springfield, Illinois: Department of Public Instruction.

NISBET, J. D. (1953) *Family Environment: a Direct Effect of Family Size on Intelligence*. Occasional Papers on Eugenics. No. 8. London: Cassell.

NISBET, J. D. (1957) 'Contribution to intelligence testing and the theory of intelligence. IV. Intelligence and age: retesting with twenty-four years interval.' *Brit. J. educ. Psychol.* **27,** 190–8.

NORRIS, D. (1961) 'Education in the training centre.' *J. ment. Subnormal.* **7,** 62–6.

NORSWORTHY, N. (1906) 'The psychology of mentally deficient children.' *Arch. Psychol.* **1,** 1–111.

OAKDEN, E. C. and STUART, M. (1922) 'Development of knowledge of time.' *Brit. J. Psychol.* **12,** 309–36.

O'BRIEN, V. and HEWSON, L. (1948) 'Analysis of psychological examinations of children with cerebral palsy.' *J. Child Psychiat.* **1,** 121–39.

O'CONNOR, N. (1951) 'Neuroticism and emotional instability in high-grade male defectives.' *J. Neurol., Neurosurg. Psychiat.* **14,** 226–30.

O'CONNOR, N. (1953) 'Brain injury and intelligence.' Unpubl. stud.

O'CONNOR, N. (1954) 'Defectives working in the community.' *Amer. J. ment. Defic.* **59,** 173–80.

O'CONNOR, N. (1956) 'The evidence for the permanently disturbing effects of mother-child separation.' *Acta Psychol.* **12,** 174–91.

O'CONNOR, N. (1957) 'Imbecility and colour blindness.' *Amer. J. ment. Defic.* **62,** 83–7.

O'CONNOR, N. and CLARIDGE, G. S. (1955) 'The effect of goal-setting and encouragement on the performance of imbecile men.' *Quart. J. exp. Psychol.* **7,** 37–45.

O'CONNOR, N. and CLARIDGE, G. S. (1958) 'A "Crespi" effect in male imbeciles.' *Brit. J. Psychol.* **49,** 42–8.

O'CONNOR, N. and HARITOS, M. (1953) 'A note on the visuo motor performance of brain damaged and normal children.' Unpubl. stud.

O'CONNOR, N. and HERMELIN, B. (1962) 'Recall in normals and subnormals of like mental age.' *J. abn. soc. Psychol.* **66,** 81–4.

O'CONNOR, N. and HERMELIN, B. (1963) *Speech and Thought in Severe Subnormality*. London: Pergamon.

O'CONNOR, N. and TIZARD, J. (1954) 'A survey of patients in twelve mental deficiency institutions.' *Brit. med. J.* **1,** 16–18.

O'CONNOR, N. and TIZARD, J. (1956) *The Social Problem of Mental Deficiency*. London: Pergamon.

O'CONNOR, N. and YONGE, K. A. (1955) 'Methods of evaluating the group psychotherapy of unstable defective delinquents.' *J. genet. Psychol.* **87,** 89–101.

OGDON, D. and ALLEE R. (1959) 'Rorschach relationships with intelligence among familial mental defectives.' *Amer. J. ment. Defic.* **63,** 889–96.

ONONDAGA COUNTY SURVEY (1955) 'A special census of suspected-referred mental retardation.' *Community ment. Hlth. Res., New York State Dept. ment. Hyg. Rep.*

ORDAHL, L. E. and ORDAHL, G. (1915) 'Qualitative differences between levels of intelligence in feeble-minded children.' *J. Psycho-asth. Monogr. Suppl.* **1,** 3–50.

ORLANSKY, H. (1949) 'Infant care and personality.' *Psychol. Rev.* **46,** 1–48.

ORME, J. E. (1961) 'The Coloured Progressive Matrices as a measure of intellectual subnormality.' *Brit. J. med. Psychol.* **34,** 291–2.

OSBORN, W. J. (1960) 'Associative clustering in organic and familial retardates.' *Amer. J. ment. Defic.* **65,** 351–7.

OSGOOD, C. E. (1957) *Contemporary Approaches to Cognition, a Behaviouristic Analysis.* Cambridge: Harvard Univ. Press.

OSTOW, M. (1950) 'Psychic function and the electroencephalogram.' *Arch. Neurol. Psychiat.* **64,** 385–400.

OWENS, W. A. (1953) 'Age and mental abilities: a longitudinal study.' *Genet. Psychol. Monogr.* **48,** 3–54.

PANTON, JAMES H. (1960) 'Beta–W.A.I.S. comparisons and W.A.I.S. subtest configurations within a state prison population.' *J. clin. Psychol.* **16,** 312–17.

PAPANIA, N. (1954) 'A qualitative analysis of the vocabulary responses of institutionalized mentally retarded children.' *J. clin. Psychol.* **10,** 361–5.

PARKER, L. P. (1957) 'The preparation for speech in the very young cerebral palsied child.' *Folia Phoniatrica* **9,** 54–7.

PARSONS, M. H. (1960) 'A home economist in service to families with mental retardation.' *Children* **7,** 184–90.

PASCAL, G. R. and SUTTELL, B. J. (1951) *The Bender Gestalt Test.* New York: Grune & Stratton.

PATAU, K., SMITH, B. W., THERMAN, E., INHARN, S. L. and WAGNER, N. P. (1960) 'Multiple congenital anomaly caused by an extra autosome.' *Lancet* **i,** 790–3.

PATERSON, D. G. (1930) *Physique and Intellect.* New York: Century.

PATTERSON, M. and MAGAW, D. C. (1936) 'An investigation of the validity of the Rorschach technique as applied to mentally defective problem children.' *Proc. Amer. Assoc. Ment. Defic.* **63,** 179–85.

PAVLOV, I. P. (1941) *Conditioned Reflexes and Psychiatry.* Trans. by W. Horsley Gantt. New York: International Publishers.

PAYNE, R. W. (1957) 'Experimental methods in clinical psychological practice.' *J. ment. Sci.* **103,** 189–96.

PAYNE, R. W. and JONES, H. GWYNNE (1957) 'Statistics for the investigation of individual cases.' *J. clin. Psychol.* **13,** 114–21.

PEARSON, K. (1914) 'Mendelism and the problem of mental defects. iii. On the graduated nature of mental defect.' *Questions of the Day and of the Fray.* IX. London: Drapers' Co. Res. Memoirs.

PECK, J. R. (1960) 'A comparative investigation of the learning and social adjustment of trainable children in public school facilities, segregated community centers, and state residential centers.' *U.S. Office of Education, Co-operative Research Program.* Project No. SAE 6430.

PEEL, E. A. (1959) 'Experimental examination of some of Piaget's schemata concerning children's perception and thinking, and a discussion of their educational significance.' *Brit. J. educ. Psychol.* **29,** 89–103.

PEIXOTTO, H. E. (1950) 'Wechsler–Bellevue subtest patterns: a note of caution.' *J. clin. Psychol.* **6,** 188–90.

PENROSE, L. S. (1938) 'A clinical and genetic study of 1280 cases of mental defect.' *Sp. Rep. Ser., Med. Res. Coun.* No. 229. London: H.M.S.O.

PENROSE, L. S. (1949) *The Biology of Mental Defect.* London: Sidgwick & Jackson. (Revised edition 1954.) See also (1963a).

PENROSE, L. S. (1950) 'Genetic influences on the intelligence level of the population.' *Brit. J. Psychol.* **40,** 128–36.

PENROSE, L. S. (1962) 'Biological aspects.' *Proc. Lond. Conf. scient. Stud. ment. Defic., 1960* **1,** 11–18.

PENROSE, L. S. (1963a) *The Biology of Mental Defect.* London: Sidgwick & Jackson (revised edition).

PENROSE, L. S. (1963b) *Outline of Human Genetics.* London: Heinemann (2nd edition).

PENROSE, L. S. (1963c) 'Finger-prints, palms and chromosomes.' *Nature (Lond.)* **197,** 933–8.

PENROSE, L. S. (1963d) 'Paternal age in mongolism.' *Lancet* **i,** 1101.

PENSE, A. W., PATTON, R. E., CAMP, J. L. and KEBALO, C. (1961) 'A cohort study of institutionalised young mentally retarded children.' *Amer. J. ment. Defic.* **66,** 18–22.

PERLSTEIN, J. A. and HOOD, P. N. (1957) 'Infantile spastic hemiplegia, intelligence and age of walking and talking.' *Amer. J. ment. Defic.* **61,** 534–43.

PFISTER, O. (1926) 'Ergebnisse des Rorschachschen Versuches bei Oligophrenen.' *Z. Psychiat.* **82,** 198–223.

PHELPS, W. M. (1948) 'Characteristic psychological variations in cerebral palsy.' *Nerv. Child.* **7,** 10–12.

PHELPS, W. M. (1958) Chap., 'The role of physical therapy in cerebral palsy.' *In Recent Advances in Cerebral Palsy.* Ed. Illingworth, R. S. London: J. & A. Churchill.

PIAGET, J. (1928) *Judgment and Reasoning in the Child.* London: Routledge.

PIAGET, J. (1948) *Le développement de la notion de temps chez l'enfant.* Paris: Presses Universitaire de France.

PIAGET, J. (1950) *The Psychology of Intelligence.* London: Routledge & Kegan Paul.

PIAGET, J. (1952) *The Child's Conception of Number.* London: Routledge & Kegan Paul.

PIAGET, J. (1953) *The Origin of Intelligence in the Child.* London: Routledge & Kegan Paul.

PIAGET, J. (1955) *The Child's Construction of Reality.* London: Routledge & Kegan Paul.

PILKEY, L., GOLDMAN, M. and KLEINMAN, B. (1961) 'Psychodrama and empathic ability in the mentally retarded.' *Amer. J. ment. Defic.* **65,** 595–605.

PINTNER, R. (1933) 'The feeble-minded child.' *In* Murchison (Ed.) (1933).

PIOTROWSKI, Z. A. (1937) 'The Rorschach inkblot method in organic disturbances of the central nervous system.' *J. nerv. ment. Dis.* **86,** 525–37.

PIOTROWSKI, Z. A. (1938) 'Rorschach studies of cases with lesions of the frontal lobes.' *Brit. J. med. Psychol.* **17,** 105–18.

PIOTROWSKI, Z. A. (1940) 'Positive and negative Rorschach organic reactions.' *Rorschach Res. Exch.* **4,** 147–51.

PITT, D. B. (1961) 'Congenital malformations and maternal rubella: progress report.' *Med. J. Aust.* **1,** 881–90.

PITT, D. B. (1962) 'Congenital malformations: a review.' *Med. J. Aust.* **1,** 82–7, 121–4.

PLUMMER, G. (1952) 'Anomalies occurring in children exposed in utero to the atomic bomb in Hiroshima.' *Pediatrics* **10,** 687–93.

POLLOCK, H. M. (1945) 'Mental disease among mental defectives.' *Amer. J. ment. Defic.* **49,** 477–80.

POPPLESTONE, J. A. (1954) 'The validity of projective interpretations of art products of mentally retarded individuals.' *Amer. J. ment. Defic.* **59,** 263–5.

PORTEUS, S. D. (1920) 'A study of the personality of defectives with a social rating scale.' *Train. Sch., Vineland.* Extension Dept.

PORTEUS, S. D. (1941) *The Practice of Clinical Psychology.* New York: Amer. Book Co.

PORTEUS, S. D. (1942) *Qualitative Performance on the Maze Test.* New York: Vineland Psychol. Corp.

PORTEUS, S. D. (1950) *The Porteus Maze Test and Intelligence.* Palo Alto: Pacific Books.

PORTEUS, S. D. (1959) *The Maze Test and Clinical Psychology.* Palo Alto: Pacific Books.

PORTNOY, B. and STACEY, C. L. (1954) 'A comparative study of negro and white subnormals on the children's form of the Rosenzweig P–F Test.' *Amer. J. ment. Defic.* **59,** 272–8.

POULL, L. E. and MONTGOMERY, R. P. (1929) 'The Porteus Maze test as a discriminative measure in delinquency.' *J. appl. Psychol.* **13,** 145–51.

PREISER, S. A. and DAVENPORT, C. B. (1918) 'Multiple neurofibromatosia (von Recklinghausen's disease) and its inheritance: with description of a case.' *Amer. J. med. Sci.* **156,** 507–40.

PRESIDENT'S PANEL ON MENTAL RETARDATION (1962) *Report to the President: a Proposed Program for National Action to Combat Mental Retardation.* Washington, D.C.: U.S. Government Printing Office.

PRICE, A. C. and DEABLER, H. L. (1955) 'Diagnosis of organicity by means of spiral after-effects.' *J. consult. Psychol.* **19,** 298–302.

PRICE, H. H. (1950) *Perception.* 2nd edition. London: Oxford Univ. Press.

PRICE, L. (1947) 'The feebleminded as child guidance patients.' *Smith Coll. Stud. soc. Wk.* **18,** 1–20.

PURCELL, C. K., DREVDAHL, J. and PURCELL, K. (1952) 'The relationship between altitude–I.Q. discrepancy and anxiety.' *J. clin. Psychol.* **8,** 82–5.

QUIBELL, E. P., STEPHEN, E. and WHATLEY, E. (1961) 'A survey of a group of children with mental and physical handicap treated in an orthopaedic hospital.' *Arch. Dis. Child.* **36,** 58–64.

RABIN, A. I. and GUERTIN, W. H. (1951) 'Research with the Wechsler–Bellevue test: 1945–50.' *Psychol. Bull.* **48,** 211–48.

RAMER, T. (1946) 'The prognosis of mentally retarded children.' *Acta Psychiat. Neurol. suppl.* **41,** 1–142.

RAPAPORT, D. (1945, 1946) *Diagnostic Psychological Testing.* Vol. I, 1945; Vol. II, 1946. Chicago: Year Book Publ.

RASMUS, M. (1946) 'The use of multi-sensory aids in guiding the slow-learning pupil in the understanding of arithmetic.' *Amer. J. ment. Defic.* **51,** 207–13.

RAVEN, J. C. (1938) *Progressive Matrices.* London: H. K. Lewis.

RAVEN, J. C. (1947) *Progressive Matrices (Coloured) Sets A, Ab, B.* London: H. K. Lewis.

RAVEN, J. C. (1956) *Standard Progressive Matrices 1938.* London: H. K. Lewis.

REGISTRAR GENERAL (1953) *The Registrar General's statistical review of England and Wales for the year 1949. Supplement on general morbidity, cancer and mental health.* London: H.M.S.O.

REITAN, R. M. (1955) 'Certain differential effects of right and left cerebral lesions in human adults.' *J. comp. physiol. Psychol.* **48,** 474–7.

RENFREW, C. and MURPHY, K. (Eds.) (1964) *The Child who does not Talk.* London: W. Heinemann.

REPORT OF THE DEPARTMENTAL COMMITTEE ON STERILISATION (1934). London: H.M.S.O.

REFERENCES

REPORT OF THE MENTAL DEFICIENCY COMMITTEE (1929), Parts I to IV. London: H.M.S.O.

REPORT OF THE ROYAL COMMISSION ON THE CARE AND CONTROL OF THE FEEBLEMINDED (1908). London: H.M.S.O.

REPORT ON LOCAL HEALTH SERVICE STATISTICS (1952–3). Society of County Treasurers.

REYNOLDS, B. and ADAMS, J. A. (1954) 'Psychomotor performance as a function of initial level of ability.' *Amer. J. Psychol.* **67,** 268–77.

REYNOLDS, M. C. and KILAND, J. R. (1953) *A Study of Public School Children with Severe Mental Retardation.* St Paul: State Department of Educ., Res. Project No. 8.

RHEINGOLD, H. L. (1956) 'The modification of social responsiveness in institutional babies.' *Monogr. Soc. Res. Child Developm.* **21,** 1–48.

RHEINGOLD, H. L. (1960) 'The measurement of maternal care.' *Child Developm.* **31,** 565–75.

RICHARDS, B. W. (1951) 'Childhood schizophrenia and mental deficiency.' *J. ment. Sci.* **97,** 290–312.

RIESE, H. (1956) 'Academic work with an eleven year old girl with an I.Q. of 41.' *Amer. J. ment. Defic.* **60,** 545–51.

RIESEN, A. H. (1947) 'The development of visual perception in man and chimpanzee.' *Science* **106,** 107–8.

RINGELHEIM, D. and POLATSEK, I. (1955) 'Group therapy with a male defective group.' *Amer. J. ment. Defic.* **60,** 157–62.

RITTMANIC, P. A. (1958) 'An oral language program for institutionalized educable mentally retarded children.' *Amer. J. ment. Defic.* **63,** 403–7.

ROBERTS, A. D. (1945a) 'Intelligence and performance test patterns among older mental defectives.' *Amer. J. ment. Defic.* **49,** 300–3.

ROBERTS, A. D. (1945b) 'Some I.Q. changes on the Stanford–Binet, Form L.' *Amer. J. ment. Defic.* **50,** 134–6.

ROGERS, C. W. (1942) *Counselling and Psychotherapy.* Boston: Houghton Mifflin.

ROGERS, L. S. (1950) 'A comparative evaluation of the Wechsler–Bellevue mental deterioration index for various adult groups.' *J. clin. Psychol.* **6,** 199–202.

ROHAN, J. C. (1954) 'A system of daily licence in a colony for mental defectives.' *Ment. Hlth. Lond.* **13,** 64–72.

ROLLIN, H. R. (1946) 'Personality in mongolism with special reference to the incidence of catatonic psychosis.' *Amer. J. ment. Defic.* **51,** 219–37.

ROSENBLATT, B. and SOLOMON, P. (1954) 'Structural and genetic aspects of Rorschach responses in mental deficiency.' *J. Proj. Tech.* **18,** 496–506.

ROSENZWEIG, L. (1954) 'Report of a school program for trainable mentally retarded children.' *Amer. J. ment. Defic.* **59,** 181–205.

ROSENZWEIG, L. (1959) 'How far have we come.' *Amer. J. ment. Defic.* **64,** 12–18.

ROSS, W. D. (1941) 'The contribution of the Rorschach method to clinical diagnosis.' *J. ment. Sci.* **87,** 331–48.

ROSSETTIE, T. M. and STRAUSS, A. A. (1945) 'Disciplinary procedures as conceived by boys in a self-determining group.' *Amer. J. ment. Defic.* **49,** 307–15.

ROSWELL HARRIS, D. (1958) 'Some aspects of cognitive and personality test changes in a group of 100 feebleminded young men.' Univ. Reading, unpubl. M.A. Thesis.

ROWBOTHAM, G. F., MACIVER, I. V., DICKSON, J. and BOUSFIELD, M. E. (1954) 'Analysis of 1400 cases of acute injury to the head.' *Brit. med. J.* **1,** 726–30.

REFERENCES

ROYAL COMMISSION ON THE DEAF AND DUMB (1889), Report of the. London: H.M.S.O.

ROYAL COMMISSION ON THE LAW RELATING TO MENTAL ILLNESS AND MENTAL DEFICIENCY, 1954–1957 (1957), Report of the. London: H.M.S.O.

ROYAL MEDICO-PSYCHOLOGICAL ASSOCIATION (1954) *Memorandum of evidence before the Royal Commission on the Law relating to Mental Illness and Mental Deficiency*. 8th Day. London: H.M.S.O.

RUDOLF, G. DE M. (1949a) 'Retesting of the I.Q. and the social age.' *J. ment. Sci.* **95,** 696–702.

RUDOLF, G. DE M. (1949b) 'Comparison of the intelligence quotient with behaviour. *J. ment. Sci.* **95,** 703–5.

RUDOLF, G. DE M. (1950) 'Improvement in mental defectives in colonies.' *J. ment. Sci.* **96,** 272–5.

RUESS, A. L. (1958) 'Some cultural and personality aspects of mental retardation.' *Amer. J. ment. Defic.* **63,** 50–9.

SACHS, M. H. (1951) 'A survey and evaluation of the existing interrelationships between speech and mental deficiency.' Univ. of Virginia, unpubl. M.A. Thesis.

SAENGER, G. (1957) *The Adjustment of Severely Retarded Adults in the Community*. Albany: New York State Interdepartmental Health Resources Board.

SAENGER, G. (1960) *Factors influencing the institutionalization of mentally retarded individuals in New York City*. Albany: New York State Interdepartmental Health Resources Board.

SAMPSON, O. C. (1962) 'Speech development and improvement in the severely subnormal child.' *J. ment. Subnormal.* **8,** 70–7.

SAMPSON, O. C. (1964) 'The conversational style of a group of severely subnormal children.' *J. ment. Subnormal.* **10,** 89–100.

SANDERCOCK, M. G. and BUTLER, A. J. (1952) 'An analysis of the performance of mental defectives on the Wechsler intelligence scale for children.' *Amer. J. ment. Defic.* **57,** 100–5.

SANGREN, P. V. (1927) *The Measurement of Achievement in Silent Reading*. Kalamazoo: West State Teachers' College.

SARASON, S. B. (1943) 'The use of the Thematic Apperception Test for mentally deficient children. I. A study of high grade girls. II. A study of high grade boys.' *Amer. J. ment. Defic.* **47,** 414–21 and **48,** 169–73.

SARASON, S. B. (1949) *Psychological Problems in Mental Deficiency*. 2nd edition 1953. New York: Harper.

SARASON, S. B. and GLADWIN, T. (1958) 'Psychological and cultural problems in mental subnormality: a review of research.' *Genet. Psychol. Monogr.* **57,** 1–284.

SARASON, S. B. and POTTER, E. H. (1947) 'Color in the Rorschach and Kohs Block Designs.' *J. consult. Psychol.* **11,** 202–6.

SARASON, S. B. and SARASON, E. K. (1946) 'The discriminatory value of a test pattern in the highgrade familial defective.' *J. clin. Psychol.* **2,** 38–49.

SARBIN, T. R. (1946) 'Spontaneity training of the feebleminded.' *In* Moreno (Ed.) (1946).

SATTER, G. (1955) 'Retarded adults who have developed beyond expectation: Part III: Further analysis and summary.' *Train. Sch. Bull.* **51,** 237–43.

SCHAEFER-SIMMERN, H. (1948) *The Unfolding of Artistic Activity*. Berkeley: Univ. Calif. Press.

SCHAEFER-SIMMERN, H. and SARASON, S. B. (1944) 'Therapeutic implications of artistic activity.' *Amer. J. ment. Defic.* **49,** 185–96.

SCHLANGER, B. B. (1953a) 'Speech therapy results with mentally retarded children in special classes.' *Train. Sch. Bull.* **50,** 179–86.

SCHLANGER, B. B. (1953b) 'Speech examination of a group of institutionalized mentally retarded children.' *J. Speech Hearing Disord.* **18,** 339–49.

SCHLANGER, B. B. (1954) 'Environmental influences on the verbal output of mentally retarded children.' *J. Speech Hearing Disord.* **19,** 339–45.

SCHLANGER, B. B. and GOTTSLEBEN, R. H. (1957) 'Analysis of speech defects among the institutionalized mentally retarded.' *J. Speech Dis.* **22,** 98–103.

SCHMIDT, B. G. (1946) 'Changes in personal, social and intellectual behaviour of children originally classified as feebleminded.' *Psychol. Monogr.* **60,** 5, 1–144.

SCHMIDT, B. G. (1948) 'A reply.' *Psychol. Bull.* **45,** 334–43.

SCHNEIDER, B. and VALLON, J. (1955) 'The results of a speech therapy programme for mentally retarded children.' *Amer. J. ment. Defic.* **59,** 417–24.

SCHONELL, F. E. (1956) *Educating Spastic Children.* Edinburgh: Oliver & Boyd.

SCHONELL, F. J. (1942) *Backwardness in the Basic Subjects.* Edinburgh: Oliver & Boyd.

SCHROEDER, P. L. (1929) 'Behaviour difficulties in children associated with the results of birth trauma.' *J. Amer. med. Assoc.* **92,** 100–4.

SCHUCMAN, H. (1960) 'Evaluating the educability of the severely mentally retarded child.' *Psychol. Monogr.* **74,** 1–32 (No. 501).

SCHUNHOFF, H. F. and MacPHERSON, J. R. (1951) 'What about the deaf or hard-of-hearing mentally deficient?' *Train. Sch. Bull.* **48,** 71–5.

'SCOTT COMMITTEE' (1962) *The Training of Staff of Training Centres for the Mentally Subnormal:* Report of the Subcommittee. London: H.M.S.O.

SCOTTISH COUNCIL FOR RESEARCH IN EDUCATION (1949) *The Trend of Scottish Intelligence.* London: Univ. London Press.

SCOTTISH COUNCIL FOR RESEARCH IN EDUCATION (1953) *Social Implications of the Scottish Mental Survey.* London: Univ. London Press.

SEGAL, C. S. (1949) *Backward Children in the Making.* London: Frederick Muller.

SEGUIN, E. (1846) *Traitement moral, hygiène et éducation des idiots et des autres enfants arrières.* Paris: J. B. Ballière.

SENDEN, M. V. (1932) *Raum und Gestalt auffassung bei operienten Blindgebornen vor und nach die Operation.* Leipzig: Berth.

SEYMOUR, A. H. and WHITTAKER, J. E. F. (1938) 'An experiment on nutrition.' *Occup. Psychol.* **12,** 215–23.

SHAFTER, A. J. (1954) 'The vocational placement of institutionalized mental defectives in the United States.' *Amer. J. ment. Defic.* **59,** 279–307.

SHAFTER, A. J. (1957) 'Criteria for selecting institutionalized mental defectives for vocational placement.' *Amer. J. ment. Defic.* **61,** 599–616.

SHAFTER, A. J. and CHANDLER, C. S. (1960) 'Merit Wards-Settings for social and vocational training.' *Amer. J. ment. Defic.* **64,** 1029–33.

SHAPIRO, A. (1962) 'Problems of psychotherapy' *Proc. Lond. Conf. scient. Stud. ment. Defic., 1960* **1,** 263–70. Dagenham: May & Baker.

SHAPIRO, M. B. (1951a) 'Experimental studies of a perceptual anomaly. I. Initial experiments.' *J. ment. Sci.* **97,** 90–110.

SHAPIRO, M. B. (1951b) 'An experimental approach to diagnostic testing.' *J. ment. Sci.* **97,** 748–64.

SHAPIRO, M. B. (1952) 'Experimental studies of a perceptual anomaly. II. Confirmatory and explanatory experiments.' *J. ment. Sci.* **98,** 605–17.

SHAPIRO, M. B. (1953) 'Experimental studies of a perceptual anomaly. III. The testing of an explanatory theory.' *J. ment. Sci.* **99,** 394–409.

SHAPIRO, M. B. (1954) 'An experimental investigation of the Block Design rotation effect.' *Brit. J. med. Psychol.* **27,** 84–8.

SHAPIRO, M. B. (1957) 'Experimental method in the psychological description of the individual psychiatric patient.' *Internat. J. soc. Psychiat.* **3,** 89–102.

SHAPIRO, M. B., BRIERLEY, J., SLATER, P. and BEECH, H. R. (1962) 'Experimental investigations of a perceptual anomaly. VII: A new explanation.' *J. ment. Sci.* **108,** 655–68.

SHELDON, W. H. (1942) *The Varieties of Temperament*. New York and London: Harper & Bros.

SHELDON, W. H. (1949) *Varieties of Delinquent Youth*. New York and London: Harper & Bros.

SHERE, M. O. (1954) 'An evaluation of the social and emotional development of the cerebral palsied twin.' Unpubl. doct. dissert. Col. Educ. Univ. Illinois. Quoted by Cruickshank and Raus (Ed,) (1955).

SHERLOCK, E. B. (1911) *The Feeble-minded*. London: Macmillan.

SHIELDS, J. (1962) *Monozygotic Twins*. London: Oxford Univ. Press.

SHIPLEY, W. C. (1940) 'A self-administering scale for measuring intellectual impairment and deterioration.' *J. Psychol.* **9,** 371–7.

SHIPLEY, W. C. and BURLINGAME, C. C. (1941) 'A convenient self-administering scale for measuring intellectual impairment in psychotics.' *Amer. J. Psychiat.* **97,** 1313–25.

SHOTWELL, A. M. and LAWRENCE, E. S. (1951) 'Mosaic patterns of institutionalized mental defectives.' *Amer. J. ment. Defic.* **56,** 161–8.

SHRAND, H. (1961) 'Treatment of lead poisoning with intramuscular edathamil calcium-disodium.' *Lancet* **i,** 310–12.

SIEGEL, S. M. (1957) 'Discrimination among mental defective, normal, schizophrenic and brain damaged subjects on the Visual-Verbal concept formation test.' *Amer. J. ment. Defic.* **62,** 338–3.

SIEGENTHALER, B. M. and KRZYWICKI, D. F. (1959) 'Incidence and pattern of hearing loss among an adult mentally retarded population.' *Amer. J. ment. Defic.* **64,** 444–9.

SIEVERS, D. J. (1959) 'A study to compare the performance of brain-injured and non-brain-injured mentally retarded children on the differential language facility test.' *Amer. J. ment. Defic.* **63,** 839–47.

SIEVERS, D. J. and ESSA, S. H. (1961) 'Language development in institutionalized and community mentally retarded children.' *Amer. J. ment. Defic.* **66,** 413–20.

SIEVERS, D. J. and ROSENBERG, C. M. (1960) 'The differential language facility test and electroencephalograms of brain injured mentally retarded children.' *Amer. J. ment. Defic.* **65,** 46–50.

SIMON, B. (1957) *Psychology in the Soviet Union*. London: Routledge & Kegan Paul.

SIMRALL, D. (1947) 'Intelligence and the ability to learn.' *J. Psychol.* **23,** 27–43.

SIRKIN, J. (1944) 'Acrocephalosyndactylia: report of a case.' *Amer. J. ment. Defic.* **48,** 335–8.

SIRKIN, J. and LYONS, W. F. (1941) 'A study of speech defects in mental deficiency.' *Amer. J. ment. Defic.* **46,** 74–80.

SKEELS, H. M. (1938) 'Mental development of children in foster homes.' *J. consult. Psychol.* **2,** 33–43.

SKEELS, H. M. and DYE, H. B. (1939) 'A study of the effects of differential stimulation on mentally retarded children.' *Proc. Amer. Assoc. ment. Defic.* **44,** 114–36.

SKEELS, H. M. and HARMS, I. (1948) 'Children with inferior social histories; their mental development in adoptive homes.' *J. genet. Psychol.* **72,** 283–94.

SKODAK, M. (1939) 'Children in foster homes.' *Univ. Iowa Stud. Child Welf.* **16,** 1–156.

SKODAK, M. and SKEELS, H. M. (1945) 'A follow-up study of children in adoptive homes.' *J. genet. Psychol.* **66,** 21–58.

SKODAK, M. and SKEELS, H. M. (1949) 'A final follow-up study of one hundred adopted children.' *J. genet. Psychol.* **75,** 85–125.

SLAVSON, S. R. (1950) *Analytic Group Psychotherapy, with Children, Adolescents and Adults.* New York: Columbia Univ. Press.

SLOAN, W. (1947a) 'Mental deficiency as a symptom of personality disturbance.' *Amer. J. ment. Defic.* **52,** 31–6.

SLOAN, W. (1947b) 'Validity of Wechsler's deterioration quotient in high-grade mental defectives.' *J. clin. Psychol.* **3,** 287–8.

SLOAN, W. (1948) 'Prediction of extramural adjustment of mental defectives by use of the Rorschach test.' *J. consult. Psychol.* **12,** 303–9.

SLOAN, W. (1951) 'Motor proficiency and intelligence.' *Amer. J. ment. Defic.* **55,** 394–406.

SLOAN, W. (1955) 'The Lincoln–Oseretsky motor development scale.' *Genet. Psychol. Monogr.* **51,** 183–252.

SLOAN, W. and CUTTS, R. A. (1945) 'Test patterns of defective delinquents on the Wechsler–Bellevue test.' *Amer. J. ment. Defic.* **50,** 95–7.

SLOAN, W. and SCHNEIDER, B. (1951) 'A study of the Wechsler Intelligence Scale for Children with mental defectives.' *Amer. J. ment. Defic.* **55,** 573–5.

SMITH, H. W. (1957) 'A sheltered employment project in an institution for mental defectives.' *Amer. J. ment. Defic.* **61,** 665–71.

SMITH, J. O. (1962) 'Group language development for educable mental retardates.' *Except. Children* **29,** 95–101.

SMITH, S. B. (1926) 'Cerebral accidents of childhood and their relationships to mental deficiency.' *Welf. Mag.* **17,** 18–33.

SMITHELLS, R. W. (1962) 'Thalidomide and malformations in Liverpool.' *Lancet* **i,** 1270–3.

SNYDER, R. and SECHREST, L. (1959) 'An experimental study of directive group therapy with defective delinquents.' *Amer. J. ment. Defic.* **64,** 117–23.

SOLOMON, P. (1954) 'A note on rigidity and length of institutionalization.' *J. clin. Psychol.* **10,** 391–2.

SOLOMON, P. (1955) 'Differential Rorschach scores of successfully and unsuccessfully placed mental defectives.' *J. clin. Psychol.* **11,** 294–7.

SPAULDING, P. J. (1946) 'Retest results on the Stanford–Binet. Form L, with mental defectives.' *Amer. J. ment. Defic.* **51,** 35–42.

SPEARMAN, C. (1923) *The Nature of Intelligence and the Principles of Cognition.* London: Macmillan.

SPITZ, H. H. and HOATS, D. L. (1961) 'Experiments on perceptual curiosity behaviour in mental retardates.' *Final Report N.I.M.H. Public Health Service Grant M5533.*

SPITZ, R. A. (1945) 'Hospitalism: an inquiry into the genesis of psychiatric conditions in early childhood.' *Psychoanalytic Stud. Child* **1,** 53–74.

SPRADLIN, J. E. (1963) 'Language and communication of mental defectives.' In *Handbook of Mental Deficiency.* (Ed. N. R. Ellis.) New York: McGraw-Hill.

SPRADLIN, J. E., CROMWELL, R. L. and FOSHEE, J. G. (1959) 'Studies in activity level: III. Effects of auditory stimulation in organics, familials, hyperactives and hypoactives.' *Amer. J. ment. Defic.* **64,** 754–7.

SPRADLIN, J. E., FOSHEE, J. G. and CROMWELL, R. L. (1960) 'The effect of auditory stimulation conditions on activity level: I Organics versus familials. II Hyperactives versus hypoactives.' *Amer. J. ment. Defic.* **65,** 754–7.

SPRINGER, N. N. (1941) 'A study of the drawings of maladjusted and adjusted children.' *J. genet. Psychol.* **58,** 131–8.

STACEY, C. L. and DE MARTINO, M. F. (Ed.) (1957) *Counseling and Psychotherapy with the Mentally Retarded.* Glencoe, Ill.: The Free Press.

STACEY, C. L. and GILL, M. R. (1954) 'The relationship between Raven's Coloured Matrices and two tests of general intelligence for 172 subnormal adult subjects.' *J. clin. Psychol.* **11,** 86–7.

STACEY, C. L. and LEVINE, J. (1951) 'Correlational analysis of scores of subnormal subjects on the Stanford–Binet and W.I.S.C.' *Amer. J. ment. Defic.* **55,** 590–7.

STANLEY, R. J. and GUNZBURG, H. C. (1957) 'A survey of residential licences from a mental deficiency hospital.' *Int. J. soc. Psychiat.* **2,** 207–13.

STEIN, Z. and SUSSER, M. (1962) 'Mental retardation: a cultural syndrome. *Proc. Lond. Conf. scient. Stud. ment. Defic., 1960* **1,** 174–8. Dagenham: May & Baker.

STEPHEN, E. (1961) 'Assessment, Training and Employment of Adolescents and Young Adults with Cerebral Palsy.' *Cerebral Palsy Bull.* **3,** 127–34.

STERN, W. (1914) *The Psychological Methods of Testing Intelligence.* Baltimore: Warwick & York.

STEVENS, G. D. (1958) 'An analysis of the objectives for the education of children with retarded mental development.' *Amer. J. ment. Defic.* **63,** 225–35.

STEVENS, H. and HEBER, R. (Eds.) (1964) *Mental Retardation.* Chicago and London: Univ. of Chicago Press.

STEVENS, S. S. (Ed.) (1951) *Handbook of Experimental Psychology.* New York: John Wiley.

STEVENSON, H. W. and ISCOE, I. (1955) 'Transposition in the feebleminded.' *J. exp. Psychol.* **49,** 11–15.

STODDARD, G. D. (1943) *The Meaning of Intelligence.* New York: MacMillan.

STOGDILL, R. M. (1938) 'Some behavior adjustment techniques in use with mentally retarded children.' *J. except. Children* **5,** 25–30.

STOLLER, A. (1961) 'Investigation of mental deficiency.' *Med. J. Aust.* 206–10.

STRAUSS, A. A. (1939) 'Typology in mental deficiency: its clinical, psychological and educational implications.' *Amer. J. ment. Defic.* **45,** 85–90.

STRAUSS, A. A. (1941) 'The incidence of central nervous system involvement in higher grade moron children.' *Amer. J. ment. Defic.* **45,** 548–54.

STRAUSS, A. A. and KEPHART, N. C. (1955) *Psychopathology and Education of the Brain-injured Child.* Vol. II. *Progress in Theory and Clinic.* By Strauss and Lehtinen. New York: Grune & Stratton.

STRAUSS, A. A. and LEHTINEN, L. E. (1947) *Psychopathology and Education of the Brain-injured Child.* 4th printing 1951. New York: Grune & Stratton.

STRAUSS, A. A. and WERNER, H. (1938) 'Deficiency in the finger schema in relation to arithmetic disability.' *Amer. J. Orthopsychiat.* **8,** 719–25.

STRAUSS, A. A. and WERNER, H. (1939) 'Finger agnosia in children.' *Amer. J. Psychiat.* **95,** 1215–25.

STRAZZULLA, M. (1953) 'Speech problems of the mongoloid child.' *Quart. Rev. Pediat.* **8,** 268–73.

STROTHER, C. R. (1944) 'The performance of psychopaths on the Wechsler–Bellevue test.' *Proc. Ia. Acad. Sci.* **51,** 397–400.

STROTHER, C. R. (1945) 'Evaluating intelligence.' *Crippled Child.* **23,** 82–3.

STUBBLEBINE, J. M. (1957) 'Group psychotherapy with some epileptic mentally deficient adults.' *Amer. J. ment. Defic.* **61,** 725–30.

STUBBLEBINE, J. M. and ROADRUCK, R. D. (1956) 'Treatment program for mentally deficient adolescents.' *Amer. J. ment. Defic.* **60,** 552–6.

STURT, M. (1925) *The Psychology of Time.* London: Kegal Paul.

SUTHERLAND, J. S., BUTLER, A. J., GIBSON, D. and GRAHAM, D. M. (1954) 'A sociometric study of institutionalized mental defectives.' *Amer. J. ment. Defic.* **59,** 266–71.

TANSLEY, A. E. and GULLIFORD, R. (1960) *The Education of Slow Learning Children.* London: Routledge & Kegan Paul.

TARJAN, G. and BENSON, F. (1953) 'Report on the pilot study at Pacific Colony.' *Amer. J. ment. Defic.* **57,** 453–62.

TERMAN, L. M. (1916) *The Measurement of Intelligence.* Boston: Houghton Mifflin Co.

TERMAN, L. M. and MERRILL, M. A. (1937) *Measuring Intelligence.* London: Harrap.

TERMAN, L. M. and MERRILL, M. A. (1960) *Stanford-Binet Intelligence Scale Manual for the Third Revision Form L–M.* Boston: Houghton Mifflin Co.

TEUBER, H. L. (1959) 'Some alterations in behaviour after cerebral lesions in man. Evolution of nervous control.' *Amer. Assoc. Adv. Sci.* 157–94.

TEUBER, H. L. and LIEBERT, R. S. (1958) 'Specific and general effects of brain injury in man: Evidence of both from a single task.' *A.M.A. Arch. Neurol. Psychiat.* **80,** 403–7.

THOMPSON, W. R. and HERON, W. (1954) 'The effects of early restriction on activity in dogs.' *J. comp. physiol. Psychol.* **47,** 77–82.

THOMSON, G. H. (1950) *Paper of the Royal Commission on Population.* Vol. V. London: H.M.S.O.

THORNDIKE, R. L. (1933) 'The effect of the interval between test and retest on the constancy of the I.Q.' *J. educ. Psychol.* **24,** 543–9.

THORNDIKE, R. L. (1940) ' "Constancy" of the I.Q.' *Psychol. Bull.* **37,** 167–86.

THORNE, F. C. (1947) 'The problem of institutional elopments.' *Amer. J. ment. Defic.* **51,** 637–43.

THORNE, F. C. (1948) 'Counseling and psychotherapy with mental defectives.' *Amer. J. ment. Defic.* **52,** 263–71.

THORNE, F. C. (1950) *Principles of Personality Counseling: an Eclectic Viewpoint.* Brandon, Vermont: J. clin. Psychol.

THORNE, F. C. and DOLAN, K. M. (1953) 'The role of counseling in a placement program for mentally retarded females.' *J. clin. Psychol.* **9,** 110–13.

THORPE, L. P. (1946) *Child Psychology and Development.* New York: The Ronald Press.

THORPE, W. H. (1956) *Learning and Instincts in Animals.* London: Methuen.

THRESHER, J. M. (1962) 'A problem for educators: arithmetical concept formation in the mentally retarded child.' *Amer. J. ment. Defic.* **66,** 766–73.

THURSTON, J. R. (1960) 'Attitudes and Emotional Reactions of Parents of Institutionalized Cerebral Palsied Retarded Patients.' *Amer. J. ment. Defic.* **65,** 227–35.

TINBERGEN, N. (1951) *The Study of Instincts.* Oxford: Clarendon Press.

TITMUSS, R. M. (1943) *Birth, Poverty and Wealth: a Study in Infant Mortality.* London: Hamish Hamilton.

TIZARD, B. (1957) *A theoretical and experimental study of the relations between higher mental processes and brain integrity.* Univ. London, unpubl. Ph.D. Thesis.

TIZARD, J. (1950) 'The abilities of adolescent and adult high-grade male defectives.' *J. ment. Sci.* **96,** 889–907.

TIZARD, J. (1951) 'The Porteus Maze test and intelligence. A critical survey.' *Brit. J. educ. Psychol.* **21,** 172–85.

TIZARD, J. (1953a) 'The effects of different types of supervision on the behaviour of mental defectives in a sheltered workshop.' *Amer. J. ment. Defic.* **58,** 143–61.

TIZARD, J. (1953b) 'The prevalence of mental subnormality.' *Bull. World Hlth. Org.* **9,** 423–40.

TIZARD, J. (1957) 'Psychological aspects.' Chap. VI *in* Hilliard and Kirman (1957).

TIZARD, J. (1962) 'The residential care of mentally handicapped children.' *Proc. London Conf. scient. Stud. ment. Defic., 1950* **2,** 659–66. Dagenham: May & Baker.

TIZARD, J. (1964) *Community Services for the Mentally Handicapped.* London: Oxford Univ. Press.

TIZARD, J. and GRAD, J. C. (1961) *The Mentally Handicapped and Their Families.* Maudsley Monographs **7,** London: Oxford Univ. Press.

TIZARD, J. and LOOS, F. M. (1954) 'The learning of a spatial relations test by adult imbeciles.' *Amer. J. ment. Defic.* **59,** 85–90.

TIZARD, J. and O'CONNOR, N. (1950) 'The employability of high-grade mental defectives.' *Amer. J. ment. Defic.* **54,** 563–76, and **55,** 144–57.

TIZARD, J. and O'CONNOR, N. (1952) 'The occupational adaptation of high-grade mental defectives.' *Lancet* **ii,** 620–3.

TIZARD, J. P. M., PAINE, R. S. and CROTHERS, B. (1954) 'Disturbance of sensation in children with hemiplegia.' *J. Amer. med. Assoc.* **155,** 628–32.

TOBIAS, J. and GORELICK, J. (1962) 'The Porteus Maze Test and the appraisal of retarded adults.' *Amer. J. ment. Defic.* **66,** 601–6.

TONG, J. E. and MACKAY, G. W. (1959) 'A statistical follow-up of mental defectives of dangerous or violent propensities.' *Brit. J. Delinq.* **9,** 276–84.

TRAPP. E. P. and HIMMELSTEIN, P. (1962) (Eds.) *Readings on the Exceptional Child.* London: Methuen.

TREDGOLD, A. F. (1909) 'The feebleminded: a social danger.' *Eugen. Rev.* **1,** 100–3.

TREDGOLD, A. F. (1949) *A Text-book of Mental Deficiency.* 7th edition reprinted. 8th edition 1952. London: Baillière, Tindall, & Cox.

TREDGOLD, R. F. and SODDY, K. (1956) *A Textbook of Mental Deficiency.* 9th edition. 10th edition 1963. London: Baillière, Tindall, & Cox.

TUCKER, J. E. (1950) 'Rorschach human and other movement responses in relation to intelligence.' *J. consult. Psychol.* **14,** 283–6.

TYLER, L. E. (1956) *The Psychology of Human Differences.* New York: Appleton-Century-Crofts. (1st edition 1947.)

UNITED NATIONS (Dept. of Social Affairs) (1953) *Study on Adoption of Children.* New York: United Nations.

URMER, A. H., MORRIS, A. B. and WENDLAND, L. V. (1960) 'The effect of brain damage on Raven's Progressive Matrices.' *J. clin. Psychol.* **16,** 182–5.

VAIL, D. J. (1955) 'An unsuccessful experiment in group therapy.' *Amer. J. ment. Defic.* **60,** 144–51.

VANDERHOST, L., SLOAN, W. and BENSBERG, G. J. (1953) 'Performance of mental defectives on the Wechsler–Bellevue and W.I.S.C.' *Amer. J. ment. Defic.* **57,** 481–3.

VAN RIPER, C. (1952) *Speech Correction*. New York: Prentice-Hall. 3rd edition 1956.

VAUGHN, C. L. (1941) 'Classroom behaviour problems encountered in attempting to teach illiterate defective boys how to read.' *J. educ. Psychol.* **32**, 339–50.

VERNON, P. E. (1953) *Personality Tests and Assessments*. London: Methuen.

VERNON, P. E. (1954) 'Symposium on the effects of coaching and practice in intelligence tests. V – Conclusions.' *Brit. J. educ. Psychol.* **24**, 57–63.

VERNON, P. E. (1955a) 'Presidential address: the psychology of intelligence and G.' *Bull. Brit. Psychol. Soc.* **26**, 1–14.

VERNON, P. E. (1955b) 'The assessment of children.' *In Studies in Education*. Univ. Lond. Inst. Educ. 7.

VOLLE, F. O. (1957) 'A proposal for "testing the limits" with mental defectives for purposes of subtest analysis of the W.I.S.C. verbal scale.' *J. clin. Psychol.* **13**, 64–7.

WAHLER, H. J. (1956) 'A comparison of reproduction errors made by brain damaged and control patients on a memory for designs test.' *J. abn. soc. Psychol.* **52**, 251–5.

WAISMANN, H. A. (1964) 'Treatment of phenylketonuria – a controlled longitudinal study.' Paper given to *Intern. Copenhagen Congress scient. Stud. ment. Retard.*

WALKER, R. G. (1956) 'The Revised Hooper Visual Organization Test; as a measure of brain damage.' *J. clin. Psychol.* **12**, 387–8.

WALLIN, J. E. W. (1924) *The Education of Handicapped Children*. Cambridge: Houghton Mifflin.

WALLIN, J. E. W. (1949) *Children with Mental and Physical Handicaps*. New York and London: Staples.

WALLIN, J. E. W. (1955) *Education of Mentally Handicapped Children*. New York: Harper & Bros.

WALLIN, J. E. W. (1956) *Mental Deficiency*. Brandon: Vt: *J. clin. Psychol.*

WALLIN, J. E. W. and HULTSCH, C. L. (1944) 'The pathognomonic significance of psychometric patterns.' *Amer. J. ment. Defic.* **48**, 269–77.

WALSH, M. N., KOCH, F. L. P. and BRUNSTING, B. A. (1938) 'The syndrome of tuberous sclerosis, retinal tumors, and adenoma sebaceum: report of case.' *Proc. Mayo Clin.* **13**, 155–60.

WALSHE, F. M. R. (1952) *Diseases of the Nervous System*. Edinburgh and London: E. S. Livingstone.

WALTON, D. (1955) 'The validity and interchangeability of Terman–Merrill and Matrices Test Data.' *Brit. J. educ. Psychol.* **25**, 190–4.

WALTON, D. and BEGG, T. L. (1955) 'Adult imbeciles.' *Lancet* **ii**, 616–7.

WARREN, S. A. and KRAUS, M. J. (1961) 'W.A.I.S. verbal minus performance I.Q. comparisons in mental retardates.' *J. clin. Psychol.* **17**, 57–9.

WATTS, A. F. (1944) *The Language and Mental Development of Children*. London: Harrap.

WEAVER, T. R. (1946) 'The incidence of maladjustment among mental defectives in military environment.' *Amer. J. ment. Defic.* **51**, 238–46.

WECHSLER, D. (1944) *The Measurement of Adult Intelligence*. 1st edition 1937, 2nd edition 1941, 3rd edition 1944. Baltimore: Williams & Wilkins.

WECHSLER, D. (1950) 'Intellectual development and psychological maturity.' *Child Developm.* **21**, 45–50.

WECHSLER, D. (1955) *Wechsler Adult Intelligence Scale*. New York: The Psychological Corporation.

REFERENCES

WECHSLER, D. (1958) *The Measurement and Appraisal of Adult Intelligence.* 4th edition. Baltimore: Williams & Wilkins.

WEDELL, K. (1960) 'Variations in perceptual ability among types of cerebral palsy.' *Cerebral Palsy Bull.* **2**, 149–57.

WEDELL, K. (1961) 'Follow-up study of perceptual ability in children with hemiplegia.' *Little Club Clinics in Developmental Medicine*, **4**, 76–85.

WEINSTEIN, S. and TEUBER, H. L. (1957) 'Effects of penetrating brain injury on intelligence test scores.' *Science* **125**, 1036–7.

WELLMAN, B. L., SKEELS, H. M. and SKODAK, M. (1940) 'Review of McNemar's critical examination of Iowa studies.' *Psychol. Bull.* **37**, 93–111.

WERNER, H. (1944) 'Development of visuo-motor performance on the marble board test in mentally retarded children.' *J. gener. Psychol.* **64**, 269–79.

WERNER, H. (1945a) 'Rorschach method applied to two clinical groups of mental defectives.' *Amer. J. ment. Defic.* **49**, 304–6.

WERNER, H. (1945b) 'Perceptual behaviour of brain-injured mental defective children: an experimental study by means of the Rorschach technique.' *Genet. Psychol. Monogr.* **31**, 51–110.

WERNER, H. (1946) 'The concept of rigidity: a critical evaluation.' *Psychol. Rev.* **53**, 43–52.

WERNER, H. and THUMA, B. D. (1942) 'A deficiency in the perception of apparent motion in children with brain injury.' *Amer. J. Psychol.* **55**, 58–67.

WERNER, H. and WEIR, A. (1956) 'The figure-ground syndrome in the brain-injured child.' *Int. Rev. Med.* **169**, 362–7.

WERTHAM, F. and GOLDEN, L. (1941) 'A differential diagnostic method of interpreting mosaics and colored block designs.' *Amer. J. Psychiat.* **98**, 124–31.

WERTHEIMER, M., HEBB, D. O. and SENDEN, M. V. (1951) 'The role of learning in perception.' *Amer. J. Psychol.* **64**, 133–7.

WEST, J. R. and KRAMER, J. G. (1955) 'Nephrogenic diabetes insipidus.' *Pediatrics* **15**, 424–32.

WEST, R. (1947) 'The neuropathologies of speech.' Chap. 8 *in* West, Kennedy and Carr (1947).

WEST, R., KENNEDY, L. and CARR, A. (1947) *The Rehabilitation of Speech.* New York: Harper.

WHETNALL, E. (1956) 'The management of deafness in the young child.' *Proc. Roy. Soc. Med.* **49**, 455–60.

WHIPPLE, S. M. (1924) *Manual of Mental and Physical Tests.* Baltimore: Warwick & York.

WHITCOMB, M. A. (1945) 'A comparison of social and intellectual levels of 100 high-grade adult mental defectives.' *Amer. J. ment. Defic.* **50**, 257–62.

WHITEMAN, M. (1950) 'Altitude as a reference point in scatter analysis.' *J. clin. Psychol.* **6**, 160–4.

WHITESIDE, S. (1934) 'Spontaneity of normal and mentally deficient subjects in selection learning.' *Proc. Amer. Assoc. ment. Defic.* **39**, 344–83.

WICKES, I. G. (1954) 'Foetal defects following insulin coma therapy in early pregnancy.' *Brit. med. J.* **2**, 1029–30.

WIDDOWSON, E. M. and MCCANCE, R. A. (1954) 'Studies on the nutritive value of bread and on the effect of variations in the extraction rate of flour on undernourished children.' *Sp. Rep. Ser., Med. Res. Coun.* No. 287. London: H.M.S.O.

WIENS, A. N., MATARAZZO, J. D. and CAVER, K. D. (1959) 'Performance and verbal I.Q. in a group of sociopaths.' *J. clin. Psychol.* **15**, 191–3.

WIEST, G. (1955) 'Psychotherapy with the mentally retarded.' *Amer. J. ment. Defic.* **59**, 640–4.

WILCOX, G. T. and GUTHRIE, G. M. (1957) 'Changes in adjustment of institutionalized female defectives following group psychotherapy.' *J. clin. Psychol.* **13,** 9–13.

WILDENSKOV, H. O. T. (1957) 'A symposium: the social adjustment of the mentally deficient – family care in Denmark – III.' *Amer. J. ment. Defic.* **62,** 304–9.

WILE, I. S. and DAVIS, R. (1930) 'A comparative study of the Kohs block design tests.' *Amer. J. Orthopsychiat.* **1,** 89–103.

WILE, I. S. and DAVIS, R. (1936) 'The use of the Kohs test as an indicator of mental confusion.' *Amer. J. Orthopsychiat.* **6,** 1–13.

WILLIAMS, A. A. (1956a) 'The education and social training of the young subnormal (Part I).' *J. Midland ment. Defic. Soc.* **2,** 56–60.

WILLIAMS, J. R. (1960) 'The effect of emotional factors on perception and concept formation in cerebral palsied children.' *Little Club Clinics in Developmental Medicine* **2,** 123–32.

WILLIAMS, J. R. and BELINSON, L. (1953) 'Neurosis in a mental defective.' *Amer. J. ment. Defic.* **57,** 601–12.

WILSON, H. (1962) *Delinquency and Child Neglect.* London: Allen & Unwin (for Sir Halley Stewart Trust).

WINDLE, C. (1962) 'Prognosis of mental subnormals.' *Monogr. Suppl. Amer. J. ment. Defic.* **66,** 1–180.

WITTENBORN, J. R. (1956) 'A study of adoptive children.' *Psychol. Monogr.* **70,** 1–115.

WITTENBORN, J. R. (1957) *The Placement of Adoptive Children.* Springfield, Ill.: C. C. Thomas.

WOLFENSBERGER, W. (1960) 'Differential rewards as motivating factors in mental deficiency research.' *Amer. J. ment. Defic.* **64,** 902–6.

WOLFF, C. (1942) *The Human Hand.* London: Methuen.

WOLFF, C. (1944) 'The hand of the mental defective.' *Brit. J. med. Psychol.* **20,** 147–60.

WOLFF, C. and ROLLIN, H. R. (1942) 'The hands of mongolian imbeciles in relation to their three personality groups.' *J. ment. Sci.* **88,** 415–18.

WOOD, A. (1929) See Report of the Mental Deficiency Committee.

WOODROW, H. (1917) 'Practice and transference in normal and feeble-minded children.' *J. educ. Psychol.* **8,** 85–96 and 151–65.

WOODROW, H. (1938) 'The relation between abilities and improvement with practice.' *J. educ. Psychol.* **29,** 215–30.

WOODROW, H. (1940) 'Interrelations of measures of learning.' *J. Psychol.* **10,** 49–73.

WOODS, G. (1957) *Cerebral Palsy in Childhood.* Bristol: Wright.

WOODWARD, M. (1955) 'The role of low intelligence in delinquency.' *Brit. J. Delinq.* **5,** 281–303.

WOODWARD, M. (1959) 'The behaviour of idiots interpreted by Piaget's theory of sensori-motor development.' *Brit. J. educ. Psychol.* **29,** 60–71.

WOODWARD, M. (1960) 'The application of Piaget's concepts to mental deficiency.' *Proc. Lond. Conf. scient. Stud. ment. Defic., 1960* **2,** 437–43. Dagenham: May & Baker.

WOODWARD, M. (1961) 'Concepts of number in the mentally subnormal studied by Piaget's method.' *J. Child Psychol. Psychiat.* **2,** 249–59.

WOODWARD, M. (1962a) 'Concepts of space in the mentally subnormal studied by Piaget's method.' *Brit. J. soc. clin. Psychol.* **1,** 25–37.

WOODWARD, M. (1962b) 'The application of Piaget's theory to the training of the subnormal.' *J. ment. Subnormal.* **8,** 17–25.

WOOLF, L. I., GRIFFITHS, R. and MONCRIEFF, A. (1955) 'Treatment of phenylketonuria with a diet low in phenylalanine.' *Brit. med. J.* **1**, 57–64.

WORLD HEALTH ORGANIZATION, UNITED NATIONS (1953) *Report on the Mental Health Aspects of Adoption*. Geneva: World Hlth. Org.

WORLD HEALTH ORGANIZATION (1954) *The Mentally Subnormal Child*. Geneva: World Hlth. Org. techn. Rep. Ser. 75.

WORLD HEALTH ORGANIZATION (1955) 'Hospitalisation of mental patients.' *Int. Dig. Hlth. Leg.* **6**, 1–100.

WORTIS, J. (1956) 'A note on the concept of the "Brain injured child" '. *Amer. J. ment. Defic.* **61**, 204–6.

WRIGHT, C. (1944) 'The qualitative performance of delinquent boys on the Porteus Maze tests.' *J. consult. Psychol.* **8**, 24–6.

WYATT, R. F. (1945) 'Improvability of pitch discrimination.' *Psychol. Monogr.* **58**, No. 267.

WYLLIE, W. S. (1951) 'Cerebral palsies of infancy.' Chap. IV *in* Feiling (Ed,) (1951).

YAMAZAKI, J. N., WRIGHT, S. W. and WRIGHT, P. M. (1954) 'Outcome of pregnancy in women exposed to the atomic bomb in Nagasaki.' *Amer. J. Dis. Child.* **87**, 448–63.

YANNET, H. (1944) 'The etiology of congenital cerebral palsy.' *J. Pediat.* **24**, 38–45.

YATES, A. J. (1954a) 'An experimental study of the Block Design Rotation Effect, with special reference to brain damage.' Univ. London, unpubl. Ph.D. Thesis.

YATES, A. J. (1954b) 'The validity of some psychological tests of brain damage.' *Psychol. Bull.* **51**, 359–79.

YEPSEN, L. N. (1929) 'The reliability of the Goodenough Drawing test with feebleminded subjects.' *J. educ. Psychol.* **20**, 448–51.

YEPSEN, L. N. (1952) 'Counseling the mentally retarded.' *Amer. J. ment. Defic.* **57**, 205–13.

YONGE, K. A. and O'CONNOR, N. (1954) 'Measurable effects of group psychotherapy with defective delinquents.' *J. ment. Sci.* **100**, 944–52.

ZANGWILL, O. L. (1960) *Cerebral Dominance and its Relation to Psychological Function*. Published for The William Ramsay Henderson Trust. Edinburgh, London: Oliver & Boyd.

ZAPELLA, M. and COWIE, V. (1962) 'A note on time of diagnosis in mongolism.' *J. ment. Defic. Res.* **6**, 82–6.

ZAPPERT, J. (1926) 'Über rontgenogene fotale mikrozephalie.' *Arch. Kinderheilk.* **80**, 34–50.

ZAZZO, R. (1960a) *Manuel pour l'examen psychologique de l'enfant*. Paris: Delachaux et Niestle.

ZAZZO, R. (1960b) 'Une recherche d'équipe sur la débilité mentale.' *Enfance* **4–5**, 335–64.

ZIGLER, E. (1962) 'Rigidity in the feebleminded.' Chap. 10 *in* Trapp and Himmelstein (Eds.).

ZOLIK, E. S. (1958) 'A comparison of the Bender Gestalt reproductions of delinquents and non-delinquents.' *J. clin. Psychol.* **14**, 24–6.

ZUBIN, J., ERON, L. D. and SULTAN, F. (1956) 'Current status of the Rorschach test. I. A psychometric evaluation of the Rorschach experiment.' *Amer. J. Orthopsychiat.* **26**, 773–91.

REPORTS AND MEMORANDA

AUTHOR INDEX

AUTHOR INDEX

AUTHOR INDEX

AUTHOR INDEX

SUBJECT INDEX

SUBJECT INDEX